edited by

GEORGE SCHLAGER WELSH and W. GRANT DAHLSTROM

DEPARTMENTS OF PSYCHOLOGY AND PSYCHIATRY, UNIVERSITY OF NORTH CAROLINA

BASIC READINGS ON THE

MMPI

IN PSYCHOLOGY AND MEDICINE

UNIVERSITY OF MINNESOTA PRESS · *Minneapolis*

Library of Congress Catalog Card Number: 56-9877

PUBLISHED IN GREAT BRITAIN, INDIA, AND PAKISTAN BY
GEOFFREY CUMBERLEGE: OXFORD UNIVERSITY PRESS, LONDON, BOMBAY, AND KARACHI

Third printing 1963

EDITORS' FOREWORD

THE sixty-six articles presented in this volume constitute, we believe, the major research and clinical developments in the use of the MMPI during the last fifteen years. The volume brings together for the first time material from diverse areas and from many different journals, some of them no longer in existence or for other reasons difficult to reach. It also contains articles not previously published, including some material on the original derivation of the basic clinical scales by one of the test authors. It is hoped that by making these data available in convenient form the painstaking efforts that went into the early work on the instrument, as well as recent developments in methods and applications in some of the latest research, can be better appreciated and understood by current users of the test.

The need for the present compilation comes in part from the impressive size of the existing literature on the MMPI (see the bibliography at the end of this volume). The tabulation below shows the publications by years. Over half of the 689 items have appeared in the years since 1950. It is becoming increasingly difficult for a new student of the test to identify and locate the papers that will provide him with a proper foundation in the use of the MMPI. One of the aims of the present volume is to provide such a selection for the beginner. In this regard it is interesting to note that the present collection contains ten of the sixteen articles starred by Hathaway and Meehl in the *Atlas for the Clinical Use of the MMPI* [307] as basic to further work with the test; these were not at that time available in reprinted form elsewhere.

Since the present collection of papers constitutes only 10 per cent of the published material on the MMPI, and we hoped to make it useful for readers at several levels, the selection of this particular set was extremely difficult. Many excellent papers had to be omitted; whenever the choice was close (as it often was), we gave preference to historical priority, completeness of analysis, representativeness of the sample, or imaginative design.

We have presented all the basic publications on the construction of the MMPI to provide these crucial papers in one convenient place for all workers with this test. These articles comprise the first two sections of this volume, on theory and development.

The place that MMPI coding procedures have already earned in the area of multivariate analysis, and the promise which they hold for future applications, have led us to place these papers in the next section. These articles should be considered as part of the basic knowledge of the MMPI worker. We have been led to introduce various minor editorial changes in the papers in other sections in relation to these coding procedures. The most important of these changes has been the insertion of codes based on the extended system of Welsh into tables reporting in-

v

dividual or mean MMPI profiles. In many instances these codes take the place of the graphically presented profiles. The benefits in clarity of communication resulting from this substitution are amply set forth in Section III. Similarly, in Section II on the development of the MMPI scales, code numbers have been used to designate the clinical scales. Some recent articles reprinted in other sections of this volume also use these code numbers in referring to the standard MMPI scales. Reference to the material in Section III will clarify this method of nomenclature.

Year	Number	Cumulative Percentage	Year	Number	Cumulative Percentage
1940.	3		1948.	67	30.6
1941.	1		1949.	55	38.6
1942.	3	1.0	1950.	78	50.0
1943.	7	2.0	1951.	79	61.5
1944.	8	3.2	1952.	76	72.6
1945.	25	6.8	1953.	82	84.5
1946.	40	12.6	1954.	100	98.9
1947.	56	20.8	Other.	9	100.0
			Total	689	

Some of the dozens of new scales developed on the MMPI since its original publication are described in Section IV. These papers illustrate variations on the usual methods of scale construction. The bases of selection included the extension of the scale development to new domains, the utilization of important new methods, and the contribution to the understanding of the sources of variance reflected in the MMPI items. In these papers we as editors have imposed some arbitrary letter designations upon the new scales. The need for uniformity in research reports on these scales cannot be underestimated; it is hoped that other workers in the field will adopt these designations in their writings.

The material on MMPI patterns is taken up next, in Sections V and VI. These papers deal with the methods of handling the configural problems and with some of the basic findings from research based on these techniques.

The remainder of the volume is devoted to papers which reflect the application of the MMPI to several important areas in psychology and medicine. Space limitations made it impossible to sample from other important areas, such as the extensive literature on dissimulation effects, on educational problems, and on applications to various industrial situations. MMPI work done in the area of juvenile delinquency has already been covered by Hathaway and Monachesi [312].

Rather than abridge articles so that more areas could be covered, we made a more limited selection. If this volume was to be of maximal use to the research worker, the basic data had to be included in full. Otherwise the selections would represent a mere catalogue of successful applications of the MMPI, and the interested reader would still have to seek out the original sources. Despite this aim, it was occasionally necessary to limit the length of some of the papers. In the case of long monographs, material had, unfortunately, to be omitted; we tried, however, to include all crucial MMPI data and to eliminate only material not germane to our purpose. One of the editorial excisions most frequently employed was the omission of the repetitive descriptions of the MMPI and its development with which early writers prefaced their articles. Since the first part of this volume provides this material in complete detail, little could be gained from reprinting these synopses throughout the remainder of the book. We hope that the excerpts selected, the occasional condensations of two papers to one, and the other minor editorial changes have not done violence to the authors' message or the reader's patience.

One further editorial policy should be explained. In the original papers each article contained its own list of references. Naturally there was a great deal of duplication in these separate lists. Since a bibliography on the MMPI as complete as possible through December 1954 had been prepared, each article reference was keyed to this master list of MMPI titles. Non-MMPI references were collected in a separate list following the main MMPI bibliography. It will be immediately apparent to the reader whether any given reference applies to the MMPI list or to the supplementary list since the latter numbers are prefaced by the letter "r" (e.g., r119). In addition, whenever authors have referred to MMPI articles included in the present volume, the reference is designated by both the MMPI bibliography number and a sectional and article number, referring to the position they occupy in the present collection. For example, [642 (see IV, 22)] means that the reference is to item 642 in the MMPI bibliography at the end of the volume and it may also be found in Section IV as article 22.

Grateful acknowledgment is made to all the authors of these articles and to the publishers of the journals and monographs from which this material has been reprinted. More specific recognition is extended to these contributors in the various sectional introductions. We would also like to express our appreciation for the help received from the professional and secretarial staff of the Departments of Psychology and Psychiatry at the University of North Carolina, and to Dr. Starke R. Hathaway for his assistance in editorial decisions as well as for his willingness to prepare the paper for this volume which covers so well the previously unpublished material on three of the basic MMPI scales. The assistance of the staff of the University of Minnesota Press has been most generously extended and gratefully received. The Institute for Research in Social Science at the University of North Carolina made possible a trip to Minneapolis for consultation with Dr. Hathaway; we wish to thank Dr. Gordon W. Blackwell, director of the Institute, for his assistance in this regard. We are indebted to our wives, Alice Welsh and Leona Dahlstrom, for patience and forbearance and their help in innumerable ways. Without their help this book would never have appeared.

G. S. W.
W. G. D.

Chapel Hill
June 1956

LIST OF CONTRIBUTORS

A. LLOYD ANDERSEN, Ph.D. Clinical Psychologist, Reno, Nevada

FRANK BARRON, Ph.D. Associate Research Psychologist, Institute of Personality Assessment and Research, University of California (Berkeley)

ARTHUR L. BENTON, Ph.D. Professor of Psychology, State University of Iowa

WILLIAM C. BIER (S.J.), Ph.D. Associate Professor of Psychology, Fordham University

JOHN D. BLACK, Ph.D. Director of the Counseling and Testing Center, Stanford University

EUGENE M. BLUMBERG, Ph.D. Clinical Psychologist, Private Practice, Long Beach, California

JOSEF BROZEK, Ph.D. Associate Professor, School of Public Health, University of Minnesota

AARON H. CANTER, Ph.D. Chief Clinical Psychologist, VA Hospital, Phoenix, Arizona

CARLOS A. CUADRA, Ph.D. Clinical Psychologist, VA Hospital, Downey, Illinois

LEWIS E. DRAKE, Ph.D. Director of the Student Counseling Center, University of Wisconsin

FRANK W. ELLIS, M.D. Chief, Oncology Section, VA Hospital, Long Beach, California

NORMAN L. FARBEROW, Ph.D. Staff Psychologist, VA Mental Hygiene Clinic, Los Angeles

MARVIN J. FELDMAN, Ph.D. Associate Professor of Psychology, University of Buffalo

JAMES J. GALLAGHER, Ph.D. Assistant Professor, Institute for Research on Exceptional Children, University of Illinois

LEONARD D. GOODSTEIN, Ph.D. Assistant Professor of Psychology, State University of Iowa

HARRISON G. GOUGH, Ph.D. Associate Professor of Psychology, University of California (Berkeley)

GEORGE M. GUTHRIE, Ph.D. Associate Professor of Psychology, Pennsylvania State University

LEO J. HANVIK, Ph.D. Clinical Psychologist, Washburn Memorial Clinic, Minneapolis

STARKE R. HATHAWAY, Ph.D. Professor and Director of the Division of Clinical Psychology, University of Minnesota

CHARLES C. HEWITT, M.D. Psychiatrist, Private Practice, New York City

HENRY BIRNET HOVEY, Ph.D. Clinical Psychologist, VA Hospital, Salt Lake City

PETER KAUFMANN, Ph.D. Counseling Psychologist, VA Hospital, Downey, Illinois

NANCY K. (ERICKSON) KJENAAS, M.A.

GEORGE F. J. LEHNER, Ph.D. Associate Professor of Psychology, University of California (Los Angeles)

CARLETON W. LEVERENZ, M.D. Practicing Physician, Internal Medicine, St. Paul

KENNETH B. LITTLE, Ph.D. Assistant Professor of Psychology, Stanford University

HERBERT McCLOSKY, Ph.D. Associate Professor of Political Science, University of Minnesota

J. CHARNLEY McKINLEY, M.D. (deceased). Formerly Head, Department of Neuropsychiatry, University of Minnesota

PAUL E. MEEHL, Ph.D. Chairman, Department of Psychology, University of Minnesota

HERBERT C. MODLIN, M.D. Senior Psychiatrist, Menninger Foundation

JOHN S. PEARSON, Ph.D. Assistant Director, Genetic Research Program, Department of Public Welfare of the State of Minnesota

WILLIAM H. PEMBERTON, Ed.D. Clinical Psychologist, Private Practice, San Francisco

DONALD R. PETERSON, Ph.D. Assistant Professor of Psychology, University of Illinois

BURTRUM C. SCHIELE, M.D. Professor of Psychiatry, University of Minnesota

HERMANN O. SCHMIDT, Ph.D. Director of Psychological Laboratories, Norwich State Hospital, Norwich, Connecticut

WILLIAM SCHOFIELD, Ph.D. Associate Professor of Psychology, University of Minnesota

WILLIAM SEEMAN, Ph.D. Chief Clinical Psychologist, Mayo Clinic, Rochester, Minnesota

EDWIN S. SHNEIDMAN, Ph.D. Assistant Chief Clinical Psychologist, VA Neuropsychiatric Hospital, Los Angeles

PATRICK L. SULLIVAN, Ph.D. Chief Clinical Psychologist, VA Mental Hygiene Clinic, Oakland, California

WILSON B. THIEDE, Ph.D. Director of Correspondence Division, University of Wisconsin

GEORGE SCHLAGER WELSH, Ph.D. Associate Professor of Psychology, University of North Carolina

PHILLIP M. WEST, M.D. Department of Biophysics, School of Medicine, University of California (Los Angeles)

WILLIAM MARSHALL WHEELER, Ph.D. Senior Psychologist, Tavistock Institute of Human Relations, London, England

DANIEL N. WIENER, Ph.D. Chief Clinical Psychologist, VA Mental Hygiene Clinic, St. Paul

HAROLD L. WILLIAMS, Ph.D. Chief, Department of Clinical and Social Psychology, Army Medical Services Graduate School, Walter Reed Army Medical Center, Washington

TABLE OF CONTENTS

xiii

BASIC READINGS ON THE

MMPI

IN PSYCHOLOGY AND MEDICINE

Theory

IT IS an interesting commentary on the present state of clinical psychology that efforts devoted to the establishment of firmer empirical bases for clinical practice by quantitative, experimental techniques are viewed in many quarters as somehow "anti-theory." Work with the MMPI has been subjected to this criticism of blind empiricism perhaps more than any other line of research in the clinical field. Yet the articles reprinted in this section, and the many others that had to be omitted or were placed arbitrarily in other sections of this volume, furnish ample refutation of this contention.

There are many affectively loaded terms used in the current psychological literature and certainly one of these is "theory." For many workers, theorizing involves the elaboration of a complicated *ad hoc* set of speculations to account for observations, either in a single clinic case or in a research study. To the extent that detailed empirical study will often demonstrate the tenuous nature of this speculative structure, such work as reported in this volume will always be in that sense anti-theory. There is no need to point out that a vast difference exists between idle speculation and healthy theorizing. The very heart of sound theory development is a set of facts to be accounted for, relations to be explicated, or discrepancies to be noted and explored. Constant reference to empirical foundations keeps theory building from degenerating into empty speculation. In this respect, there can be no theory without empirical data, and there can be very little meaning to raw empirical data without theory.

Another emotionally toned term in current psychological usage is "projective." The semantic analysis required to clarify the many connotations of that term is the problem Meehl takes up in the first article in this section. By placing the emphasis in their writings on the procedures for drawing the sample of behavior, many of the writers on projective techniques have obscured the entry of the projective element into the testing procedure. Meehl very clearly demonstrates that neither the stimulus channel nor the response class involved carries the projective burden, but rather the inference made from the observation. A test item is structured only if the interpretation made from it is fixed on an a priori basis. To the extent that the valid variance is identified by open-minded empirical study, to that extent any item is projective.

An amplification of this insight leads the workers with questionnaire items to an understanding of the multiphasic nature of all inventory statements like those in the MMPI. All the items in such a battery have a large number of validities. The importance of this viewpoint is elaborated in a later section on the construction of the MMPI.

Another important implication is taken up in great detail in the second article

3

4 THEORY

in the present section. Meehl and Hathaway review the many attempts to identify and minimize the extraneous sources of variance operating in test items. They proceed to a discussion of suppressor variables and the development of the present K scale. Their search involved the identification of subsets of items which have very little of the variance of the criteria under investigation, but which do contain the variance that operates as error in the other items reflecting the true score variance. This advanced treatment of inventory item work contains many as yet unresolved problems, but the paper of Meehl and Hathaway is clearly a classic in the field.

The notion of subtlety in item operation stems from the realization that the item content itself does not necessarily provide an adequate basis for inference about validity. The relationship of item replies to nontest behavior is the only sound basis for such interpretations. This concept of subtlety was applied with considerable success in practical clinical problems by Harmon and Wiener (see IV, 22, below). In the third article in this section, Seeman demonstrates the utility of this designation on a subset of items from the MMPI. He is also able to show how stable these classes are in the face of formal instruction to a group of graduate students.

Further empirical support for the subtlety in operation of the MMPI items is advanced in Gough's article at the end of this section. He is able to extend his earlier work on the level of scale scores [235] to the level of specific items with excellent success. He also points up the practical significance of this material in the identification of dissimulation.

The articles in this section came from the following sources: article 1 from P. E. Meehl, The dynamics of "structured" personality tests, *Journal of Clinical Psychology*, 1945, 1, 296–303; article 2 from P. E. Meehl and S. R. Hathaway, The K factor as a suppressor variable in the MMPI, *Journal of Applied Psychology*, 1946, 30, 525–564; article 3 from W. Seeman, "Subtlety" in structured personality tests, *Journal of Consulting Psychology*, 1952, 16, 278–283, and Concept of "subtlety" in structured psychiatric and personality tests: an experimental approach, *Journal of Abnormal and Social Psychology*, 1953, 48, 239–247; and article 4 from H. G. Gough, Some common misconceptions about neuroticism, *Journal of Consulting Psychology*, 1954, 18, 287–292. We are indebted to the authors and to the publishers of the journals for permission to reproduce these articles in this form.

ARTICLE 1 *The Dynamics of "Structured" Personality Tests*

IN A recent article [r83] Lt. Max L. Hutt of the Adjutant General's School has given an interesting discussion of the use of projective methods in the army medical installations. This article was part of a series describing the work of clinical psychologists in the military services, with which the present writer is familiar only indirectly. The utility of any instrument in the military situation can, of course, be most competently assessed by those in contact with clinical material in that situation, and the present paper is in no sense to be construed as an "answer" to or an attempted refutation of Hutt's remarks. Nevertheless, there are some incidental observations contained in his article which warrant further critical consideration, particularly those having to do with the theory and dynamics of "structured" personality tests. It is with these latter observations rather than the main burden of Hutt's article that this paper is concerned.

Hutt defines "structured personality tests" as those in which the test material consists of conventional, culturally crystallized questions to which the subject must respond in one of a very few fixed ways. With this definition the present writer has no quarrel, and it has the advantage of not applying the unfortunate phrase "self-rating questionnaire" to the whole class of question-answer devices. But immediately following this definition, Hutt goes on to say that "it is assumed that each of the test questions will have the same meaning to all subjects who take the examination. The subject has no opportunity of organizing in his own unique manner his response to the questions."

These statements will bear further examination. The statement that personality tests assume that each question has the same meaning to all subjects is continually appearing in most sources of late, and such an impression is conveyed by many discussions even when they do not explicitly make this assertion. It should be emphasized very strongly, therefore, that while this perhaps has been the case with the majority of question-answer personality tests, it is not by any means part of their essential nature. The traditional approach to verbal question-answer personality tests has been, to be sure, to view them as self-ratings; and it is in a sense always a self-rating that you obtain when you ask a subject about himself, whether you inquire about his feelings, his health, his attitudes, or his relations to others.

However, once a "self-rating" has been obtained, it can be looked upon in two rather different ways. The first, and by far the commonest approach, is to accept a self-rating as a second best source of information when the direct observation of a segment of behavior is inaccessible for practical or other reasons. This view in effect forces a self-rating or self-description to act as surrogate for a behavior sample. Thus we want to know whether a man is shy, and one criterion is his readiness to blush. We cannot conveniently drop him into a social situation to observe whether he blushes, so we do the next best (and often much worse) thing and simply ask him, "Do you blush easily?" We assume that if he does in fact blush easily, he will realize that fact about himself, which is often a gratuitous assumption; and secondly, we hope that having recognized it, he will be willing to tell us so.

Associated with this approach to structured personality tests is the construction of items and their assembly into scales upon an a priori basis, requiring the asssumption that the psychologist building the test has sufficient insight into the dynamics of verbal behavior and its relation to the inner core of personality that he is able to predict beforehand what certain sorts of people will say about themselves when asked certain sorts of questions. The fallacious character of this procedure has been sufficiently shown by the empirical results of the MMPI alone, and will be discussed at greater length below. It is suggested tentatively that the relative uselessness of most structured personality tests is due more to a priori item construction than to the fact of their being structured.

The second approach to verbal self-ratings is rarer among test-makers. It consists simply in the explicit denial that we accept a self-rating as a feeble surrogate for a behavior sample, and substitutes the assertion that a "self-rating" constitutes an intrinsically interesting and significant bit of verbal behavior, the nontest correlates of which must be discovered by empirical means. Not only is this approach free from the restriction that the subject must be able to describe his own behavior accurately, but a careful study of structured personality tests built on this basis shows that such a restriction would falsify the actual relationships that hold between what a man says and what he *is*.

Since this view of question-answer items is the rarer one at the present time, it is desirable at this point to elucidate by a number of examples. For this purpose one might consider the Strong Vocational Interest Blank, the Humm-Wadsworth Temperament Scales, the MMPI, or any other structured personality measuring device in which the selection of items was done on a thoroughly empirical basis using carefully selected criterion groups. In the extensive and confident use of the Strong Vocational Interest Blank, this more sophisticated view of the significance of responses to structured personality test items has been taken as a matter of course for years. The possibility of conscious as well as unconscious "fudging" has been considered and experimentally investigated by Strong and others, but the differences in possible interpretation or *meaning* of items have been more or less ignored — as well they should be. One is asked to indicate, for example, whether he likes, dislikes, or is indifferent to "conservative people." The possibilities for differential interpretation of a word like "conservative" are of course tremendous, but nobody has worried about that problem in the case of the Strong. Almost certainly the strength of verbs such as "like" and "dislike" is variably interpreted throughout the whole blank. For the present purpose the MMPI will be employed because the present writer is most familiar with it.

One of the items on the MMPI scale for detecting psychopathic personality (Pd) is "My parents and family find more fault with me than they should." If we look upon this as a rating in which the *fact* indicated by an affirmative response is crucial, we immediately begin to wonder whether the testee can objectively evaluate how much other people's parents find fault with them, whether his own parents are warranted in finding as much fault with him as they do, whether this particular subject will interpret the phrase "finding fault" in the way we intend or in the way most normal persons interpret it, and so on. The present view is that this is simply an unprofitable way to examine a question-answer personality test item. To begin with, the empirical finding is that individuals whose past history and momentary clinical picture is that of a typical psychopathic personality tend to say "Yes" to this much more often than people in general do. Now in point of fact, they probably should say "No" because the parents of psychopaths are sorely tried and probably do not find fault with their incorrigible offspring any more than the latter deserve. An allied item is "I have been quite independent and free from family rule," which psychopaths tend to answer False — almost certainly opposite to what is actually the case for the great majority of them. Again, "Much of the time I feel I have done something wrong or evil." Anyone who deals clinically with psychopaths comes to doubt seriously whether they could possibly interpret this item in the way the rest of us do (cf. Cleckley's [r37] "semantic dementia"), but they *say* that about themselves nonetheless. Numerous other examples such as "Someone has it in for me" and "I am sure I get a raw deal from life" appear on the same scale and are significant because psychopaths tend to *say* certain things about themselves, rather than because we take these statements at face value.

Consider the MMPI scale for detecting tendencies to hypochondriasis. A hypochondriac says that he has headaches often, that he is not in as good health as his friends are, and that he cannot understand what he reads as well as he used to. Suppose that he has a headache on an average of once every month, as does a certain "normal" person. The hypochondriac says he often has headaches, the other person says he does not. They both have headaches once a month, and hence they must either interpret the word "often" differently in that question, or else have unequal recall of their headaches. According to the traditional view, this ambiguity in the word "often" and the inaccuracy of human memory constitute sources of error; for the authors of the MMPI they may actually constitute sources of discrimination.

We might mention as beautiful illustrations of this kind of relation the nonsomatic items in the hysteria scale of the MMPI [423 (see II, 9)]. These items have a statistical homogeneity and the common property by face inspection that they indicate the person to be possessed of unusually good social and psychiatric adjustment. They are among the most potent items for the detection of hysterics and hysteroid temperaments, but they reflect the systematic distortion of the hysteric's conception of himself, and would have to be considered invalid if taken as surrogates for the direct observation of behavior.

As a last example might be mentioned some findings of the writer [435] in which "normal" persons having rather abnormal MMPI profiles are differentiated from clearly "abnormal" persons with equally deviant profiles by a tendency to give statistically rare as well as psychiatrically "maladjusted" responses to certain other items. Thus a person who says that he is afraid of fire, that windstorms terrify him, that people often disappoint him, stands a better chance of being normal in his nontest behavior than a person who does not admit to these things. The discrimination of this set of items for various criterion groups, the intercorrelations with other scales, and the content of the items indicate strongly that they detect some verbal-semantic distortion in the interpretation and response to the other MMPI items which enters into the spurious elevation of scores achieved by certain "normals." Recent unpublished research on more subtle "lie" scales of the MMPI indicates that unconscious self-deception is inversely related to the kind of verbal distortion just indicated.

In summary, a serious and detailed study of the MMPI items and their interrelations both with one another and with nontest behavior cannot fail to convince one of the necessity for this second kind of approach to question-answer personality tests. That the majority of the questions seem by inspection to require self-ratings has been a source of theoretical misunderstanding, since the stimulus situation seems to request a self-rating, whereas *the scoring does not assume a valid self-rating to have been given*. It is difficult to give any psychologically meaningful interpretation of some of the empirical findings on the MMPI unless the more sophisticated view is maintained.

It is for this reason that the possible differences in interpretation do not cause us any a priori concern in the use of this instrument. Whether any structured personality test turns out to be valid and useful must be decided on pragmatic grounds, but the possibility of diverse interpretations of a single item is not a good *theoretical* reason for predicting failure of the scales. There is a "projective" element involved in interpreting and responding to these verbal stimuli which must be recognized, in spite of the fact that the test situation is very rigidly structured as regards the ultimate response possibilities permitted. The objection that all persons do not interpret structured test items in the same way is not fatal, just as it would not be fatal to point out that "ink blots do not look the same to everyone."

It has not been sufficiently recognized by critics of structured personality tests that what a man says about himself may be a highly significant fact about him even though we do not entertain with any confidence the hypothesis that what he says would agree with what complete knowledge of him would lead others to say of him. It is rather strange that this point is so often completely passed by, when clinical psychologists quickly learn to take just that attitude in a diagnostic or therapeutic interview. The complex defense mechanisms of projection, rationalization, reaction formation, etc., appear dynamically to the interviewer as soon as he begins to take what the client *says* as itself motivated by other needs than those of giving an accurate verbal report. There is no good a priori reason for denying the possibility of similar processes in the highly structured "interview" which is the question-answer personality test. The summarized experience of the clinician results (one hopes, at least) in his being able to discriminate verbal responses admissible as accurate self-descriptions from those which reflect other psychodynamisms but are not on that account any the less significant. The test analogue to this experience consists of the summarized statistics on response frequencies, at least among those personality tests which have been constructed empirically (MMPI, Strong, Rorschach, etc.).

Once this has been taken for granted we are prepared to admit powerful items to personality scales regardless of whether the rationale of their appearance can be made clear at present. We do not have the confidence of the traditional personality-test maker that the relation between the behavior dynamics of a subject and the tendency to respond verbally in a certain way must be psychologically obvious. Thus it puzzles us but does not disconcert us when this relation cannot be elucidated, the science of behavior being in the stage that it is. That "I sometimes tease animals" (answered False) should occur in a scale measuring symptomatic depression is theoretically mysterious, just as the tendency of certain schizophrenic patients to accept "position" as a determinant in responding to the Rorschach may be theoretically mysterious. Whether such a relation obtains can be very readily discovered empirically, and the wherefore of it may be left aside for the moment as a theoretical question. Verbal responses which do not apparently have any *self*-reference at all, but in their form seem to request an objective judgment about social phenomena or ethical values, may be equally diagnostic. So, again, one is not disturbed to find items such as "I think most people would lie to get ahead" (answered False) and "It takes a lot of argument to convince most people of the truth" (answered False) appearing on the hysteria scale of the MMPI.

The frequently alleged "superficiality" of structured personality tests becomes less evident on such a basis also. Some of these items can be rationalized in terms of fairly deep-seated trends of the personality, although it is admittedly difficult to establish that any given depth interpretation is the correct one. To take one example, the items on the MMPI scale for hysteria which were referred to above as indicating extraordinarily good social and emotional adjustment can hardly be seen as valid self-descriptions. However, if the core trend of such items is summarily characterized as "I am psychiatrically and socially well adjusted," it is not hard to fit such a trend into what we know of the basic personality structure of the hysteric. The well-known *belle indifférence* of these patients, the great lack of insight, the facility of repression and dissociation, the "impunitiveness" of their reactions to frustration, the tendency of such patients to show an elevated "lie" score on the MMPI, may all be seen as facets of this underlying structure. It would be interesting to see experimentally whether to the three elements of Rosenzweig's "triadic hypothesis" (impunitiveness, repression, hypnotizability) one might add a fourth correlate — the chief nonsomatic component of the MMPI hysteria scale.

Whether "depth" is plumbed by a structured personality test to a lesser extent than by one which is unstructured is difficult to determine, once the present view of the nature of structured tests is understood. That the "deepest" layers of personality are not verbal might be admitted without any implication that they cannot therefore make themselves known to us via verbal behavior. Psychoanalysis, usually considered the "deepest" kind of psychotherapy, makes use of the dependency of verbal behavior upon underlying variables which are not themselves verbalized.

The most important area of behavior considered in the making of psychiatric diagnosis is still the form and content of the *speech* of the individual. I do not mean to advance these considerations as validations of any structured personality tests, but merely as reasons for not accepting the theoretical objection sometimes offered in criticizing them. Of course, structured personality tests may be employed in a purely diagnostic, categorizing fashion, without the use of any dynamic interpretations of the relationship among scales or the patterning of a profile. For certain practical purposes this is quite permissible, just as one may devote himself to the statistical validation of various "signs" on the Rorschach test, with no attempt to make qualitative or really dynamic personological inferences from the findings. The tradition in the case of structured personality tests is probably weighted on the side of nondynamic thinking; and in the case of some structured tests, a considerable amount of experience and clinical subtlety is required to extract the maximum of information. The present writer has heard discussions in case conferences at the University of Minnesota Hospitals which make as "dynamic" use of MMPI patterns as one could reasonably make of any kind of test data without an excessive amount of illegitimate reification. The clinical use of the Strong Vocational Interest Blank is another example.

In discussing the "depth" of interpretation possible with tests of various kinds, it should at least be pointed out that the problem of validating personality tests, whether structured or unstructured, becomes more difficult in proportion as the interpretations increase in "depth." For example, the validation of the "sign" differentials on the Rorschach is relatively easier to carry out than that of the deeper interpretations concerning the basic personality structure. This does not imply that there is necessarily less validity in the latter class of inferences, but simply stresses the difficulty of designing experiments to test validity. A very major part of this difficulty hinges upon the lack of satisfactory external criteria, a situation which exists also in the case of more dynamic interpretations of structured personality tests. One is willing to accept a staff diagnosis of psychasthenia in selecting cases against which to validate Pt scale of the MMPI or the F% as a compulsive-obsessive sign on the Rorschach. But when the test results indicate repressed homosexuality or latent anxiety or lack of deep insight into the self, we may have strong suspicions that the instrument is fully as competent as the psychiatric staff. Unfortunately this latter assumption is very difficult to justify without appearing to be inordinately biased in favor of our test. Until this problem is better solved than at present, many of the "depth" interpretations of both structured and unstructured tests will be little more than an expression of personal opinion.

There is one advantage of unstructured personality tests which cannot easily be claimed for the structured variety, namely, the fact that falsehood is difficult. While it is true for many of the MMPI items, for example, that even a psychologist cannot predict on which scales they will appear or in what direction certain sorts of abnormals will tend to answer them, still the relative accessibility of defensive answering would seem to be greater than is possible in responding to a set of inkblots. Research is still in progress on more subtle "lie" scales of the MMPI and we have every reason to feel encouraged on the present findings. Nevertheless the very existence of a definite problem in this case and not in the case of the Rorschach gives the latter an advantage in this respect. When we pass to a more structured method, such as the TAT, the problem reappears. The writer has found, for example, a number of patients who simply were not fooled by the "intelligence-test" set given in the directions for the TAT, as was indicated quite clearly by self-references and defensive remarks, especially on the second day. Of course such a patient is still under pressure to produce material and therefore his willingness to reveal himself is limited in its power over the projections finally given.

In conclusion, the writer is in hearty agreement with Lieutenant Hutt that unstructured personality tests are of great value, and that the final test of the adequacy of any technique is its utility in clinical work. Published evidence of the validity of both structured and unstructured personality tests as they had to be modified for convenient military use does not enable one to draw any very definite conclusions or comparisons at the present time. There is assuredly no reason for us to place structured and unstructured types of instruments in battle order against one another, although it is admitted that when time is limited they come inevitably into a very real clinical "competition" for use. The present article has been aimed simply at the clarification of certain rather prevalent misconceptions as to the nature and the theory of at least one important structured personality test, in order that erroneous theoretical considerations may not be thrown into the balance in deciding the outcome of such clinical competition.

P. E. MEEHL AND S. R. HATHAWAY

ARTICLE 2 *The K Factor as a Suppressor Variable in the MMPI*

History and Problem

AMONG the very large number of structured personality inventories which have been published, it is by now quite generally admitted that there are relatively few which are of practical value in the clinical situation. There are a number of reasons, both obvious and subtle, for this fact, some of which will be developed by implication in the present paper. One of the most important failings of almost all structured personality tests is their susceptibility to "faking" or "lying" in one way or another, as well as their even greater susceptibility to unconscious self-deception and role-playing on the part of individuals who may be consciously quite honest and sincere in their responses. The possibility of such factors having an invalidating effect upon the scores obtained has been mentioned by many writers, including Adams [r1], Allport [r5, r6, r7], Bernreuter [r17, r18, r19], Bills [r20], Bordin [r22], Eisenberg and Wesman [r53], Guilford and Guilford [r67], Humm and Humm [r79], Humm and Wadsworth [r81], Kelly, Miles, and Terman [r88], Laird [r92], Landis and Katz [r93], Maller [r110], Olson [r130], Rosenzweig [r139, r140], Ruch [r142], Strong [r156], Symonds [r159], Vernon [r164], Washburne [r165], Willoughby [r171], and others. One of the assumed advantages of the projective methods is that they are relatively less influenced by such distorting factors, although this assumption should be critically evaluated.

The existence of a distorting influence in test-taking attitude is so obvious that it has been thought hardly necessary to establish it experimentally, although a number of investigations have demonstrated the effect. Frenkel-Brunswik [r60] investigated tendencies to self-deception in rating oneself, finding in some cases marked negative relations between self-judgments and the evaluation of others. Hendrickson [r74], cited by Olson [r130], reported that a group of teachers earned significantly more stable, dominant, extroverted, and self-sufficient scores on the Bernreuter scales when instructed to take the test as though they were applying for a position than when under more neutral instructions. Ruch [r142] showed that college students could fake extroversion on the Bernreuter to the extent of achieving a median at the 98th percentile of Bernreuter's norms, as contrasted with a "naive" median at the 50th percentile. Bernreuter [r18] found that college students could produce marked shifts in their Bernreuter scores in the "socially approved" direction, although he interpreted this finding as indicating the comparative unimportance of the faking tendency. His reasoning was that had the need for giving socially approved responses operated in the first administration to any appreciable extent, the effect of special instructions to take this attitude should not have been great. This reasoning seems rather tenuous, inasmuch as the occurrence of a shift merely shows that conscious and permitted faking can produce greater effects than those which may have been operating in the "naive" original testing. The insignificant correlations between naive and faked scores were also used by Bernreuter to support his view, an argument which is not comprehensible to the present writers, especially in view of the probably gross skewness of the faked scores. What is clear from his investigation is that people are able to influence their scores to a considerable extent if they choose to, and that the average student's stereotype of what is "socially desirable" seems to be an individual who is dominant, self-sufficient, and stable. Maller [r110], Metfessel [r118], Olson [r130], and Spencer [r152] have studied the effects of anonymity on responses to self-rating situations and shown that the requirement of signing one's name has a definite effect on the scores. Kelly, Miles, and Terman [r88] demonstrated the great ease with which scores on the Terman-Miles Masculinity-Femininity Test could be "faked" in either direction once the subjects had been let in on the secret of what the test measured. Strong [r156], Bills [r20], Steinmetz [r153], and Bordin [r22] have presented evidence on the ability of subjects to distort their interest patterns when taking the Strong Vocational Interest Blank.

It is a significant sociological fact about psychologists that in spite of the strong reasons, both a priori and experimental, for accepting the reality of this phenomenon in objective personality testing, very few systematic efforts have been made to correct for it or to overcome it. In published articles one continually finds brief and inadequate references to the "assumption of frankness" and the necessity for arousing a "sincere desire to know oneself better," but the treatment is usually extremely sketchy and no very concrete suggestions are given for producing such test-taking attitudes or, what is almost as important in practice, for determining the extent to which they have been present. It almost seems as though we inventory-makers were afraid to say too much about the problem because we had no effective solution for it, but it was too obvious a fact to be ignored so it was met by a polite nod. Meanwhile the scores obtained are subjected to varied and "precise" statistical manipulations which impel the student of behavior to wonder whether it is not the aim of the personality testers to get as far away from any unsanitary contact with the organism as possible. Part of this trend no doubt reflects the lack of clinical experience of some psychologists who concern themselves with personality testing, and the very strong contemporary trend which stresses the statistical interrelationships of item responses much more than the relation of the latter to external nontest criteria. The establishment of "validity" (*sic!*) in terms of various criteria of internal consistency naturally leads to an unconscious neglect of the problem of nontest behavior correlates.

Among the many authors who recognize the problem there are a few who have made specific suggestions for its solution. The inclusion of special exhortations to frankness and objectivity in the test directions themselves is common, but we have no evidence as to its effectiveness. Obviously, if a subject is consciously determined to fake, he will do so; whereas if his motivation to distortion is of a more subtle, non-verbalized nature, such exhortations can hardly be expected to be efficacious. Another method is to attempt disguise of the items, so that the "significance" of a given response is less obvious. Traditional approaches to the measurement of personality render this technique practically impossible, inasmuch as the items are selected to begin with for their *obvious* psychological significance and hence, unless changed so greatly as to no longer elicit the desired information, almost inevitably continue to betray their origin. An effective use of a set of "subtle" items is only possible when the initial item pool is very large and the *initial selection* (not only the final validation) of items is ruthlessly empirical. Those items whose significance would not have been guessed by the test-maker will then be equally mysterious to the testee. When the projective and role-playing components of test-taking behavior are clearly seen to be present in objective personality inventories [433 (see I, 1)], this approach to the problem is very fruitful. A simple stratagem along the item-disguise line is to state about half of the items negatively, so that an affirmative response is not consistently a "bad" or maladjusted one. However, such techniques cannot eliminate the problem entirely.

A spurious anonymity using secret coding for identifying the testee is a possibility suggested by the studies cited above, but is clinically impractical for obvious reasons. The deception involved is not desirable, and in any case the clinical patient, unlike the sophomore student, knows perfectly well that the examiner is interested in *his* score individually. Instead of anonymity, it has been suggested by Olson [r130] that the name be signed at the conclusion of the administration instead of at the top of the page. This suggestion was carried into practice by Maller [r111] in his Character Sketches. This investigator also stated the questions in the "indirect" (third person) form, requiring the subject to indicate whether he was the *same* or *different* from the person described. Maller presents evidence that this procedure aroused considerably less annoyance in his subjects, although direct proof that this decrease in annoyance led to increased validity is lacking. For reasons which have been given in more detail elsewhere [433 (see I, 1)], it is doubtful whether the removal of personal reference is wholly desirable, since there is reason for believing that the same role-playings and self-deceptions which operate to invalidate *some* of our measurements are an important factor in making *other* measurements possible.

Another technique for reducing the effect of signing one's name is to have the items printed on cards which are then sorted by the subject, making all writing unnecessary and possibly lessening the feeling that one is making a permanent record of his personal failings. This has been done by Maller in a revised test (Personality Sketches) and by Hathaway and McKinley in the MMPI [303].

Although all these stratagems may have a considerable value, especially in the aggregate, the fact still remains that they do not by any means remove the possibility of "faking." What is much more important, they are mainly directed at the sort of *conscious* falsehood which most writers have stressed, while ignoring the more subtle tendencies to self-deception which are probably of even greater importance in affecting scores. In the third place, they neglect to stress the existence of trends in the opposite direction — namely, those trends which exaggerate the apparent abnormality or maladjustment of the individual rather than soft-pedaling it. It is only natural that the tendency of a testee to put himself in a favorable light should have received more attention than the contrary tendency, which makes much less "sense" psychologically at least from a superficial point of view. There is evidence that this latter tendency does exist, however, and that it is a much more important factor in determining scores on personality inventories than has generally been supposed. Some of this evidence will be presented in the present paper, while other indications have been given elsewhere [435]. It is also probable that certain systematic differences in item interpretation, not necessarily a function of personality dynamics of the defensive or self-critical sort but relatively "neutral" psychologically (e.g., semantic variation), lead to score deviations that are misleading. Such problems have been investigated by Benton [r16], Eisenberg [r52], and Eisenberg and Wesman [r53].

A more fruitful attitude was taken by Rosenzweig [r139] in which he reiterated that self-ratings are untrustworthy and indicated that instead of trying to eliminate completely these sources of error we should recognize them and attempt to "correct" for them in interpreting the results. He says:

> Astute phraseology in the instructions and questions of the test have sometimes been resorted to, but such expedients are rarely very effective. Might it not be more effective to recognize at the outset that such tests have certain limitations that can never be completely circumvented and then go on to the measurement of these limiting factors themselves, thus obtaining information by which a correction may be applied to the subject's answers? [r139]

Rosenzweig's specific proposal for achieving this end was to include among the usual self-rating items a set of items of the form "I should like to be the sort of man who . . ." on the theory that if we knew something of the strength of certain "ideal-self" trends in the person, we could make appropriate correction for these trends in interpreting responses to the traditional items. Rosenzweig never carried this idea into practice and there is no way of telling whether or not it would have worked. It seems to the writers that it would be relatively ineffective, since what is desired is not a statement of the strength or number of ideals for the self, but a measure of the extent to which they are allowed to distort responses. In other words, a subject might easily have quite lofty ideals verbally expressed, but might be too honest, insightful, objective, or self-critical to distort his responses into agreement with these ideals. It is, for example, rather characteristic of psychasthenic persons to express high and often unattainable ideals of perfection and achievement; whereas at the same time they are prone to be excessively self-critical, a fact which is psychometrically reflected in the negative correlation of the Pt (psychasthenia) scale of the MMPI with some of the subtle "lie" scales which will be discussed below.

Maller [r111] attempted to solve this problem in another way in his Character Sketches, by including a small set of items which were supposed to measure the subject's "readiness to confide." The occurrence of very normal, well-adjusted scores in combination with a low measured "readiness to confide" would lead one to be skeptical of the validity of the measurement. This was a material advance in principle, except that the "readiness to confide" items were themselves self-ratings on that very readiness. In the later form called Personality Sketches Maller does not make use of this procedure so we may assume that it was unsuccessful or at least did not materially improve validity.

To carry Rosenzweig's thinking to its logical conclusion, the obvious procedure is to give the subject a good *chance* to distort his answers in accordance with some self-picture or conscious façade, and observe the extent to which he does so. The difficulty here is that such a procedure requires a knowledge of the objective facts (and the subjective facts!), which are usually inaccessible to us. Here there are three possibilities open to the test-builder. First, he may sidestep the problem of getting directly at the objective truth, and attempt to establish falsehood by obtaining internal contradictions. This was another technique employed by Maller in his earlier test. Cady [r29], in his application of a modified form of the Woodworth Psychoneurotic Inventory to the measurement of juvenile incorrigibility, had earlier made use of repeated items to increase reliability of the scores, although the aim of detecting inconsistency of the "fake" sort was not explicit in his rationale. Each question appeared twice, once in each section of the test, except that in the second appearance the question was phrased in the negative. Theoretically the subject's response should also be reversed; and the number of failures to reverse is an indication of some inconsistency and hence, Maller assumes, of noncooperation or dishonesty. The "inconsistency score" obtained in this way was to be subtracted from the adjustment score to get a sort of corrected score as proposed by Rosenzweig. It is by no means obvious that the shift to a negative form of item will leave the projective properties of the stimulus simply reversed in meaning, so that the fact of an "inconsistency" in the strict logical sense would not necessarily imply lack of cooperation or dishonesty. However, it would seem reasonable that a very large number of such inconsistent pairs would cast grave suspicion upon the scores, either for dishonesty or for some other equally serious reason. This technique also was abandoned by Maller in his revised instrument.

The second method of using distortion is to present opportunities for answering in a very favorable way but in a way which could almost certainly not be true. This idea was employed by Hartshorne and May in the Character Education Inquiry [r70]. Since there are very few aspects of behavior for which one could have complete confidence that no subject would be "ideal" in them, it is necessary to present a considerable number of such opportunities and progressively reduce the probability that any flesh-and-blood individual would be as described. Everyone has at least a few highly desirable traits, and no one has all of them. Without knowing anything whatsoever about a particular person, we can write down on commonsense grounds a list of extremely good and rare human qualities which it is statistically absurd to suppose will all or in large part be his. If he says, however, that he has all (or a very great many) of them, we decide that he is not telling the truth. To practically clinch this argument it is only necessary to choose desirable attributes which will very rarely belong, even singly, to anyone, and which furthermore relatively few normal persons claim for themselves when given the chance. In the mass the answers to these items may yield very strong evidence of deception. "I sometimes put off until tomorrow what I ought to do today" can be answered False by *very* few honest people. If a subject gives such responses with some considerable frequency, the inference is obvious. A more detailed discussion of this approach will be given below in the section on the L scale.

The Humm-Wadsworth Temperament Scales and the MMPI have both made use of this method, the latter more explicitly. Humm and Wadsworth [r81] deserve credit for having been among the first investigators of structured personality measurement to lay great stress upon the problem of detecting noncooperation and distortion of response when evaluating a particular profile of scores. They were also among the first to adopt an explicit and uncompromising empiricism in selecting items from a large initial pool. The two scales which serve as "checks" or "correctors" for the remainder of the profile on the Humm-Wadsworth are the "Normal" component and the "no-count." The Normal component is rather difficult to evaluate from the theoretical point of view, for reasons which have been given elsewhere by one of the present writers [435]. It is sufficient here to indicate merely its function as described by Humm and Wadsworth, which is to assess the strength of a general inhibiting, controlling, or normalizing factor in personality which serves to act as a "brake" upon strong abnormal tendencies on the other variables. This means that in interpreting a given profile, the significance of any deviation on one of the abnormal components must be established with the size of the Normal score in mind. To the extent that the Normal component measures what the authors claim for it, it is not especially relevant to the present problem; but if it actually operates by detecting something other than the personality component they describe, it would perhaps be of significance here. For a more detailed discussion of this question the reader is referred to the study cited above.

The "no-count" is based upon the number of items to which the subject responds in the negative. Inasmuch as approximately 76 per cent of the scored items (87 per cent of the total pool) of the Humm-Wadsworth are "obviously" suggestive of abnormality when replied to affirmatively, the no-count is to some extent a measure of the testee's tendency to avoid, consciously or otherwise, saying "bad" things about himself when taking the test. That this relationship obtains is further supported by the tendency for the no-count to correlate positively (.77) with the Normal component and negatively (—.39 to —.72) with the various abnormal components [r81]. If the no-count is excessively great, the inference is that the subject has responded in a very defensive or possibly (as in some psychotics) stereotyped fashion; and therefore the particular testing is of doubtful validity. In another article, Humm and Wadsworth state that as high as 25 or 30 per cent of normals seem to invalidate their scores in this way, a proportion which would seem to be impractically high for clinical purposes. In a later article [r80] they attempt to reduce the proportion of useless tests by a "correction" for the no-count based upon multiple regression procedures. Humm and Wadsworth state that in a subsequent group of cases "well known" to them, the improved validity of profiles thus corrected was demonstrated. An unpublished study of hospitalized psychiatric cases by Arnold [r10] indicated that even the exclusion of cases with "invalid" no-count did not result in any greater validity clinically than was obtained using all cases. Humm (in a personal communication) states that improved multiple regression techniques have resulted in a very marked reduction in the proportion of test misses and of uninterpretable profiles. These more recent data on the Humm-Wadsworth have not been published. On present evidence it is difficult to say to what extent the use of the multiple regression technique was successful in improving validity.

Washburne, in revising his "Test of Social Adjustment" (OSPA), included a set of 21 items modeled after the "lie" items of Hartshorne and May and referred to the total score on this set as *objectivity*. This score was included to detect both lying and unintentional inaccuracy, and the author reports that interviews with people having very low objectivity scores showed that "it was useless to question them." A very low objectivity score was said to invalidate the test as a whole, and a weighted objectivity score was included in the total score on the entire test [r166].

Another application of the second method for detecting invalidity by identifying the presence of distortion was the "lie" scale (and its complement, F) of the MMPI, which will be discussed in detail in the section below on the L scale.

The third technique available is the empirical derivation of a "fake" scale by making use of the item shifts obtained when persons take a test under normal "naive" conditions and then are retested with instructions to fake. This method has been used by Ruch to construct an "honesty" key for the Bernreuter. It is interesting that a procedure so logical and straightforward, invented to solve a problem so obvious and insistent, should have been employed for the first time over twenty years after the appearance of the first personality inventory. Ruch says:

The argument is rather simple. If answers to items on a test like the Bernreuter can be faked at all, the chances are that some are easier to fake than others. Therefore, it should be possible to give each item a weight to represent the extent to which it can be faked by the average college student. This was done by tabulating the frequency of each answer to each question for the standard condition and for the influenced condition. These frequencies were converted into percentages, and an "honesty" weight was assigned to each reply according to the magnitude of the critical ratio of the difference between the frequency of the reply in the honest and in the influenced condition. [r142]

In applying this honesty scale to a new group he was able to show that all cases of "real" introverts would be detected in an attempt to make themselves appear extroverted on the test. There are a number of interesting problems presented by this method, such as the extent to which the key would work if the subjects were not under actual instructions to fake extrovert but were being more subtle and actually trying to deceive an examiner in a real-life situation. Presumably the deviation toward dishonesty would not be as great under such circumstances. The use of the critical ratio as a basis for weighting items might also be open to some question. In any event, Ruch seems to have been the first investigator to attempt empirical derivation of a fake key for a question-answer personality inventory. The results of applying this procedure to work on the MMPI will follow in the present article.

As was mentioned earlier, there is some evidence of a tendency in the opposite direction in taking personality tests. It is difficult to characterize such a tendency, especially since it may occur on several different bases. A patient in the hospital may, for instance, engage in a sort of psychiatric malingering for strictly conscious reasons, presenting a profile on a test such as the MMPI which shows abnormalities out of all reasonable proportion to what is apparent from other considerations. Again, there may be somewhat general traits of verbal pessimism or self-deprecation which, while of some relevance personologically, act so as to distort systematically the results of personality measurement. We shall dichotomize the test-attitude continuum by the two opposed terms "defensiveness" and "plus-getting," not implying anything as to the degree of conscious, deliberate deception involved in either. The corresponding *extremes*, where such deliberate deception seems likely, we shall refer to as "faking good" and "faking bad" respectively. It is recognized that, like the defensive tendency, the plus-getting tendency may exist in all degrees from a mild self-criticality or merely objectivity to a deliberate, conscious attempt to make oneself look psychiatrically abnormal. Whether this represents simply the extreme of a continuum with faking good at the opposite end, or an entirely new and different factor, we shall for the moment leave aside. At any rate it would be desirable to develop a scale for detecting these tendencies to put oneself in a bad light when answering a personality inventory, so that allowance might be made in such cases in the light of a deviant score obtained on such a scale. The F scale of the MMPI was not originally developed with this in mind, but subsequent evidence showed that it could be used in this way (see below). Presumably the two "correction" scales C_H [420 (see II, 6)] and C_D [301 (II, 7)] which were found necessary in the early attempts to detect hypochondriasis and symptomatic depression were at least partially dependent upon the operation of such a plus-getting tendency.

A systematic investigation of the plus-getting tendency was attempted by one of the present writers, which resulted in the development of a somewhat more generalized correction scale which was called N. The details of derivation and interpretation of this scale are reported elsewhere [435] and will not be repeated here. Suffice it to say that from a study of the item responses made by a group of presumably normal persons who showed abnormal MMPI profiles as contrasted with a group of clinically abnormal persons with matched profiles, a group of items was isolated which could be used to quantify in a rough fashion the plus-getting tendency. It was found that normal persons who show distinctly abnormal (maladjusted) profiles on the personality scales proper tended to answer this selected set of N items in the "obviously" maladjusted direction, which was with few exceptions also the direction of response given by a minority of the unselected normal population. In other words, a person who is clinically normal in spite of having an abnormal profile shows a tendency to give statistically uncommon answers which are also "maladjusted" answers in the sense that by inspection they would be considered evidence of psychiatric involvement. For example, about 48 per cent of the unselected general population normals answer True to the item "A windstorm terrifies me." Yet we find that among those normals selected specifically for showing apparently *abnormal* profiles on the personality scales proper, about 62 per cent give an affirmative answer to this question. Persons having MMPI profiles no more deviant than these plus-getting normals, but who are actually abnormal clinically, give an affirmative answer about 26 per cent of the time. Thus if a person shows an otherwise deviant profile but states that he is terrified by windstorms he stands a better chance of being clinically normal than one who gives the a priori more "normal" or "adjusted" response. Similar items on the N scale include such things as "I am afraid of fire," "I have a fear of water," "People often disappoint me," "I did not like school," and so on. Inspection of these items and an examination of the correlations between N and the other MMPI scales led to a conviction that the N scale was actually detecting a diffuse plus-getting tendency of the sort described. It was further shown that either the inspectional or the mechanical use of the N scale in order to under-interpret profiles having the plus-getting tendency led to a reduction in the number of false positives in identification of psychiatric cases. However, the N scale was rather long, and was also apparently loaded with genuine psychiatric factors which led to an undesirable under-interpretation of profiles belonging to grossly abnormal persons. It is therefore to be seen merely as a beginning attempt which was supplanted by K, as will be described below.

MMPI Scale F

The MMPI variables F and L were not formally validated originally, but were presented on face validity, that is, we assumed their validity on a priori grounds. The F variable was composed of 64 items that were selected primarily because they were answered with a relatively low frequency in either the true or false direction by the main normal group; the scored direction of response is the one which is rarely made by unselected normals. Additionally, the items were chosen to include a variety of content so that it was unlikely that any particular pattern would cause an individual to answer many of the items in the unusual direction. A few examples are these: "Everything tastes the same." (True) "I believe in law enforcement." (False) "I see things, animals, or people around me that others do not see." (True) The relative success of this selection of items, with the deliberate intent of forcing the average number of items answered in an unusual direction downward, is illustrated in the fact that the mean score on the 64 items runs between two and four points for all normal groups. The distribution curve is, of course, very skewed positively; and the higher scores approach half the number of items. In distributions of ordinary persons the frequency of scores drops very rapidly at about seven and is at the 2 or 3 per cent level by score twelve. Because of this quick cutting off of the curve the scores seven and twelve were arbitrarily assigned T-scored values of 60 and 70 in the original F table.

From the first it was recognized that F represented several things. Most simply, since the subject would need to sort almost all the items according to expectation in order for these low scores to result, any error in recording, such as mistaking true items for false items and the like, would raise the F score appreciably. Similarly, if a subject could not understand what he was reading adequately enough to make conventional answers to these items, the F score would obviously be higher. It was felt to be axiomatic that this method would eliminate as invalid records of subjects who could not read and comprehend or who refused to cooperate sufficiently to make expected placements.

In addition, however, it was early discovered that schizoid subjects and subjects who apparently wished to put themselves in a bad light also obtained high scores. The schizoid group obtained high scores because, owing to delusional or other aberrant mental states, they said very unusual things in responding to the items and thus obtained high F scores. This is referred to as distortion since we feel that an impartial study would not justify the patient's placements. Among more normal persons some high scores were also observed where the individual had rather unusual ways of responding to conventional stimuli such as are represented by the items involved. For example, to the item "I have had periods in which I carried on activities without knowing later what I had been doing," most persons answered False. Some persons, however, included periods of sleep in the implication of the item. One might argue that such ways of thinking are often allied to schizoid mentation generally and that the answers in this case indicate a true abnormality. At the very least, however, the person is responding to some items in a way that differs from that of most individuals. Such persons might, therefore, not be appropriately approached through this method of personality measurement. It seems a reasonable enough possibility that there are individuals whose habitual ways of reacting to items are so different from their fellows that measurement of their personalities through the use of verbal items of this type would reflect the unusualness of their reactions to the items more than any clinical abnormality. This semantic factor has been treated more completely elsewhere [r16, r52, 435]. Insofar as such a possibility may exist we have not yet separated it from the clinically more important abnormality expressed in the Sc scale. Parenthetically, one of the most persistent difficulties with developing the Sc scale was this very fact, that an appreciable number of individuals obtained high scores on Sc without being marked by a clinically important degree of abnormality. They nevertheless, as indicated above, were responding differently from other people about them as represented by the original data from the general population. It appears that the essential difference clinically is concerned with the particular manifestation of unusual mentation in the individual. If this is not too clearly counter to society's mores, the person may not be thought of as schizoid by those about him though he is often recognized as queer.

Clinical experience suggests that the usual critical score of $T = 70$ is too low in the case of F. We have found that scores ranging up to $T = 80$ (raw score 16) are more often a reflection of "validly" unusual symptoms and attitudes than an indication of invalidity in the rest of the profile due to misunderstanding, etc. Raw scores much above this, however, strongly suggest an invalid record.

With the problems of measurement that developed in the armed forces where a subject might be expected frequently to attempt to put himself in a bad light in answering the MMPI, the F score became especially interesting. It was, of course, immediately possible to consider the F score as an evidence of this attempt to malinger and obtain fallaciously bad scores on other scales. As a check on this interpretation, a group of 54 ASTP men who had completed a considerable portion of their training in psychology were asked to take the MMPI twice. The group took it in the usual way and also took it under instructions to assume that they wished to avoid being accepted in the draft and in order to be rejected they were to obtain adverse scores without giving themselves away. Half the group took it with "fake" instructions first, half second. Through this plan we had a "faked bad" record and a "normal" record. The data showed that 96 per cent of the "faked bad" records had a raw score F of 15 or more ($T \geqq 78$), indicating that even these men who were somewhat cognizant of psychological measurements betrayed themselves when they attempted to fake a bad record. The resulting profiles were nearly all unusually abnormal in character, and to one who has seen a large number of abnormal profiles, most of them would have appeared invalid from their pattern alone.

From this experiment it appeared that F was a very good device for identifying the intentional faking that could be set up in an experimental situation. It still seemed desirable, however, to attempt to separate among the individuals obtaining relatively high F scores those who were of the above-described schizoid type or who were simply overpessimistic in their view of themselves, from those who for one reason or another faked a bad score or did not understand the items.

The L Scale

The original 15 L items making up the L scale were selected under the inspiration of the work of Hartshorne and May. Each of the items presents a situation desirable socially, but rarely true of the individual. For example in the item "I read all the editorials in the newspaper every day," we have a type of behavior that might be generally considered desirable but which is true of only a small percentage of the population. It was recognized that very conscientious persons would frequently have more than the average number of these L items truly positive but for a person to have six or eight of them seemed almost impossibly good. The 15 items of this type scattered among the main body of the items constituted a fairly subtle trap for anyone who wanted to give an unusually good impression of himself.

Among the various normal groups the mean score on the L items lies between three and five. As in the case of F the frequency curves are all skewed sharply in the positive direction. Very few individuals obtain raw scores of seven or more, and the 2 or 3 per cent level is at about ten. These values were arbitrarily called the 60 and 70 T-score points, respectively. As the L score was used in the clinical setting and as some data began to accumulate from personnel workers in industrial situations, it became apparent that the assumptions regarding the meaning of L were in the main correct, but that there were also other valid interpretations of L, at least in the range from T score 56 to 70. In fact we found ourselves placing considerable emphasis on T scores of 56 to 60, which indicated that the original arbitrary assignment of T scores had been too conservative. On the other hand while the positive presence of the rise in the L score seemed quite valid as an indicator that the individual taking the test was being dishonest and might be somewhat unreliable, if no rise in L was observed, the finding could not be so positively and clearly interpreted. The L score was a trap for the naive subject but more sophisticated subjects easily avoided it.

To check the assumption that L would not identify the more sophisticated subject an experiment was performed with ASTP psychology students. As in the study cited above, 53 men were given the MMPI twice. The "faked good" data were obtained by instructing the men to make certain in taking the test that they would be acceptable to army induction. These records showed no appreciable rise in L. It is also true, however, that the majority of the profiles were only slightly, if any, better than the corresponding non-fake profiles. This experiment would have been improved if persons whose true profiles were abnormal had been used. Some data have been collected from such cases but the number is small. At least, one may conclude that the intent to deceive is not often detectable by L when the subjects are relatively normal and sophisticated.

The K Scale

In summary there were two basic lines of experimental approach to the problem of identifying the attitude a subject takes toward the items that he is faced with in the personality inventory [642 (IV, 22)]. Each of these two approaches permits a subdivision into several methods. First, we may have the subject deliberately assume a generally defined attitude, as in the study by Ruch. For example, we may ask him to attempt deliberately to obtain adverse scores while not betraying his in-

tention, and secondly, we may choose records in which there is presumptive likelihood that a special attitude has been assumed. The first approach may be subdivided
into those experiments in which the "faking" is directed toward obtaining adverse
scores and the approach in which the intention is to obtain desirable scores. In both
latter cases an additional set of responses must be obtained relatively simultaneously with the "faked" responses in which the individual assumes his ordinary attitude. The "faked" and "normal" records can then be contrasted for study. One may
make an item analysis to discover the items that are most frequently changed from
the "normal" records as contrasted to the "fake" records. By use of these "fake"
approaches, several scales were derived.

It was found that the items indicating an attempt to obtain a bad record are not
necessarily those derived by analysis of records where the subjects attempted to
obtain a good record. Our first finding in this regard was that either of these procedures provided a scale that would be about as good for the other type of faking
as it was for the one from which it was derived when such scales were applied to
test cases not used in the original derivations. It was further found that using two
such scales separately did not materially increase the predictive value. As has already been pointed out, it was also found that the original F scale was as effective as
was needed to identify those persons who intentionally attempted to obtain a bad
score, at least within the range of the experiments that we conducted. Conversely,
the L scale was not effective nor were any of the specially derived scales especially
effective in identifying sophisticated persons who deliberately attempted to obtain
better scores. In all these experiments the findings were so complex and the time devoted to many subprojects was so great that we shall only present data for the final
scale K (see below).

In the second line of experimental approach there are also several subdivisions.
One may find among presumably functional and normal records those records which
are so abnormal as to indicate that the individual should have been in a hospital
and attempt to discover the items among these records that will differentiate them
from the records of actually abnormal persons. For the counterpart to this approach
one chooses cases who were in the hospital but whose records show a normal profile.
These may likewise be compared by item analysis to the records of hospital patients
with suitably abnormal profiles who would be assumed to have had no interfering
test-taking attitude. Using this approach we also derived several scales and made
many experimental tests of them. Again the details of all of these are not worthy
of the complex presentation they would require and these preliminary results will
merely be summarized.

The first and most important finding was that whichever of these methods was
used, as was the case with the "faked" approach above, the resultant scales were
about equally effective and about equally unsatisfactory regardless of the approach
and of the particular item content. These scales were also rather effective in differentiating the "fake" group and in some cases were just as valid for that purpose
as were the scales derived by that approach. After some two years of this experimentation all the scales that had shown any promise were reconsidered by applying
them to various available groups that had not been used in their derivation and
from among them all a single scale which was originally called L$_6$ was chosen as
the best. It should be recognized that L$_6$ was not entirely satisfactory but its action

in several of the sample situations resulted in its tentative adoption. Although as indicated in the above summary the particular derivation does not seem to play an important part since we could not easily distinguish a scale as having been derived by a special process when we examined its action, nevertheless it may be desirable to tell how L_6 was derived. It must not be forgotten that several other scales resulting from the other methods were very nearly as good as was L_6, especially the plus-getting scale N. However, when the N scale and L_6 were compared and even applied to the test situation set up for the N scale, L_6 was a close competitor to N and in several instances was actually better.

In brief, L_6 was derived by an item analysis of the responses of 25 males and 25 females in a psychopathic hospital whose profiles showed an L score of T = 60 or more and who, with the exception of six normal cases, had diagnoses indicating the probability that they should have had abnormal profiles but whose profiles were in reality within the normal range. The diagnoses given to these cases by the psychiatric staff were mostly psychopathic personality, alcoholism, and allied descriptive terms indicating behavior disorders rather than neuroses. In general one would expect persons with such diagnoses to be rather more likely to be defensive in taking a personality test than cases of psychoneurosis. There are a few exceptions, however, in the case of hysteria where as has been pointed out in previous papers [423 (see II, 9), 433 (I, 1), 435] there is a tendency for the hysteria to be based upon something closely allied to the assuming of an overly perfect attitude in answering personality items. A particular listing of the diagnoses among these cases is not given here because the diagnostic categories are not clear enough to be of additional value. In summary, two criteria were employed in the selection of the criterion group. Practically all of them were individuals known to be characterized by deviant behavior but they obtained relatively normal profiles and were thus what we have called misses for the MMPI; and all of these criterion cases were also characterized by having a tendency to obtain elevated scores on the original L scale.

The item responses of these fifty cases handled separately for males and females were compared to the male and female item frequencies from the general group of males and females that has been used in past scale derivations. In all, 22 items were chosen as a result of this comparison. All these items showed a percentage difference of 30 or more between the criterion cases and the control group.

These 22 items are given below with a T or an F to indicate the direction of the answer that would agree with the tendency of the criterion group. Since the criterion group is assumed to be a group with intent to obtain good scores the larger raw scores on these items are in the same direction as the larger raw scores on the original L scale. The content of these items would seem to suggest an attitude of denying worries, inferiority feelings, and psychiatrically unhealthy symptoms, together with a disposition to see only good in others as well as oneself. The over-all impression is one of "impunitiveness" if we may apply Rosenzweig's term in a situation where no particular frustration is involved.

B-55. I have very few quarrels with members of my family. (T) C-18. I worry over money and business. (F) C-27. It makes me impatient to have people ask my advice or otherwise interrupt me when I am working on something important. (F) C-33. It takes a lot of argument to convince most people of the truth. (F) D-53. I think nearly anyone would tell a lie to keep out of trouble. (F) D-54. Most people will use somewhat unfair means to gain profit or an advantage rather than to lose it. (F)

E-43. When in a group of people I have trouble thinking of the right things to talk about. (F) E-44. I find it hard to make talk when I meet new people. (F) E-52. People often disappoint me. (F) F-8. It makes me uncomfortable to put on a stunt at a party even when others are doing the same sort of things. (F) F-33. Often I can't understand why I have been so cross and grouchy. (F) F-34. Criticism or scolding hurts me terribly. (F) F-43. At periods my mind seems to work more slowly than usual. (F) F-46. I frequently find myself worrying about something. (F)

G-18. I have periods in which I feel unusually cheerful without any special reason. (F) G-29. I get mad easily and then get over it soon. (F) G-30. At times my thoughts have raced ahead faster than I could speak them. (F) G-31. At times I feel like smashing things. (F) I-22. I have often met people who were supposed to be experts who were no better than I. (F) I-31. I have sometimes felt that difficulties were piling up so high that I could not overcome them. (F) I-37. I certainly feel useless at times. (F) I-38. I often think "I wish I were a child again." (F)

Following the final choice of L_6 as the best of the scales available, we subjected it to more careful study and went back through hospital and normal records to find out if it seemed to be of any help in interpreting individual profiles. There were relatively few data on normal cases but on hospital cases a fairly extensive symptomatic summary was available that would permit us to judge whether or not a patient should have had a normal profile. We could then look up the profile and if it was normal we could check to see if the L_6 deviated in an upward direction indicating that the patient had attempted to place himself in a good light. As a result of this study L_6 appeared effective but left much to be desired.

Since in the summary of scales when L_6 was chosen for intensive study it had seemed about as adequate for the detection of plus-getting as was N or any of the other experimental scales, the records of a new series of presumably normal persons showing deviant profiles were examined and it was again true that L_6 appeared to work at the plus-getting end of the test-attitude continuum. That is to say, a relatively low score on L_6 could be used to under-interpret an otherwise deviant profile and so avoid some of the presumably false positives in the normal population sample. Thus L_6 seemed useful at "both ends" of the test-attitude continuum, defensiveness and plus-getting.

The most outstanding difficulty in such a procedure was that L_6 tended to be low on severe depressive or schizophrenic patient records and thus led to an under-interpretation in spite of the fact that the patients were very grossly abnormal. To partly correct for this tendency, items were added that would work in the opposite direction. To choose these we studied the item tabulations for the group of ASTP men who had attempted to fake good and bad scores. In this study there were many items which showed no tendency to change with an alteration in the test-taking attitude. That is, the percentage of true or false, as the case might be, remained constant whether the attitude was the normal one or the faked one. From among these items, a subgroup was chosen which showed differences between schizophrenic and depressive criterion groups and general population normals. The procedure rested upon the admittedly somewhat shaky assumption that any item that did not appear to be much affected by the test-taking attitude as approached by a normal person attempting consciously to "fake" good or bad but which did occur as a frequent item to differentiate depressed or schizophrenic patients would be useful in correcting the tendency of our L_6 scale to go too low for schizophrenic and depressed patients. Of course such an item was scored in a way that would make it work against the tendency of the L_6 scale. Eight items were selected by this method. The effect of adding these 8 items to the 22 on L_6 was to elevate slightly the mean score of normals and make it more nearly approach the mean score of abnormal cases on the complex of all 30 items. The 8 items chosen by this procedure are given below. The letter F indicates the response scored in the "lie" direction, and in the direction characteristic of schizophrenic and depressed cases.

A-3. I have never felt better in my life than I do now. (F) C-28. I find it hard to set aside a task that I have undertaken, even for a short time. (F) D-48. I think a great many people exaggerate their misfortunes in order to gain the sympathy and help of others. (F) D-51. I am against giving money to beggars. (F) F-7. What others think of me does not bother me. (F) F-20. I like to let people know where I stand on things. (F) G-23. At times I am all full of energy. (F) J-51. At times I feel like swearing. (F)

As a final step these 8 items were combined with the 22 L_6 items into a single scale which we have called K. The K scale represents the final outcome of many experiments in the general field of measuring test attitude. The K scale is far from perfect for its purpose as measured by the various available data. Generally speaking it is about as good as any other single scale derived for any one of the single purposes that have been described. In individual applications it is inferior now to one scale and now to another but the differences are never great enough to be very significant practically and the small number of items in this scale gives it a distinct advantage over one or two of the longer scales such as N. Finally, as was stated above it is not expedient to present more than a single scale although a slight advantage could have been gained if two scales analogous to the original L and F scales had been separately presented.

The construction of K being what it was, odd-even or Kuder-Richardson reliabilities were not computed. Test-retest coefficients were .72 and .74 computed on two groups, one of which was retested at intervals varying from one day to over a year, the other after a lapse of 4–15 months.

Since the K scale was derived as a correction scale or suppressor variable [r76, r115] for improving the discrimination yielded on the already existent personality scales, it was not assumed to be measuring anything which in itself is of psychiatric significance. Actually, its relationship with such clinical variables as the subtle Hy items (see below) might suggest an interpretation of K alone; further, it is presumably a significant fact about a person that, in answering a personality inventory, he tends to behave as a "liar" or a "plus-getter." However, the real function of K is intended to be the correction of the other scores, and validity will be discussed with reference to this function only.

It is first necessary to choose criterion cases of the sort on which K can conceivably be of value. It is clear that such cases will be characterized by the presence of what may be called *borderline* profiles, i.e., those showing T scores, say, between 65 and 80. The reason for this is that in studying hundreds of deviant profiles after the addition of K, almost no individuals were found with T scores above 80 in the normal sample, and it was not statistically profitable to correct elevations of such magnitude to the point of calling them normal. On the other hand, when a curve shows no elevations at all above 65, even the presence of a high K score does not enable the clinician to form any adequate notion of what the peak, if any, would have been, had the K factor not been operating to distort the results. In other words, there are upper and lower limits beyond which deviations on K cannot effectively operate. Profiles showing scores above 80 are to be interpreted as probably "abnormal" no matter how low K falls; while if a profile shows no scores above 65 we cannot tell whether a high K means the profile should be adjusted toward more severe scores or is merely that of an actually normal person who for some reason or other took a defensive attitude when being tested. The kind of curve which gives interpretative difficulty and which could conceivably be improved by knowledge of the influence of K would be a curve in the doubtful, borderline region. Accordingly, a group of cases from the normal and hospital groups was chosen on the basis of having achieved such borderline curves. We selected for this study all cases in the files showing at least one personality component (excluding Mf) elevated as high as T = 65, but no component elevated to T > 80. Among the normals, there were 174 having such borderline curves, of which 71 were males and 103 were females. Corresponding to these cases, 129 males and 208 females with similar borderline profiles were located among our clinically abnormal cases. The data for the two sexes were treated separately.

The analysis of these data was in terms of the ability of the K scale, used mechanically as will be described, to separate the curves of the actual normals from those of the actual abnormals. For each sex group, the procedure was to arrange the whole set (normals and abnormals combined) in order of the magnitude of their K scores. The distribution of K was cut on the basis of the proportion of normals and abnormals in the sample, with all cases above the cut called "abnormal" and all those below "normal." A fourfold table was set up on this basis, and chi squares of 20.436 for the males and 29.540 for the females were obtained. Both of these are highly significant (p < .001) with 1 df. If, instead of locating an optimal cutting score, the K distribution is cut at the mean of the general population K distribution (i.e., at T = 50 regardless of the present samples) the cutting point of the males is unchanged, whereas that for the females shifts enough to lower their chi square to 17.750, which is still highly significant. In other words, if one considers miscellaneous profiles which lie in the borderline range between 65 and 80, regardless of the kind of elevation and irrespective of the clinical diagnosis of those who are clinically abnormal, he can separate them into "actual" normals and abnormals significantly better than chance by using a cutting score on K. It must be emphasized again that K in this instance is operating chiefly as a suppressor of certain test-taking tendencies, since K by itself does not practically differentiate unselected normal and abnormal cases (difference of 1 to 2½ raw score points between means for various samples). In terms of percentages, it was found that for the males 72 per cent of the abnormals and 61 per cent of the actual normals were correctly identified. For the females, 66 per cent of the abnormals were identified as such and 59 per cent of the normals were so classified. These percentages are based upon the separations at a K = 50, and take, therefore, no account of the actual normal-abnormal proportions among the present cases.

Evidence from examination of the test misses spotted by K in the above data, combined with our knowledge of the correlation between K and other MMPI scales, indicated that the K correction was more important in the case of some scales than of others. Therefore, it was decided to analyze the borderline groups in terms of the peak elevation of their profiles, in the attempt to identify those particular curves on which K could be used with profit.

The entire group of 511 borderline curves (males and females, normals and abnormals pooled) was divided into eight subgroups, each subgroup being composed of cases having the peak score on the same one of the eight personality components. Thus, there were 60 curves having the peak on Hs, 91 on D, 119 on Hy, 66 on Pd, 38 on Pa, 25 on Pt, 28 on Sc, and 52 on Ma. (The difference between this total of 479 cases and the 511 used in getting the over-all chi square is due to the exclusion of 32 profiles on which no "peak" could be fairly assigned, since two or more of the components showed identical T scores and these were the highest on the given curve.)

The normals and abnormals having borderline curves with the same peak score were then separated mechanically by the use of a cutting score on K, the proportion of cases above the cutting score being determined on the basis of the proportion of actual abnormals versus normals in each subgroup. This was unavoidable in the present analysis because the relative proportions of actual normals and abnormals varied widely from scale to scale and the use of the mean of K would have been grossly misleading since in some instances the proportions were extremely asymmetrical [r176]. For the eight groups studied in this manner, only three showed a significant chi square (p < .01), namely those having peaks on Hs, Pd, and Sc. The Ma group yielded a chi square between the .10 and .20 level of significance. On D, Hy, Pa, and Pt the chi squares were all below the .20 level of significance; and the pooled chi square for these five scales (5 df) gave a p > .22. It would seem, therefore, that the K factor may be used with profit in interpreting some kinds of profiles but not others. Of course, the failure to discriminate with K when grouping profiles by peak score does not establish that a K correction might not be profitably added to the single scores themselves. This problem will be treated at length in a sequel to the present paper [424 (see II, 11)].

One other validating study was done on K. In this instance, we made use of a group of 22 normals and 22 abnormals employed in a previous study [435]. The normals in this set consisted of a random selection from a large group of profiles showing any elevation of 70 or over (excluding Mf). The abnormals consisted of a heterogeneous group also having at least one score over 70, and included seven psychoneurotics, seven schizophrenics, three psychopaths, two alcoholics, two manic-depressives (depressed), and one paranoid state, chosen randomly from recent hospital cases. These groups had been selected for a different purpose and had not entered into the derivation of K in any way. They can also be considered, therefore, a fair test group for validation purposes. Without regard for any other information concerning the profiles, all cases showing K > 50 were arbitrarily guessed as abnormals, whereas those with K < 50 were called normals. The cutting score was therefore also independent of the statistics of the present group. Here the

K scale worked phenomenally well, being much better than the N scale (which was derived on cases some of which were included in this blind diagnosis study). Of the entire group of 44 cases, 37 were correctly classified when K was used in this way, a total of 85 per cent hits. It will be recalled that we are here trying to separate normals and abnormals all of whom have deviant profiles, so that this percentage is quite impressive considering the task set for K. Of the seven errors in classifying, six are "false positives," i.e., cases of normals showing elevated profiles and K >50, called therefore abnormal. The chi square for the fourfold table of these data is 21.569 which with 1 df is highly significant (p < .001). This corresponds to a contingency coefficient of .57. Here we have striking evidence of the validity of K when used to differentiate between deviant curves of actual normals and abnormals. We are not prepared to explain the superiority of this result to that given by the analysis previously discussed, except to say that the range of abnormal scores in the present analysis was from 70 to 90 whereas in the previous analysis we used "borderline" scores defined as lying between 65 and 80. In what way this could make K appear to function more effectively in the one case than the other is not clear. Also the present study involved only males, on whom K in general seems to work a little better than on females.

The fact that K is less effective as applied to some scales than others would suggest separate interpretations or cutting scores depending upon the kind of profile with which one is confronted. Furthermore, the rough classification into "normal" and "abnormal" on the basis of a single arbitrary cutting score obviously sacrifices some quantitative information about the actual magnitude of the personality scale elevations with respect to the magnitude of the K score. We do not intend to propose such a rough cutting method as the most efficient manner of application for K, but are using that form here simply to indicate that K has differentiating power for what it was hoped to differentiate. The optimal mathematical procedure in using K as a suppressor involves complex issues which we shall have to reserve for a later publication.

Relation of K to Other Test Variables

The correlation of the K scale with other MMPI variables should throw some light upon the question of its differential efficiency on these scales, as well as give us some insight into its psychological nature. Table 1 below shows the intercorrelations of K with the other personality components measured by the MMPI. These correlations are based upon 100 cases, chronological ages 26–45, in each of the four groups indicated, excluding records having "?" > 70 or F > 80.

Of interest in this table are the following facts. With the exception of Hy and one of the four coefficients of D, the correlations are consistently negative. This is

Table 1. Intercorrelations of K with Other MMPI Variables

Group	Hs	D	Hy	Pd	Pa	Pt	Sc	Ma	Mf
Normal males.........	−.30	.15	.48	−.17	−.07	−.67	−.59	−.36	
Normal females.......	−.35	−.03	.30	−.06	−.02	−.64	−.58	−.28	
Abnormal males.......	−.42	−.29	.11	−.26	−.19	−.60	−.60	−.37	−.08
Abnormal females.....	−.17	−.16	.17	−.21	−.13	−.63	−.58	−.38	.04

of course to be expected if K represents the defensive, lying, or self-deceptive test-taking attitude it was derived to measure. The negative correlations with Hs combined with the positive correlations with Hy indicate that there must be a fairly high positive correlation between K and those nonsomatic items on Hy which have been previously referred to — the "zero" items on Hy or what Harmon and Wiener [645] have called "Hy-subtle" (henceforth designated Hy-S). Since this latter set of items, although derived by its empirical separation of clinical hysterias from normals, seems to reflect the self-deceptive and impunitive attitude of the hysterical temperament, it is consonant with our interpretation of K that it should be markedly correlated with Hy-S. The direct evidence on this point will be reported below. The only correlations of very impressive magnitude which appear in this table are those with Pt and Sc. Here they are high negative — the person who makes responses characteristic of compulsive and schizoid persons has the opposite of the self-deceptive and defensive attitude. In other words, he tends to be a plus-getter and in this way is distinctly unlike the hysteric. These correlations are also in harmony with our clinical knowledge of the components in question, especially in the case of the psychasthenia. The Pt scale has never been considered very satisfactory, and it has been shown in unpublished studies that Pt can actually be used as a correction scale in the way in which N was used. It is perhaps significant that of all the MMPI scales, Pt is the only one for which, since there was not a sufficiently large criterion group, methods of internal consistency were employed in the item selection. Here again we would expect to get a greater operation of nonclinical test-taking factors of the K variety.

It might be thought that such low correlations as occur in the table above would preclude any possibility of the use of K as a suppressor. There is a tendency for the scales on which K seems "valid" by the chi square test to show the higher correlations, with the exception of Pt. It will be shown in a subsequent paper that, for the use to which K is put, correlations as low as .20 can be utilized to yield very significant and useful improvements in discrimination [424 (see II, 11)].

At this point we may briefly review some of the previously developed scales which are now known to be saturated with what we may call the K factor, since their diverse sources and methods of derivation furnish additional strong evidence for our theoretical interpretation of K. Two of these scales have never been published, so that their derivation and properties must be briefly summarized here. About three years before research on the test-taking attitude was begun, Hathaway and W. K. Estes, using a variant of the method of internal consistency, developed a scale called G. This scale is the only MMPI scale which was derived without the use of any kind of criterion external to the test; like those personality tests being developed by factor analytic methods at the present time, the selection and scoring of items were based wholly upon the intercorrelations among the items themselves. Essentially, the procedure consisted in locating among a group of 101 unselected normals those individuals who, when their answer sheets were used as scoring keys, produced the maximum variance of the other 100 scores. The assumption was that these persons were the most extreme deviates on whatever factor or factors contributed most heavily to the variance and covariance of the total pool of MMPI items. From the evidence adduced by Mosier [r124], it is of course clear that the "purity" or factorial unity of this hypothetical underlying continuum is by no means guaranteed by such a procedure. Another way of looking at this procedure is to consider the fact that one maximizes the variance of a set of items by scoring them in such a direction as to maximize their mean covariance—since the item variances are unaffected by the direction of scoring. Instead of actually calculating the variances for the 2^{550} ways of scoring the test, we select *individuals* who approximate the optimal scoring key. It was found that the scoring keys for some 10 individuals selected by this method tended to form two distinct clusters, each of which consisted of keys (individuals) showing high correlations with one another and high negative correlations with the members of the other cluster. An item analysis was then carried out on these two small groups, and the items resulting were combined into a scale called G (general factor).

The G scale had a number of interesting properties which were not interpretable at the time of its derivation. It showed a very large variability, both in absolute terms and as indicated by a coefficient of variation. The scores *among normals* ranged from those who answered none of the items in the scored direction, to those who answered all but 8 of the 62 items in the scored direction—a phenomenon unheard of in the other MMPI scales. The odd-even reliability of G was about .93, which is considerably higher than the coefficients we typically find in the MMPI scales. The item content was that of the typical "neurotic" or "maladjustment" sort which predominates on a priori scales such as the Thurstone or Bernreuter B_1N. Examples of items are these: "When in a group of people I have trouble thinking of the right things to talk about" (T); "I cry easily" (T); "I am certainly lacking in self confidence" (T). It is perhaps significant that the most powerful single item in the internal consistency sense—which happens in the sample studies to have a correlation of 1.00 with the entire G scale—is almost a distilled essence or prototype of so-called neurotic schedule items: "I am easily embarrassed" (T). The G scale, although derived without recourse to any clinical group whatever, nevertheless showed a correlation of .91 with Pt. The mean MMPI curves for unselected normals with high G (the "neurotic" end) showed elevations on F, Hs, D, Pd, Pa, Pt, Sc, and Ma, especially on Pt and Sc, whereas L (raw score) and Hy tended to fall below the mean. The mean profile for normals with low G was almost an exact mirror image of this curve. However, G was not found to be very effective in the detection of any clinical group or to be particularly useful for any purpose; and since at that time no theoretical basis was available for interpreting it, the scale was abandoned. Another scale, called + ("plus"), was derived in a similar but not identical manner.

In the derivation of the original hypochondriasis key, there was developed a correction scale called C_H, the function of which was to separate actual clinical hypochondriacs from a group of nonhypochondriacal abnormals (mostly schizophrenic and depressed) who attained spuriously elevated scores on H. The item content of this C_H key was quite puzzling, because although the correction was successful, the items did not seem to refer to anything either hypochondriacal or anti-hypochondriacal. In fact it was difficult to see what psychological homogeneity, if any, they possessed. For a more detailed description of this scale (now no longer in use since the appearance of the modified Hs key) the reader is referred to the original article [420 (see II, 6)]. For present purposes it is merely necessary to state that the great majority of the items on C_H were scored if answered in the statistically rare and obviously "maladjusted" direction and that they apparently measured some nonsomatic component of test responses which resulted in spuriously elevated H scores in persons who were not actually hypochondriacal.

Still another scale of the same general sort was derived by Meehl and called N. To repeat briefly what has been said above, this scale differentiated normals showing elevated profiles from clinical abnormals showing no greater profile elevations, and was interpreted as detecting a plus-getting test attitude for which scores on the personality components proper should be corrected. The type of item occurring on the scale N has been discussed above.

Lastly, we recall to mind the Hy-S items which have been described above as reflecting this kind of component, although scored in the opposite direction from N, C_H, and G.

It is of considerable interest to examine the correlations between K and these other variables, derived in their diverse ways. Table 2 presents the correlations between K and the various scales thought to be loaded with the factor in question; the correlations are based upon scores of 100 individuals ages 26–45 in each of the groups indicated.

Table 2. Correlations of the K Scale with Other Variables
Thought to Be Loaded with the "K Factor"

Group	+	G	N	C_H	Hy-S
Normal males..........	−.64	−.76	−.70	−.67	.81
Normal females.........	−.62	−.73	−.64	−.63	.78
Abnormal males........	−.70	−.75	−.69	−.64	.74
Abnormal females.......	−.70	−.81	−.72	−.71	.74

Considering the relative unreliability of some of these variables, the above is a very impressive group of intercorrelations. We have two scales (G and +) which were derived wholly by internal item relationships and without regard to criteria of any nontest behavior; a scale (N) which corrects for the self-criticality of certain plus-getters who show deviant profiles; a scale (C_H) which differentiates hypochondriacs from nonhypochondriacal abnormals who have elevated H scores; and a subset of items (Hy-S) which were chosen because they differentiate a clinical group—hysterics. There is, however, a considerable item overlap among these scales, tending to raise these correlations. On the other hand, it will be recalled that the scale K is not actually "pure" for the hypothetical test-taking attitude because it is a composite of the test-taking scale L_6 plus the eight "psychotic" items. This would presumably tend to lower the correlations. Accordingly, we have substituted L_6 for K, removed the item overlap among the scales G, N, C_H, L_6, and Hy-S, and calculated correlations among these reduced keys. Table 3 shows the interrelations among these five nonoverlapping keys, based upon the responses of 150 unselected normal males between the ages of 26 and 45; records with ? > 70 or F > 80 were rejected. All scales were scored so as to render the correlations positive.

This correlational matrix has been subjected to a factor analysis, repeated three times in successively approximating the communalities because of the small number of tests. The first factor extracted leaves no residuals larger than .049, and the SD of the residuals is .032, which is less than the SE of .041 attached to the mean r in the matrix. When the significance of the residuals was tested by the formula chi square $= \Sigma(z_0 - z)^2 (n - 3)$ the chi square on the deviation of observed r's from those predicted with the first factor loading was not significant (chi square $= 5.101$, 5 df, p $> .30$). It appears that one common factor is quite sufficient to account for the intercorrelations of these scales. The factor loadings of the scales G, C_H, L_6, N, and Hy-S are .927, .868, .847, .818, and .770 respectively. It is interesting to find such a powerful factor running through scales derived by such diverse methods. It is

Table 3. Intercorrelations of Five Scales Thought to Be Loaded
with the Test-Taking Attitude, No Item Overlap
(N = 150 Normal Males)

Scale	G	C_H	L_6	N
C_H	.82			
L_6	.76	.71		
N	.78	.73	.66	
Hy-S	.70	.63	.70	.59

also worth noticing that the largest loading of the K factor is in the one scale constructed wholly by "internal consistency" methods, whereas the smallest loading is that of the clinical variable Hy-S. If we extract a second factor just to see what it looks like, none of the loadings is over .20 and the meaning of the second factor would be quite uninterpretable on our data. Although we have been thinking in terms of a "K factor" on the basis of the apparent community of practical function shown by these various scales, it is reassuring to find that the term "factor" may be used here without doing violence to the more technical meaning of that term as used by factor analysts.

Considering the nature of the items which are involved in scales such as L_6, N, and G, this finding perhaps sheds some light on the relative inadequacy of "neurotic" inventories such as the B_1N when applied to clinically diagnosed neurotics. Here we have a kind of item which, while it does not (in its own right) appear to discriminate normal from abnormal individuals very successfully, does reflect some kind of a test-attitude or self-critical component. Those "neurotic" persons who happen to be characterized by this particular manifestation of self-criticism, such as certain compulsives, will probably be differentiated by such a set of items. On the other hand, other equally "neurotic" persons such as hysterics, who are characterized by the opposite attitude, will not be successfully spotted by the scale. If anything, they should be discriminated backward! Furthermore, the central tendency of abnormals in general is the same as that of normals, and it is quite possible that in developing personality questionnaires set up in the traditional, a priori fashion and "refined" by statistical manipulation we are merely setting up groups of items to differentiate among people with respect to various test-attitude continua of little or no psychiatric relevance. It will be recalled that the scale G consisted of items having the heaviest loading with whatever factor (or factors) contribute most to the variance and covariance of the entire 550 items in the MMPI pool. Yet this scale turns out to have little or no clinical value (*except* as a suppressor) and to be the scale most saturated with respect to the test-taking attitude. We feel that psychologists have tended to forget the fact that when one constructs a personality inventory by studying the item associations, whether by old-fashioned methods of internal consistency or by factor analysis of item correlations, he is merely locating certain covariations in verbal behavior. When a final scale based upon that kind of derivation is presented to the clinician, all that the clinician can be assured of is that *persons who say certain things about themselves also have a tendency to say certain other things about themselves.*

Willoughby's argument [r170] that the non-chance covariation of item responses establishes "validity" with respect to *some* underlying, common trait which gives rise to the covariation may be admitted without contradicting what we have just said. That items should exhibit consistency in this covariant sense in spite of not being valid for the traits sought, or in fact even being negatively valid, has been shown by many studies, most particularly those of Landis and his associates [r93, r94, r131]. The "underlying disposition" which leads a subject to respond in a certain way to such questions may or may not be identical with the dispositions we recognize as clinical variables, or with those that might be suggested by the item content. It is quite clear on present evidence that this identification cannot be established by an assumed equivalence between nontest behavior and the verbal report. Hence, as has been repeatedly stressed by the present writers, both a priori selection of items and the psychological naming of a statistically homogenous scale from its item content are fraught with possibilities of error.

An obvious line of investigation which is suggested by these considerations is the systematic study of the relationships which exist among variables such as K, G, and N, which are fairly definitely known to be chiefly test-taking variables, and other personality scales which have been developed by variants of the method of internal consistency. Because of the influence of socioeconomic or educational level upon the K factor (see the section below) such studies should ideally be carried out upon subjects from the general population. At present, we can only report a few preliminary studies which seem to have some bearing upon this question. All these studies happen to be concerned with the batteries developed by Guilford and Martin (GAMIN, STDCR, and the Personnel Inventory). We wish to emphasize that the presentation of these scattered data on our part is intended simply to raise some questions concerning the construction of scales by internal consistency methods where factors such as K are probably in operation; the validity of the Guilford-Martin scales must of course be assessed upon other grounds. We wish further to stress that in comparing these tests with the MMPI we do not intend to set the latter up as a "criterion," although it does of course have the advantage that each item is known to differentiate certain defined criterion groups which literally define the scales on which the item occurs. It should also be made clear that Guilford, as one of the foremost contributors to the factor analytic approach to personality test construction, has explicitly called attention to the importance of the problem of test-taking attitudes as "factors," when he says:

We must constantly remember that the response of a subject may not represent exactly what the question implies in its most obvious meaning. Subjects respond to a question as at the moment they think they are, with perhaps a lack of insight in many cases as to their real position on the question. They also respond as they would like themselves to be and as they would like others to think them to be and as they wish the examiner to think them to be. They also respond with some regard to self-consistency among their own answers. Whether these determining factors are sufficiently constant to set up individual differences which are uniform in character and so constitute common factors in themselves is difficult to say. Should any one of them be so pervasive it should introduce an additional vector in the factor analysis. [r67, p. 118]

It is our opinion that the data we have presented indicate that the answer to Guilford's question is in the affirmative, and that the inclusion of a few K-type scales in a factor analysis would probably result in a somewhat different interpretation of the other tests and factors than would otherwise be the case.

Elaine Wesley [628] has studied the relationships existing between the Guilford-Martin Personnel Inventory of traits O-Ag-Co and the MMPI scales, using the test records of 110 presumably normal college women. The three traits measured by the Personnel Inventory are called *objectivity, agreeableness,* and *cooperativeness* by their authors. High scores are in the direction of the traits named, and low scores indicate the presence of what is called in composite the "paranoid" personality. Wesley found that the composite Personnel Inventory score correlated only .11 with the MMPI Pa scale which, while still in a preliminary stage, does consist of items which are empirically known to distinguish clearly paranoid groups of persons from people in general. Together with this rather disconcerting finding, she also discovered that the "paranoid" score on the Personnel Inventory correlated .50 and .57 with the MMPI scales Pt and Sc—both of which are relatively weak scales from the standpoint of clinical differentiation but are known to be heavily loaded with the K factor. The correlations of "objectivity" with Pt and Sc were both —.62, which led her to correlate trait O with the correction scale N, leading to the same figure. None of the other correlations of the Guilford scales with MMPI scales exceeded .45, and the majority of them were under .20. The mean MMPI profile of subjects selected on the basis of having low raw scores on N (the "defensive" end) showed a pattern hardly distinguishable from that of subjects selected for having high scores on factor O. It is interesting to note in passing that of the seven items of very similar wording which occur on both the Guilford-Martin Inventory and the MMPI Pa scale, five are scored as "paranoid" in the opposite direction on the two scales. For example, to say that most people inwardly dislike putting themselves out to help others, that most people would tell a lie to get ahead, that some people are so bossy and domineering that one feels like doing the opposite of what they tell him to do, are responses scored as paranoid on the Guilford-Martin; whereas it is found empirically that these verbal reactions are actually significantly *less* common among clinically paranoid persons than they are among people generally. This kind of finding suggests that paranoid deviates are characterized by a tendency to give two sorts of responses, one of which is obviously paranoid, the other "obviously" not. But these two sorts of responses are negatively correlated among people generally, and hence appear scored oppositely on scales developed by internal consistency methods.

It is of course possible to begin the development of scales by internal consistency or item-intercorrelation procedures, and having built a scale by these methods, to apply it to various criterion groups for validation. But it would seem that if the aim is to find items which will optimally perform such a discriminating function, the most direct route to that goal is immediate empirical item selection from the start.

It may be agreed that scales developed through item-correlation techniques have more statistical "purity" and hence are in a certain special sense better for what they *do* measure. One's attitude toward this problem is likely to reflect his more fundamental views as to the nature of a so-called measurement in personality testing, complete discussion of which would take us beyond the present paper. It seems clear that the results of factor analysis to date have not, whatever their theoretical validity, made possible the construction of single personality items which can be called even approximately "pure." For example, in Guilford's factor analysis of 89 personality items originally chosen (on the basis of suggestions from a previous factor analysis) to sample seclusiveness, thinking introversion, and rhathymia, after the extraction of nine different factors the majority of the items still showed communalities less than .50. Torrens [593], Wesley [628], and Loth [399] all found that the typical scale intercorrelation among the variables of the Guilford-Martin batteries STDCR, GAMIN, and the Personnel Inventory is actually higher than the typical intercorrelations of scales on the MMPI which were developed with almost no consideration for questions of scale purity or freedom from item overlap.

Louis Wesley (in a personal communication) has suggested that the contrast between the two methods of scale derivation is between *maximal measurement* and *meaningful measurement*. By this is meant that internal consistency methods lead to scales which measure whatever they measure with high consistency, large variance, great discrimination. This is "maximal" measurement. It is suggested that the most important nontest behaviors, which it is the aim of the test to predict, may not be associated with the same variables that lead to the kind of consistency involved. We may, as in the case of the Pa scale, have to sacrifice the desire to have high item intercorrelations in order to score items so as to achieve the more fundamental aim of criterion discrimination. Since scales are so very "impure" at best, there does not seem to be any very cogent reason for sacrificing anything in pursuit of the rather illusory purity involved.

There are multiple determiners which enter into a subject's decision when he answers a personality item. One might say that all but a very few personality items have an inherently "multiphasic" character, exceptions being such items as "I am a male." Obviously, if there existed or could be invented verbal items which were even approximately pure, the "scales" of such items could be extremely short and in fact the practical value of substituting an inventory for a few brief oral questions would be much in doubt. But the items are not uniquely determined. This simple behavioral fact imposes certain limitations upon the progress of personality measurement, as has been pointed out by many critics. From the common-sense point of view, the situation is not very different from what occurs in medical diagnosis or in the psychiatric interview. Almost all the symptoms or responses which are in evidence are known to arise upon diverse bases.

During a psychological interview, a woman may miscall her husband by the name of a former suitor, a phenomenon which is in itself ambiguous; perhaps she has recently seen the man in question, perhaps she has been reading a novel in which that name appears, and perhaps—the psychiatrically significant possibility— she feels somewhat regretful for not having married him instead. Later, we find that she developed a headache on her wedding anniversary, also an ambiguous datum if it stands alone. Again, she is excessively effusive about how happy her married life is, and so on. It is through the hypothesis of marital dissatisfaction that these different behaviors find a common explanation. When we accumulate such single items about her behavior, we are merely piling up the probabilities. It seems a little foolish to locate these behavior particles or their "sum" on a continuum of measurement, except in the most crude ordinal and probability sense. It is further quite likely that important configurational properties are also involved here, so that the significance to be assigned to one of these single facts should be a function of the other facts we know.

The traditional scoring procedure of simply counting *how many* responses belonging to a certain class have been made seems to be very crude; fortunately it has been repeatedly found that the various weightings, compositions, and nonlinear refinements which the behavioristic logic might suggest do not usually make sufficient practical difference in the ordering and sorting of people to be worth doing. The fact that we find it convenient to treat these behaviors in certain mathematical ways (independent scoring, unit weights, summation, linear transformations, etc.) should not mislead us into supposing that we are doing anything very close to what the physicist does when he cumulates centimeters. From this point of view, methods aimed at either "purity" or "internal consistency" are not easy to justify. At the very best, we have a rather heterogeneous collection of verbal responses which have a rough tendency to covary in strength. It may or may not be true that the most important (powerful) determiners of this tendency to covary are clinically relevant or personologically significant. For example, disliking one's husband is not the most powerful "factor" in determining the frequency of headaches among people generally. Nor is it the most potent factor in determining whether one calls him by the wrong name. Furthermore, the tendency to do these two things may not be covariant at all among people in general. None of these reasons, however, would lead us to reject the two facts in trying to evaluate the hypothesis of marital unhappiness.

From both the logical and statistical points of view, the best set of behavior data from which to predict a criterion is the set of data which are among themselves not correlated. This is well known and made use of in the combination of scales into batteries; but for some reason psychologists are uncomfortable if the same reasoning is applied within scales. The statistical considerations are of course quite general, applying as well to items as to scales. It is likely that the insistence upon high internal consistency and "item validity" in the item-test correlation sense springs in part from a feeling that all the items ought to be "doing the same thing." This certainly sounds like a reasonable demand as it stands, but it requires clarification. As is clear from the factor analysis studies, one simply cannot find any appreciable number of nonidentical verbal items which all "do the same thing." Every one of them depends upon many things, and the item as a unit is like the old-fashioned atom—uncuttable and hence permanently impure. Items "do the same thing" when they are so combined in pools that it is very unlikely that the subject will answer many of them in the scored direction unless he is characterized by a certain strength or range of nontest behaviors which in turn depend upon the one (or few) "variables" that are common to the items. It may still (unfortunately) be the case that the heaviest contribution to each item consists of variables other than the ones we are interested in. That this is in fact true is indicated by the typical values of item communalities.

It is this state of affairs which we believe imposes limitations upon the efficiency of such suppressor scales as K. Since we cannot find items which depend upon only clinical abnormality, we try to find items which depend upon abnormality to an appreciable extent even though they unavoidably depend upon other things as well. The suppressor consists of items which unavoidably depend to some slight degree upon clinical abnormality, but to a greater extent upon the objectionable factors in the first set. By cumulating responses to the second set of items, we hope to get an indication of the strength of these other factors, which information is then used to correct for their undesired contribution to a score attained on the first. The impurity of the suppressor itself, however, sets limits to the efficiency of such a process. Thus, a subject may obtain a high depression score because he is a plus-getter. The strength of his plus-getting tendency is assessed by items such as those of K. However, a sufficiently great degree of depression will yield considerable deviations on K, since the K items themselves are not pure for the plus-getting tendency but are also slightly loaded with clinical abnormality. In such cases K operates against us. It is interesting to note that the K scale, itself a suppressor, also *contains* a suppressor in the form of the eight "psychotic" items—but here also the effort to suppress the unwanted components of the suppressor can only be imperfectly carried out. No refinements of statistical technique enable us to escape the basic psychological fact that our smallest behavior units, the responses made to single items, are inherently of this multiphasic character.

Relation of K to Age, Intelligence, and Socioeconomic Status

In the study of the correction scale N it had been observed that college students (actually, high school graduates tested at the university Counseling Bureau prior to actual matriculation) showed a distinct elevation in the "lie" direction, averaging about one sigma above the general population mean. It was also found that the younger age group (16–25) showed a similar although smaller deviation, which was accounted for by the presence of a considerable number of medical students in that group. Furthermore, college graduates who had been some ten years out of college showed a mean T score of about 60 on the N scale. A similar trend is discernible in the case of K. The mean T score of a group of 84 medical students is at 62, a deviation which is significant at the .01 level. Both male and female precollege cases average a T of 57 on K. This tendency falls in line with the fact that the mean MMPI curve for several college and precollege groups, including some obtained elsewhere than at Minnesota, is a curve with a slight but consistent elevation on Hy, in spite of having an Hs below the mean. This indicates, as usual, a tendency to respond in the hysteroid fashion which elevates Hy-subtle enough to more than counteract the tendency to answer the somatic items on Hy in a nonhypochondriacal fashion. We are not prepared on present evidence to give an interpretation of this phenomenon. That it is not primarily a reflection of intelligence differences is suggested by a correlation of only .04 between K and ACE score among the precollege cases, which, even taking their relative homogeneity into account, should be higher if intellect as such is the reason for the difference. If the factor at work here is not intelligence, or the mere fact of being in college when tested, two other possibilities are socioeconomic status and chronological age. A group of WPA workers in the young age group 16–25 showed no elevation on K whatsoever, which would favor the socioeconomic interpretation. The mean K of a group of 50 normals aged 16–25, excluding college graduates and persons in college, was 13.5 (T = 52). These figures would seem to eliminate mere chronological age as the chief basis of differentiation. We are left with socioeconomic status as the most plausible remaining variable. What is needed is a study of a group of persons in the upper socioeconomic group who are not college students and have never been college educated. Unfortunately, we do not have a large enough sample of such persons to enable us to draw conclusions with certainty. The mean raw score on K for a group of 18 normal subjects classified in Groups I and II in the Goodenough classification, who were not, however, college graduates or attending college, was 18.50, which corresponds to a T score of 61. In spite of the small N, this difference is great enough so that a t ratio comparing their mean with that of 156 unselected normals from the other economic classes was highly significant (t = 6.055, p < .01). It seems plausible that the college, precollege, and college-educated elevation is reflecting chiefly a difference in socioeconomic status, although further evidence on this topic should be collected. If this is confirmed by subsequent investigation, it will be interesting to speculate upon the possible ways in which membership in the upper classes generates the particular kind of defensiveness involved.

Summary and Conclusions

The general problem of test-taking attitudes in their effect upon scores obtained on structured personality inventories is discussed. The literature on the subject is briefly surveyed, and a discussion given of the various approaches which have been taken in an effort to solve this problem. The final result of many efforts to derive special scales for measuring various attitudes in the taking of the MMPI is presented, with some indication of its validity. The relationship of this scale, called K, to other variables is used as a basis for discussing certain general problems in the theory of personality measurement. Conclusions are as follows:

1. The conscious or unconscious tendency of subjects to present a certain picture of themselves in taking a personality inventory has a considerable influence upon their scores.

2. We may distinguish two directions in this test-taking attitude: the tendency to be defensive or to put oneself in a too favorable light, and the opposed tendency to be overly honest and self-critical (plus-getting). The extremes of these tendencies are deliberate, conscious efforts to fake bad or lie good.

3. The defensive tendency appears to be related to the clinical picture of hysteria, whereas plus-getting is related to the picture of psychasthenia.

4. The MMPI scales L and F, while relatively effective in detecting extreme distortion, do not seem to be sufficiently subtle to detect the more common and often unconscious varieties of defensiveness or plus-getting. It has been found convenient to begin interpretation of L in the range of T scores 55 or 60, whereas F does not clearly establish invalidity even up to T score 80 (raw score about 16).

5. By contrasting item frequencies of abnormal persons showing normal MMPI profiles and elevated L scores with the records of unselected normals, an empirical key called K has been derived which is relatively successful in detecting the influence of disturbing test-taking attitudes and can be used to improve the discrimination between normals and abnormals.

6. In studying the intercorrelations among a group of scales derived by various means but all functioning with some effectiveness to detect such attitudes, it was found that one common factor is sufficient to account for all the intercorrelations. The scale (G) which has the largest factor loading was derived by a method of internal consistency and without recourse to any external criterion. Since K is the scale being used to measure this factor, the factor in question has been called the K factor.

7. On the basis of these findings and study of the relationship of the MMPI to certain of the Guilford-Martin scales, it is suggested that perhaps the construction of personality inventories by means of item-correlation and factor analytic methods leads to the development of tests which are excessively loaded with such test-taking attitudes. The procedure of internal consistency in its various forms is called into question as a profitable method for the construction of personality inventories.

◆──

ARTICLE 3 *Subtlety in Structured Personality Tests*

IN AN early paper on projective techniques Frank argued that a defining property of such a technique consists in this distinctive feature of the stimulus situation: "[It is] designed or chosen because it will mean to the subject, not what the experimenter has arbitrarily decided it should mean (as in most psychological experiments using standardized stimuli in order to be 'objective'), but rather whatever it must mean to the personality who gives it, or imposes upon it, his private, idiosyncratic meaning and organization." [r58, p. 403]

In a later review of the nature and theory of projective methods Sargent correctly recognized that "the very wording of the above definition implies a controversy: it presents projective techniques not only as an addition to our present stock of instruments; it also implies that they are set up in opposition to something" [r143, p. 257]. This "opposition" character is observed frequently both in the literature and in discussion among clinical psychologists. For example, Hutt stated that structured tests are characterized by the presence of "culturally crystallized questions" which, it is assumed, "will have the same meaning to all subjects" [r83, p. 135]. A very considerable defect which Hutt assigned to such structured tests lies in their presumed failure to "offer access to the personality make-up or to its processes" [r83, p. 136].

It is the "meaning" property of the stimuli in structured personality tests which is the subject of this investigation, and the term "subtlety" will be used to refer to the degree to which this "meaning" can or cannot be arbitrarily assigned in a priori fashion. As an example consider two items from the MMPI: "It takes a lot of argument to convince most people of the truth" and "I have a habit of counting things that are not important, such as bulbs on electric signs and so forth." To the extent that the psychodynamic meaning of the second item can easily be established with a high degree of interpersonal agreement (that is, most individuals who have had the requisite psychological or psychiatric training would agree that this is an obsessive-compulsive mode of defense) whereas this is not true of the first item, the first item would by definition be properly characterized as "more subtle" than the second. For experimental purposes this definition will prove adequate although it does not provide for a complete ordering of a hierarchy of subtlety should occasion ever require such an ordering. But in this respect such items are no different from projective instruments, as will soon be apparent to anyone who tries to order in a hierarchy of subtlety such instruments as the Bender Gestalt, the various sentence completion tests, the Thematic Apperception Test, and the Rorschach; or who tries to establish such a hierachy for the TAT cards. It seems clear, however, that subtlety is a quality which cannot be dichotomized in all-or-none fashion, but rather that there are degrees of this property.

It is this property of subtlety in which structured personality instruments have been commonly presumed to be deficient. And, indeed, those structured tests in which the items operate as self-ratings and behavior-surrogates, and to which it is presumed that the psychodynamic significance can be assigned a priori may well be lacking in such subtlety. It is, however, most essential to recognize that this approach to structured personality instruments constitutes a historical accident rather than a defining property of such tests. In the theoretical analysis of the dynamics of structured personality tests Meehl has this to say about the self-rating a priori approach:

Associated with this approach to structured personality tests is the construction of items and their assembling into scales upon an a priori basis, requiring the assumption that the psychologist building the test has sufficient insight into the dynamics of verbal behavior and its relation to the inner core of personality that he is able to predict beforehand what certain sorts of people will say about themselves when asked certain sorts of questions. The fallacious character of this procedure has been sufficiently shown by the empirical results of the Minnesota Multiphasic Personality Inventory alone. . . . It is suggested tentatively that the relative uselessness of most structured personality tests is due more to a priori item construction than to the fact of their being structured. [433 (see I, 1)]

An alternative approach to the building of structured personality or psychiatric instruments is one which considers all items to be stimuli, the nontest correlates (that is, psychodynamic "meaning") of which must be laboriously searched out experimentally. Since such a procedure repudiates the a priori assignment of "meaning," it is obvious that it opens the way for the introduction of subtle items into the test.

All the items used in the investigation to be reported were taken from a structured test which was built along these empirical lines, the MMPI. From this test were selected 30 items; of these, 15 were "obvious" items such as the counting item referred to earlier in this paper. They were designated as obvious items because their psychological meaning was considered to be quite clearly recognizable by psychologically trained individuals. The other 15 items were designated subtle items because it was considered that their meaning and psychological significance would not be detected by the same persons. The items, the manner of presentation, and the directions are described in the following paragraphs:

PART 1. *Directions*: This is an experiment in which your assistance is being enlisted. The problem is to identify items which, in your opinion, would be of diagnostic value on some psychiatric scale of a structured type of psychological test. A "psychiatric scale" is to be regarded as a category such as "schizophrenia," "hysteria," "depression," and so forth.

Read each item and decide whether the answer "true" or "false" to that item would render the item of value in any of the psychiatric categories listed with it. If you decide it belongs on a certain diagnostic scale, put an X before that category. If you think the item would be of no value for any of the categories listed, place the X before "none." As an example consider the item: "I am happy most of the time."

The answer "false" would help to identify this as a depressed person and so would belong on the "Depression" scale of the test.

The items in part 1 are as follows:

1. I believe I am being plotted against. __a. Depression __b. Obsessive-compulsive __c. Paranoid schizophrenia __d. Hysteria __e. None

2. I have had periods in which I carried on activities without knowing later what I had been doing. __a. Schizophrenia __b. Paranoid state or condition __c. Hysteria __d. Obsessive-compulsive __e. None

3. Peculiar odors come to me at times. __a. Hypomania __b. Schizophrenia __c. Depression __d. Obsessive-compulsive __e. None

4. Much of the time my head seems to hurt all over. __a. Paranoid state __b. Obsessive-compulsive __c. Depression __d. Hysteria __e. None

5. I am neither gaining nor losing weight. __a. Hysteria __b. Depression __c. Hypomania __d. Schizophrenia __e. None

6. It takes a lot of argument to convince some people of the truth. __a. Paranoid schizophrenia __b. Obsessive-compulsive __c. Paranoid state __d. Hysteria __e. None

7. Most people will use somewhat unfair means to gain profit or an advantage rather than lose it. __a. Hysteria __b. Depression __c. Hypomania __d. Schizophrenia __e. None

8. Most nights I go to sleep without thoughts or ideas bothering me. __a. Hypomania __b. Paranoid schizophrenia __c. Obsessive-compulsive __d. Hysteria __e. None

9. I almost never dream. __a. Depression __b. Obsessive-compulsive __c. Paranoid state __d. Hypomania __e. None

10. I often feel as if things were not real. __a. Hysteria __b. Schizophrenia __c. Hypomania __d. Paranoid state __e. None

11. I have a habit of counting things that are not important such as bulbs on electric signs and so forth. __a. Obsessive-compulsive __b. Hysteria __c. Schizophrenia __d. Mania __e. None

12. Someone is hypnotizing me and has control of my mind. __a. Depression __b. Hysteria __c. Obsessive-compulsive __d. Paranoid schizophrenia __e. None

13. I commonly wonder what hidden reason a person may have for doing something nice for me. __a. Obsessive-compulsive __b. Hypomania __c. Hysteria __d. Depression __e. None

14. Sometimes some unimportant thought will run through my mind and bother me for days. __a. Obsessive-compulsive __b. Hysteria __c. Schizophrenia __d. Depression __e. None

15. I get mad easily and then get over it. __a. Hysteria __b. Paranoid state __c. Hypomania __d. Obsessive-compulsive __e. None

16. I am very seldom troubled by constipation. __a. Hysteria __b. Depression __c. Hypomania __d. Obsessive-compulsive __e. None

17. I like to flirt. __a. Hysteria __b. Paranoid schizophrenia __c. Depression __d. Hypomania __e. None

18. I can be friendly with people who do things which I consider wrong. __a. Obsessive-compulsive __b. Depression __c. Hypomania __d. Hysteria __e. None

PART 2. *Directions*: In each of the items below indicate how the item should be scored for the category mentioned. In every instance T means *True*, F means *False*, and ? means *Cannot say*. For example, the item below has the F in parentheses to indicate that the answer *False* is scored in the direction of *Depression*.

"I seem to be as capable and smart as most others around me." T (F) ?

1. The item "Most people inwardly dislike putting themselves out to help other people" would be scored as a paranoid answer if answered T F ?

2. The item "I wish I could be as happy as others seem to be" would be scored as a depressed answer if answered T F ?

3. The item "I never worry about my looks" would be scored for hypomania if answered T F ?

4. "I dream frequently about things that are best kept to myself" would be scored as depressive if answered T F ?

5. "Someone has been trying to influence my mind" would be scored for paranoid schizophrenia if answered T F ?

6. "I do not blame a person for taking advantage of someone who lays himself open to it" would be scored in the direction of depression if answered T F ?

7. "Some people are so bossy that I feel like doing the opposite of what they request even though I know they are right." This item would be scored as paranoid if answered T F ?

8. "Much of the time I feel as if I have done something wrong or evil" would be scored as obsessive-compulsive if answered T F ?

9. "I usually have to stop and think before acting even in trifling matters" would be scored obsessive-compulsive if answered T F ?

10. "I drink an unusually large amount of water every day" would be scored for hysteria if answered T F ?

11. "Bad words, often terrible words, come into my mind and I cannot get rid of them." This item would be scored as obsessive-compulsive if answered T F ?

12. "Most people are honest chiefly through fear of being caught" would be scored in the paranoid direction if answered T F ?

The subjects in this investigation were 58 students in a graduate and advanced undergraduate course in clinical psychology at the University of Minnesota. The prerequisites for this course included, among other courses, two quarters of abnormal psychology in which the standard nosological categories are described and studied at some length. Three of the students did not fulfill these requirements and in some of the statistical tests their responses were not considered. It will be obvious, however, that the inclusion or exclusion of these three members of the class would in no way change the results of the test.

Results

Table 1 presents the responses of the subjects to the first 18 items, indicating the manner in which each item was assigned to the psychiatric categories. Since the asterisk indicates the MMPI scale from which the item was actually taken, it is clear that "success" in identification of the appropriate scale will be indicated when the number of students assigning the item to that scale exceeds the number assigning the item to any other scale. It might be fruitful, before proceeding, to make a brief analysis of how these items may be expected to behave in the light of the concept of subtlety. It is, in the first place, quite obvious that the failure of those items designated as subtle to behave in a discriminably different manner from the obvious items would (at least so far as this experiment is concerned) lend little support to the validity of the concept. There are, however, several ways in which the concept may be experimentally supported. In the first place, one would expect that the "none" category should be used with a significantly greater frequency for the subtle items than for the obvious items, either in consequence of the innocuous character of some of the items or in consequence of the ambiguity of their meaning. A second and obvious way in which the concept would receive experimental support has already been, in part, indicated; that is, a significantly greater success is to be expected in the assignment of psychiatric categories for the obvious items than for the subtle items. Third, a *chance* assignment to the psychiatric categories for the subtle items might be expected in some instances, in consequence of the ambiguity of "meaning." Finally, if one were to consider the 15 subtle and the 15 obvious items as two separate subtests, one would expect a significantly different distribution of scores, considering the number of correct identifications as a score.

Table 1. Success and Failure in Identifying Appropriate Psychiatric Scales as Achieved by 58 Clinical Psychology Students

Item [b]	Psychiatric Scale [a]								p [c]
	D	Hy	Pa	O-C	PaSc	Sc	Ma	None	
1............	1	1		2	53°			1	<.01
2............		24	0	5		26°		3	<.01
3............	3			12		31°	2	10	<.01
4............	10	37°	3	0				8	<.01
5(S)	10	8				0	2°	38	<.01
6(S)		3°	24	7	11			13	<.01
7(S)	11	7°				10	2	28	<.01
8............		0		29°	2		5	22	<.01
9(S)	5		5	12°			6	30	<.01
10............		2	2			37°	4	13	<.01
11............		0		56°		0	1	1	<.01
12............	0	2		3	53°			1	<.01
13(S)	17	1°		8			0	32	<.01
14............	2	2		54°		0		0	<.01
15(S)		8°	3	2			31	14	<.01
16(S)	11	16°		1			4	26	<.01
17(S)	1°	4			8		26	19	<.01
18(S)	4	6°		13			9	26	<.01

[a] The appropriate scale with the MMPI used as the criterion is indicated by an asterisk.
[b] (S) indicates "subtle" items.
[c] Probability of obtaining the indicated distribution for each item assuming theoretical N = one fifth of the total N for each choice in that item.

There can be no question that Table 1 does provide considerable experimental support for the concept of subtlety in structured items. Comparison of the frequencies in the starred categories for subtle and obvious items reveals that in every instance the frequencies for the obvious items in the correct category exceed the frequencies in any other category, whereas there are no instances in which this is true of the subtle items. It does not appear to strain matters to characterize these results as striking. Furthermore, analysis of the frequencies in the category "none" reveals that whereas the subtle items were assigned here 43.3 per cent of the time, the obvious items were so assigned only 11.1 per cent of the time; this is a difference significant at the .01 level, and in the direction required by this formulation.

Table 2 presents similar data for the 12 items in Part 2. Again we note that in every instance the responses to obvious items are correctly assigned as judged by the criterion. For the subtle items five of the six are incorrectly assessed; one (item 6) meets the previously indicated criterion of chance distribution of responses, the chi square being 1.79 with 3 df. So that here, again, the evidence is strikingly in support of the concept of subtlety as defined in this paper.

What, now, is the nature of the evidence when the items are considered as two separate subscales? The answer to this question, as indicated in Tables 3 and 4, is quite unequivocal. Table 3 presents the distribution of scores for subtle and obvious subscales for both parts of the test. It is obvious immediately that the distributions are virtually nonoverlapping in character. Since the distributions are so obviously skewed it seemed wise not to apply the test of significance of difference between means, which involves the assumption of normality. It is, however, possible and

Table 2. Direction of Responses to "Subtle" and "Obvious" Items Indicated by 58 Students in Clinical Psychology [a]

Item	T	F	?	p
1(S)	50	2°	6	<.01
2	55°	2	1	<.01
3	41°	7	10	<.01
4(S)	46	4°	8	<.01
5	56°	2	0	<.01
6(S)	18	24°	16	>.05
7(S)	37	7°	14	<.01
8	51°	6	1	<.01
9	45°	7	6	<.01
10(S)	41	4°	13	<.01
11	31°	1	26	<.01
12(S)	48	5°	5	<.01

[a] An asterisk indicates correct scoring on the MMPI criterion.

appropriate to apply the chi square test, provided suitable precautions are taken to ensure independence of categories. This was done by breaking down the entire group into two random subgroups. The data for all items are presented in Table 4, and it is clear that the differences are in the required direction and well beyond the .01 level of significance.

We may take it, then, that the phenomenon of subtlety in structured psychological instruments is an experimentally verifiable one; or, alternatively stated, that the concept of subtlety can be shown to have an empirical basis. The significance of this has been discussed at some length by Meehl [433 (see I, 1)] and has been noted by Wiener [642 (IV, 22)] and by Hathaway and McKinley (305); it therefore requires no extended further discussion here. Suffice it to underscore the point that those features which appear to have been primarily accountable for the frequently noted weaknesses and failures of structured psychological tests were to a considerable extent a function of the a priori construction procedures which *ipso facto* rule out the concept of subtlety of items.

There remain, however, two problems of such significance that they must be disposed of at this point. Let us consider two hypothetical critics, the first of whom argues in the following manner: it is true that the items designated as subtle behave in an experimentally specifiable fashion differently from the obvious items. This, however, may simply show that they are personologically without validity, whereas the obvious items are valid. And indeed, it is a somewhat analogous argument which Allport [r6] makes. Our hypothetical critic goes on to assert that one can obviously see that the items are without psychological or psychiatric significance. To such an argument we can only reply that it defines validity as face validity, requires the construction of structured tests in a priori fashion, and leaves no room for subtlety of items. Our second hypothetical critic, however, cannot be disposed of in such a cavalier fashion. His argument is something like this: the experimental verification of the concept of subtlety rests, in the last analysis, on the assumption of the validity of the criterion. What if the MMPI were not a valid test? Our answer to this would be an unhesitating denial that the validity of the MMPI is crucial to the validity of the concept advanced in this paper. At most, the invalidity of the MMPI (were it demonstrated) would indicate that these specific items might be faulty. It seems unlikely that our hypothetical critic will wish to maintain that in principle and for theoretically weighty reasons it would be impossible to build a valid multiphasic instrument. But with the possibility of building such an instrument the experimental validity of the subtlety of concept remains secure.

A further experimental test of the concept presents results of the readministration of the same items to the same group of students after completion of an additional two quarters of clinical psychology at the University of Minnesota. Almost an entire quarter is devoted to a study of the MMPI through readings and lectures given by Dr. Paul Meehl.

Table 3. Distribution of Scores on Subtle
and Obvious Subscales

	Part 1		Part 2	
Score	Subtle	Obvious	Subtle	Obvious
9.....................		4		
8.....................		9		
7.....................		23		
6.....................		12	1	30
5.....................	1	4	0	17
4.....................	2	1	0	6
3.....................	2	2	2	2
2.....................	10		6	
1.....................	18		18	
0.....................	22		28	

Table 4. Frequency of Subjects' Having Scores above or below the Midpoint
on Subtle and Obvious Scales

	Part 1			Part 2	
Score	Subtle	Obvious	Score	Subtle	Obvious
>5.5..............	0	23	>3.5..............	1	25
<5.5..............	28	4	<3.5..............	27	2
	$x^2 = 41.1$			$x^2 = 44.0$	
	df = 1			df = 1	
	p < .01			p < .01	

The primary question to be answered by the results of this experimental treatment is whether, after a quarter of study of the MMPI, the items designated as subtle maintain their subtlety. This question will be answered, of course, by comparing the behavior of the two types or sets of items. The failure of the subtle items to behave in a discriminably different manner from the obvious items would indicate that whatever the degree of subtlety inherent in the former set of items, it was not sufficient to withstand the instruction in the course work. On the other hand, the concept of subtlety may be said to receive experimental verification if such differences *can* be demonstrated. The definition of subtlety as developed here requires, rather obviously, that a significantly greater success be achieved by the subjects in the categorizing of the items as well as in indicating the direction of scoring for the specified category. One might expect, also, that the "none" category would be used with a significantly greater frequency for the subtle than for the obvious items, either on the ground that the former are innocuous or because of the ambiguity of their meaning. One might expect, also, that occasionally *a chance* assignment of the subtle items should occur, in consequence of the ambiguity of their meaning. Finally, if one were to consider the 15 subtle and the 15 obvious items as two separate subtests, one would expect a significantly different distribution of scores, considering the number of correct identifications as a score.

Table 5 indicates the manner in which the items in Part I (the first 18 items) were assigned to the various psychiatric categories. The MMPI criterion scale is, in each case, indicated by an asterisk, so that the number in that cell indicates the number of correct identifications of the item, that is, the number of students who assign the item to the same scale as the criterion. It is quite evident from a study of

Table 5. Success and Failure in Identifying Appropriate Psychiatric Scales as Achieved by 48 Clinical Psychology Students after Course Discussion on the MMPI

Item [b]	Psychiatric Scale [a]								p [c]
	D	Hy	Pa	O-C	PaSc	Sc	Ma	None	
1............					47°			1	.01
2............		23	1	2		21°		1	.01
3............	1			4		39°		4	.01
4............	8	29°		1				10	.01
5(S).........	7	19					3°	18	.01
6(S).........		3°	21	22	2				.01
7(S).........	7	20°					3	18	.01
8............		3		34°	1		2	8	.01
9(S).........	2			13°	10		4	19	.01
10............		1				47°			.01
11............				48°					.01
12............				1	47°				.01
13(S).........	10	6°		13				19	.01
14............	1			45°		1		1	.01
15(S).........		18°		2			24	4	.01
16(S).........	13	19°		4			4	8	.01
17(S).........	4°	10			3		25	6	.01
18(S).........	1	22°		7			11	7	.01

[a] The appropriate scale with the MMPI used as the criterion is indicated by an asterisk.
[b] (S) indicates "subtle" items.
[c] Probability of obtaining the indicated distribution.

the table that the degree of success achieved in assignment of the obvious items is markedly greater than that achieved in assignment of the subtle items. This is an agreement with the concept of subtlety previously developed, and suggests that even instruction in the MMPI by an individual thoroughly conversant with its structure does not close the gap between the subtle and the obvious items. If one arranges the responses in a contingency table indicating the agreement of choices with criterion scales and computes mean square contingency coefficients, one finds that for the obvious items $C = .83$, whereas for the subtle items, $C = .50$, a striking difference. Or, alternately, if one selects an arbitrary criterion of 75 per cent correct for each item, the resulting differences (Table 6) between the two sets of items are significant at the .01 level. Furthermore, the difference between the two sets of items for the "none" category is 17.2 per cent, a difference significant at the .01 level.

Table 6. Breakdown of Subtle and Obvious Items in
Parts 1 and 2 According to Whether 75 Per Cent
Success Was Achieved or Not

Degree of Success	Subtle	Obvious
>75%.........................	0	12
<75%.........................	15	3
	$x^2 = 20$	
	$p < .01$	

Table 7. Distribution of Scores on Subtle
and Obvious Subscales

Score	Part 1		Part 2	
	Subtle	Obvious	Subtle	Obvious
9.....................		3		
8.....................		21		
7.....................		15		
6.....................	1	6		28
5.....................	4	3		14
4.....................	6		8	4
3.....................	8		3	2
2.....................	12		6	
1.....................	7		21	
0.....................	10		10	

Table 8. Frequency of Subjects' Having Scores above or below the
Midpoint on Subtle and Obvious Scales

	Part 1			Part 2	
Score	Subtle	Obvious	Score	Subtle	Obvious
>5.5..........	0	23	>3.5........	1	22
<5.5..........	24	1	<3.5........	23	2
	$x^2 = 46$			$x^2 = 36.8$	
	$p < .01$			$p < .01$	

Consider, next, the character of the evidence when the two sets of items are regarded as two different subscales, and the number of successes is considered as a score for each individual on each subscale, yielding four scores for each student. Tables 7 and 8 leave little doubt about the unequivocal nature of the answer to this question. The modal score for the obvious subscale one is readily seen to be eight, whereas the modal score for the subtle subscale one is considerably below this. Similarly, the modal score for the obvious subscale two is six, whereas the modal score for the subtle subscale two is one. Although the skewed nature of the distribution renders it incorrect to use normal curve procedures, it can, nevertheless, readily be shown by use of nonparametric statistics that these distributions are different, significant at the .01 level. The procedure followed in this case was the following: The entire group was broken down into eight random subgroups and the means for the subtle and obvious subscales were computed. These were then ranged in order of magnitude as suggested by Moses [r123], and the Mann-Whitney U test was applied, the resulting U falling well beyond the .01 level of significance. It is possible, also, to apply the chi square test of significance provided precautions are taken to ensure independence of categories. This was done by assigning the members of the entire sample in random fashion to two subgroups. The chi square was then computed with the criteria indicated in Table 8, the difference being in the required direction and well beyond the .01 level of significance.

It seems clear from all the evidence reviewed above that the concept of subtlety in structured tests can be given solid experimental meaning. It has been demonstrated that those items designated as subtle not only behaved in a discriminably different fashion on the occasion of their initial presentation, but that this difference was manifested after the students were given additional instruction, virtually one full quarter, which consisted of lectures on the structure of the MMPI by an unusually competent lecturer.

ARTICLE 4 *Some Common Misconceptions about Neuroticism*

A RESPECTABLE science of psychopathology needs to be based upon, among other things, a thorough and accurate knowledge of what particular beliefs, values, self-definitions, attitudes, and self-conceptions are characteristic of persons diagnosable as maladjusted. Theories about process, about the "self," about motivations, and about therapeutical techniques can hardly be evolved without some minimum pre-establishment of "facts" in this realm. That is, for example, if one is to develop a theory to account for the contention that most neurotics say that they get a "raw deal" from life, then we must first make sure that most neurotics *do*, in fact, express this belief.

It is rather surprising, if one reviews the psychological literature of the past twenty years, to discover how little has been done to determine the characteristic and differentiating beliefs and attitudes of persons classified with respect to their psychological adjustment. We have some general notions, for example, that neurotics feel misunderstood, that they often have bad dreams, that they often expect to fail in what they do, that they desire more sympathy than they get, that they find it hard to concentrate, and so forth. Yet, in spite of the diffusion of ideas such as these, there are only a few studies which have actually asked patients for responses on these issues and then compared the frequency of their agreements with those of control groups.

The few studies done, such as those of Page, Landis, Katz, and Zubin [r93, r94, r131], and Hathaway and McKinley [300 (see II, 5), 303, 423 (II, 9)] have revealed findings strikingly discrepant from the pervasive stereotypes of both professional and lay persons. The clinical stereotype about what patients would say and think appeared, in both series of studies, to be so wide of the mark as to lead not only to irrelevant designations, but to erroneous ones. For example, in one paper of Page, Landis, and Katz [r131], a fifty-item scale for schizophrenia based on expert psychiatric judgment actually yielded *higher* scores for a control sample of nonhospitalized adults than it did for a group of diagnosed schizophrenics. Clearly something is amiss in the clinical conceptions of verbal behavior in psychopathology if errors of this magnitude can appear.

None of the studies mentioned, however, was primarily devoted to specifying and outlining the details of the conventional sterotypes about neuroticism, although all of them revealed something of the grossness of the errors of prevailing opinion. The decision was made, accordingly, to attempt an extensive survey of specific stereotypes about neuroticism and then, by comparing the stereotype with the observed reactions of diagnosed patients, to delineate some of the discrepancies between opinion and fact. In making such a search for discrepancies, the broader the sampling of beliefs and attitudes the better. The MMPI [303], by reason of its systematic coverage of many areas of self-definition and personal values, is exceptionally well suited to the task at hand, and was therefore selected as the research instrument.

Method of Analysis

Seven samples of subjects were obtained in order to conduct the analysis. Four of these samples consisted of patients psychiatrically diagnosed as "psychoneurotic," and the remaining three were experimental samples requested to take the role of a patient experiencing a psychoneurotic reaction and to answer the test items accordingly. The samples were constituted as follows:

I. Males
  A. Patients
    1. Thirty-nine patients from the University of California Langley Porter Psychiatric Clinic.
    2. Forty-six patients from the Oakland VA Mental Hygiene Clinic.
    3. Forty patients from a U.S. Army station hospital.
  B. Dissimulators
    1. Fifty students from a University of California, Berkeley, class in abnormal psychology.
    2. Eleven professional workers from the Army hospital.
II. Females
  A. Patients.
    1. Fifty-one patients from the Langley Porter Psychiatric Clinic.
  B. Dissimulators
    1. Fifty students from the class in abnormal psychology.

For each of the items in the MMPI, the proportion in each of the above samples replying True was calculated, and then three internal comparisons (I.A.1 and I.A.2 vs. I.B.1; I.A.3 vs. I.B.2; and II.A.1 vs. II.B.1) were made. All items yielding similar and statistically significant differences in each comparison were selected. These items, then, could be said to embody the fallacious stereotypes of the experimental samples. The entire statistical table is too long to be given here, but a few selected items are listed in Table 1 to indicate the impressive magnitude of error observed. Note, for example, item number 35: "If people had not had it in for me I would have been much more successful." In the stereotype about what patients will say, this sentiment features strongly, and yet, in the actual responses of patients, it is almost nonexistent. In the light of this particular finding what is one to make of a theory which attempts to account for the "fact" that psychoneurotic patients tend to harbor such feelings, and to express them on inquiry?

Altogether, 74 items were identified which met the criterion of significance. These items, and the direction of response given more frequently by the simulators, are listed below:

10. There seems to be a lump in my throat much of the time. (T) 14. I have diarrhea once a month or more. (T) 16. I am sure I get a raw deal from life. (T) 19. When I take a new job, I like to be tipped off on who should be gotten next to. (T) 23. I am troubled by attacks of nausea and vomiting. (T) 24. No one seems to understand me. (T) 29. I am bothered by acid stomach several times a week. (T) 31. I have nightmares every few nights. (T) 35. If people had not had it in for me I would have been much more successful. (T) 42. My family does not like the work I have chosen (or the work I intend to choose for my life work). (T)

44. Much of the time my head seems to hurt all over. (T) 47. Once a week or oftener I feel suddenly hot all over, without apparent cause. (T) 50. My soul some-

Table 1. Sample Items Revealing Erroneous Conceptions about Neuroticism

MMPI Item	Percentage of Dissemblers Saying "True"			Percentage of Patients Saying "True"			
	Professional Workers (N = 11)	Male Students (N = 50)	Female Students (N = 50)	Langley Porter Males (N = 39)	Oakland VA Clinic Males (N = 46)	Army Males (N = 40)	Langley Porter Females (N = 51)
16. I am sure I get a raw deal from life	64	82	90	8	7	28	12
35. If people had not had it in for me I would have been much more successful	36	68	86	0	4	2	0
88. I usually feel that life is worth while	36	28	10	79	74	60	59
212. My people treat me more like a child than a grown-up	45	76	76	15	20	2	22
257. I usually expect to succeed in things I do	27	36	10	72	76	88	67
459. I have one or more bad habits which are so strong that it is no use in fighting against them	73	80	88	8	13	15	12

times leaves my body. (T) 53. A minister can cure disease by praying and putting his hand on your head. (T) 68. I hardly ever feel pain in the back of the neck. (F) 73. I am an important person. (T) 83. Any man who is able and willing to work hard has a good chance of succeeding. (F) 88. I usually feel that life is worth while. (F) 93. I think most people would lie to get ahead. (T) 96. I have very few quarrels with members of my family. (F)

97. A times I have a strong urge to do something harmful or shocking. (T) 104. I don't seem to care what happens to me. (T) 125. I have a great deal of stomach trouble. (T) 137. I believe that my home life is as pleasant as that of most people I know. (F) 179. I am worried about sex matters. (T) 206. I am very religious (more than most people). (T) 207. I enjoy many different kinds of play and recreation.

(F) 210. Everything tastes the same. (T) 211. I can sleep during the day but not at night. (T) 212. My people treat me more like a child than a grown-up. (T)

216. There is very little love and companionship in my family as compared to other homes. (T) 226. Some of my family have habits that bother and annoy me very much. (T) 241. I dream frequently about things that are best kept to myself. (T) 246. My neck spots with red often. (T) 247. I have reason for feeling jealous of one or more members of my family. (T) 257. I usually expect to succeed in things I do. (F) 297. I wish I were not bothered by thoughts about sex. (T) 303. I am so touchy on some subjects that I can't talk about them. (T) 306. I get all the sympathy I should. (F) 320. Many of my dreams are about sex matters. (T)

325. The things that some of my family have done have frightened me. (T) 328. I find it hard to keep my mind on a task or job. (T) 341. At times I hear so well it bothers me. (T) 344. Often I cross the street in order not to meet someone I see. (T) 352. I have been afraid of things or people that I knew could not hurt me. (T) 360. Almost every day something happens to frighten me. (T) 375. When I am feeling very happy and active, someone who is blue or low will spoil it all. (T) 388. I am afraid to be alone in the dark. (T) 405. I have no trouble swallowing. (F) 419. I played hooky from school quite often as a youngster. (T)

422. I have felt embarrassed over the type of work that one or more members of my family have done. (T) 433. I used to have imaginary companions. (T) 438. There are certain people whom I dislike so much that I am inwardly pleased when they are catching it for something they have done. (T) 443. I am apt to pass up something I want to do because others feel that I am not going about it in the right way. (T) 453. When I was a child I didn't care to be a member of a crowd or gang. (T) 458. The man who had most to do with me when I was a child (such as my father, stepfather, etc.) was very strict with me. (T) 459. I have one or more bad habits which are so strong that it is no use in fighting against them. (T) 466. Except by a doctor's orders I never take drugs or sleeping powders. (F) 471. In school my marks in deportment were quite regularly bad. (T) 475. When I am cornered I tell that portion of the truth which is not likely to hurt me. (T)

476. I am a special agent of God. (T) 480. I am often afraid of the dark. (T) 481. I can remember "playing sick" to get out of something. (T) 485. When a man is with a woman he is usually thinking about things related to her sex. (T) 518. I have often felt guilty because I have pretended to feel more sorry about something than I really was. (T) 519. There is something wrong with my sex organs. (T) 524. I am not afraid of picking up a disease or germs from door knobs. (F) 525. I am made nervous by certain animals. (T) 528. I blush no more often than others. (F) 535. My mouth feels dry almost all the time. (T)

541. My skin seems to be unusually sensitive to touch. (T) 543. Several times a week I feel as if something dreadful is about to happen. (T) 545. Sometimes I have the same dream over and over. (T) 565. I feel like jumping off when I am on a high place. (T)

The similarity of these items to a conventional neuroticism questionnaire is obvious. Most observers, professionally trained or not, would probably identify the items at once as pertaining to maladjustment. Nevertheless, the inference seems justified that they do *not* pertain to neuroticism and maladjustment, but rather to the prevailing *stereotypes* about neuroticism.

For each of the specific instances listed, neurotic patients answer in precisely the opposite direction from what is predicted for them. They do not, in other words, respond True to questionnaire items like "No one seems to understand me," "I don't seem to care what happens to me," and "I have one or more bad habits which are so strong that it is no use in fighting against them," and they do respond True to items like "I get all the sympathy I should," and "I usually expect to succeed in things that I do." Even such a short listing as this should serve to highlight the dangers that are involved in any a priori decisions about how patients will answer questions such as these. Indeed, as will be shown below, the way to identify psychoneurotic predispositions as they are manifested on the above list would not be to accept current theory in scoring each item, but rather to reverse it in every instance and score each item backwards.

In order to simplify and condense the list of 74 items, the writer has attempted a subjective clustering. The groupings which were derived are as follows:

1. Numerous physical complaints and dysfunctions.
2. Feelings of victimization, injustice, and misunderstanding; lack of hope for and faith in the future.
3. Exaggerated irritability, petulance, tenseness, fear, and anxiety.
4. Lack of independence and self-sufficiency; inability to face issues squarely.
5. Dissatisfaction with family background and childhood.
6. Sexual conflicts and preoccupations.
7. Bizarre, eccentric ideas; excessive religiosity.

These clusters, then, summarize to some extent the kinds of emphases which are given too much weight in the typical stereotypes about the expressed beliefs and attitudes of maladjusted persons.

Cross-Validating Samples

The separate item discriminations achieved in the analyses were sufficiently striking to suggest trying them as a scale for dissimulation. For this purpose a number of new samples were obtained. The results are indicated in Table 2. Of the 13 samples in Table 2, only one, the 11 Army dissemblers, was used in the item analyses just reported. All the other samples include cross-validating cases only, so that the

Table 2. Means and Standard Deviations on the 74-Item Dissimulation Scale for the Samples Indicated

Sample	N	M	SD
Dissemblers			
Professional workers	11	46.82	11.21
Students in abnormal psychology	302	53.96	11.52
Students in personality in society and culture	41	57.34	11.90
Clinical cases			
Army psychiatric patients	250	18.87	10.94
Ft. Snelling VA Hospital males	99	16.91	11.45
Oakland VA Hospital males	103	13.40	10.20
San Francisco VA Mental Hygiene Clinic males	62	17.45	9.33
Langley Porter Psychiatric Clinic males	100	15.05	9.21
Langley Porter Psychiatric Clinic females	100	16.25	9.58
University of Minnesota Psychiatric Division males	101	12.31	7.02
University of Minnesota Psychiatric Division females	100	13.59	6.86
Nonclinical samples			
High school freshmen	223	16.89	8.32
High school seniors	284	15.08	7.48

results are probably similar to what would be anticipated in most subsequent applications of these items as a scale.

The analysis of variance over 13 separate samples yielded an F ratio of 374.17, significant well beyond the .01 probability point. The clinical samples and the student samples both average near the lower end of the scale, with the dissimulators all scoring much higher.

If the eight clinical samples are pooled in a composite (N = 915), a mean of 15.94 and a standard deviation of 9.99 are obtained. For the student samples the combined figures (N = 507) are 15.88 and 7.90. The difference between the means is .06, and the CR is 0.125. This is an important finding, for it indicates that patients diagnosed as psychoneurotic actually achieve mean scores on this scale nearly identical with those attained by a large nonhospitalized sample. Patients not only do not respond to the questions in the manner indicated by usual conceptions, but are

Table 3. Proportion of Cases Falling in the Scoring Categories Indicated

Scores	Dissemblers (N = 354)	Clinical Cases (N = 915)	Students (N = 507)	Scores	Dissemblers (N = 354)	Clinical Cases (N = 915)	Students (N = 507)
70–74	4.2			25–29	2.0	7.2	7.5
65–69	15.2			20–24	0.6	12.5	14.8
60–64	19.4			15–19	0.3	17.5	23.2
55–59	16.9			10–14	0.3	21.5	24.6
50–54	14.7	0.4		5–9		19.8	19.3
45–49	11.0	0.8	0.2	0–4		10.1	3.9
40–44	7.3	1.8	0.6				
35–39	4.2	2.6	1.2	M	54.13	15.94	15.88
30–34	3.7	5.3	4.5	SD	11.69	9.99	7.90

actually indistinguishable from normals in reacting to the set of 74 statements. Furthermore, both patients and the control samples score considerably below the mean achieved by subjects asked to simulate a psychoneurotic reaction.

The distributions of scores for the three consolidated samples—dissemblers, clinical cases, and students—are presented in Table 3.

The F ratio for the threefold breakdown represented in Table 3 was 2141.04, a clearly significant value. The screening efficiency of the Ds scale for these cross-validation samples (all were cross-validating cases except for the 11 Army dissimulators) can be exampled by a cutting score of 35. Ninety-three per cent of the dissemblers scored at or above this point, whereas only 6 per cent of the clinical cases and 2 per cent of the students did so.

The results obtained in treating the differentiating items as a *scale* further underscore the erroneousness of the particular aspects of the clinical stereotypes of neuroticism they embody. The opinions and sentiments contained in the items are not expressed, or more accurately, assented to, with any *more* frequency by diagnosed psychoneurotic patients than by control samples, and, furthermore, are agreed with much *less* frequently than the conventional conceptions of neuroticism would presage.

Summary

An investigation of typical conceptions of neuroticism was conducted by having subjects take the role of a psychoneurotic patient in responding to a personality inventory. Significant discrepancies between what diagnosed patients did, in fact, report on this inventory and the stereotypes given by the simulators were discovered.

The argument was advanced that errors of the magnitude observed suggested a considerable degree of misinformation in the prevailing conceptions about neuroticism.

Finally, it was possible, by consolidating the items individually tapping these misconceptions, to develop a measuring instrument yielding similar scores for both patient and control samples, and differentiating each from samples based on dissembled records.

Construction

THERE is currently a great deal of pressure on test authors and publishers to publish enough of the validational data to enable others to judge the value of the test scales for various purposes and to determine its appropriateness for the avowed aims of the instrument or its efficiency in separating groups, classifying subjects, or predicting behavior [r181]. No personality test published to date has more adequately met these requirements for publication of the construction data than the MMPI. Anyone proposing to use the MMPI in clinical work or research should familiarize himself with the information contained in the following papers.

In this section the articles covering the derivation of the nine clinical scales are presented in the same sequence as the original publication chronology. One of the reasons we have kept the chronological sequence is to illustrate the gradual changes that emerged with further experience in scale development by the Minnesota group. It is obvious that there could be no analysis of a profile until a number of scales had been developed and the focus had to be on scale derivation per se until that time. In article 9 we have for the first time a reference to scales 1, 2, and 3 together as the "neurotic trio" in connection with the patterning properties of those three scales. In article 11 the phrase now more commonly employed is introduced: "neurotic triad."

In article 9, it may also be noted, there is one of the first explicit allusions to the use of the entire profile as a frame of reference for judging the significance of a scale elevation rather than the absolute magnitude of a single score. It is pointed out that peak scores may fall below 70, a sort of arbitrary standard line of significance, and still prove crucial as a predictor or measure of "significant" behavior deviation.

Article 5 takes up some of the basic methods of procedure in the development of the MMPI. In article 6 the older H—C_H scale is discussed; it should be noted that the Hs scale currently used is a modification of the H scale. Articles 7 and 8 deal with D and Pt respectively while 9 includes three scales: Hy, Ma, and Pd. The next article, 10, was written especially for this volume since the material on the derivation of Mf, Pa, and Sc had not previously been made public. One of the validating scales, K, appears in article 11; other material on K, and also on L and F, appears in Section I, article 2 of the present volume.

The evidence for the use of K as a "correction" scale presented in article 11 raises some crucial questions for present-day users of the MMPI (see I, 2). It is apparent that the derivation of the various weights of K to be applied to "correct" five of the clinical scales followed a crude, even though ingenious, empirical procedure. This is clearly pointed out by the authors. Nor is any apology for the use of practical empiricism necessary. Throughout all the articles in this section may be seen the advantages of methods of scale construction and development which were not hamstrung by rigid adherence to a priori theoretical notions and overly rigorous statistical refinements.

58

If the value of a scale is to be judged by its utility — in the case of the MMPI, its ability to separate a criterion psychiatric group from a normal population — then lack of strenuous statistics or theoretical niceties cannot be invoked and argued against the use of the scale. It is on the basis of utility, however, that we question the routine use of the specified K "correction." Evidence is adduced, it is true, to indicate the amount of improvement over the "uncorrected" values in discriminating criterion groups. But it must be noted that the suggested weights of K to be applied are optimal for the populations used by the authors. They themselves point out that the *same* weights would not very likely be found to operate in other populations.

The evidence as to the utility of K is by no means unanimous; such studies as that of the Schmidt [529] or Hunt *et al.* [341] fail to demonstrate any improvement in differential diagnosis when the total profile with K added is used. Even in article 11 it is mentioned, although unfortunately dismissed, that for Capwell's cases [112] the differentiation was less successful when K was applied. Further comments by Meehl [436 (see V, 31)] testify to its ineffectiveness with certain clinical cases. We believe that the last paragraph in the article, suggesting the routine application of K to all records, is gratuitous. The evidence presented is persuasive but not compelling. Our suggestion is that we follow the lead of many experienced MMPI workers and draw both the regular and the K-corrected profile. It is awkward to do so on the recording sheets now provided by the Psychological Corporation (which are set up only for K-added profiles) since the regular scores have been relegated to tables in the *Manual* [305]. But many errors in interpreting profiles which have been distorted rather than corrected may in this way be avoided. The clinician should remember that the derivation of K was based on the "borderline" range of scores around 70; it was not designed to correct profiles with scores far above or below this point.

One further point must be mentioned: that the improvement with K is demonstrated in article 11 scale by scale. Only with scales 1 and 3 is any possible patterning effect discussed. There was a good deal of experience by that time to underscore the need for a total and configural approach to the MMPI profile and yet the efficiency of K was taken up piecemeal.

In this section the reader will note in the article titles that we have replaced scale names with digits. These refer to the coding system which is dealt with at some length in Section III. It will be necessary to remember the appropriate code digits, a point we have discussed in the Foreword to this volume.

The articles in this section came from the following sources: article 5 from S. R. Hathaway and J. C. McKinley, A multiphasic personality schedule (Minnesota): I. Construction of the Schedule, *Journal of Psychology,* 1940, 10, 249–254; article 6 from J. C. McKinley and S. R. Hathaway, A multiphasic personality schedule (Minnesota): II. A differential study of hypochondriasis, *Journal of Psychology,* 1940, 10, 255–268; article 7 from S. R. Hathaway and J. C. McKinley, A multiphasic personality schedule (Minnesota): III. The measurement of symptomatic depression, *Journal of Psychology,* 1942, 14, 73–84; article 8 from J. C. McKinley and S. R. Hathaway, A multiphasic personality schedule (Minnesota): IV. Psychasthenia, *Journal of Applied Psychology,* 1942, 26, 614–624; article 9 from J. C. McKinley and S. R. Hathaway, The MMPI: V. Hysteria, hypomania, and psychopathic deviate, *Journal of Applied Psychology,* 1944, 28, 153–174; article 10 is an original manuscript prepared for this volume; and article 11 from J. C. McKinley, S. R. Hathaway and P. E. Meehl, The MMPI: VI. The K scale, *Journal of Consulting Psychology,* 1948, 12, 20–31. We are indebted to the authors and to the publishers of the journals for permission to reproduce these articles in this form.

S. R. HATHAWAY AND J. C. McKINLEY

✦

ARTICLE 5 *Construction of the Schedule*

FOR several reasons it has seemed that a multiphasic personality schedule might be constructed which would be of greater value in the medical or psychiatric clinic than is true of personality inventories already available. It is desirable that more varied subject matter be included to obtain a wider sampling of behavior of significance to the psychiatrist, rather than to utilize independent sets of items for special purposes such as one might use in studying any particular reaction type. Then, too, in dealing with clinic patients, there seemed to be a need for simpler wording and a simpler method of presentation than is usually the case, in order to stay within the comprehension of those individuals who are not of high intellectual or cultural level. Finally, it seemed desirable to create a rather large reservoir of items from which various scales might be constructed in the hope of evolving a greater variety of valid personality descriptions than are available at the present time.

The individual items were formulated partly on the basis of previous clinical experience. Mainly, however, the items were supplied from several psychiatric examination direction forms, from various textbooks of psychiatry, from certain of the directions for case taking in medicine and neurology, and from the earlier published scales of personal and social attitudes. The original list consisted of more than one thousand items. By deletion of duplicates and of those items which seemed to have relatively little significance for the purposes of this study, the inventory finally contracted to its present form of 504 items.

The separate items were formulated as declarative sentences in the first person singular. The majority were placed in the positive, the remainder in the negative. Interrogative sentences were not used. Simplified wording constituted the language of the items, the words used being selected as far as possible from those in most frequent use according to standard word frequency tables. Also, the statements were restricted to matters of "common knowledge." Idiomatic expressions were included when the idioms were common in the English language. Grammatical form was occasionally sacrificed in the interests of brevity, clarity, and simplicity. Each item was printed with its number in large type (16-point boldface) on a 3- x 5-inch card.

As a matter of convenience in handling and in avoiding duplication, the items were arbitrarily classified under 25 headings, though it was assumed that an item was not necessarily properly classified merely because it had been placed under a given subdivision. The arrangement was as follows: General Health (9 items); General Neurologic (19 items); Cranial Nerves (11 items); Motility and Coordination (6 items); Sensibility (5 items); Vasomotor, Trophic, Speech, Secretory (10 items); Cardiorespiratory (5 items); Gastrointestinal (11 items); Genitourinary (6 items); Habits (20 items); Family and Marital (29 items); Occupational (18 items); Educational (12 items); Sexual Attitudes (19 items); Religious Attitudes (20 items); Political Attitudes – Law and Order (46 items); Social Attitudes (72 items); Affect, Depressive (32 items); Affect, Manic (24 items); Obsessive, Compulsive (15 items); Delusions, Hallucinations, Illusions, Ideas of Reference (31 items); Phobias (29 items); Sadistic, Masochistic (7 items); Morale (33 items); and items modeled after suggestions of Hartshorne, May, and Shuttleworth [r71] to indicate whether the individual is trying to place himself in an improbably acceptable or unacceptable light (15 items).

For purposes of recording and subsequent interview with the patient, a separate mimeographed booklet of the items in classified form with their appropriate code was constructed.

Since a considerable number of the statements were in the negative, an answer by the subject of False would produce a double negative. Our subjects report that they experienced little difficulty in dealing with these double negatives.

The pack of 504 cards was split into two sections, each approximately one half of the total. Each section was placed in a separate box and marked respectively Section 1 and Section 2. Three guide cards were placed in each box marked True, False, and Cannot Say. The following directions were pasted into the inner side of the cover of the box and these directions were called to the patient's attention by reading them to him at the time of handing him the cards for sorting.

DIRECTIONS

Take the cards out from the front, one at a time and decide whether each is true or not.

If it is *mostly* true about you, put it *behind* the card that says *TRUE*.

If it is *not mostly* true about you, put it *behind* the card that says *FALSE*.

If a statement does not apply to you, or is something that you don't know about, put it *behind* the card that says *CANNOT SAY*.

There are no right or wrong answers.

Remember to give *your* opinion of *yourself*.

There are two boxes in this set.

In order that we may use your results, both boxes must be completed.

After the cards are sorted by the subject into the three categories, the responses are recorded on a tabulation sheet. The left-hand lower corner of each card bearing a statement which is significant if filed as False is clipped, whereas the right-hand lower corner is clipped in the case of cards with significance if filed as True. Thus, in each of the true or false categories it becomes possible by breaking the deck over these clipped corners to separate the psychiatrically significant from the nonsignificant responses. Only the significant and the Cannot Say responses need be recorded. Each section of cards is marked by a distinctively colored ink stripe along the top side of the pack from front to back. Thus, it becomes possible to locate at a glance a card which has crept into the wrong deck, been reversed, or turned upside down.

After each administration of the inventory the sections are weighed to demonstrate whether or not all the cards for that section are still in the box. Before administration to another subject, each section is thoroughly shuffled so that the items come to the attention of the subject in random order. In this way no item has a constant effect on a subsequent item through any series of individual administrations. Theoretically, therefore, it should be possible either to delete old items or add new ones without producing any constant effect in the subsequent use of the inventory.

Subjects for standardization and development of scales are being obtained from several sources:

1. A normal group from the University Hospitals and the outpatient department (724 cases). These are individuals who themselves are not ill but are bringing relatives or friends to the clinic. They constitute the bulk of our so-called normal cases. The assumption is made, of course, that these people are in good health, which may not always be the case. To help establish them as real normals we ask them whether or not they are receiving treatment for any illness. Only those who say they are not under a physician's care are accepted in this group.

2. A normal group from the university Testing Bureau (265 cases). These are mainly precollege high school graduates who came to the Testing Bureau for precollege guidance, but there are a number of representatives from various college classes as well.

3. A group of normals whom we were able to contact through the courtesy of the local WPA (265 cases). These are all skilled workers from local projects.

4. Patients in the general wards of the University Hospitals (254 cases). These are individuals mainly on the medical service but also in lesser numbers from other services of the hospital whom we have contacted through the courtesy of the various members of the staff of the University Hospitals. Of course, most of these patients are in the hospital for one or another physical disease. Some of these were suffering acute illnesses such as upper respiratory infections, jaundice, and the like; others were chronically ill with carcinoma, gastric ulcer, leukemia, and a variety of other conditions. All of these have been checked so that they do not include obvious psychiatric conditions.

5. Patients in the psychopathic unit of the University Hospitals and the outpatient neuropsychiatric clinic (221 cases). All the inpatients who are not too disturbed or otherwise unusable become subjects of the inventory regardless of the diagnosis.

On all normal groups the person's identity is withheld if the subject does not care to reveal his name, but information is obtained on age, sex, school level reached, occupational level, marital state, and children. The subjects report upon the presence of mental deficiency or of psychoses in the family. On the hospital patients one of two procedures is used. For those patients not seen and diagnosed by the neuropsychiatric staff, the hospital record is carefully read and an independent judgment is made as to the presence of mental disorder. If a disorder is present, a tentative diagnosis is made; if not present the case is classified "physical normal." This indicates a relatively normal mental state in a patient with a physical disease.

For those who have received full clinical work-up by the neuropsychiatric staff, the responsible clinician fills out a mimeographed symptomatic tabulation sheet of the patient's essential symptoms and problems and writes the diagnostic summary

Table 1. Ages and Marital Status of Two Groups of Normals

	Male		Female	
Age	Single	Married	Single	Married
Group 1: Outpatient Department and Hospital				
16–25	62	45	70	28
26–43	39	194	26	123
44–54	8	61	5	38
55–65	2	14	0	9
Group 2: Testing Bureau				
16–25	152	0	113	0

Separate items tabulations are being made on these subjects, divided into convenient subgroups. The groupings and the present state of the records as they relate to Groups 1 and 2 are indicated in Table 1.

Some of these groups are still much too small to afford adequate norms or standards, but the general normals and hospital classes are being enlarged daily. The tabulations being made show the percentage frequencies of each of the three possible answers.

It is the authors' ultimate intention to publish the complete list of items with all the frequency statistics for the various normal groups when the number of cases becomes sufficiently large to provide adequate samples. We also plan to establish a series of scoring keys so that differential quantitative scales can be made available as an aid in differential psychiatric diagnosis. The problem of reliability and validity of each scale to be developed will receive special attention so that the strengths and weaknesses of this multiphasic personality schedule will be disclosed. Continued research will then make possible continued refinements and the overcoming of weaknesses.

ARTICLE 6 *Scale 1 (Hypochondriasis)*

AS THE first group of clinical cases for study with the multiphasic schedule [300 (see II, 5)], we have chosen our available cases of hypochondriasis. Since such individuals constitute a psychiatric and sociological problem of major interest and importance, it is fortunate for our purposes that they were the most numerous among our pathological groups. They were also favorable material for study in that they constituted one of the simpler and more definite nosological units from the clinical standpoint and thus represented a relatively stable clinical concept.

Hypochondriasis is defined for the purposes of this study as abnormal, psychoneurotic concern over bodily health. Our present usage is given authority in the American Psychiatric Association's *Classification of Mental Disorders* under the heading "Psychoneurosis, hypochondriasis." Thus we have arbitrarily limited statistical differentiation to the diagnostic group under the psychoneuroses and have excluded the symptomatic implications of the term as applied to the psychoses. This restriction to the narrower meaning added somewhat to our difficulties in the selection of cases by automatically eliminating many in which hypochondriasis as a symptom was prominent but was associated with other severe personality disturbances. Nevertheless, it was advantageous in that it provided us with a reasonably clear-cut concept.

Construction of the Scale for Hypochondriasis ($H-C_H$ Scale)

The group of pathological cases for scale construction was selected with meticulous care to exclude those with manifestations of the major psychoses; as far as it was possible for us to determine, only pure, uncomplicated hypochondriasis was included. All the cases had been studied intensively as inpatients in the psychopathic unit of the University of Minnesota Hospitals. Medical, neurological, psychiatric, and frequently psychometric surveys were followed through in detail. Diagnostic homogeneity was thus satisfactorily established. Though only 50 cases of this sort were available, the number was probably adequate, at least for our initial purposes, considering the care exercised in their selection. Fifty cases were inadequate, of course, for statistical analysis of the effect of such factors as social and marital status, sex, and intelligence. They were selected, however, to exclude the extremes of age or other obviously disturbing influences.

64

The series of "normal" or control cases from which the hypochondriacal cases were to be differentiated was as follows:

First, 109 males and 153 females between the ages of 26 and 43 inclusive. They were all married persons but seldom man and wife. These were from the group of individuals visiting patients in the hospital or bringing them to the various surgical and medical clinics of the outpatient department. They all asserted that they were not under a physician's care. In general, they represented a social stratum comparable with that of the patients in the hospital; both patients and this normal group belonged to the somewhat underprivileged classes. They came from all parts of Minnesota, both urban and rural.

Second, 265 college students from the University of Minnesota, mainly entering freshmen. These were not broken down into subcategories; they represented obviously an adolescent, unmarried group. They served as a control in the selection of scale items for the avoidance of inconsistent differentiations ascribable to differences in marital or parental status, age, socioeconomic level, intelligence, and education.

The procedure for identification of the differential items was set up in the usual manner. For each of the normal criterion groups, the percentage frequency of arbitrarily scored significant responses was recorded for each of the 504 separate items of the whole schedule. An item was selected tentatively for scale construction only if it showed a percentage frequency difference between the criterion group and the normal group which was at least twice its standard error; for most of the items selected, the differences were considerably more than twice the standard errors. The frequency of the significant response in nearly all the scale items was above 10 per cent for both groups; thus doubtful and rarely occurring responses were largely excluded. In a few of these items, the percentage of occurrence in the college group equaled or exceeded that of the hypochondriacal group, though both were significantly different from the adult normals. Such items were deleted on the basis of no differentiation between college students and hypochondriacal individuals. Where differences appeared to be obviously on such bases as marital status, or attitude toward one's children, the items were excluded on the ground that they did not apply generally in the population. Through similar reasoning a few more items were rejected on inspection of the list. Inter-item correlations were not calculated.

After experimenting with several tentative scales made up of items chosen in the manner described, the following items were finally settled upon as providing the best measure. The letter following each item indicates the answer (T = true; F = false) which is characteristic of the hypochondriacal response. Partly on the basis of the reliability of the percentage differences and partly on the basis of clinical judgment, evaluations were attempted with several weighted scales but they failed to show any superiority over unweighted items. Thus, each of the items is merely given a value of "one" in deriving this portion of the total score for an individual case.

1. During the past few years I have been well most of the time. (F) 2. I am in just as good physical health as most of my friends. (F) 3. I do not tire quickly. (F) 4. I seldom worry about my health. (F) 5. I believe I am no more nervous than most others. (F) 6. I have very few headaches. (F) 7. Much of the time my head seems to hurt all over. (T) 8. Often I feel as if there were a tight band about my head. (T)

9. There seems to be a fullness in my head or nose most of the time. (T) 10. The top of my head sometimes feels tender. (T) 11. I am troubled by attacks of nausea and vomiting. (T)

12. I seldom or never have dizzy spells. (F) 13. My judgment is better than it ever was. (F) 14. I cannot keep my mind on one thing. (T) 15. My eyesight is as good as it has been for years. (F) 16. I can read a long while without tiring my eyes. (F) 17. I do not often notice my ears ringing or buzzing. (F) 18. I feel weak all over much of the time. (T) 19. I have never been paralyzed or had any unusual weakness of any of my muscles. (F) 20. I have had no difficulty in keeping my balance in walking. (F) 21. I have little or no trouble with my muscles twitching or jumping. (F) 22. I frequently notice my hand shakes when I try to do something. (T)

23. I have few or no pains. (F) 24. Parts of my body often have feelings like burning, tingling, crawling, or like "going to sleep." (T) 25. I have numbness in one or more regions of my skin. (T) 26. I hardly ever feel pain in the back of the neck. (F) 27. My hands and feet are usually warm enough. (F) 28. Once a week or oftener I feel suddenly hot all over, without apparent cause. (T) 29. I cannot understand what I read as well as I used to. (T) 30. I sweat very easily even on cool days. (T) 31. I am almost never bothered by pains over the heart or in my chest. (F) 32. I hardly ever notice my heart pounding and I am seldom short of breath. (F) 33. There seems to be a lump in my throat much of the time. (T)

34. I have a good appetite. (F) 35. I have a great deal of stomach trouble. (T) 36. I am bothered by acid stomach several times a week. (T) 37. I am troubled by discomfort in the pit of my stomach every few days or oftener. (T) 38. I am very seldom troubled by constipation. (F) 39. I have had no difficulty in starting or holding my bowel movement. (F) 40. I have had no difficulty in starting or holding my urine. (F) 41. I wake up fresh and rested most mornings. (F) 42. My sleep is fitful and disturbed. (T) 43. Most nights I go to sleep without thoughts or ideas bothering me. (F) 44. I am about as able to work as I ever was. (F)

45. People generally demand more respect for their own rights than they are willing to allow for others. (F) 46. I enjoy social gatherings just to be with people. (F) 47. No one seems to understand me. (T) 48. I am usually calm and not easily upset. (F) 49. I cannot do anything well. (T) 50. I have had periods of days, weeks, or months when I couldn't take care of things because I couldn't "get going." (T) 51. It makes me nervous to have to wait. (T) 52. I have had periods of such great restlessness that I cannot sit long in a chair. (T) 53. Sometimes without any reason or even when things are going wrong I feel excitedly happy, "on top of the world." (F) 54. The sight of blood neither frightens nor makes me sick. (F) 55. I certainly feel useless at times. (T)

The preliminary score (H score) as above determined was then obtained on all the hospitalized psychiatric cases to whom the complete schedule had been administered. As one would expect on clinical grounds, many cases of frank psychosis (depression, for example) obtained high hypochondriacal scores. Contrary to expectation, however, a fair number of cases obtained high scores although the psychiatric staff had failed to elicit adequate evidence for the presence of hypochondriasis. On this basis, a correction scale seemed indicated and the following approach was undertaken for its construction.

Fifty cases with the highest H scores were selected from among the group of hospitalized psychiatric patients who clinically showed little or no hypochondriasis. The percentage frequency of the arbitrarily scored significant responses was recorded on each of the 504 separate items of the total schedule. The items showing significant percentage frequency difference between this group and the original group of 50 hypochondriacal individuals were then located. Those few items reappearing with differences in this comparison that had been included in the H scale were avoided; the remainder of the items with significant differences were collected into a separate grouping which we called the C_H scale (correction of the H scale). The C_H scale items are as follows with T or F chosen so that the item, answered as true or false, indicates differentiation between the groups in the direction of the nonhypochondriacal group:

1. I have had blank spells in which my activities were interrupted and I did not know what was going on around me. (T) 2. My hearing is apparently as good as that of most people. (F) 3. My speech is the same as always (not faster or slower, or slurring; no hoarseness). (F) 4. I drink an unusually large amount of water every day. (F) 5. The members of my family and my close relatives get along quite well (F) 6. At times I have very much wanted to leave home. (T) 7. Once in a while I feel hate toward members of my family whom I usually love. (T) 8. I have been disappointed in love. (T) 9. I am apt to pass up something I want to do when others feel that it isn't worth doing. (T) 10. I have often lost out on things because I couldn't make up my mind soon enough. (T) 11. Religion gives me no worry. (F) 12. It is all right to get around the law if you don't actually break it. (F)

13. I am likely not to speak to people until they speak to me. (T) 14. I prefer to pass by school friends, or people I know but have not seen for a long time, unless they speak to me first. (T) 15. I should like to belong to several clubs or lodges. (F) 16. I am a good mixer. (F) 17. I seem to make friends about as quickly as others do. (F) 18. I do many things which I regret afterwards. (I regret things more or more often than others seem to.) (T) 19. What others think of me does not bother me. (F) 20. I have sometimes stayed away from another person because I feared doing or saying something that I might regret afterwards. (T) 21. I am so touchy on some subjects that I can't talk about them. (T) 22. I have at times had to be rough with people who were rude or annoying. (T) 23. Even when I am with people I feel lonely much of the time. (T) 24. I have difficulty in starting to do things. (T)

25. I am apt to take disappointments so keenly that I can't put them out of my mind. (T) 26. I feel anxiety about something or someone almost all the time. (T) 27. I have met problems so full of possibilities that I have been unable to make up my mind about them. (T) 28. I am not easily angered. (F) 29. At times I feel like picking a fist fight with someone. (T) 30. I usually have to stop and think before I act even in trifling matters. (T) 31. I sometimes keep on at a thing until others lose their patience with me. (T) 32. I am sure I get a raw deal from life. (T) 33. I have often felt that strangers were looking at me critically. (T) 34. Someone has been trying to influence my mind. (T) 35. I believe I am being plotted against. (T) 36. I have had very peculiar and strange experiences. (T)

37. People say insulting and vulgar things about me. (T) 38. If given the chance I could do some things that would be of great benefit to the world. (T) 39. I have been afraid of things or people that I knew could not hurt me. (T) 40. I have no fear of water. (F) 41. I am afraid when I look down from a high place. (F) 42. I feel uneasy indoors. (T) 43. My plans have frequently seemed so full of difficulties that I have had to give them up. (T) 44. I often must sleep over a matter before I decide what to do. (T) 45. I have several times given up doing a thing because I thought too little of my ability. (T) 46. It makes me feel like a failure when I hear of the success of someone I know well. (T) 47. I have sometimes felt that difficulties

were piling up so high that I could not overcome them. (T) 48. I am certainly lacking in self confidence. (T)

These items in an individual score were counted each as "one" and the total subtracted from the H score. The final, corrected score for hypochondriasis could thus be expressed as $H-C_H$. The superiority of the $H-C_H$ scale is demonstrable on the basis of empirical results. Comparison of the statistics of the H scale with those of $H-C_H$ shows that the latter provides differentiations from normals which are as good as the former for groups clinically characterized either by hypochondriasis as a clinical entity or by hypochondriasis as a symptom of other psychiatric conditions. On the other hand, $H-C_H$ permits exclusion of many cases from the hypochondriacal group which are not clinically hypochondriacal but which obtain high H scores. The pertinent data for comparing the two scores are shown in Table 1.

Table 1. Relative Differentiations of Various Psychiatric Groups from a Normal Group by H and $H-C_H$ Scores

		H Score			$H-C_H$ Score			Diff/SE_{diff}	
Group	N	M	SD	Diff from Normals	M	SD	Diff from Normals	H Score	$H-C_H$ Score
A. Normal married males, ages 26–43	123	10.9	6.56		−3.9	5.64			
B. Hypochondriasis criterion group	50	29.1	7.88	18.2	14.3	7.80	18.2	15.4	14.9
C. C_H criterion group	50	26.2	7.58	16.1	0.3	8.76	6.1	13.0	4.5
D. Hypochondriasis, new cases for test	25	29.1	6.36	18.2	14.0	6.30	17.9	13.0	13.1
E. Psychiatric cases with symptomatic hypochondriasis	28	20.9	10.20	10.0	3.6	7.24	7.5	5.0	5.1
F. Psychiatric cases with high H score but without symptomatic hypochondriasis	17	22.3	3.82	11.4	1.2	5.46	5.1	10.4	3.6

The principal points of interest in Table 1 have to do with the critical ratios in the last two columns. As might be expected, there is some decrease of the critical ratio of the $H-C_H$ score as compared with the H score of the criterion group of hypochondriacs (B in Table 1). The loss is evidently not appreciable, however, because a new group of hypochondriacs (D) shows slight improvement of the critical ratio of $H-C_H$ over the H score. The group of cases (C) by means of which C_H was derived tested high with the H score but were not clinically hypochondriacal though they were psychiatric cases; they were chosen as criterion cases for this reason. It is obvious that the $H-C_H$ score has pulled them away from the hypochondriacal group, as would necessarily be the case. A similar group of new psychiatric cases (F) behaves in like fashion when put to the test of the two scores. On the other hand, a group of psychiatric cases with symptomatic hypochondriasis occurring coincidentally in other psychiatric states (E) appears to be collectively as hypochondriacal with the $H-C_H$ score as with the H score alone. From these and other data, we conclude that some factor other than body concern is corrected out by the subtraction of C_H from H. Although we do not hold that two persons are alike whose final $H-C_H$ scores are both 20, the one with H = 20 and C_H = 0, the other with H = 40 and C_H = 20, we have been unable to disclose any difference between them related to hypochondriasis.

Application of the $H-C_H$ Score to Normal and Pathological Case Material

The $H-C_H$ score was now obtained on all other persons who had been subjects of the entire schedule. The normal individuals were divided into the groups as shown in Table 2. Since skewness was very slight in the frequency distributions, the numerical expressions of mean and standard deviation as given in the table represent very closely the true distributions. The range of the means of the various groups of normals is not large, though in a few cases the differences are statistically significant. We hesitate to draw conclusions on the basis of these differences in view of our relative clinical inexperience with the scale at the present time. Certain of the more consistent trends do seem to justify comment, however. For example, in com-

Table 2. $H-C_H$ Scores on Normal Cases

Group Designation	Marital Status	Sex	Age	Number	Raw Score Mean	SD
Normal clinic visitors.	S	F	16–25	62	−3.5	6.34
Normal clinic visitors.	M	F	16–25	45	−3.1	6.68
Normal clinic visitors.	S	M	16–25	70	−4.3	4.82
Normal clinic visitors.	M	M	16–25	28	−3.0	6.28
Normal clinic visitors.	S	F	26–43	39	−3.9	5.12
Normal clinic visitors.	M	F	26–43	194	−1.5	6.58
Normal clinic visitors. . . . :.	S	M	26–43	26	−5.2	5.10
Normal clinic visitors.	M	M	26–43	123	−3.9	5.64
Normal clinic visitors. . . . . .M & S		F	44–54	69	+0.5	6.84
Normal clinic visitors. . . . . .M & S		M	44–54	43	−2.4	7.54
Normal college students. . . . . .M & S		F	16–25	113	−2.3	5.52
Normal college students. . . . . .M & S		M	16–25	152	−2.9	4.50

paring married and single individuals in each of the age groups where numbers permit their separation, the mean scores for married individuals were higher (more hypochondriacal) than for the corresponding unmarried persons. Likewise the scores for females are, without exception, higher than for the corresponding males. One might indulge in considerable speculation on these findings, but since the validity of the test within the normal group is at present in process of study, and the differences themselves are slight, we are not prepared to draw any conclusions as to the meaning of such differences.

Application of the Test to Clinical Cases

Since all the available hospitalized cases were used or culled over for the construction of the scale, we were limited in the selection of cases on which to put the scale to test to those patients who were admitted to our hospital wards after its construction and to the less desirable material from the outpatient department. The latter group was less satisfactory because of less complete clinical recording and the relative haste in clinical work-up demanded in the press of outpatient department practice. The test series consisted of 25 clinically diagnosed cases of hypochondriasis, 7 of which received intensive inpatient neuropsychiatric investigation, and the remaining 18 the routine outpatient work-up. The scores of the test cases are shown in Table 3 relative to the scores of two normal groups, the one without and the other with concomitant physical disease, and also to the scores of a group of miscellaneous psychiatric cases.

Table 3. Frequency Distributions of T Scores on the $H-C_H$
Scale for Four Groups

T Scores	Normals (N = 699)	Hypochondriacs (N = 25)	Physical Disease Normals (N = 50)	Miscellaneous Psychiatric Patients (N = 45)
97–99		1		
94–96		0		
91–93		0		
88–90		0		
85–87		5		
82–84		2	2	
79–81	2	1	0	
76–78	5 (1%)	1	3	2
73–75	7	4	1	2
70–72	19 (5%)	5	2	2
67–69	18	0	3	4
64–66	37 (10%)	2	5	1
61–63	50	1	5	2
58–60	57	2	8	6
55–57	61	1	4	9
52–54	98 (50%)		2	2
49–51	95		4	4
46–48	63		3	2
43–45	77		4	6
40–42	46		3	0
37–39	24		0	1
34–36	20		1	0
31–33	9			2
28–30	5			
25–27	5			
22–24	0			
19–21	1			

The normal group without physical disease is the same as Group 1, as described in our first paper [300 (see II, 5)], and that with physical disease the same as Group 4. The first group is made up of 699 cases; 50 cases make up the second. The 45 miscellaneous psychiatric cases were all inpatients who had been given detailed clinical study. The basic data for comparison with Table 3 are given in Table 4. It is obvious from simple inspection of the table that the scores of the hypochondriacal cases are distributed decidedly higher than any of the other groups. While overlap occurs, 8 of the 25 cases are beyond the highest score of any normal. Furthermore, the lowest score in the hypochondriacal group is above the mean of the normals. Since the selection of normals was really a random sample of functioning individuals who stated they were not under a physician's care, it is not surprising to note that a considerable number of them score within the distribution of the clinically hypochondriacal range. This coincides with and is at least a partial statistical verification of the frequently expressed opinion in medical and psychiatric circles that an appreciable proportion of the so-called normal population is suffering with hypochondriacal and other psychoneurotic disturbances.

The normals with physical illness constitute an especially important group. Since at the time of testing many of them were suffering physical pain, anxiety, and other reactions to organic diseases, one might expect a marked elevation of their scores. Only moderate elevation occurs; the group is much nearer the normals than it is the hypochondriacs. One concludes from this that physical symptoms alter the personality pattern only moderately in the direction of hypochondriasis.

The distribution of the 45 miscellaneous psychiatric cases also provides important data. These were individuals from the inpatient psychiatric service who had not been used in constructing or testing the scale. The only exclusion was the removal

Table 4. The Statistics of the Standard Score Equivalents of the
Three Test Groups [a]

Group Designation	Number	Standard Score Mean	Standard Score SD	Critical Ratio to Normal
Hypochondriacal cases	25	74.2	10.23	10.9
Normals with physical disease	50	58.1	11.34	4.0
Miscellaneous psychiatric cases ..	45	55.7	10.98	2.5

[a] Age and sex are corrected out. See also Table 3.

of psychoneurotic hypochondriacal cases and, of course, patients who could not cooperate. It is to be remembered that hypochondriasis as a symptomatic concomitant of other obvious psychiatric disorders was not excluded from this group. In our opinion, this group constitutes a most exacting test of the discriminatory power of the scale. Thus, depressive patients, as is well known, frequently exhibit hypochondriacal symptoms together with feelings of guilt, nihilistic delusions, and other self-depreciatory trends as the syndrome of the condition; similar comment is possible in relation to other included psychotic conditions. Yet the score distribution of these miscellaneous psychiatric cases is only slightly higher than that of the normal group and is definitely lower than that of the hypochondriacal cases. Thus, the group of clinically diagnosed hypochondriacs is differentiated by the schedule almost as well from the psychotic group as it is from the normal.

Conclusions

Differential study of groups of persons by a scale for hypochondriasis derived from our multiphasic personality schedule reveals that:

1. Significant separation of hypochondriacal cases from normals can be demonstrated.

2. A sizable proportion of the so-called normal population nevertheless overlaps the hypochondriacal group as is often stated in medical and psychiatric opinion.

3. The presence of physical disorder does not greatly raise the scores over the normal distribution in the direction of hypochondriasis.

4. The distribution of the hypochondriacal scores of psychotic patients is only slightly higher than that of the normals.

Addendum

In a personal communication S. R. Hathaway has outlined the subsequent modification of $H - C_H$.

It had been noted in the course of derivation of a scale for hysteria that the new scale 3 (Hy) differed from the hypochondriasis scale mainly in the items related to the correction C_H for H. Scale 1 (Hs) was therefore arbitrarily made into a somatic item scale by eliminating the C_H items and some of the old H items that did not stand up on further analysis. This decision was intended to make the diagnosed hysterics score high mainly on scale 3. When K was tried on scale 1, the results showed that the corrected scale improved the differentiation between hypochondriasis and hysteria. It appeared that too extreme a purification had been made when *all* the C_H items were taken out. The addition of .5K helped correct this error. As indicated in the K article [441 (see I, 2)] the C_H items correlated well with K; the correlation was negative because the items were scored inversely. In short, modern Hs + .5K is a compromise between a pure somatic scale and the old $H - C_H$.

ARTICLE 7 *Scale 2 (Depression)*

THE complete set of items in the MMPI has now been administered to about 3000 individuals of various normal and abnormal classifications. The chief normal group against which all hospitalized abnormal groups are considered is comprised of adults to whom the items were administered when they came as visitors to or brought patients to the University Hospitals. The only requirement for inclusion of these persons as normal was that they said they were not under a doctor's care at the time of testing. The word "normal" as used hereafter never implies more than this. The normal group so obtained represents a reasonably accurate cross section of the Minnesota population. The modal scholastic achievement is eighth grade, and socio-occupational ratings indicate that the modal occupational level is approximately that of the general adult population.

One scale has already been derived and published [420 (see II, 6)]. This scale measures symptomatic hypochondriasis and yields a score indicating the degree to which the clinical picture of hypochondriasis is present in the individual. Hypochondriasis was chosen for the first scale because it was relatively clear-cut clinically and because good clinical cases were relatively easy to obtain.

Derivation of the Depression Scale

The present paper deals with the development of a scale for measuring symptomatic depression. The term "symptomatic" is used here because the authors wish to avoid the identification of the term "depression" with anything other than the presence at the time of testing of a clinically recognizable, general frame of mind characterized by poor morale, lack of hope in the future, and dissatisfaction with the patient's own status generally. In fact, such a clinical picture might result from economic or vocational frustration, from personal problems, from a depressive phase of a cycloid personality, or from any one of the other commonly known clinical backgrounds of depression. As seen in this way, the measured depression might represent a less stable trait in the individual than would the measured hypochondriacal tendency or, in fact, most other measured personality characteristics. It is well recognized that a few patients with a marked degree of depression on one day may change toward normal within twenty-four hours. The same tendency to shift is notable in a few individuals who may never develop a clinically important depth of depression. All these factors make rather difficult the problem of obtaining a group of patients clearly depressed at the time of testing.

73

The subjects for scale derivation consisted of (a) 139 normal married males between the ages of 26 and 43 and 200 normal married females between the ages of 26 and 43, (b) a group of 265 college students as a check for the effect of age on item frequency, (c) 40 normal persons having a high depression score on a preliminary depression scale, (d) a group of 50 patients without clinically observed depression but with a tendency to score high on the preliminary depression scale, and finally (e) a group of 50 carefully chosen depressed patients to serve as a criterion group.

The 50 patients of the criterion depression group (e), most of whom were in the depressed phase of a manic-depressive psychosis, had all been thoroughly investigated medically and psychiatrically and, as far as possible, represented relatively pure cases of depression. This group of depressed patients will hereafter be referred to as the criterion group. The group of male and female normals (a) against which comparisons were made will be referred to as the normal group. It should be noted that in the final presentation of the results of the scale, many more normals are included than are included in the normal group as described above. The college students (b) were mostly first- or second-year students and also included were a number of college applicants just out of high school. The 40 normal persons (c) who were depressed on the preliminary depression scale will be referred to hereafter as the depressed normal group. Some of these may have been true depression cases not in the hospital or under a doctor's care. The 50 University Hospitals patients (d) with high preliminary scores but with no clinically observed depression will be described later as the nondepressed group.

In deriving the significant items for depression, the preliminary statistical procedure consisted in listing the percentage occurrence among the normal group of each answer, True, False, and Cannot Say, for each item alongside the similar percentages for the criterion group. Analysis then included the checking of all items having a reliable difference between the percentages for normal and criterion groups. At this point in the derivation the requirement for reliability was that the difference be more than twice its standard error. After the items had been checked for the presence of a reliable difference, each was inspected and any item that had too great a sex difference, or that failed to differentiate between the criterion and college groups was eliminated. A few other items were eliminated because of some apparent inconsistency or because they seemed inappropriate. This left 70 items which were used as a preliminary depression scale.

All available psychiatric and normal cases were next scored on the preliminary scale. As was the case with hypochondriasis, it was found that when all other clinic patients were scored on this preliminary depression scale and their scores were compared with the scores made by normals in general, a number of clinically studied cases scored high who had not been found by the psychiatric staff to present any important degree of depression. Since it was felt that, as had been true also of the hypochondriacal scale, extraneous factors were influencing the scores, a correction was necessary. This correction was derived by choosing from among carefully studied clinical cases 50 individuals to form the nondepressed group. The nondepressed group was selected as indicated above (d) on the basis of a high score on the preliminary depression scale, contrasting with an absence of depression as seen clinically. The percentage occurrence of all items for this group was now tabulated alongside the above tabulations for the criterion and normal groups. A depressed normal group of 40 persons (c) was next selected from among the large normal group. Those in this category were selected merely on the basis of having scored highest among the normals on the preliminary scale. All item tabulations of this group were also added to the above array, completing the data for the selection of the final scale items.

In choosing items for the final scale, the following requirements had to be met by the accepted item. First, each depressive item had to show a progressive increase in frequency from the normal groups through the depressed normal group to the criterion group since it was assumed that the depressed normals would be less depressed than the criterion cases but more than general normals. In all items primarily indicating depression, the difference in percentage between the normal and the criterion was 2.5 or more times its standard error. Second, the nondepressed group percentage for the item was required to approach that for normals. After careful analysis of all percentages for each of the 504 items, 60 items were chosen as the final depression scale.

The above procedure was devised to eliminate stray items that might occur beyond statistical limits if only two groups were used and to avoid items that would fail to differentiate in the desired direction under special conditions. Especially, the nondepressed group was used to assure the inclusion of correction items to hold the scores down on cases not belonging to the clinical category. In the present scale the correction is achieved without minus items, in contrast to the hypochondriasis scale although the same basic procedure is followed. In all, 11 of the 60 items of the present scale are primarily correction items and not especially indicative of depression. By this is meant that they showed little increase in percentage from normal to depressed but did clearly differentiate the nondepressed from the depressed group. Other items serve both purposes at the same time. By using the depressed normal group in the scale development, it was hoped that a more certain validity could be established for intermediate scale values between normal and clearly abnormal than would have been true for a scale contrasting the two extreme groups alone.

In the final scale all items are simply counted $+1$ when answered in the depressed direction. If any item is answered Cannot Say it is disregarded since there are few such responses. The following list contains all the final items with a T or an F after each to indicate the scored answer. Those items for which the chief function is correction rather than depression are starred.

1. During the past few years I have been well most of the time. (F) 2. I am in just as good physical health as most of my friends. (F) 3. I have never felt better in my life than I do now. (F) 4. I am neither gaining nor losing weight. (F) 5. I seldom worry about my health. (F) 6. I believe I am no more nervous than most others. (F) 7. I am troubled by attacks of nausea and vomiting. (T) °8. I have never had a fit or convulsion. (F) 9. I seem to be about as capable and smart as most others around me. (F) 10. My judgment is better than it ever was. (F)

11. My memory seems to be all right. (F) 12. I feel weak all over much of the time. (T) 13. I cannot understand what I read as well as I used to. (T) °14. I sweat very easily even on cool days. (F) °15. Sometimes, when embarrassed, I break out in a sweat which annoys me greatly. (F) °16. I do not have spells of hay fever or asthma. (T) °17. I have never vomited blood or coughed up blood. (T) 18. I have a

good appetite. (F) 19. I am very seldom troubled by constipation. (F) 20. My sleep is fitful and disturbed. (T)

21. Most nights I go to sleep without thoughts or ideas bothering me. (F) 22. I am easily awakened by noise. (T) 23. I dream frequently about things that are best kept to myself. (F) 24. I am about as able to work as I ever was. (F) 25. I have at times stood in the way of people who were trying to do something, not because it amounted to much but because of the principle of the thing. (F) 26. It takes a lot of argument to convince most people of the truth. (F) 27. I like to flirt. (F) °28. I go to church almost every week. (F) °29. I believe in the second coming of Christ. (F) °30. Everything is turning out just like the prophets of the Bible said it would. (F)

31. I do not blame a person for taking advantage of someone who lays himself open to it. (F) 32. I prefer to pass by school friends, or people I know but have not seen for a long time, unless they speak to me first. (T) 33. I am a good mixer. (F) 34. I enjoy many different kinds of play and recreation. (F) 35. Criticism or scolding hurts me terribly. (T) 36. I wish I could be as happy as others seem to be. (T) 37. I usually feel that life is worthwhile. (F) 38. My daily life is full of things that keep me interested. (F) 39. I have difficulty in starting to do things. (T) 40. I have had periods of days, weeks, or months when I couldn't take care of things because I couldn't "get going." (T)

41. I brood a great deal. (T) 42. I cry easily. (T) 43. I don't seem to care what happens to me. (T) 44. I am happy most of the time. (F) 45. I have periods in which I feel unusually cheerful without any special reason. (F) 46. At times I am all full of energy. (F) 47. Sometimes without any reason or even when things are going wrong I feel excitedly happy, "on top of the world." (F) 48. At times I feel like smashing things .(F) 49. At times I feel like picking a fist fight with someone. (F) °50. I sometimes keep on at a thing until others lose their patience with me. (F)

°51. When I leave home I do not worry about whether the door is locked and the windows closed. (F) 52. I do not worry about catching diseases. (F) 53. I am afraid of losing my mind. (T) °54. I sometimes tease animals. (F) 55. I find it hard to keep my mind on a task or job. (T) 56. I work under a great deal of tension. (T) 57. I certainly feel useless at times. (T) 58. I am certainly lacking in self-confidence (T) 59. Once in a while I laugh at a dirty joke. (F) 60. At times I feel like swearing. (F)

For clinical use, the raw scores are transformed into standard scores in which the means of each of the whole normal groups of males and females between the ages of 16 and 45 are given the value 50; other raw scores are transformed so that the standard deviation will be 10. Larger scores than the mean, denoting more depression, are assigned to the range above 50 and those below the mean to the range below 50. In basing the standard scores on the age range of 16–45 inclusive, the whole population is well characterized even though there is a change with age. It is more acceptable clinically to permit a higher average score on depression with increasing age. The standard scores also eliminate the sex difference present in raw scores.

Evidences of Validity and Incidental Findings

In order to test the scale for validity, a group of 35 cases observed in the clinic subsequent to the scale derivation was selected. These are called test cases. The test cases were not all clear cases of depression but they were satisfactory to the extent that they should, as a group, be clearly different from normals although individuals might have recovered from their depression before testing. It was not possible to tell from the clinical record whether or not the rated depression was present at the precise time of administration of the inventory. As a further test of validity, a group of patients who had not actually received the diagnosis "depression" but who were marked by the staff as having or having had during their illness some degree of abnormal depression was selected from among the psychiatric records. This group, hereafter called the symptomatic depression group, probably includes some definitely depressed patients as well as some with little depression (especially at the time of testing). It also includes schizoid and neurotic patients in whom the depression was overshadowed by some other component. On the whole, the sympto-

Table 1. Frequency Distributions of T Scores on Scale 2 (D) for Minnesota Normals and the Depressed Test Cases

T Scores	Normals (N = 690)	Depressed Test Cases (N = 35)	T Scores	Normals (N = 690)	Depressed Test Cases (N = 35)
97–99	0	3	61–63	34	2
94–96	1	2	58–60	39	2
91–93	1	3	55–57	52	1
88–90	0	2	52–54	61	0
85–87	2	2	49–51	69 (50%)	0
82–84	3 (1%)	5	46–48	79	1
79–81	7	1	43–45	70	
76–78	10	2	40–42	65	
73–75	11 (5%)	2	37–39	53	
70–72	13	2	34–36	44	
67–69	17	2	31–33	21	
64–66	26 (10%)	3	28–30	10	
			25–27	2	

matic group would be expected to score above all groups except the more definitely diagnosed depressed criterion and test groups.

Table 1 shows the results on 690 normals of ages 16–65. The scale is in the above standard score values and the 1, 5, 10, and 50 per cent points are marked as they were obtained with the origin at the depressed end of the distribution. Because of skewness, these are not at the standard values predicted from a normal curve. Distributed on the same standard scale are the scores of the 35 test depression cases. These provide the best available test of validity. The shape of the distribution for the normals is probably typical for personality traits where deviations in the normal direction are restricted relative to abnormal deviation.

Table 2 gives the raw score means and standard deviations for the groups described above, together with the probability values for several of the differences between the means. The groups are arranged according to the value of the mean raw score. As was indicated in Table 1, the test group shows a clear difference from normals. This difference is second in magnitude only to that of the criterion group. The statistics of the symptomatic depression group — which is a further test of validity since its members had depression as a symptom — are also given. In reality, this group is a very heterogeneous one, including many depressed patients who had other symptoms that were favored in their diagnosis as well as patients with little real evidence of depression. It is apparent that although there is some overlap the scale yields scores that differentiate at least 50 per cent of the test cases from normals and even from other psychiatric cases although the latter are, reasonably enough, more depressed than normal. Twenty-four of the 35 test cases made a standard score greater than 70.

Unfortunately, the nondepressed group also still shows a large and significant difference. Whether this is because they were really depressed and not observed by the clinicians to be so or whether they represent true errors of measurement cannot be determined. The former alternative is not unreasonable, however, since all of the score that could be corrected as being spurious was so corrected and since certain depressed patients are notably able to hide depression. The nondepressed were not frequent among all cases seen in the clinic and do not constitute a practical problem after partial correction.

Table 2. The Means and Standard Deviations of Various Groups

Group	N	M	SD	Diff [a]	Diff/SE$_{diff}$ [a]
Criterion	50	36.68	4.7	18.54	26.9
Test depressed	35	32.49	7.4	14.35	11.0
Nondepressed	50	28.86	6.3	10.72	11.8
Symptomatically depressed	223	28.20	7.3	10.06	19.0
Random psychiatric cases	413	24.44	7.2	6.30	15.8
Physically ill	229	21.70	5.2	3.56	8.9
Normals	690	18.14	4.9		

[a]The differences and their reliability values are in contrast with the statistics of the normal group.

The group in Table 2 called random psychiatric cases is made up of all clinic cases not diagnosed as any type of depression; but it does include the 223 symptomatic depression cases in whom some depression was observed. The random psychiatric cases as a group contrast with the physically ill cases of Table 2 which are from other wards of the hospital. To be on a psychiatric ward seems to increase the score. In reality, this difference is observable clinically among the psychiatric cases as is shown by the fact that it mostly disappears when the symptomatically depressed group is left out. The subjects in the physically ill group were patients on the open wards who were not special problems psychiatrically but who were in the hospital because of one or more physical complaints. These patients are often observably depressed as a reaction to their illness, which could be anything from a mild respiratory infection to very serious conditions. This group is reliably more depressed than the normal. Of special interest among this group is the relative standing of the men and the women. When the scores are transformed into standard scores, 18 per cent of the males but only 6 per cent of the females exceed the 5 per cent point of the normal group. The mean standard score of the males is 60 ($+1$ sigma) and that of the females is 55 ($+.5$ sigma). This finding shows the especial reaction of the males to a disabling illness.

In consideration of Tables 1 and 2, another factor may play a part in the overlap of normal and test cases. The normal group included many persons who were visiting relatives or friends in the hospital for serious illnesses and consequently might themselves be reactively depressed. Although fluctuations of a more temporary sort would not be likely to greatly affect many traits, the depression scale is surely sensitive to them. There is no practical way to estimate from our available data the effect of the factor upon the overlap of the curves.

Table 3 gives some raw score means and standard deviations with the significance of the differences from the criterion group. As a group, the nondepressed are significantly different, showing that some correction has occurred, since there was no difference on the preliminary scale.

Although the primary approach has been through the establishment of what is best described as the clinical validity of the scales, some evidence of test-retest reliability is available. Although many retests have been recorded on our clinical material, these are not suitable for reliability correlations for obvious reasons. For 40 normal cases, the reliability coefficient is .77 ± .044. On the basis of this reliability the probable error of a score is 1.9 points.

For the previously published scale of hypochondriasis, $H-C_H$, the test-retest reliability coefficient is .80 ± .038 for the same group. The two tests on these normals were separated in time by never less than three days and up to more than a year. All of these 40 normals were employees and staff members but none knew that the test was to be repeated until they were asked to take it again. The range of the group was small on both scales.

Among a sample of 50 random normal cases in the age range 26 to 35, the intercorrelation with hypochondriasis as measured by $H-C_H$ is .29 ± 0.87. On another sample of 50 from the normal group in the age range 16 to 25, the same procedure gives a correlation of .16 ± .093. This value rises to .62 ± .041 on a sample of 100

Table 3. Means and Standard Deviations of Several of the Groups in Contrast with the Statistics of the Criterion Group

Group	N	M	SD	Diff	Diff/ SE_{diff}
Criterion	50	36.68	4.7		
Test depressed	35	32.49	7.4	−4.19	3.0
Nondepressed	50	28.86	6.3	−7.82	7.0
Random psychiatric cases	413	24.44	7.2	−12.24	16.3
Normals	690	18.14	4.9	−18.54	26.9

random psychiatric cases. Part of the rather small degree of correlation for normals is no doubt due to overlap of the measuring instruments. In all, 22 items are common to both scales but five of these are counted oppositely. This leaves approximately 12 items working in a common direction if one corrects for the effect of the opposing items. That the two factors can be dynamically interrelated is shown when abnormal cases are used. One can hardly be deeply concerned over his health even on a delusional basis without being somewhat depressed as a result.

Among normal groups there are several differences that are of interest. Table 4 gives the raw score means and standard deviations for some of the subgroups. The college group appears here for the first time since it was not included in the general normal data presented above. These mixed college and precollege cases have the lowest scores of any subdivision. Among the general normals there is an age difference with a clear tendency for a higher score at higher ages. The most constant difference, however, is that between sexes. At present the authors are not willing to interpret this difference but it may be due to some general bias in response that is not particularly related to depression.

Table 4. Age and Sex Differences in Mean Score

Group	Males			Females		
	N	M	SD	N	M	SD
College students	155	14.77	3.70	115	16.90	4.2
General population (by age)						
16–25.....................	110	16.15	4.39	118	18.57	5.4
26–35.....................	111	16.63	3.90	165	19.08	4.6
36–45.....................	73	17.36	4.11	113	20.23	5.6
46–55.....................	40	18.93	5.47	59	19.25	4.8
56–	13	21.46	6.43	19	21.58	6.0

Conclusions

Differential study of groups of persons by a scale for depression derived from our multiphasic personality schedule reveals that:

1. Significant separation of clinically depressed patients from normals can be demonstrated for a large percentage of cases.

2. Patients having only moderate degrees of depressive trend without specific abnormality can also be differentiated.

3. Depression scale scores are significantly higher for females than for males and they become higher with increasing age.

4. Unselected patients on a psychiatric ward test higher on depression than do patients on other wards and the latter are higher than the normal.

J. C. McKINLEY AND S. R. HATHAWAY

ARTICLE 8 *Scale 7 (Psychasthenia)*

THE psychiatric classification of psychasthenia is applied to a group of individuals whose thinking is characterized by excessive doubt, by compulsions, obsessions, and unreasonable fears; these persons are often seen in psychiatric hospitals but are encountered much more frequently among normal groups by counselors and personnel workers. Certain phobias such as the fear of spiders, of snakes, or of windstorms are widespread among the population, but similar phobias become so strong and so numerous in some persons as to afford a source of considerable maladjustment vocationally, socially, or otherwise. Often a psychasthenic individual is characterized not so much by well-marked fears of individual things or acts as by great doubts as to the meaning of his reactions in what seems to be a hostile environment. In other cases the phobia becomes attached to certain acts or thoughts of the subject in such a way that he is forced through fear to compulsively perform needless, disturbing, or personally destructive acts or to dwell obsessively upon lines of thought which have no significance for his normal activities.

Compulsive acts are always characterized by the need felt by the subject to perform them without regard to rational considerations. For example, he may always be forced to count objects or to touch a certain spot on a wall or to avoid stepping on sidewalk cracks. If he fails to do these things he feels uncomfortable; if he does them he is forced to rationalize and justify his acts. Obsessive thinking is itself commonly accompanied by anxiety so that the patient may be tense and anxious over the content of his thoughts as when he thinks over and over again that he is useless. Similarly, he may find himself anxiously obsessed with such ideas as the impending likelihood that he will faint or that something terrible or threatening is about to happen. Again, he may be forced to think things which, while not in themselves producing anxiety, through his impatience and preoccupation with the fact that he cannot stop thinking them, do secondarily produce an anxious reaction; for example, compulsive counting itself has little attached anxiety since the patient is merely forced to count everything that he sees, but he may worry so much over his inability to stop counting as to have anxiety as a large component in his thinking. The general reaction type characterized by these compulsive and obsessive acts and thoughts is called psychasthenia. The word derives from the concept of a weakened will that cannot resist the behavior regardless of its maladaptive character.

The development of a scale for the measurement of the general symptomatic

81

traits which are classed under the psychiatric designation of psychasthenia has demonstrated that there is an identifiable personality pattern underlying the varying symptomatic picture from case to case. Many of the items making up the psychasthenia scale are clearly much more general than the specific compulsions or phobias and apply to a more general personality make-up of which the subject is usually entirely unaware.

The methods of derivation for the present scale differ only in detail from the methods used in the scales reported earlier [420 (see II, 6), 301 (II, 7)]. Unfortunately for the present study not many entirely satisfactory criterion cases of psychasthenia come into the closed wards of a psychiatric clinic. Many more are seen in the outpatient clinic or are advised by lay counselors and are never severely handicapped. Because we have felt unsure in the use of even carefully studied inpatients for purposes of scale derivation, we have avoided using criterion cases from the outpatient clinic. The criterion group is thus small and not entirely homogeneous. At least one of the cases appears to have been incorrectly diagnosed. Fortunately, the trait itself is the most homogeneous one so far described so that correlations of items with total score could be used as a guide. Otherwise, we would hesitate to publish the results with so few criterion cases.

The chief subjects for scale derivation consisted of (a) 139 normal married males between the ages of 26 and 43, and 200 normal married females between the ages of 26 and 43, (b) a group of 265 college students as a check of the effect of age on item frequency, and (c) a group of 20 psychiatric patients carefully selected as probable psychasthenia cases.

The criterion group included patients who had been intensively studied medically and psychiatrically and for whom the final diagnosis was psychasthenia in one or another form. Unfortunately, as mentioned above, it was necessary not only to use a rather small criterion group, but also to include in the group several persons who, as it subsequently developed, were probably not appropriate. For example, the two of this group who received the lowest final scores were young persons, one of 16 and the other of 17 years. One of these was not at all similar in item responses to the remainder of the criterion group. It is probable that this 16-year-old boy was wrongly diagnosed.

A preliminary step in deriving this scale was the tabulation of the item responses of the criterion group in contrast to the norm groups of men and women and the college students considered as a mixed normal group selected for age and for scholastic aptitude. All items that showed a differentiation of two or more times the standard error of the difference between the criterion and all of the normal groups were chosen as a preliminary scale for psychasthenia. All available normal and psychiatric cases were then scored on this preliminary scale. It was possible at this point to check whether or not the scale seemed to be working in the right direction and to determine its apparent variability. Since the scale as derived in this preliminary fashion appeared to be unusually homogeneous and since there were other potentially useful items that had been doubtful in the statistics of the comparison of criterion and normal groups, item correlations were used to test all preliminary scale items as well as certain of the doubtful items not included in the preliminary scale.

Tetrachoric correlations were obtained for every preliminary item and all the doubtful items against total scores on the preliminary scale for a sample of 100 normal persons and for a sample of 100 randomly selected psychiatric patients. These data combined with the original comparison data of criterion and normal cases permitted us to select a final scale of 48 items. The following list contains all of these final scale items each followed by a T or an F to indicate the direction of the scored answer. After each item is given the tetrachoric correlation of the item with total score on the preliminary scale. The first figure is the correlation from normal cases and the second that from psychiatric cases. It was assumed that items were valid if they correlated with either group. In some cases only one correlation is given since the cell frequencies for a response might be too low to obtain a valid indication of the other correlation. A few of the items with low correlations were retained because the item had appeared very strong in the criterion group. The items are merely counted +1 when answered in the indicated direction.

Item		100 Normals	100 Psychiatric Patients
I seldom worry about my health	F	40	65
At times I have fits of laughing and crying that I cannot control	T	59	47
I seem to be about as capable and smart as most others around me	F	80	47
My memory seems to be all right	F		71
I feel weak all over much of the time	T	75	61
I cannot understand what I read as well as I used to	T	43	63
There seems to be a lump in my throat much of the time	T	80	50
I wake up fresh and rested most mornings	F	65	80
Most nights I go to sleep without thoughts or ideas bothering me	F	32	77
I almost never dream	F	40	53
I like to study and read about things that I am working at	F		51
I do many things which I regret afterwards (I regret things more or more often than others seem to)	T	65	72
In school I found it very hard to talk before the class	T	57	44
I am easily embarrassed	T	56	70
I am more sensitive than most other people	T	77	53
I easily become impatient with people	T	52	
Even when I am with people I feel lonely much of the time	T	55	81
I wish I could be as happy as others seem to be	T	60	67
My daily life is full of things that keep me interested	F	41	74
I have had periods of days, weeks, or months when I couldn't take care of things because I couldn't "get going"	T	66	66
I frequently find myself worrying about something	T	85	76
Most of the time I feel blue	T	80	82
Much of the time I feel as if I have done something wrong or evil	T	76	
I feel anxiety about something or someone almost all the time	T	52	
Once a week or oftener I become very excited	T	90	72
I have periods of such great restlessness that I cannot sit long in a chair	T	79	75
Sometimes I become so excited that I find it hard to get to sleep	T	63	50
I forget right away what people say to me	T	16	74
I usually have to stop and think before I act even in trifling matters	T	52	
I have a habit of counting things that are not important such as bulbs on electric signs, and so forth	T	45	67
Sometimes some unimportant thought will run through my mind and bother me for days	T	82	62
Bad words, often terrible words, come into my mind and I cannot get rid of them	T	48	71

Item		100 Normals	100 Psychiatric Patients
Often I cross the street in order not to meet someone I see ..	T	80	80
I have strange and peculiar thoughts	T	63	79
I get anxious and upset when I have to make a short trip away from home	T	58	55
Almost every day something happens to frighten me	T		82
I have been afraid of things or people that I knew could not hurt me	T	41	20
I have no dread of going into a room by myself where other people have already gathered and are talking	F	35	44
I am afraid of losing my mind	T		60
My hardest battles are with myself	T	45	50
I have more trouble concentrating than others seem to have ..	T	90	72
I have several times given up doing a thing because I thought too little of my ability	T	53	
I find it hard to keep my mind on a task or job	T	36	79
I am inclined to take things hard	T	56	53
Life is a strain for me much of the time	T	50	84
I certainly feel useless at times	T	70	74
I am certainly lacking in self confidence	T	52	
Once in a while I think of things too bad to talk about	T	46	70

The distributions of Table 1 show the scores of the normal, the criterion cases, and fifty symptomatic cases on the final scale. The scores used in Table 1 are standard score equivalents derived from the statistics for 293 normal males and 397 normal females between the ages of 16 and 45. Two standard score tables were used, one for the males and one for the females. This cancels the sex differences. (See Table 2.) The standard scores were fitted to a mean of 50 and a standard deviation of 10.

Table 1. Frequency Distributions of the T Scores on Scale 7 (Pt) for Minnesota Normals and Two Criterion Groups

T Scores	Normals (N = 690)	Criterion Psychasthenics (N = 20)	Symptomatic Cases (N = 50)
88–90............		1	
85–87............	1	1	3
82–84............	1	1	1
79–81............	5 (1%)	1	1
76–78............	3	3	5
73–75............	11	3	3
70–72............	14 (5%)	2	4
67–69............	21	3	4
64–66............	34 (10%)	1	4
61–63............	29		
58–60............	39	2	4
55–57............	66	1	7
52–54............	58		4
49–51............	63 (50%)		5
46–48............	69		1
43–45............	96		3
40–42............	65		
37–39............	72		1
34–36............	39	1	
31–33............	4		

Table 2. Changes in Score with Age and Sex

Group	Males			Females		
	N	M	SD	N	M	SD
College students	155	7.27	5.8	115	8.93	6.0
General population (by age)						
16–25....................	110	9.10	7.4	118	13.00	7.9
26–35....................	110	10.54	7.2	165	12.19	7.7
36–45....................	73	10.12	6.5	114	14.47	7.4
46–55....................	40	10.90	7.8	59	12.31	6.7
56–65....................	13	12.38	8.8	19	14.16	7.4

Validity and Incidental Findings

There was relatively little change in score with age. Table 2 shows the raw score statistics for ten-year intervals from 16 to 65. The college student group deviates markedly from the group of similar age chosen at random from the population. There is some difference between the sexes as observed with other scales but without further study no special significance should be attached to this difference.

It is, unfortunately, not possible to estimate the validity of the psychasthenia scale by testing it on a new group of psychiatric patients diagnosed psychasthenia only but not used in the derivation of the scale. A few new cases have been diagnosed by the clinic but another year will be required for the accumulation of a sufficiently large group to permit this type of statistical validation. Nevertheless additional individuals so far obtained by clinical diagnosis have been deviates on the scale.

The evidence of validity as given by the psychiatric cases with clinical symptoms of some degree of psychasthenia is relatively clear and positive. This has been shown by experience in the clinic but is more graphically shown in Table 1. The distribution marked symptomatic cases represents 50 psychiatric cases very heterogeneous in diagnosis but with the one common characteristic that they were marked by the staff as having some symptomatic evidence of obsessions or compulsions. Since none of these cases were finally diagnosed psychasthenia and since the clinician frequently overemphasizes symptoms as seen in a person otherwise abnormal, the cases should not be expected to be uniformly high in the scale. Nevertheless the trend toward high scores for the group is clearly significant. Only 10 per cent fall below the mean for the normal group.

Table 3 lists the means and standard deviations of several groups in comparison with the normal group. In contrast to previously derived scales, the physically ill individuals from other portions of the hospital test very little above normals not in the hospital. Psychiatric cases without recorded evidence of psychasthenia test above the normal average but the staff frequently fails to record the presence of some psychasthenic traits even though they are observed since the trends are not disabling.

Several measures of reliability are available. For a group of 47 normal cases retested at intervals of never less than three days and up to more than a year, the test-retest reliability coefficient is .74 ± .15. Most of these cases were employees and staff but none knew that the test was to be repeated. The standard deviation of this group was 4.9 on the first test as compared with over 7 on general normals and undoubtedly the coefficient obtained represents a low limit rather than a true test-retest correlation value. The split half coefficient obtained from a group of 200 random normal cases is .84 ± .07. When a similar sample of 100 psychiatric cases selected at random is used, the correlation is .89 ± .10. When these two correlations are statistically corrected to a full-length test, they are .91 ± .07 and .94 ± .10.

Table 3. Means and Standard Deviations for Several Groups

Group	N	M	SD	Diff	Diff/ SE_{diff}	Percentage Reaching or Exceeding Mean of Normals
Normals	690	11.70	7.7	....	..	..
Criterion psychiatric	20	27.05	9.4	15.35	7.2	95
Symptomatic psychiatric ..	50	21.02	9.1	9.32	7.1	90
Other psychiatric	576	16.15	10.1	4.45	8.6	63
Physically ill	266	12.12	7.9	0.42	0.7	48
College students	270	7.99	6.0	−3.71	7.9	28

The test intercorrelation with hypochondriasis as measured by H—C_H is .06 ± .10 as obtained from 100 normals. The intercorrelation with depression as measured by D on the same group was .44 ± .10. When 100 miscellaneous psychiatric cases are used, these two correlations are, with H—C_H, .28 ± .10 and, with D, .69 ± .10. The rise in the correlation with depression for psychiatric cases is probably to be expected since the complaint factors involved in psychasthenia are dynamically related to depression so that many persons tend to have the psychasthenic type of fears in greater degree as their morale becomes lower, and conversely to be reactively more depressed as they are troubled by psychasthenia.

Summary

The psychiatric designation psychasthenia as used in the present study refers to a group of individuals who are frequently troubled by compulsions, obsessions, and phobias and who are often disabled by vacillation, excessive worry, and lack of confidence. Through the differential study of persons having psychiatric evidences of psychasthenia, a scale was derived which is internally homogeneous and which differentiates clinic patients from normals in a large percentage of cases. Further evidence of validity is given by the fact that, on the average, persons exhibiting psychasthenic symptoms to only a minor degree score significantly higher than normals.

ARTICLE 9 *Scales 3 (Hysteria), 9 (Hypomania), and 4 (Psychopathic Deviate)*

THE basic plan of approach in the development of the MMPI has been presented elsewhere [300 (see II, 5)]. Three scales have been described as developed according to that plan [420 (II, 6), 301 (II, 7), 421 (II, 8)] and the present paper will present some salient points regarding three more scales for the detection respectively of hypomania, psychopathic deviation, and hysteria. These scales have been in preliminary use [303].

The procedures for the derivation of the three scales are similar and can be presented generally for the three. It is essential to note that the details of scale development have involved many tentative trials with subsequent validating studies and finally the adoption of the best scale for inclusion in the inventory. A description of this process would be too detailed for profitable publication. It follows, though, that the establishment of validity of a scale becomes most important; consequently the scale descriptions rest more than is usual upon the establishment of clinical validity. Clinical criteria for validity present many potential pitfalls. There must be reasonable assurance that the clinical opinion and the scale derivation process are separated for each new validating case; the clinical diagnoses must be based upon valid and generally applicable concepts and one must be assured that the diagnostic judgments are not determined on a knowledge of the item content of the scale to be validated. When all the work of derivation and validation of a scale is centered in one laboratory the dangers in establishing validity are avoided only with difficulty. The following scales are presented with a full realization that their final validity and general usefulness will depend upon the experience of others, though we have endeavored to avoid obvious pitfalls.

The problems to be solved by the scales of the MMPI are frankly those of detecting and evaluating typical and commonly recognized forms of major psychological abnormality. The terminology and classification system are largely drawn from ordinary psychiatric practice. Where there are correlations between clinical syndromes, the scales tend to show correlation; where the clinically recognized diagnosis is impure the scales will tend to be impure. These are usually, therefore, not statistically pure scales. They often contain deliberately diverse types of items. One additional point should be especially stressed. Every item finally chosen differentiates between criterion and normal groups and that is the reason for acceptance or rejection of the items. They are not selected for their content or theoretical import. Frequently the authors can see no possible rationale to an item in a given scale; it is nevertheless accepted if it appears to differentiate. Some scales have been selected and put into experimental use in our clinic before the items were studied for content. Occasionally, items that differentiate have been rejected to eliminate some undesirable statistical trend. Thus items from the depression scale tend naturally to recur in most other scales and must be omitted in part at least if the intercorrelation is not to be undesirably high.

Specifically, the derivation of scales begins with the selection of a criterion group or groups. These persons have all been examined and diagnosed by the staff of the department of neuropsychiatry as patients in the inpatient service of the University Hospitals. The size of the criterion group varies usually between 25 and 50. For some scales it required several years to collect a sufficient number of cases to permit satisfactory scale derivation. These criterion cases are selected to be as representative as possible of the classical concept of the given syndrome. In practice, as any thoughtful clinician will agree, clear and uncomplicated cases of such common diagnostic classes as hysteria and mania are rare. There is most frequently an admixture of symptoms of other syndromes and commonly it is not at all certain that another skilled interviewer would agree as to the main diagnosis. To be psychologically abnormal in one recognized way seems to increase greatly the appearance of other psychologically abnormal states. This is easily understood in the case of depression but the connection is more obscure for other syndromes. It is to be emphatically understood that these scales are recognized to partake of the same defects that are found in the classification system now in general use. It would doubtless be more pleasing to the theoretically minded person if an approach were adopted involving a new nosology based on experimentally determined categories. All that can be said in our defense is that as a matter of practicality in the clinical setting of today the criterion groups correspond to the types that are now being generally recognized and the scales are deliberately prepared to aid in the kind of diagnostic judgments we now understand. It is to be hoped that the future will see much improvement in classification and when that time comes, new scales and possibly new techniques will need to be developed for better performance.

For each scale the responses of the criterion group or groups to each of the 550 items of the MMPI were tabulated to show the percentage frequency of occurrence of each possible answer — True, False, Cannot Say. These response frequencies were tabulated for comparison with expected frequencies as determined on normal groups.

The normal groups most commonly used for item by item contrast were composed of 339 persons selected from among general Minnesota normals and of 265 precollege cases from among high school graduates applying for admission to the university. The general sample was divided into 139 men and 200 women, tabulated separately to show sex differences. These persons were between the ages of 26 and 43 inclusive and were all married. They declared themselves to be not under a doctor's care at the time of taking the inventory and are considered normal on that single basis. The modal number of years of schooling was 8 and few had gone beyond high school. These particular persons were used because they were felt most likely to be stable and representative. The tabulation for the entering college students was based upon 151 men and 114 women. These latter tabulations were invaluable in controlling the strong tendency of responses to certain items to vary widely in accordance with age or intelligence, or both.

For all scales the percentages for the criterion groups were compared with each of the normal percentages and an initial reservoir of items was selected which included all those showing a consistent difference. Statistically no item was chosen that showed a difference less than twice its standard error and most items yielded differences greater than three times their standard errors. The steps in the selection of the final scale items were more variable and in part will be presented more completely with the descriptions of the separate scales.

To establish the validity of the various scales as they were derived, their power to differentiate test cases from normals was used as an indicator. "Test cases" is the term used in this paper to designate cases identified relatively or entirely independently of the criterion groups. For the most part, these cases were drawn from among hospitalized patients who were diagnosed routinely by the staff during the preliminary derivation of items and before any scale was made available. Where possible, test cases were taken from records and diagnoses made in an entirely different clinical setting. Naturally these latter cases are most desirable and where they were not available in suitable numbers for these scales, it is to be hoped that other workers will supply the necessary final validation. At least one such study has already been published [386 (see VII, 42)].

It is important to note, nevertheless, that test cases were not so carefully selected as the criterion cases to represent either the pure syndromes or careful evaluation by the staff. This was necessary because of the small percentage of good clinical cases among all those seen. It was assumed that the best scale was the one which would most effectively separate test cases from normals and from other types of abnormals. The chief criterion for excellence of separation was the amount of overlap of the groups. It was recognized that even a perfect scale could not completely separate these test cases from normals since some of them were borderline and probably no worse than some of the "normal" group and some of them may have been incorrectly diagnosed clinically. Some also changed radically between the time of diagnostic summary and the time of testing. In considering the data presented showing the standard scores of test cases against the normal groups, it can usually be assumed that the data given represent a poorer picture than would be yielded if the cases could have been more carefully selected and the normals more adequately proved normal.

Scale 3 (Hysteria)

A scale for aid in the clinical diagnosis of hysteria was one of the earliest problems undertaken in the development of the MMPI. Almost at once, a promising preliminary scale was developed and many hours were then directed toward its improvement. Although the original scale was bettered somewhat, most of the series of experimental hysteria scales were differentially less effective than the original and it rapidly became apparent that our difficulty was due considerably to lack of definition in the clinical concept, to the concurrence of hysterical phenomena with other neurotic symptoms in the same individual, or to downright inability of the psychiatric staff to be sure of hysterical reactions in individuals who were under suspicion of developing organic disease.

The persons comprising the criterion groups were drawn mainly from the in-patient service of the psychiatric unit of the University of Minnesota Hospitals. They had each received the diagnosis psychoneurosis, hysteria, or had been especi-ally noted as having characteristic hysterical components in the personality disturb-ance. In the assignment of these diagnostic terms the neuropsychiatric staff followed, as closely as possible, current clinical practice. Where cases showed a simple con-version symptom such as aphonia, an occupational cramp, or a neurologically irra-tional anesthetic area, the diagnosis was usually well agreed upon. In some cases there remained a doubt as to whether there was a true organic illness such as mul-tiple sclerosis present or whether the syndrome reflected hypochondriasis or an early schizophrenic reaction.

Several tentative criterion groups were selected from these diagnosed cases. The final chief group was made up of 50 cases; the items finally selected were re-peatedly identified, however, by the several criterion groups. The observed fre-quencies of True or False responses to all items were compared in percentages between criterion and normal groups; a basic pool of items was established.

The items could immediately be seen to belong to several categories. There was a strong group referring to somatic complaints and another negatively correlated consisting of statements tending to show that the patient considered himself un-usually well socialized. Examples of the somatic items were complaints of headache, spells of dizziness, and tremor of the hands. The social items were well illustrated by his saying False to such items as "I frequently have to fight against showing that I am bashful," "I get mad easily and get over it soon," "Some people are so bossy that I feel like doing the opposite of what they request even though I know they are right." In spite of their implication of a very socialized make-up the items include "unhappy" and "blue" admissions. These latter items are to be contrasted with those in which the patient says that he is not repressed or shy with others. Besides the foregoing item types there were certain others that persistently appeared in the statistical studies but for which we have no adequate interpretation. It was at once apparent that the correlation of any final scale adopted would be rather high with that previously developed for hypochondriasis (now Hs, formerly H—C_H in the *Manual*). It seemed desirable to decrease this correlation by eliminating as many of the overlapping somatic items as possible.

In order to test the results of various changes in item content of the several trial scales, test cases were accumulated. These cases were obtained from several sources. A number of newly diagnosed and therefore independent cases were available from the neuropsychiatric clinic. In addition, two separate small groups of records were obtained through the cooperation of Dr. Burton P. Grimes and Major Carleton Leverenz. The latter cases had been received in an army station hospital and diag-nosed psychoneurosis, hysteria.

Elimination of the somatic items resulted in a marked drop in the number of test cases identified and introduced another disturbing difficulty; if only the non-somatic items were used, there was a strong relation with age and education. The mean score was more than a half sigma higher for the college group than for older persons. These results forced the inclusion of some somatic items in the final scale with consequent high correlation ($r = .52$ normals and $r = .71$ clinic cases) between Hs (hypochondriasis) and Hy (hysteria). Some relation still remains between age and intelligence and the Hy score. The relation seems valid clinically.

One of the reasons why the compromise intercorrelation was forced can be illustrated by the behavior of the two scales on two test groups. The first test group was composed of 75 cases diagnosed hypochondriasis. Of these, 13 per cent received a T score of 70 or above on Hs *alone*. (T scores are standard scores with the mean of normals adjusted to 50 and the standard deviation adjusted to 10; 70 represents plus two sigma.) In all, 76 per cent received a score of 70 or above on Hs alone or on *both* Hs and Hy. Finally, only 12 per cent had such a score on Hy *alone*. Contrast these data with the results on a test group of 60 cases diagnosed hysteria. Of these, 32 per cent received a T score of 70 or above on Hy *alone*. In all, 72 per cent received a T score of 70 or above on Hy alone or on *both* Hy and Hs. Finally only 7 per cent had such a score on Hs *alone*. Study of these figures shows among other things that if Hy were discarded because of correlation with Hs in favor of using only the latter, 32 per cent of the test group of hysteria cases would have been missed. Part of these data are illustrated in Table 1. This shows the standing of the two test groups against the scores of normals for Hy. Table 1 also shows the standing of the two test groups on Hs. It will be seen that Hy discriminates the

Table 1. Frequency Distributions of T Scores on Scale 3 (Hy) for Minnesota Normals and for Hy and Hs Test Cases (T Scores on Scale 1 (Hs) Are Also Shown for Comparison)

T Scores	Normals on Scale 3 (N = 690)	Hy on Scale 3 (N = 60)	Hs on Scale 3 (N = 75)	Hy on Scale 1 (N = 60)	Hs on Scale 1 (N = 75)
103–105			2		
100–102			2		
97–99		1	4		1
94–96		1	1	1	2
91–93		1	2		5
88–90		0	7	2	1
85–87	2	4	3		9
82–84	1	8	10	1	10
79–81	2	7	4	5	7
76–78	2 (1%)	9	7	4	6
73–75	3	8	6	4	10
70–72	11	4	5	6	4
67–69	14 (5%)	2	7	11	9
64–66	34 (10%)	2	1	5	4
61–63	48	2	5	2	2
58–60	63	1	3	5	1
55–57	76	2	3	3	3
52–54	89 (50%)	5	1	2	
49–51	95	3	1	3	
46–48	73			4	1
43–45	61			2	
40–42	42				
37–39	33		1		
34–36	18				
31–33	11				
28–30	4				
25–27	7				
22–24	1				

hypochondriac as an abnormal as well as does Hs itself. It is possible from these results to omit scoring cases on Hs in situations where no clinical follow-up is intended.

Although the above and other statistical points contributed to the continued use of both Hy and Hs, the most important determiner was clinical experience. All clinicians who used both scales were emphatic that there was indubitably a valid clinical difference between two persons having high scores on Hs and Hy but differing in that one score was higher. There was a different prognosis and treatment indicated for the two. Where Hs was higher the physical complaints were diffuse and frequently required much less study to establish the presence of an important psychological factor in the disability. On the other hand, when Hy was dominant, the person frequently appeared normal psychologically and his physical complaints were likely to mimic closely or be accompanied by some common physical syndrome of the type now called psychosomatic. The final decision will lie with other clinics. The scale is presented with the expectation that others will check these clinical and admittedly subjective impressions.

The 60 items selected for the final Hy scale are as follows; each is followed by a T or an F to indicate the direction of the hysterical response.

1. During the past few years I have been well most of the time. (F) 2. I am in just as good physical health as most of my friends. (F) 3. I have never felt better in my life than I do now. (F) 4. I do not tire quickly. (F) 5. I have very few headaches. (F) 6. Much of the time my head seems to hurt all over. (T) 7. Often I feel as if there were a tight band about my head. (T) 8. I am troubled by attacks of nausea and vomiting. (T) 9. I seldom or never have dizzy spells. (F) 10. I have never had a fainting spell. (F) 11. My eyesight is as good as it has been for years. (F) 12. I can read a long while without tiring my eyes. (F) 13. I feel weak all over much of the time. (T) 14. I have had no difficulty in keeping my balance in walking. (F) 15. I have little or no trouble with my muscles twitching or jumping. (F)

16. I frequently notice my hand shakes when I try to do something. (T) 17. I have few or no pains. (F) 18. My hands and feet are usually warm enough. (F) 19. Once a week or oftener I feel suddenly hot all over, without apparent cause. (T) 20. I am almost never bothered by pains over the heart or in my chest. (F) 21. I hardly ever notice my heart pounding and I am seldom short of breath. (F) 22. There seems to be a lump in my throat much of the time. (T) 23. I have a good appetite. (F) 24. I wake up fresh and rested most mornings. (F) 25. My sleep is fitful and disturbed. (T) 26. I drink an unusually large amount of water every day. (F) 27. I believe that my home life is as pleasant as that of most people I know. (F) 28. I am about as able to work as I ever was. (F) 29. I have often lost out on things because I couldn't make up my mind soon enough. (F) 30. It takes a lot of argument to convince most people of the truth. (F)

31. I like to read newspaper articles on crime. (F) 32. I enjoy detective or mystery stories. (F) 33. I am worried about sex matters. (T) 34. My conduct is largely controlled by the customs of those about me. (F) 35. I am always disgusted with the law when a criminal is freed through the arguments of a smart lawyer. (F) 36. I think a great many people exaggerate their misfortunes in order to gain the sympathy and help of others. (F) 37. I think most people would lie to get ahead. (F) 38. Most people will use somewhat unfair means to gain profit or an advantage rather than to lose it. (F) 39. I feel that it is certainly best to keep my mouth shut when I'm in trouble. (F) 40. I am likely not to speak to people until they speak to

me. (F) 41. When in a group of people I have trouble thinking of the right things to talk about. (F) 42. I find it hard to make talk when I meet new people. (F) 43. It is safer to trust nobody. (F) 44. I can be friendly with people who do things which I consider wrong. (T) 45. I wish I were not so shy. (F)

46. What others think of me does not bother me. (F) 47. I frequently have to fight against showing that I am bashful. (F) 48. I resent having anyone take me in so cleverly that I have had to admit that it was one on me. (F) 49. Often I can't understand why I have been so cross and grouchy. (F) 50. My daily life is full of things that keep me interested. (F) 51. Most of the time I feel blue. (T) 52. I am happy most of the time. (F) 53. I have periods of such great restlessness that I cannot sit long in a chair. (T) 54. I get mad easily and then get over it soon. (F) 55. In walking I am very careful to step over sidewalk cracks. (F) 56. Some people are so bossy that I feel like doing the opposite of what they request, even though I know they are right. (F) 57. I commonly wonder what hidden reason another person may have for doing something nice for me. (F) 58. The sight of blood neither frightens me nor makes me sick. (F) 59. I find it hard to keep my mind on a task or job. (T) 60. At times I feel like swearing. (F)

The raw score mean and standard deviation for 475 normal females were M = 18.80, SD = 5.67, and for 345 males they were M = 16.50, SD = 5.50.

Test-retest data from 47 cases with an interval of three days to more than a year gave an r of only .57. On a group of 98 high school girls retested after about one year the value was only r = .47. (Data were provided by courtesy of Dora Capwell and the Minnesota State Bureau for Psychological Services.) These low values also need explanation. Test-retest values for other scales of a comparable number of items are above .70. Again the above clinical arguments must be resorted to. It has not been proved so by other objective tests but clinically observed exacerbations and recessions of the symptomatic picture of hysteria in a given case are marked. An apparently normal person placed under sufficient strain will surprise everyone by developing symptoms. A case with a clear paralysis may get well momentarily and be undetectable except on the basis of the history.

Assuming the validity of the scale, the implications in routine testing of the foregoing discussion are interesting. If at the time of testing, the subject is under strain and experiencing symptomatic evidence of hysterical conversions, the scale identifies him. If he is always on the borderline he is probably identified but if he is not under strain at the time he may not show the potentiality. It may be that similar thinking could explain the observed clinical fact that some cases of uncomplicated and obvious hysterical conversion are not identified by this scale or by any that could be derived in the present studies.

It is pertinent to introject that the statistical thinking derived from aptitude and achievement testing should be amended when personality tests are considered. Many traits of personality are highly variable. Otherwise there would be little meaning to psychotherapy or preventive mental hygiene. Test-retest data on MMPI scales are more a measure of trait variance than of reliability of scales. In some cases scales correlate consistently much higher with other scales than with themselves. This will need future expanded interpretation but it at once indicates that several factors of personality commonly vary together. Again common observation recognizes these variations as they are seen in those about us.

Table 2 gives the intercorrelations of Hy with all other scales as obtained from random normal and clinic records. The higher correlations with Hs and D are apparent. The rise of these for the abnormal group indicates the dynamic factor alluded to above. In clinical practice the three scales constitute a kind of "neurotic trio" that characterizes the greater number of the cases observed.

In summary, a scale called Hy for aid in identification of hysterical tendency has been derived. This scale appears to measure a rather variable trait which is closely allied to and likely includes the earlier scale of hypochondriasis. The person who is especially characterized by Hy tends to be less obviously neurotic and to have, during disabled periods, a more specific set of physical symptoms.

Table 2. Correlations of Hy with Other Scales

Group	Hs	D	Pd (rev.)	Pa	Pt	Sc	Ma
100 normal cases	.52	.55	.37	.44	.13	.28	.05
100 psychopathic hospital cases	.71	.68	.18	.40	.33	.23	−.13

Scale 9 (Hypomania)

Hypomania refers to the milder degrees of manic excitement occurring typically in the manic-depressive psychoses. The cardinal symptoms of maniacal conditions are generally stated to be an elated but unstable mood, psychomotor excitement, and flight of ideas. Hypomanic trends follow the same pattern in general, but in lesser degrees that may be at times so unobtrusive as not to impress even an expert. Thus, among normal individuals one may recall acquaintances who tend at times to be overtalkative, distractible, restless. Such a person may feel and appear to be extraordinarily well, enthusiastic, and energetic, but the use of his energy is likely to be inefficient because he tries to do too many things at a time. He is usually full of ideas which may be basically sound but they are not adequately worked out and if put into execution are seldom carried through to a satisfactory conclusion. Emotionally he may be a bit elated and too happy, he may be impatient and irascible or he may express ideas of feeling gloomy and somewhat frustrated; commonly the mood swings rapidly within minutes or hours from one to another of these attitudes, often without any corresponding environmental explanation for the shifts. Viewed over a longer period of time it is often discernible that these persons tend to have periods of definite depression rather than elation or euphoria. Along with these characteristics, there is often egocentricity, lack of appreciation of the ineptitude of his behavior in given settings, and a certain obvious disregard for others. In many respects these patients, during their episodes, are reminiscent of the asocial type of psychopathic personality. In some of the cases their abnormal characteristics disappear completely between attacks.

A group of 24 such cases was selected for scale construction. These criterion cases had all been studied intensively as inpatients in the psychopathic unit of the University Hospitals. Only manic patients of moderate or light degree were usable, since the more severe cases could not cooperate adequately in sorting the inventory items. The clinical diagnoses were either hypomania or mild acute mania, depending on the severity of the case. Care was exercised to exclude individuals with delirium, confusional states, or with excitements associated with other psychoses such as schizophrenia; the agitated depressions were likewise excluded. Naturally, routine but searching medical, neurologic, psychiatric, and psychological studies were performed on these patients as indicated. The number of cases is obviously too small to permit an analysis of the effects of factors like sex, age, marital status, and economic level, but as a criterion group they are satisfactorily uniform for scale construction purposes.

The selection of the differential items was done by essentially the same methods as for previously reported scales. The percentage frequency of significant responses was obtained on the normal and criterion groups of persons for each of the 550 separate items of the inventory. Several scales were tentatively constructed and the following 46 items were finally selected as representing the best scale for hypomania. The hypomanic response is indicated for each item according to the answer being True (T) or·False (F). As in all scales each item has been assigned a value of "one" in obtaining the raw score.

1. I have had periods in which I carried on activities without knowing later what I had been doing. (T) 2. I have had attacks in which I could not control my movements or speech but in which I knew what was going on around me. (T) 3. I have had blank spells in which my activities were interrupted and I did not know what was going on around me. (T) 4. At times I have fits of laughing and crying that I cannot control. (T) 5. My speech is the same as always (not faster or slower, or slurring; no hoarseness). (F) 6. I sweat very easily even on cool days. (T) 7. A person should try to understand his dreams and be guided by or take warning from them. (T) 8. I drink an unusually large amount of water every day. (T) 9. My people treat me more like a child than a grown-up. (T) 10. Some of my family have habits that bother and annoy me very much. (T) 11. At times I have very much wanted to leave home. (T) 12. I have often had to take orders from someone who did not know as much as I did. (T) 13. It makes me impatient to have people ask my advice or otherwise interrupt me when I am working on something important. (F) 14. I have at times stood in the way of people who were trying to do something, not because it amounted to much but because of the principle of the thing. (T) 15. I believe women ought to have as much sexual freedom as men. (F)

16. I have been inspired to a program of life based on duty which I have since carefully followed. (T) 17. I feel that I have often been punished without cause. (T) 18. When I was a child I belonged to a crowd or gang that tried to stick together through thick and thin. (T) 19. I have never done anything dangerous for the thrill of it. (F) 20. I am always disgusted with the law when a criminal is freed through the arguments of a smart lawyer. (F) 21. I do not blame a person for taking advantage of someone who lays himself open to it. (T) 22. If several people find themselves in trouble, the best thing for them to do is to agree upon a story and stick to it. (T) 23. I don't blame anyone for trying to grab everything he can get in this world. (T) 24. At times I have been so entertained by the cleverness of a crook that I have hoped he would get by with it. (T) 25. It wouldn't make me nervous if any members of my family got into trouble with the law. (T) 26. When I get bored I like to stir up some excitement. (T) 27. When in a group of people I have trouble thinking of the right things to talk about. (F) 28. I find it hard to make talk when I meet new people. (F) 29. I never worry about my looks. (T) 30. It makes me uncomfortable to put on a stunt at a party even when others are doing the same sort of things. (F)

31. It is not hard for me to ask help from my friends even though I cannot return the favor. (T) 32. Something exciting will almost always pull me out of it when I am

feeling low. (T) 33. I have met problems so full of possibilities that I have been unable to make up my mind about them. (T) 34. Once a week or oftener I become very excited. (T) 35. I have periods of such great restlessness that I cannot sit long in a chair. (T) 36. At times I feel that I can make up my mind with unusually great ease. (T) 37. At times my thoughts have raced ahead faster than I could speak them. (T) 38. I sometimes keep on at a thing until others lose their patience with me. (T) 39. At times I have a strong urge to do something harmful or shocking. (T) 40. Some people are so bossy that I feel like doing the opposite of what they request, even though I know they are right. (T) 41. I am an important person. (T) 42. I know who is responsible for most of my troubles. (T) 43. I am afraid when I look down from a high place. (F) 44. I work under a great deal of tension. (T) 45. Sometimes when I am not feeling well I am cross. (F) 46. My table manners are not quite as good at home as when I am out in company. (F)

Some of these items are obviously enough applicable to the usual concept of hypomania, but others are not explicable at present. The raw score mean and standard deviation from 379 females were $M = 13.65$, $SD = 4.50$, and the values from 294 normal males were $M = 14.51$, $SD = 4.42$.

Elated, overactive, or clearly hypomanic cases rarely occur among the neuropsychiatric clinic cases available to test the Ma scale. From among nearly a thousand clinic cases only 38 valid records are available on persons marked by the staff as having some overactivity or elation. These exclude of course the criterion cases. Of the 38 only 5 were diagnosed manic-depressive psychosis. They received scores of 77, 75, 79, 66, and 61; the latter two were marked "mild hypomanic." The remainder of the whole group received various diagnoses, chiefly some form of schizophrenia. There was evidence that hypomanic cases are more difficult for the staff to diagnose than are others. As might be expected from clinical experience, there were a number of cases called psychopathic personality.

Among more than 900 available clinic cases 30 received scores of 70 or more without any clinical note especially indicating hypomania. These cases also illustrate the tendency for psychopathic personality to be indicated by the hypomanic scale since 10 of them received this diagnosis or were chronic alcoholic cases. There also appeared to be a tendency for cases with organic deterioration of the brain to receive high scores.

Table 3 shows the distributions of the scores of the patients with overactivity or elation (the criterion cases), 300 randomly selected psychiatric clinic cases, and the whole normal group. In several of the criterion patients with low scores there is a high probability that the manic state has been superseded by a normal or depressed phase at the time of testing. The summary of symptoms made by the staff was not correlated in time with the administration of the inventory so that if a patient alternated between manic and depressive or normal phases, his state at the particular time of testing cannot now be determined. The evidence for the validity of Ma is certainly not conclusive. There is, however, a tendency for persons with hypomanic symptoms to secure high scores. It is to be hoped that the scale would appear distinctly better if the criterion cases were better. This is one of several scales that will need to be checked further before final acceptance. Table 4 gives the correlations of Ma with other scales as observed on normal and clinic cases.

The correlation with D is slightly negative as might be expected. In clinical practice it is common to find both depression and manic overactivity in the same patient at the same time as is the case with some of the agitated depression patients. This was seen frequently on the test profiles; it probably explains the low correlation. As was indicated in the validity study above there is a degree of positive relationship between Ma and Pd.

The test-retest correlation for Ma is .83. This indicates that the trait has a surprising degree of stability in normal persons. No test-retest is available on clinic cases. There is probably an important constant personality factor represented together with a variable factor. The constant factor is likely to be something akin to what is commonly called optimism. Among our acquaintances, those whom we think of as optimists are rather consistently so, as are the pessimists. Apart from optimism there is also a variable tendency related to the usually episodic excitement of mania or hypomania which is seen in abnormal degree. The abnormal factor comes and goes and seems not to be strong among normal persons. Further analysis is needed to develop these theories.

Table 3. Frequency Distributions of T Scores on Scale 9 (Ma) for Minnesota Normals and Three Psychiatric Groups

T Scores	Normals (N = 690)	General Psychiatric Cases (N = 300)	Ma Criterion Cases (N = 24)	Ma Test Cases (N = 38)
94–96	1	1		
91–93		2	1	
88–90		2		
85–87	2	1	2	
82–84	1	1	1	
79–81	1	4	2	4
76–78	2 (1%)	1	2	1
73–75	6	4	2	4
70–72	10	5	1	3
67–69	18 (5%)	21	5	2
64–66	28 (10%)	13		3
61–63	56	19	3	10
58–60	51	14	1	2
55–57	72	29		1
52–54	97 (50%)	25	1	1
49–51	96	23	1	1
46–48	80	39		1
43–45	69	44	2	
40–42	41	25		
37–39	26	13		3
34–36	17	8		
31–33	8	3		
28–30	5	1		
25–27	2	2		
22–24	1			

Table 4. Correlations of Ma with Other Scales

Group	Hs	D	Hy	Pd	Pa	Pt	Sc
100 normal cases	.28	−.02	.05	.49	.30	.39	.56
100 psychiatric hospital cases	.08	−.21	−.13	.43	.31	.14	.36

The Ma scale has proved to be quite useful in the clinic. The juvenile delinquent, the overactive adult, and the agitated depression with ambivalent affect are not frequent but nevertheless important to recognize. The delinquent with a high Ma score and lower Pd has seemed more likely to benefit by counseling and being given another chance. The rather good prognostic indications in the adult case with an isolated Ma score are apparently in accord with general psychiatric opinion.

In spite of the small number of criterion and test cases available, a scale for hypomania is presented. It is the best that we could derive from the patients seen over a five-year period. The scale is certainly valid as to trend and it has proved distinctly useful in the clinic. The correlations with other scales are low.

At least two factors are apparently measured. These are dominant constant factors allied to ebullient optimism and a more variable factor that accounts for abnormal periods.

Scale 4 (Psychopathic Deviate)

It is not our intention in this paper to add to the already long list of definitions of the general clinical group "psychopathic personality." Our study has accepted, as a basic group, those persons seen by us who fit approximately into the asocial type of psychopathic personality as decribed by Henderson [r73], Cleckley [r37], and others.

Among these psychopathic personalities it was early recognized that there was an important subgroup, composed of individuals who were probably identifiable by a questionnaire. A preliminary study [r72] indicated that these persons were partly characterized by a tendency to answer in ultra-perfect ways, as shown by such general scales as the B_1N component on the Bernreuter Personality Inventory. Subsequent to this earlier work five trial scales for the identification of these persons have been developed. The best of these is now referred to as Pd (revised).

The chief criterion group consisted of patients diagnosed psychopathic personality, asocial and amoral type, after study by the staff of the department of neuropsychiatry. They were from both sexes and were mostly within the approximate age range 17 to 22 years. None was psychotic or neurotic, and most of the hysterical and clearly schizophrenic cases were eliminated.

The symptomatic backgrounds of the criterion cases were highly varied but can be characterized in several ways. Most often the complaint was stealing, lying, truancy, sexual promiscuity, alcoholic overindulgence, forgery, and similar delinquencies. There were no major criminal types. Most of the behavior was poorly motivated and poorly concealed. All the criterion cases had long histories of minor delinquency. Although many of them came from broken homes or otherwise disturbed social backgrounds, there were many in whom such factors could not be seen as particularly present. Among the criterion cases there was a somewhat larger proportion of girls than of boys; this may have been due to the social selection that results from differential treatment by courts of boy and girl delinquents. This factor, if it operated, could account for the larger number of girls since many of the cases came for study on request of the courts.

Response frequencies to items as observed on the criterion group were compared with similar response frequencies observed on a sample of the married Minnesota population and the sample of college applicants. A number of items were then selected. This tentative list included many items later discarded. These items were studied further as individual items and more extensively as they fell into subgroups. Examples of such subgroups are items related to home difficulty, such as "My parents and family find more fault with me than they should," and social trouble items, such as "I played hookey from school quite often as a youngster." From numerous minor studies a preliminary scale was derived. The scale was immediately valuable in the clinic. The clinical demand was dependent in part upon the uncertainty of the average clinician when he attempts to examine a case of suspected psychopathic personality.

Two groups of test cases were available. One group was composed of patients in the psychopathic unit of the University of Minnesota Hospitals who had been studied subsequent to the selection of the criterion cases. These were not so carefully checked to eliminate doubtful cases since it was assumed that the group as a whole should show the desired tendency. For the other test group, we were fortunate in obtaining records from 100 men prisoners at a federal reformatory. These cases were collected by H. D. Remple, psychologist, with the cooperation of the medical staff and released to us for study through the courtesy of Dr. John W. Cronin and the United States Public Health Service. All the reformatory cases had received a psychiatric diagnosis of psychopathic personality. It is important to note, however, that they were not differentiated as to type and could not be expected to be uniformly of the asocial type although their presence in a reformatory would indicate that the majority might be so.

The test groups were used to try the excellence of various combinations of items (but these groups were not used to select individual items), and 50 items were eventually chosen as the final scale. These items make up the Pd (revised) scale. The following list gives the final items together with a T or an F to indicate the abnormal answer.

1. I am neither gaining nor losing weight. (F) 2. I have used alcohol excessively. (T) 3. My family does not like the work I have chosen (or the work I intend to choose for my life work). (T) 4. I believe that my home life is as pleasant as that of most people I know. (F) 5. There is very little love and companionship in my family as compared to other homes. (T) 6. I have been quite independent and free from family rule. (F) 7. My parents have often objected to the kind of people I went around with. (T) 8. My parents and family find more fault with me than they should. (T) 9. I have very few quarrels with members of my family. (F) 10. At times I have very much wanted to leave home. (T) 11. My relatives are nearly all in sympathy with me. (F) 12. I have been disappointed in love. (T) 13. I liked school. (F) 14. My sex life is satisfactory. (F) 15. I like to talk about sex. (F) 16. In school I was sometimes sent to the principal for cutting up. (T) 17. During one period when I was a youngster I engaged in petty thievery. (T)

18. My conduct is largely controlled by the customs of those about me. (F) 19. I am always disgusted with the law when a criminal is freed through the arguments of a smart lawyer. (F) 20. I am against giving money to beggars. (F) 21. I have never been in trouble with the law. (F) 22. I have never been in trouble because of my sex behavior. (F) 23. No one seems to understand me. (T) 24. When in a group of people I have trouble thinking of the right things to talk about. (F) 25. I find it hard to make talk when I meet new people. (F) 26. I do not mind being made fun of. (F) 27. I do many things which I regret afterwards (I regret things more or more

often than others seems to). (T) 28. I wish I were not so shy. (F) 29. What others think of me does not bother me. (F) 30. It makes me uncomfortable to put on a stunt at a party even when others are doing the same sort of things. (F) 31. I wish I could be as happy as others seem to be. (T) 32. My daily life is full of things that keep me interested. (F) 33. Much of the time I feel as if I have done something wrong or evil. (T) 34. I have not lived the right kind of life. (T)

35. I am happy most of the time. (F) 36. I have periods in which I feel unusually cheerful without any special reason. (F) 37. Sometimes without any reason or even when things are going wrong I feel excitedly happy, "on top of the world." (F) 38. At times my thoughts have raced ahead faster than I could speak them. (F) 39. If people had not had it in for me I would have been much more successful. (T) 40. Someone has it in for me. (T) 41. I am sure I get a raw deal from life. (T) 42. I am sure I am being talked about. (T) 43. I have had very peculiar and strange experiences. (T) 44. I know who is responsible for most of my troubles. (T) 45. I have very few fears compared to my friends. (F) 46. These days I find it hard not to give up hope of amounting to something. (T) 47. My hardest battles are with myself. (T) 48. I am easily downed in an argument. (F) 49. I find it hard to keep my mind on a task or job. (T) 50. My way of doing things is apt to be misunderstood by others. (T)

Inspection of the final scale items will show them to fall naturally into several general groupings. For one, social maladjustment items are prominent. Another group is made up of items related to depression and the absence of strongly pleasant experiences. There are also a number of items suggesting paranoid trends. All these subgroupings were found to contribute to validity. The composite scale weights of the groups as expressed in the number and occurrence frequencies of their items are apparently nearly optimal in the final scale. It was difficult to account for or predict variations in validity that were observed among the earlier scales; this indicates that the diagnosis is based upon a complex of factors rather than upon any one. Also, unlike the scale for psychasthenia, the items do not show a strong tendency to be highly intercorrelated. The final scale is, therefore, certainly not pure but deliberately mixed in factor content to yield greater clinical usefulness.

Table 5 shows the standing on the final scale of 294 males and 397 females of the general norm group. As is common with frequency curves from personality traits having one end recognized as abnormal, there is a slight negative skewness of the curve. About 4.6 per cent of these normal cases fall above 70 (two sigma above the mean). In these normative data there is no significant mean score change with increasing age, but it is probably significant that 56 per cent of the cases with standard scores above 70 are from the 16 to 25 age range; these young people make up only 33 per cent of the total norm group. The raw score sex difference amounts to 0.45 of a point between means and 0.23 between standard deviations. These differences are probably insignificant but a correction in standard score is made for sex since the observed values are still the most likely correct. The means and standard deviations for raw scores are $M = 13.44$, $SD = 4.23$, for 397 females and $M = 12.99$, $SD = 4.00$, for 294 males.

Table 5 also shows the standard score standings of the two groups of test cases. There are 78 cases diagnosed psychopathic personality from the psychopathic unit and 100 prisoners from the reformatory. Again it must be emphasized that the scale was expected to identify only the asocial fraction of these miscellaneous cases. The separation of the prison group is better than that of the clinic group, chiefly because of the selective factor determining a greater frequency of the asocial type among the prisoners. Among the prisoners 59 per cent obtained scores at or above 70 and among the clinic cases 45 per cent of the scores were above that level. The mean raw scores and the standard deviations are $M = 22.61$, $SD = 4.43$, for prisoners and $M = 21.44$, $SD = 6.23$, for clinic cases.

The validity of the scale appears still better if the whole profile of each test case is inspected. The profile is made up of all scores at present obtained from the MMPI. When the other personality components are graphically presented in the same standard scores, a number of the test cases scoring below 70 on the present scale show up as plainly outstanding. Thus, it is common for scores on other scales to be uniformly from one-quarter to one-half standard deviation distance below the mean, leaving the Pd score clearly dominant. It is possible that this effect, which appears to be a general reduction in the measured abnormality, is produced by overly scrupulous, conscious avoidance of any betrayal by abnormal answers on the part of the subject. More likely these persons simply feel themselves to be overly perfect. Evidence for the latter suggestion lies in the fact that they seem clinically to be characterized by great self-esteem and self-interest.

Table 5. Frequency Distributions of T Scores on Scale 4 (Pd) for Minnesota Normals, Federal Reformatory Inmates, and Pd Clinic Test Cases

T Scores	Normals (N = 690)	Federal Reformatory Cases (N = 100)	Pd Clinic Test Cases (N = 78)
103–105			1
100–102			1
97–99			
94–96			4
91–93		7	5
88–90			1
85–87	1	5	2
82–84	1	6	2
79–81	2	4	4
76–78	3 (1%)	13	3
73–75	13	15	8
70–72	15 (5%)	9	4
67–69	16	7	4
64–66	18 (10%)	7	8
61–63	35	8	8
58–60	47	11	7
55–57	58	1	1
52–54	64	6	3
49–51	72 (50%)		5
46–48	87	1	3
43–45	81		
40–42	65		3
37–39	49		
34–36	34		1
31–33	18		
28–30	8		
25–27	2		
22–24	1		

Inspection of the items in the scale shows that there is a group of items on which the significant answer shows this over-perfect tendency. Consider, for example, the item "I find it hard to talk when I meet new people." Most of the normal group admit such failings but the psychopath has no such reaction. It is interesting that these persons who might be most likely to attempt consciously to hide their character are partly identifiable by the attempt itself. It is, however, unlikely that such reactions are conscious; they are more likely completely submerged from the conscious level by the insightless egocentricity.

The test-retest correlation obtained for the scale is 0.71; this was obtained on a normal sample of 47 cases repeated with an interval of a few days to more than a year. The correlations with other scales commonly used on the MMPI are given in Table 6. It is interesting that, contrary to what is true with other MMPI scales, the correlations are smaller as obtained from the psychopathic unit cases.

The random cases from the psychopathic unit included a few psychopathic personality diagnoses; they were predominantly neurotic and schizophrenic. Although

Table 6. Correlations of Pd (revised) with Other Scales

Group	Hs	D	Hy	Pa	Pt	Sc	Ma
100 normal cases..............	.42	.29	.37	.38	.48	.60	.49
100 psychopathic unit cases....	.37	.14	.18	.40	.23	.31	.43

the increase is slight, the correlations with paranoia and mania are somewhat higher than with other scales. This is in accord with clinical experience. The hypomanic patient often gets into trouble during one of his attacks in ways that are confusingly similar to the behavior of the psychopathic personality. Similarly, the case with a psychopathic personality is frequently somewhat paranoid. Being basically confident of his abilities, he naturally often feels persecuted by society when he is punished for behavior he thinks he will be able to control in the future.

The introductory sentence to the present section of this paper stated that we did not wish to add to the list of definitive statements about psychopathic personality. Yet it seems apparent from the foregoing facts that an appreciable percentage of clinically recognized cases are identified on the Pd (revised) scale. Generally speaking, these persons are those diagnostically classified in most clinics as psychopathic personality, asocial type. Nevertheless, to avoid confusion we have named the scale psychopathic deviate (Pd). The term implies a variation in the direction of psychopathy. The scale itself is a definitive device and the following descriptive material is merely an attempt to state some general facts about cases selected by the scale.

Most prominently the typical case has a shallow emotional life. The clinician may work very hard and become intensely interested in the patient but fail to receive in return more than a transitory and superficial loyalty. Sexual and other appetitive drives are not deeply effective in the patient's life. For example, although there may be promiscuity or actual prostitution, the female is frequently frigid and engages in sexual acts primarily as a means to social entertainment. Females are often masculine in interests. The psychopathic deviate seems to the observer to seek more and more dangerous or embarrassing experiences in the attempt to feel emotion like that of the normal. They sometimes commit suicide or more often nearly do so. This is again from shallow emotional sources rather than deep depression or normal recognition of failure.

As they become older it is common for many of these cases to avoid more successfully real conflict with society. The lying, alcoholism, sexual promiscuity, or other behavior may persist; but it is somewhat more restrained and also society seems to feel less outraged. While these persons can usually verbalize as to the consequences of their behavior, there is often a failure to appreciate its significance for them in terms of their long-time social adjustment. Depression, when present, is usually expressed as fear of immediate punishment and loss of liberty rather than any reaction in guilt, regret, or the like. The tendency to blame others or to excuse themselves for their predicament is common. They claim in self-extenuation that they were misled by others who took advantage of their innocence, that the family discipline had been too severe so they rebelled, or some similar explanation.

In clinical practice, the Pd scale has been most valuable. So many of the cases with high scores are recidivists in delinquency that it is helpful to be put on guard. If the person is 16 to 19 years of age and has a score twenty T points above most other scores on the profile, there is little likelihood that the person can stay out of trouble if not under rigid discipline. Older persons, however, more often avoid open breaks. In therapy, young persons with a high Pd should not be pushed toward maximal scholastic or vocational levels even when they have the capacities for training.

One special advantage in the prediction afforded by the scale is that the type identified is so often characterized by a relatively appealing personality together with good intelligence and background. These factors are misleading to clinicians so that a halo effect operates toward a too lenient view of the clinical problem. The overly optimistic treatment is not only wasteful of social resources but also permits the fixation of undesirable habits in the patient; furthermore, the patient is permitted to continue until a more serious offense requires penal action.

In summary, a final scale has been developed which will identify half or somewhat more of the cases routinely classed psychopathic personality clinically. The cases best identified are those with strong asocial trends. The scale is called psychopathic deviate to indicate that it is not expected to differentiate all the cases of psychopathic personality. The scale appears to have fair reliability and intercorrelations with other scales are low.

It is in the clinic, however, that the value of the scale is best illustrated. The clinician usually finds himself at a loss in the diagnostic evaluation of the psychopathic personality, and the scale has been found to be particularly useful in this regard.

ARTICLE 10 *Scales 5 (Masculinity-Femininity), 6 (Paranoia), and 8 (Schizophrenia)*

MATERIAL relative to the derivation and validity of three MMPI scales, Mf, Pa, and Sc, has not hitherto been published. These three scales were characterized as preliminary in the earlier *Manual*. The intent was to indicate that revised scales together with the appropriate derivational and validity data would later be prepared and published in final form.

Some principles of derivation of MMPI scales have also not been published. It is impossible to describe fully the steps in selection of the MMPI scale items. As emphasized in earlier publications, all the items were empirically selected by contrast of criterion groups with other clinical groups and with various normal groups. All scales were tested by one or more cross-validation samples. Frequency distributions of the cross-validation samples were constructed to show the separation of the criterion abnormal type from normals, from patients who were physically ill (but not obviously with mental symptoms), and finally from miscellaneous psychiatric cases having diagnoses other than the one being studied. This multiple checking of items and scales is probably the most characteristic general procedure relative to the derivation. Beyond this, specific steps in scale development were so varied that they cannot be completely described.

As a first step, the criterion group item frequencies were compared with frequencies on normals and miscellaneous psychiatric patients. In this initial comparison, items that showed consistent and statistically reliable response differentiation of the criterion were chosen as a basic pool from which the scale would later be selected. These items were then followed in successive tabulations showing the frequencies of significant answers as observed in other samplings by diagnosis. The items were also checked to make certain that college students did not behave in some way that might detract from the validity of the item.

An important point is that a great many good basic pool items were eliminated from a final scale because they showed overlap in validity with some other clinical syndrome. Clinical depression samples, for example, show significant answers for numerous items that discriminate schizophrenia. In order to hold down the intercorrelation of scales, groups of items that seemed to be contributing equally to two scales were eliminated from both scales or used in only one. In some cases, as with scales Pt and Sc, an arbitrary decision had to be made about the proper amount

104

of overlap. These scales correlate and the syndromes as observed in clinical cases also overlap. It would be undesirable to eliminate this correlation in measurement of the syndromes. The correlation was deliberately built in by leaving in each scale certain items that had been observed to be valid for the other syndrome. No statistical or theoretical preciseness was available to determine the optimal size of the intercorrelations.

These intercorrelations are the basis for the pattern effects that are thought to be so characteristic of MMPI profiles. Certain scales are expected to vary together; when they do not, unfamiliar configurations occur that indicate less routine interpretation than usual. Fortunately these intercorrelations decrease the number of different profiles one is likely to encounter; they increase the frequency of some profiles. If the ten regular MMPI scales were more independent, experience with profiles would be so limited that one could not expect to become proficient on the basis of having seen a number of a given kind. Ten variables with low intercorrelations would so rarely provide two similar profiles that no practical number of cases would provide experience with populous classes of profile.

If the ten variables of the MMPI were independent, there would be 90 different but equally probable variations of the two highest coded points on profiles. If each variable showed a 5 per cent frequency greater than 70 T score, the rate of occurrence of each of these moderately deviant profile types would be one in 18,000. It could be that deviant personality is recognizably divisible into 18,000 different classes, but if so the use of a statistical method of analysis or prediction would require electronic memory systems. Of course if one had as few as six independent variables, then the number of different patterns of the two highest points would be only 30. It would not be hard to remember these, but deviant ones would still be infrequent. In passing, it seems unlikely that every profile type would be about equally probable as is implied in the zero covariance condition.

The above argument is based upon the assumption that clinically significant variables are really patterned [440], that they cannot be combined in a simple manner to arrive at useful evaluation of the personality. Among other things, this assumption means that one could not go across the profile and add appropriate positive adjectives for the position of each scale to end up with a meaningful description. On the contrary, it is assumed that a person with greatest deviation on variable one is definitely different even in the expression of the implied correlates of variable one by the fact that no other variable is so deviant. The proper descriptive adjectives (see III, 17) are peculiar to the profile, not to the unique deviant value of variable one.

Another procedure that contributed an arbitrary element to the derivation of scales concerned the treatment of highly intercorrelated item groups. When several items were intercorrelated so that the answer to one of them was determinative of answers to the others, part or all of the group were accepted or rejected according to the same principles that governed the acceptance or rejection of one item; the group would be considered as an unusually valid item and much thought often went into decisions about it because of the extra scale variance involved. If it should happen that four items were perfectly correlated, then their contribution to scale variance would be four times that of a single item with comparable individual variance. If such multiple-item clusters are clearly and broadly valid, they are very important to a scale. Often, however, they are valid for only a single symptom that, though itself valid, would not be broad enough. For example, several items might relate to having delusions of reference. Such delusions are highly valid as evidence of paranoid mentation but such ideas are not present in the majority of paranoid patients. Construction of a scale would require consideration of the effect of four such items on both the mean and the variance since they might overemphasize this one symptom. In this one way manifest item content did enter at times into decisions about item choice for scales.

Perhaps it should again be stated that except for items with high covariance, derivation of the items for a scale did not appreciably depend upon the manifest content of the item. The break from the face validity approach to item selection for a scale was the result of a conscious decision. No item was ever eliminated from a scale because its manifest content seemed to have no relation to the syndrome in question; conversely no item was arbitrarily accepted if the validating evidence for the item was not strong.

This method of scale derivation is not possible unless one has a considerable supply of clinical cases and adequate staff study of them to assure that the validity criterion will represent a broadly based opinion. It is unlikely that all the syndromes of the MMPI scales will survive the next comparable study. Several are probably basic; of these, a likely example is Pd. But within the relatively large clinical staff where considerable democracy prevailed in the assessment of the people who made up the criterion groups, there may have been a greater than usual degree of coherence in the classifications. MMPI scales were *ad hoc*. Clinical practice as it occurred in the psychiatric unit indicated the variables that were needed for routine work and for statistical accounting. The patients were short-time residents who stayed an average of twenty days, and they differed through the whole range of severity and diagnosis. Mostly the ones used for scale derivations were not psychotic and many of them were not even very ill. More often than not they were in a mental hospital for the first time. Few were private cases and the majority had less than a high school education. A few were sent in by courts for study as an aid in evaluation of the significance of their unlawful acts.

Growing recognition of the complexity of the validity issue in personality scale derivation has made it hard to say when a scale is satisfactory. We do not yet know causes of mental disorders, and prognosis or specific treatments do not provide a convincing basis for classification. No real evidence has established the usefulness of the theory that factor purity is either characteristic of personality or the choice basis for a classificatory system. We are handicapped by indecision. It has not been established whether criteria should be based upon overt social behavior, upon the self-evaluation, or upon subtle and intrinsic aspects of mentation. Every clinician knows that social and self-evaluations are not perfectly correlated. Where a person considers himself to be maladjusted and inferior and his associates consider him to be reasonably like others, one scale value cannot properly represent the two aspects.

It could be that an MMPI scale like Sc is more valid than we have yet discovered. Consider an analogous illustration from physical medicine. When a test specific to a disorder is discovered, it is often found that there are many persons who are positive on the test but negative on clinical symptomatology. The typhoid bacillus is closely related to the severe clinical syndrome of typhoid fever. Suppose that the bacillus had been discovered long before the typhoid fever patient could be differentially separated from patients with similar sicknesses. A criterion group of sick persons (some of whom actually had another disease) would have shown a higher than average percentage with the bacillus but not all would have had it. In our test terminology these would be called false negatives. Also, since many persons carry the bacillus without developing symptoms, the well group of controls would show false positives.

Except for patients who try for high scores with an ulterior purpose, patients who obtain a high T score on a scale are *ipso facto* validly like the group from which the scale was derived. This indisputable statistical validity should be more widely recognized and studied by clinicians. A case record is called a false positive if it is deviant on a scale that derived its validity from persons to whom the given case does not seem sufficiently similar. False positives on a scale are false only in the first instance. They initially appear so from the observation that certain expected correlates of the scale score are not clearly present in the observed behavior. There is a possibility that we do not recognize the pertinent core of the syndrome.

The symptoms of many deviant persons do not happen to get them into trouble. There is no necessity for assuming a high correlation between mental aberration and behavior judged to be socially undesirable. Some clinicians seem to be unaware of this fact and without qualification they classify a person as normal or average in pattern of personality simply because he is undistinguished in his social behavior. But it would be equally fallacious to assume that all high-scoring persons on some MMPI scale are usefully categorized by the fact.

Since criteria are not closely intercorrelated, the validity problem depends upon the use to which a scale is to be put. For some purposes scale deviation alone may be useful; such a situation is simplest but is rare. The variables represented by MMPI scales or by any other substitute for the validating behavior always fall below perfect relationship. This is clearly illustrated in the more mature context of the measurement of intelligence. No intelligence test shows a perfect correlation with any behavior that it is expected to predict. With some applications a close correlation is expected; with others only a loose relationship. Too high a validity for one use may prejudice the validity for another. MMPI scales can be related in varying degree to various criteria. Probably the most common criterion in clinical work relates them to social adjustment as seen by the clinician or the family. But it may be just as common and useful to relate them to the patient's self-evaluation. It is a little surprising that they are at all valid when one considers the dissimilarity between answering test items and the complexity of social and personal adjustment. What apparently preserves the relationship is the power of the self-concept expressed in the "I am" statements of the items that determines a degree of identity between the manifest or latent content of these and social behavior.

Sooner or later psychometric devices must be perfected either against criteria such as specific cause, specific treatment, or specific course of disease or, less desirably, they must be perfected by the boot-straps [r 40] effect. Intelligence scales began by reference to inferior criteria but, by the boot-straps effect, lifted themselves into the criterion position. The original criteria are now evaluated against the scales. The boot-straps effect depends upon the discovery of a number of correlates of a personality scale so that it comes to have a broad construct validity. A possible example may be found in the Pd scale. This is related to success in practice teaching [261 (V, 36)], to social responsibility [259], to fear of mental patients [331 (V, 34)], and to delinquency [312] among already known correlates discovered from various approaches.

The foregoing discussion is intended as a rationale for the continued use of scales that do not show high validity against the clinical diagnosis criterion. If a scale accounts for some useful variance in a number of criterion situations, one may excuse its failure to account for more variance of any particular criterion. It is recognized that this is a dangerous doctrine. Obviously the validities for critical applications must be reasonably better than those available by other scales. In addition, the useful validity must be evaluated against the economic use of clinician manhours.

Scale 8 (Sc)

No scale received more attention in the attempt to identify a useful variable than was the case with the Sc scale. The folders of data on the derivation of this scale contain at least two basic stocks of items from which at least four basic scales were derived and from which more than twelve differential scales were attempted. The basic scales and the stock items were all derived from two partly overlapping groups of 50 patients who had been diagnosed schizophrenia. These cases were of assorted diagnostic subtypes and included about 60 per cent females and 40 per cent males. The final Sc scale was derived from a stock group of 152 items all of which showed statistically reliable differences for the schizophrenia criterion cases but many of which also differentiated depression cases, hypochondria cases, and other special groups.

From the very first it was found that differential cuts on cross-validation groups could not be pushed above a positive 50 to 60 per cent of the diagnosed cases identifiable with an apparently false positive rate of 10 or 15 per cent out of general normal cases. Because the early Sc scales did not work as well as had been the case for other MMPI scales, efforts were made to improve them by breaking down the criterion into component parts. These parts were at first the subclassifications of schizophrenia: catatonic, paranoid, simple, and hebephrenic. Separate scales were derived for each of these groups. These more limited scales were tested both as basic scales and as secondary scales to modify the score on general Sc scales. None of these systems was successful in raising the cross-validation ratio of true to false positive cases. More than twelve of these subscales were tried out in the various combinations.

Another seemingly fruitful line was the attempt to derive a subscale from patient records that were false negatives among the original criterion groups. These test misses were used as a criterion to develop "miss" scales. Several of these miss scales were checked both as independent scales and in combination with basic scales. Again no manipulation could effect much change in the basic percentage of cross-validation cases that were identified.

As a result of all these efforts, which consumed hundreds of hours of clerical work, the published scale was the best among the basic Sc scales. This final scale was originally Sc 4, the fourth basic scale derived, and it was only slightly better than were the ones that were rejected. As time passed, no appreciable change in the published scale seemed justified and the matter was at a standstill until the work on the K scale was undertaken.

The K scale, an outgrowth of Meehl's work on the derivation of a scale for a normal control component in behavior, finally provided a device by which the discrimination of the Sc scale could be sharpened. Data given in the K article [424 (see II, 11)] illustrate the status before and after development of the K correction. The 91 cross-validation cases that were used for these tables were assorted psychiatric cases diagnosed schizophrenia but many of these would not have been suitable for criterion cases because of one or another doubtful aspect of the clinical syndrome. They should not therefore be expected to be as highly differentiated by any scale as would more carefully selected examples of the diagnostic category. Only 31 per cent of these cases obtained a T score on Sc of 70 or greater. On the original norm distribution this score was reached or exceeded by 4.5 per cent of the normals. The K correction raised the percentage of cross-validation cases reaching or exceeding T score 70 to 59 and the corresponding percentage of normals dropped to 2 per cent. With these cases the K correction effected a marked improvement in the discriminative ability of the original scale. Even with the correction, a considerable number of the cross-validation cases managed to stay below the T score 61.

Various investigators have found the clinical diagnosis of schizophrenia to be reproduced independently on the same patients by different clinicians in only 30 to 60 per cent of the cases. These figures are certainly not too low if less psychotic patients are used for the experiment. The MMPI Sc scale suggests, as do similar scales on other inventories, about the same degree of reproduction of the diagnosis in such clinical groups. There is no accepted way to assert that either the scale or the diagnosis is wrong. In the long run the decision should rest upon the useful correlates of test and diagnosis. The better diagnostic device will provide the more useful correlates with such items as therapeutic response and prognosis.

Scale 8 correlates highly with scale 7. This correlation has been variously given from .68 [312] to .84 [146, 144]. The two syndromes are clinically similar but as the *Atlas* diagnostic tables illustrate, a definite discrimination is possible [307]. *Atlas* cases with a diagnosis of psychasthenia show a rate of 57 per cent for scale 7 occurring highest or second highest in code position; for scale 8 the corresponding rate is only 32 per cent. By contrast, the cases diagnosed schizophrenia have scale 7 high or second high 17 per cent of the time and scale 8 in those positions 48 per cent of the time.

Relative to the same point, follow-up data from ninth-grade public school MMPI records indicate reliable differences in behavior between boys with high 7 and those with high 8 codes. The high 8 boys have a larger delinquency rate and their delinquent acts tend to be more severe. In particular, truancy, running away from home, and violation of probation show the relatively largest differences. High 8 boys also get into trouble at an earlier age than is true of the high 7 boys.

Scale 6 (Pa)

Scale 6 was derived from patient samples judged to have paranoid symptoms. Diagnostically these were rarely called paranoia. The most common diagnoses were paranoid state, paranoid condition, and paranoid schizophrenia. Symptomatically they tended to have ideas of references, to feel that they were persecuted by individuals or groups, and to have grandiose self-concepts. Milder symptoms included suspiciousness, an excess of interpersonal sensitivity, and an underlying rigidity of opinions and attitudes.

As with other scales, several different scales were derived and tested by cross-validation. This cross-validation was always disappointing and the published scale was considered weak although it was the best that could be developed. One factor that seemed to justify at least temporary use of the scale was that there were few false positives. When a person had a high score, he tended to be diagnosed as paranoid or at least he was felt to be sensitive and rigid in personal relationships.

As was at first true with scale 8, the hope that the temporary scale 6 would be bettered was not rewarded. Even the K variable failed to sharpen the differentiation. It was felt that the K correction did not help because more than 20 per cent of the scale 6 items were already subtle in character [424 (see II, 11)].

Scales 6 and 8 were in progress of derivation at the same time and attempts were made to derive a special scale for the patients diagnosed paranoid schizophrenia. No single scale operated as well to distinguish these patients as did the combination of 8 and 6.

Scale 5 (Mf)

The difficulty in deriving a better Mf scale centered in the problem of a criterion by which the validity could be established. The published scale was derived by contrasting item frequencies from a small group of 13 homosexual invert males with those of average males and also by contrasting a group of more feminine males as determined from the Terman and Miles I Scale [r 160] with average males. A final less important criterion was the comparison of male and female frequencies. At first it seemed reasonable to collect relatively large samples of homosexual invert males and of homosexual females for more complete criterion evidence. The plan went awry because it became apparent that the homosexual samples were too heterogeneous. As we worked with the homosexual males and females, we came to feel that the groups were much more obviously divisible into several subtypes than was true for other clinical categories. For example, there is a pseudo-homosexual type where neurotic features related to inferiority seem to be dominant; there is a psychopathic variety with a strong tendency to high scores on Pd; and there is an invert group in which a constitutional factor seems probable. These and possibly other subgroups seem definite enough so that clinical study could separate them and much better and purer Mf scales might be derived. Because the task was dependent upon having a comparatively large number of cases of each type and also because of the press of other research, this project was never finished. In the meantime, the Mf scale has become widely used and although it was omitted from much of our experimental work, it contributes considerably to routine clinical interpretations.

One attempt was made to improve the Mf scale. A number of records from women whose personal problems included homosexuality as one issue were used as a criterion group. A scale designated Fm was derived by a process similar to that used for Mf. The new scale correlated .78 to .95 with Mf on a number of samples. This correlation and the fact that cross-validation did not particularly favor the new scale, even for identification of homosexual females, indicated its abandonment.

Discussion

By this time a number of papers on the validity of these scales have been published by others. Evidence is varied, some positive and some negative. It is not helpful merely to list the relative frequency of positive and negative findings. Some of the designs and hypotheses were so ill-conceived as to be inappropriate for evidence. The *Atlas* [307] was intended as a primary source on the validity of scales 6 and 8 as well as the other clinical scales. Some evidence can also be found relative to scale 5. Those who must interpret profiles that show a high 6 or 8 should read the *Atlas* cases with these codes. If the reader finds coherence among such case records, then this is the best clinical preparation and evidence of validity.

In addition to the *Atlas*, Cottle's review [146] suggests other sources. The bibliography and reviews in the present volume are useful as source material on the application of all MMPI scales for various purposes. The above brief discussion of the problem of validity should make it clear that no one validity has wide meaning. Every different application invokes a different validity concept.

The reliability of the three scales has been best estimated by Rosen [498]. He obtained test-retest data on 40 male VA hospital cases tested within a short interval. These reliabilities were scale 5 (Mf) .64; scale 6 (Pa) .75; and scale 8 (Sc) .86. Cottle [143], using a group with smaller scale 6 and scale 8 variance (68 male and 32 female college students), got these values: scale 5, .91; scale 6, .56; and scale 8, .86. Holzberg and Alessi [322] got correlations of .76 for scale 5, .78 for scale 6, and .89 for scale 8 on psychotic state hospital patients. It is always difficult to evaluate any of the usual reliability data on personality measures that are likely to show valid time-related variance in the individual subjects. All the MMPI scales are sensitive to therapeutic and other effects. Since both the motivation and the life situation of the subjects are likely to change almost momentarily, it is always possible that an observed change in score is valid variance instead of error variance.

J. C. McKINLEY,
S. R. HATHAWAY, AND P. E. MEEHL

◆ ────────────────────────────────────

ARTICLE 11 *The K Scale*

THE K scale of the MMPI was developed in an attempt to correct the scores obtained on the personality variables proper for the influence of attitudes toward the test situation. The rationale of the approach as well as the empirical procedure employed in deriving K has been presented in a previous publication [441 (see I, 2)] and will not be dealt with here except very summarily. The present paper is to be read as a sequel to the original and aims chiefly to present norm data on K for various groups, an improved technique for applying K statistically, and certain miscellaneous observations such as its effects on the validity and intercorrelations of the other scales of the MMPI.

The K scale was derived by studying the item response frequencies of certain diagnosed abnormals who had *normal* profiles. It was here assumed that the occurrence of a normal profile was suggestive of a defensive attitude in the patient's responses. The response frequencies were contrasted with those from an unselected sample of people in general ("normals"). The differentiating items were then scored so that a high K score would be found among abnormals with normal curves, whereas a low score would be found in clinical normals having deviant curves. In this operational sense, it can be said that a high K score is indicative of a defensive attitude, and a low K score suggests unusual frankness or self-criticality ("plus-getting"). The extremes of defensiveness and plus-getting may be called "faking good" and "faking bad" respectively.

The earlier procedure for applying K was one of subjectively correcting profiles on the basis of the K score. Thus, a given borderline curve would be "underinterpreted" if K was considerably below the mean, since the examinee would be presumed to have achieved a bad curve because of his plus-getting tendency. If the same profile occurred in the presence of an elevated K, the clinician would assume that the curve ought to be "over-interpreted," since the examinee showed evidence in his high K of having been defensive.

In the following presentation we will first give the more practical data referent to the routine use of K. Following the description of the determination of K-correction factors and specific data on validity we will return to the more general facts bearing on clinical interpretation integrated with the whole profile.

The original method of using K was admittedly vague and inspectional, and would require considerable experience on the part of the individual clinician. It was

112

clear that the influence of the K factor upon scores was not the same for all MMPI variables, so that the optimal interpretation of the personality scales proper on the basis of a given K deviation varied. It is obvious that the amount of experience required to make a satisfactory use of K in profile interpretation would be very great, even assuming that the clinician would be able subjectively to record, retain, and analyze the welter of impressions with reference to the nine personality components. For this reason, it seemed that a more rigorous and objective procedure for taking account of the K score would be desirable.

Since high K scores represent the defensive or "fake good" end of the test attitude continuum, the most obvious approach to the problem is to add K (or some function of K) to the raw score on each personality variable, i.e., increase the score in the direction of abnormality. Thus, a psychopath who is very defensive in taking the test is presumed to have attained a lower raw score on the Pd scale than he "should" have, i.e., than he would have had he been less defensive. This defensiveness will also tend to reflect itself as a high K score. The obtained score on Pd should accordingly be corrected by adding some amount, the amount added being dependent upon the degree of defensiveness present as indicated by K. The problem is simply one of determining the optimal weight for the K factor with respect to any given scale, taking a linear function as an adequate approximation for practical purposes.

Our first attempt was crude in that it treated K as what may be called a "pure" suppressor, whose only contribution lay in its correlation with the noncriterion components of the personality variable [r 107, r 115]. In a preliminary study of the Hs scale, using an unusually carefully selected group of diagnosed hypochondriacs, the Hs score was increased by a fraction of K proportional to the regression weight of Hs on K among the normals. In other words, in place of Hs alone we now were using the *residual* of Hs regressing on K, i.e., that part of Hs which is K independent. This procedure is inexact since it assumes that K itself is uncorrelated with the dichotomous criterion, and also because it neglects the correlation of Hs with K among the abnormals. In spite of this crudeness, it was encouraging to find that the corrected Hs score now enabled us to detect 89 per cent of the hypochondriacs as contrasted with about 70 per cent of the same sample when Hs was used alone. This separation was achieved on a test group which had not entered into the derivation of either Hs or the K weight, and involved no increase in the number of false positives among normals (about 5 per cent in both cases).

The desirability of taking account of the correlation of K with the personality scales among both normals and abnormals, as well as any differentiating power of its own which K might have on certain sorts of cases, suggests the use of the discriminant function for determining the optimal weight. In the present problem, the variances among normals and abnormals were not always alike, nor was it convenient to restrict our analysis to the usual case of equi-numerous groups. We experimented with a modification of the discriminant function which added variances rather than sums of squares, but decided to reject this also for the following reason: The region in which differentiation is clinically most important is around 60 to 80 T score. There is little or no basis at present for interpreting the personality scores which are below the mean. All methods which are based upon maximizing the ratio of the variance of criterion group means to some type of pooled variance *within* groups will be taking account of the entire distribution. This results in a K weight based upon information which there seems to be no reason to include. The skewness of MMPI variables and the obvious doubts one might have as to the influence of K at different points of the distribution led us to determine the optimal weight by a study of a more restricted region, within which refinement was of greatest consequence. It is unfortunate that this decision entails procedures which are mathematically inelegant and in sore need of analytic justification but we have not been able as yet to devise acceptable alternatives. It is hoped that the procedure now to be described will seem reasonable, and that others will attempt a formally simple solution and will study the sampling distribution of the test employed. In the present case, there is reason to suspect that a general maximizing solution is impossible without making assumptions regarding distribution form which are empirically inadmissible.

Consider a given personality variable, represented in deviate score form by x, where the deviation is from the mean of normals. Let the K deviate score be represented by z. Let λ be an arbitrary weight, whose optimal value is to be determined. *Optimal value* refers here to the λ which achieves the best differentiation between a criterion group of abnormals diagnosed as having the abnormality in question (e.g., hypochondriasis) and a sample of unselected normals. In other words, we are here considering the personality variables singly, by specific diagnosis, rather than "abnormals" as a whole. Then the deviate *corrected* score on the given abnormal component is

$$y = x + \lambda z$$

Let us now restrict our attention to the cases scoring above the mean of *normals* on y, i.e., consider only cases such that $x + \lambda z > 0$. We now define a sum of squares for those abnormals whose corrected score is above the *normal* mean. That is, for cases such that $x + \lambda z > 0$, we define a sort of "half sum of squares,"

$$SS_a = \Sigma_a(y)^2 = \Sigma_a(x + \lambda z)^2$$

The same quantity is computed for the normals,

$$SS_n = \Sigma_n(y)^2 = \Sigma_n(x + \lambda z)^2$$

The ratio of these two sums of squares, which we shall call the *differential ratio*,

$$\frac{SS_a}{SS_n} = \frac{\Sigma_a(x + \lambda z)^2}{\Sigma_n(x + \lambda z)^2}$$

is then taken as an index of the degree of differentiation achieved by a given value of λ.

It can almost be seen by inspection that a straightforward analytic solution for the optimal λ cannot be carried through by maximizing this ratio, since the number of cases involved in numerator and denominator will occur in the resulting derivative and will itself fluctuate with the choice of a λ in a manner that cannot be known without special specifications of the joint distribution of x and z. Even if special assumptions are made, such as normal bivariate surface and equal correlation for normals and abnormals (neither being true in this sort of material), the solution of the problem presents serious mathematical complications. We hope to be able to make further progress in this direction and invite more mathematically competent readers to attack the general case. We fell back upon a straight trial-and-error method. We assigned arbitrary values of λ ($= .1, .2, .3, .4$, etc.) and for each of these values we distributed y for normals and criterion cases separately. The ratio SS_a/SS_n was then calculated for each of these λ values, and these ratios were plotted as a function of λ. A smooth curve was drawn by inspection through the plotted points, and a rough maximum was estimated therefrom. Where several different samples of abnormals were available, such curves were drawn separately for each, in the hope of having more confidence in the estimated maximum on the basis of agreement in curve "trend."

One further qualification needs to be mentioned. Since squares emphasize extreme deviations, and in view of what has been said above concerning "clinically important range," it was felt desirable to limit the influence of extreme deviations upon the ratio. Therefore, after the distribution of y for a given λ had been obtained, all scores of the normal and abnormal groups lying above three standard deviations on the basis of a given $x + \lambda z$ normal distribution (corrected T score of 80) were arbitrarily reduced to that value. A change in λ which produced further elevations of abnormals already at three sigma would therefore not result in further improvement in the differential ratio. It is possible that four sigma should have been chosen instead, since recent work on pattern analysis in differential diagnosis among abnormals suggests that elevations above three sigma may be important. In fact, we would not be prepared to defend vigorously the use of this restriction at all.

The graphical method used gave opportunity to observe the behavior of the differential ratio as λ was varied, and to check the degree of disparity with other indicators of separation. In general, it was found that the λ which maximized the ratio tended to agree fairly well with that selected by such measures as percentage of abnormals above the top decile of normals. Research on a different problem suggests that the differential ratio gives results similar to but not identical with the critical ratio. In the present study, the λ's finally chosen were sometimes based upon compromises between the curve maxima of the differential ratio for various criterion groups, as well as counting measures of overlap.

Table 1 shows typical data on the differential ratio as applied to Sc $+ \lambda K$. Groups I and II are composed of 25 and 28 males diagnosed schizophrenia and Groups III and IV of 24 and 14 female cases respectively. There were some minor differences in the clinical constitution of the four groups but since the curves were similar in maximum points these differences can be disregarded. From these data we chose the λ weight for Sc to be 1K.

The K weights which were finally adopted by these procedures are given below:

$$Hs + .5K \qquad Sc + 1.0K$$
$$Pd + .4K \qquad Ma + .2K$$
$$Pt + 1.0K$$

It must be emphasized that these weights are optimal, within our sample, for the differentiation of largely inpatient psychiatric cases of full-blown psychoneurosis and psychosis from a general Minnesota "normal" group. For other clinical purposes it is possible that other λ values would be more appropriate. Thus, it seems likely that for the best separation of "maladjusted normals," such as those which abound in a college counseling bureau and would be formally diagnosed in a psychiatric clinic as *simple adult maladjustment*, other weights might be better.

The mode of applying these weights has been described already in the supplementary manual for the MMPI published by the Psychological Corporation [295]. This manual contains a set of tables to be used in making the K correction, and new test blanks are also available to be used with K. Briefly one determines the weighted K value by referring to the table, which is based directly upon the proportions just cited. Thus, in correcting Hs for K, one begins by determining .5K either mentally or from the table (K here is the *raw* score). This quantity is then added to the original *raw* score on Hs, to yield Hs + .5K. This sum is called the *corrected raw score* on Hs. This corrected raw score is then entered in a second table of Tc (cor-

Table 1. Values of the Differential Ratio as a Function of the K Weight (λ) for the Sc Scale

λ	Schizophrenic Group			
	I	II	III	IV
0.0	.08	.07	.04	.04
0.1	.23	.19	.15	.08
0.2	.39	.35	.27	.14
0.3	.54	.49	.37	.19
0.4	.69	.63	.46	.25
0.5	.86	.79	.59	.34
0.6	.98	.76	.69	.39
0.7	1.13	.95	.81	.45
0.8	1.18	1.18	.91	.52
0.9	1.28	1.33	1.03	.61
1.0	1.23	1.35	1.06	.63
1.1	1.18	1.36	1.07	.62
1.2	1.13	1.32	1.05	.68
1.3		1.22	.97	.53
1.4			.88	.57
1.5			.81	.60

rected T scores). This T table is of course based upon the mean and standard deviation (on general normals) of the quantity Hs + .5K. Similar processes are involved in the case of the other scales.

It will be noted that only five scales receive a K correction. The scales D, Hy, and Pa are uncorrected. (Mf was not studied in this respect.) It may seem paradoxical that in the original article on K, we found only three scales on which K would "work." This finding was based on a crude test using a single cutting score and a chi-square analysis. In the case of Pt, the sample studied originally was very small and significance hard to attain. The present K weights are to be accepted as the best indication of the "improvement" achieved by K, rather than the chi squares cited previously.

We see then that Pt and Sc are most affected by K, Hs and Pd mediumly, Ma least, and D, Hy, and Pa not at all. It is interesting to speculate upon this hierarchy. It will be recalled that the scale D already contains a correction scale, called Cd [301 (see II, 7)]. Hy already contains the K factor in the Hy-subtle items [441 (I, 2), 423 (II, 9)]. While Pa has no explicit correction scale, almost one fourth of the Pa items are of the Hy-subtle type (eight being actually "0" items on the scoring key). These items, with the indicated response scored for Pa, are as follows:

B-54. My mother or father often made me obey even when I thought that it was unreasonable. (F) D-46. Most people inwardly dislike putting themselves out to help other people. (F) D-50. Most people are honest chiefly through fear of being caught. (F) D-52. I think most people would lie to get ahead. (F) D-53. I think nearly anyone would tell a lie to keep out of trouble. (F) D-54. Most people will use somewhat unfair means to gain profit or an advantage rather than to lose it. (F) D-55. The man who provides temptation by leaving valuable property unprotected is about as much to blame for its theft as the one who steals it. (F) G-50. Some people are so bossy that I feel like doing the opposite of what they request, even though I know they are right. (F) H-9. I tend to be on my guard with people who are somewhat more friendly than I had expected. (F)

If one calculates the percentage of "0" items for each of the eight personality scales (excluding Mf), the proportion of such items per scale is Hs = 0%, Sc = 3%, Pt = 4%, Ma = 15%, Pd = 16%, Pa = 20%, D = 27%, Hy = 33%.

These figures at least suggest that the proportion of zero items per scale tends to be negatively associated with the K weight found to be optimal. One way of looking at this finding is to say that scales which are more *subtle* are less subject to distortion by such test attitudes as K, and hence cannot be improved much by application of a K correction. It cannot be decided on present evidence whether this is the correct view rather than the view that the subtle items, although not derived as suppressors, already contain "suppressor" components for the obvious items.

The Effect of the K Correction on Validity as Related to Diagnosis

Table 2 gives an idea of the diagnostic effect achieved by the K correction. The cases designated "test cases" were not always clear cases of the given diagnostic category but represented patients who were noted by the psychiatric staff as being at least in part characterized by traits belonging to the category. Hence it is probably fair to assume that the percentages of these cases lying above the three given T values are smaller than would be true of more carefully selected patients. The 200 standard sample normal records used as reference were made up of 100 males and 100 females from the general normative files who were specially selected to be representative of the whole population.

For Hs and Hs + .5K, the data are given on both Hs and Hy test groups. The figures for these groups as distributed by Hy are also included. (See also Table 3.) One may compare not only the Hs with Hs + .5K but also Hs + .5K with Hy. It is apparent from Table 2 and from correlational data that the addition of K to Hs makes it act more like Hy. This could be predicted from the communality of K and Hy-subtle [441 (see I, 2)]. In terms of the group data of Tables 2 and 3, one is justified in using both scales. As was argued in an earlier publication [423 (see II, 9)], clinical evidence is at present in favor of the continued use of both scales because they are complementary when operating in the individual case. For example, Table 3 indicates that the joint use of both scales results in the identification of more hypochondriacs and hysterics than would the use of either separately. We hope soon to publish further data relative to the clinical significance of the two scales used together.

The gains for Pd + .4K over Pd are most marked at the 5th and 10th percentiles. This results from a flattening of the frequency curve for the normals in the range of 60 to 70 T score. We have already tended to interpret Pd as having clinical signifi-

Table 2. The Effect of the Final K Corrections on Test Case Groups Contrasted to a Standard Sample of 200 Normal Cases (The Values Given Are the Percentages of Cases at or above the Given T-Score Points)

T Score	Hs 200 Normals	Hs 101 Hs Test Cases		T Score	Hs + .5K 200 Normals	Hs + .5K 101 Hs Test Cases
70.0.........	3	59		70.0.........	5.5	74
69.8.........	5	62		70.3.........	5	72
65.0.........	10	69		62.9.........	10	89

T Score	Hy 200 Normals	Hy 101 Hs Test Cases		T Score	Hs 200 Normals	Hs 74 Hy Test Cases
70.0.........	4	64		70.0.........	3	38
67.5.........	5	74		69.2.........	5	42
63.3.........	10	79		65.0.........	10	55

T Score	Hs + .5K 200 Normals	Hs + .5K 74 Hy Test Cases		T Score	Hy 200 Normals	Hy 74 Hy Test Cases
70.0.........	5.5	54		70.0.........	4	53
70.3.........	5	51		67.5.........	5	62
62.9.........	10	69		63.3.........	10	66

T Score	Pd 200 Normals	Pd 89 Pd Test Cases		T Score	Pd + .4K 200 Normals	Pd + .4K 89 Pd Test Cases
70.0.........	5	52		70.0.........	3.5	55
70.0.........	5	52		67.5.........	5	65
65.0.........	10	65		62.7.........	10	76

T Score	Pt 200 Normals	Pt 36 Pt Test Cases		T Score	Pt + 1K 200 Normals	Pt + 1K 36 Pt Test Cases
70.0.........	6.5	42		70.0.........	4	61
71.5.........	5	40		68.5.........	5	67
67.2.........	10	47		64.0.........	10	67

T Score	Sc 200 Normals	Sc 91 Sc Test Cases		T Score	Sc + 1K 200 Normals	Sc + 1K 91 Sc Test Cases
70.0.........	4.5	31		70.0.........	2	59
69.0.........	5	31		64.0.........	5	69
62.5.........	10	43		61.2.........	10	75

T Score	Ma 200 Normals	Ma 89 Ma Test Cases		T Score	Ma + .2K 200 Normals	Ma + .2K 89 Ma Test Cases
70.0.........	8	62		70.0.........	2.5	65
66.3.........	5	72		65.7.........	5	74
61.8.........	10	79		63.1.........	10	84

cance at around T = 65 when it appears as a clear "spike" or when certain other values (especially the neurotic triad) are below 50. The above data probably add justification to this interpretation.

The increased validity of Pt + 1K is a function of both increased normality in the frequency curve for normals and relatively higher scores for the test cases. The Pt + 1K is likely to be more clearly a "clinical" scale than was the Pt. We have pointed out [441 (I, 2)] that Pt is a rather good measure of the K factor and one would expect partial removal of this variance to result in a remainder "purer" for the real clinical component. Good clinical data on psychasthenia relatively independent of schizophrenia are difficult to obtain and we can give no further evidence at this time.

Sc was never a very satisfactory scale (see II, 10) in terms of the number of schizophrenic patients identified, although when it is elevated Sc is quite valid. When Sc + 1K is used, a very gratifying improvement is apparent. These gains with a K correction are from all standpoints the best of the five scales.

The improvement of Ma + .2K over Ma is not great but if the effect upon the frequency curve for normals is combined with that on the test group, it is definitely worth while to use the correction. Ma is the most common single deviate score in both high and low directions. Among the profiles of unselected normals, Ma occurs

Table 3. Comparison of the Action of Hs + .5K and Hy on Test Cases Diagnosed Psychoneurosis, Hypochondriasis, and Psychoneurosis, Hysteria

	Percentage of Hs Test Cases with T Score 70 and above	Percentage of Hy Test Cases with T Score 70 and above
On Hs + .5K alone..	16	9
On Hy alone........	6	12
On both scales......	58	41

as a "peak" score more often than does any other scale, and it also occurs as a lowest score more often than any other. This is presumably a statistical consequence of the fact that Ma correlates with the other scales less than they tend to correlate among themselves. Ma probably has more independent clinical significance than any other single scale. These facts add to the importance of any gains in validity.

The General Interrelationship of K and K-Corrected Scales

Table 4 shows the means and standard deviations for various groups. We attribute no certain significance to the variations that can be observed in these statistics. The normals designated in this table are the general normals that have been described elsewhere in publications on the MMPI as a reasonably satisfactory cross section of Minnesota residents. While there are several possible sex difference trends as seen in the separate age groups, a grand compilation of all these normal males contrasted with all the females shows no appreciable differentiation.

The two groups referred to as "mixed psychiatric" included all diagnoses observed in the psychiatric unit and are not necessarily typical of a psychiatric hospital of the usual type. Many of the patients presented behavior problems of types that would not be committed to an institution for the insane and in general the group would be a borderline group between the obviously psychotic and the normal. The moderate rise in the means for these groups is chiefly contributed by the psychopathic personality and criminal individuals who would make up about 20 per cent of the whole number. University students have a relatively higher mean as contrasted with general normals of their age range. An interesting point is evident in the means for the Capwell [112] girls. Here the reform school cases obtain a higher mean than otherwise similar adolescents in high school. This low mean is contradictory to the tendency that we observed in adult offenders which is illustrated by the reformatory women whose mean score is somewhat higher than the general norm. It is of interest in this connection that a K correction slightly decreased the differentiation of the Capwell cases from their matched partners when the Pd scale was used as a discriminator. We have no explanation at present for this finding.

The largest mean that we have observed was obtained from the graduate electrical engineers. These men were studied during the war and were mostly around 30 years of age. They were exempted from military duty in order to carry on aviation research and at the time of testing were applying for special airplane control

Table 4. The K Means and Standard Deviations of Various Groups

Group	N	Sex	M	SD
Normals age 16–25 inc.	115	F	12.61	4.96
Normals age 16–25 inc.	73	M	13.79	5.27
Normals age 26–35 inc.	153	F	12.82	5.21
Normals age 26–35 inc.	105	M	12.41	5.85
Normals age 36–45 inc.	105	F	10.41	4.60
Normals age 36–45 inc.	69	M	12.49	5.14
Normals age 16–45 inc.	373	F	12.08	5.07
Normals age 16–45 inc.	247	M	12.84	5.64
Mixed psychiatric	372	M	14.57	5.85
Mixed psychiatric	596	F	14.34	5.21
University	50	M	16.10	5.15
University	50	F	15.66	5.01
University (Drake, Wisconsin)	379	F	15.58	4.20
High school (Capwell)	73	F	14.96	5.46
Reform school (adolescent) (Capwell)	88	F	12.77	4.99
Reformatory (adult) (Capwell)	34	F	14.18	4.86
Graduate electrical engineers (Minneapolis-Honeywell)	100	M	16.72	4.19
Miscellaneous employed (American Airlines)	100	F	15.38	6.05

testing at high altitude. The final group of miscellaneous employed was obtained from a sample of airline employees most of whom were college graduates or had several years of college work. These were in skilled clerical or minor administrative type positions.

We have described elsewhere [441 (see I, 2)] experiments in which ASTP men and several other groups were asked to fake good and bad profiles on the MMPI. In these experiments half the class faked a good or bad profile and the other half took the inventory in a supposedly honest way. At a subsequent session of the class, the roles of these two groups were reversed. All the subjects were naive in regard to personality inventories and in regard to the MMPI in particular.

This procedure afforded a check upon the action of F and L as well as K. In brief, it was found that F was very efficient in distinguishing faked bad records but L was not at all effective in detecting a faked good record among the men and was only moderately effective with women. We at first presumed that the failure of L for men was in part due to the relatively obvious items of which L is composed.

Among 48 student nurses asked to fake a good record, 16, or 33 per cent, obtained a raw score L greater than or equal to 7 (T score greater than or equal to 60) in contrast to only one out of 48 when the same girls took the test with a supposedly honest attitude. If a raw score L greater than or equal to 6 (T score greater than or equal to 56) is used, these figures become 54 per cent identified as faked for the faked records, as contrasted with 10 per cent "false positive" among the honest records. This finding accords with our clinical experience that it is profitable to begin interpretation of L at T = 60 or even lower [441 (see I, 2)].

When we turn to the K distributions for these two groups, the most interesting findings are that the mean K score for the 48 nursing students taking the MMPI "honestly" is 18.3, standard deviation 3.80, and the corresponding statistics for 107 ASTP men are 19.8 and standard deviation 4.10. These two means correspond to general normal T values of about 61 and 63 respectively. These means are definitely larger even than the means of college students in general as given in Table 2. Some factor seems to have operated on these two experimental groups to produce an unusually high average value of K when they were supposedly taking the test with an honest attitude.

As might be expected, when data were obtained from the 54 of the ASTP men faking a bad profile, the mean K values shifted markedly downward. The statistics for this group of faked bad data are a mean of 8.1 and standard deviation 4.04. The mean corresponds to a normal T value of 41. We have no corresponding statistics for women. K is in this case equally sensitive with F in differentiating the faked bad profiles. By contrast, the average K score for the 53 ASTP men who attempted to fake a good score was very little different from their normal mean as given above. The mean of this group's faked good records was 20.2 and the standard deviation 3.66. The mean would correspond to a normal T of 64. This result was similar to the finding among the student nurses who obtained a mean K score of 19.7 and a standard deviation of 3.90 on faked good records. The normal T score for this mean is about 64. It should be kept in mind that when the ASTP men attempted to fake a bad profile the resulting profiles were very severe, differed to a remarkable extent from the individual's "honest" profile, and could be recognized as invalid from the profile form alone. In contrast again to this, neither the men's nor the women's faked good profiles could readily be distinguished in any consistent way from their honest profiles, or from the ordinary profiles of normal persons in general. The obvious experiment in which one would take a group who had deviant profiles and ask them to attempt to fake good was not performed. Further evidence on the behavior of K and F in the "fake bad" situation can be found in a recent article by Gough [235].

In consideration of these data, it seems justifiable to postulate that in these experiments the differentiation of the faked good profiles by the use of K is impossible because the "honest" was already in some sense faked good. The evidence that the "honest" represented something already related to faking can be derived from the fact that the "honest" means of both these groups were more than a standard deviation elevated in terms of the general normal mean statistics for K and at least half a standard deviation in T score above the means obtained from other college data. This elevation over the three other means given in Table 2 would be even greater in standard scores on the basis of the college data considered as norms. Some unidentified factor related to K must have operated in the experimental situation where the faking data were obtained. This latter assumption would be more certain if the rise in the means had not been observed from such different groups as student nurses and ASTP men. It is possible, however, to link these two groups provisionally in one significant element. Both the nurses and the men were under impulsion not to jeopardize in any possible way their continuance in the war-related programs that they were following. This pressure would contrast with the situation of the miscellaneous college students who were tested either before or after the war and probably in even greater degree with the attitudes of the general MMPI norm groups that provided the normative statistics for the T table of K.

The nearest approach to data on faked good scores as obtained from persons with *initially* deviant profiles is embodied in some incidental data obtained from our records where psychiatric hospital patients repeated the MMPI for one reason or another. By searching the duplicate records, we were able to find a few cases where patients had taken the inventory twice and where the K raw score for the second test was four or more points higher than that for the first test. Most of these patients had originally deviant profiles. The obtained differences are not worthy of statistical analysis but all scales show a tendency to decrease in T score under these conditions. The most marked changes occurred on Hs, D, Pt, and Sc. Naturally, since these patients were not asked to fake a good score, the finding yields only presumptive evidence.

Correlational Data

The test-retest correlation of K is available on two groups. For a group of 85 high school girls (Capwell data) retested at an interval of 110 to 410 days the correlation was .72. For a group of miscellaneous normals retested after four days to one year the correlation was .74. It is of course impossible to say to what extent these coefficients are to be viewed as indicators of "reliability."

A second question that may be raised regards the effect of the K correction upon the intercorrelations of the other MMPI scales. Table 5 gives the correlation coefficients for the same group with and without the K correction having been made before correlating. The intercorrelations for the original scores are indicated in ordinary type, while the corresponding coefficient upon the same sample after making the K correction is indicated immediately to the right of the originals in italic. These coefficients are based upon a sample of 100 normal males, all college graduates, employed as engineers in an industrial concern (Honeywell cases of Table 4). We see that some of the correlations are raised by the K correction, that others are lowered, and that this is true whether they are considered in the absolute or algebraic sense. The increases preponderate over the decreases. Inspection suggests that the greatest shifts occur in the case of pairs of scales one of which suffers a considerable K correction and the other none (e.g., Hy and Pt). We are not prepared to give any special interpretation of this table and include it here only for the sake of completeness.

Summary and Conclusions

Specific arguments and data are presented establishing the rationale of using the K factor as a suppressor on certain MMPI clinical scales. Five scales seem to be improved by the correction, as indicated by increased correspondence between scores and clinical status. The scales Pt, Sc, Hs, Pd, and Ma receive K corrections of varying amounts. The scales Hy, D, Mf, and Pa are not so treated nor is it established that the K score should be taken into account subjectively in evaluating them. A new statistic was used to determine the K-correction factors. This statistic, called the differential ratio, is described as appropriate to establishing maximal differentiation between two distributions with emphasis upon the region of their overlap.

Normative statistics on the distributions of K for various groups are presented.

The chief finding of interest here is a tendency for college and college-educated persons to deviate in the upward direction between one-half and one standard deviation. It was suggested in the original article on K that this difference is chiefly a function of socioeconomic status.

Table 5. Correlations among Scales before and after K Correction, with the Latter in Italic. (N = 100 Employed Male College Graduates)

	Hs	D	Hy	Pd	Mf	Pa	Pt	Sc	Ma
Hs									
D	33 *33*								
Hy	33 *65*	31							
Pd	28 *37*	36 *37*	25 *47*						
Mf	27 *17*	26	21	28 *22*					
Pa	08 *22*	17	37	15 *24*	33				
Pt	47 *47*	28 *45*	−17 *38*	33 *43*	41 *44*	16 *45*			
Sc	51 *59*	20 *26*	−03 *51*	31 *44*	45 *32*	19 *39*	72 *66*		
Ma	25 *04*	−07 *−05*	−13 *00*	32 *01*	30 *34*	06 *12*	50 *26*	53 *21*	
K	−25	08	53	09	−08	22	−65	−46	−42

Some evidence was presented to show that K behaves in the expected manner when persons attempt to fake a "bad" profile, although the corresponding effect in faking "good" was not demonstrated on any experimental group. Some clinical support for this latter effect had been found.

The addition of K had a variable effect on the intercorrelations of clinical scales. There seems to be some indication that the optimal amount of K correction for a given clinical scale is inversely related to the proportion of "subtle" items the scale already contains.

It is suggested that the K correction should be made routinely by users of the MMPI and that old records should be scored and redrawn if any research or validation study is to be carried on.

SECTION III Coding

AS EXPERIENCE with the clinical scales (discussed in Section II) grew and as the nonmedical applications proved increasingly successful, it became clear that the implications of the scales had to be extended and their original psychiatric emphasis redirected. That is, instead of referring to "the schizophrenia scale" the simple label Sc was frequently used. This helped free the scale from many of the obvious, and in some ways unfortunate, connotations of the concept of schizophrenia. It had become apparent with widespread testing that many people who scored high on the Sc scale were by no means clinically schizophrenic and it was misleading to attribute to them the usual implications of the term.

Now, with the substitution of the nonevaluative code digit 8 for the Sc scale, it is possible to get even further from these restrictive connotations. In this section some of the work is reported that has led to an amplification of interpretive implications of the various scales. Coding as exemplified in these articles is more than a substitution of numbers for scale names. It is a positive approach to both clinical and research problems with the MMPI. The former is illustrated in Hathaway and Meehl's *Atlas* [307] and the latter in *Analyzing and Predicting Juvenile Delinquency* by Hathaway and Monachesi [312]. In a review of the *Atlas*, Welsh [623] expressed the belief that it "should encourage clinical workers to utilize the profile patterning and configural approach to the MMPI and should discourage the unprofitable adherence to the diagnostic terminology of the individual scales. It will then be possible to determine empirically and without psychiatric bias the personality correlates — both normal and abnormal — of the various profile patterns." We feel that the articles in this section demonstrate how interesting and how useful such an approach has been.

In this section the first two articles, 12 and 13, take up the mechanics of a profile coding system, while the remaining articles show the application of coding to various problems. Welsh demonstrates in article 14 that coding may reveal profile configurations which are obscured by graphic or tabular listing of T scores; he points out that erroneous inferences drawn from imperfect realization of the actual profile configuration due to limitations of the two common methods of presenting data may often be avoided by the use of coding. In article 15 Hathaway and Meehl group psychiatric patients according to frequent profile code types and summarize the salient features of the clinical picture; tables are also presented of the frequencies of all two-digit codes for psychiatric patients and Minnesota normals. Guthrie in article 16 groups by two-digit codes patients who sought help from a specialist in internal medicine; the clinical data are supplemented by an item analysis of the code types. The use of an adjective check list with one- and two-digit codes is described by Black in article 17 utilizing a population of female college undergraduates. In

124

the last article, 18, Drake studies the frequency with which certain profile codes occur in male counselees when they have been grouped according to outstanding behavioral features as noted by the counselors. It is of great interest to notice both similarities and certain differences in characteristics of profile codes on the three kinds of populations: psychiatric, medical, and normal.

A word is necessary about the two coding procedures, the original method of Hathaway and Welsh's extended code. We believe the latter to have many clear-cut advantages over the earlier method. These are summarized in a table at the end of article 13. Throughout this volume, as we have indicated earlier in the Foreword, the extended coding method has been used wherever possible. It may be noted in both articles 16 and 18 how data available for study had to be reduced because of unfortunate limitations of the original method. Article 17 does not suffer this loss, since the extended method was utilized. Both the *Atlas* and *Analyzing and Predicting Juvenile Delinquency* are much less useful than they could have been because of adherence to the earlier coding system [623]. The reader is urged to adapt his own procedure with MMPI profiles to the extended coding method so that maximum information can be conveniently retained.

The articles in this section came from the following sources: article 12 from S. R. Hathaway, A coding system for MMPI profiles, *Journal of Consulting Psychology*, 1947, 11, 334–337; article 13 from G. S. Welsh, An extension of Hathaway's MMPI profile coding system, *Journal of Consulting Psychology*, 1948, 12, 343–344; article 14 from G. S. Welsh, Some practical uses of MMPI profile coding, *Journal of Consulting Psychology*, 1951, 15, 82–84; article 15 from S. R. Hathaway and P. E. Meehl, The Minnesota Multiphasic Personality Inventory, in *Military clinical psychology*, Dept. of the Army Technical Manual TM 8:242 and Dept. of the Air Force Manual AFM 160-145, Washington: U.S. Govt. Printing Office, 1951; article 16 from G. M. Guthrie, Common characteristics associated with frequent MMPI profile types, *Journal of Clinical Psychology*, 1952, 8, 141–145; article 17 from J. D. Black, The interpretation of MMPI profiles of college women, Ph.D. dissertation, University of Minnesota, 1953; and article 18 from L. E. Drake, MMPI profiles and interview behavior, *Journal of Counseling Psychology*, 1954, 1, 92–95. We are indebted to the authors and to the publishers of the journals for permission to reproduce these articles in this form.

ARTICLE 12 *A Coding System for MMPI Profile Classification*

FOR some time there has been a need for a more efficient method of classifying MMPI profiles. Certain problems of behavior, such as alcoholism, are likely to be symptomatic of basic personality patterns represented by several different profile types. If one averages the profile scale values obtained in such symptomatic groups, definitive information may be lost. A complete analysis should include both the averages and some kind of interscale variability study.

In the development of the MMPI scales, the particular scale has been stressed rather than the profile. This was in part due to the fact that the scales were serially derived, making it impossible to speak of profiles in earlier work. It has been common practice, however, for the experienced users of the inventory to evaluate profiles rather than separate scales. No one has seriously doubted the general validity of this profile approach but experimental verification or even simple transmission of one person's experience to another has been nearly impossible from lack of "profile language."

Gough [234 (see VI, 38)], Harris [292], Meehl [436 (V, 31)], and Schmidt [528 (VI, 39)] have all presented clinical data of profile-descriptive type, but their descriptions were very hard to apply to a particular profile and it would be a real problem for another investigator to locate in his files the profiles most nearly fitting the descriptions.

Du Mas [r45] has discussed the problems of profile analysis and concludes, among other points, "If prediction or diagnosis is to be maximally good, both intensity and pattern must be operative in a profile."

The coding system presented here expresses intensity and pattern but effects a compromise between too much detail on scale elevation and equally undesirable detail as to profile shape. If either elevation or shape is too fully expressed, the nine clinical scales of the MMPI provide an unusually cumbersome number of classes. On the other hand, one must preserve enough detail to include the "type" information that may later be found in the profiles.

From the code to be presented, one at once knows for any coded profile all scales that deviate farther upward than a standard score of 54. These are listed in order of their deviation magnitude with the most extreme first and others in succession. A mark is also provided to show the point at which this descending series of scale

126

values crosses the 70 line. Following the listed high points a dash initiates a list of the low points which are in order from lowest upward to standard score 46. No specific indication is provided for variation of scales within the range of the middle nine standard score points (T = 46 to 54 inclusive).

The first step in classification is the substitution of number digits for the nine scale symbols. The Hs scale becomes scale 1, D becomes 2, and so on across the profile ending with Ma represented by the number 9. Using these numbers to refer to the scales, one may begin to write the code for a particular profile.

Consider the hypothetical profile that would result from the T scores of A in Table 1. The code for this profile would be 32′17–69. This code is obtained by writing first the code number of the highest score and successively the numbers of the next

Table 1. Hypothetical Profile Data and Codes

Case	Hs (1)	D (2)	Hy (3)	Pd (4)	Mf (5)	Pa (6)	Pt (7)	Sc (8)	Ma (9)	Code
A...............	65	70	75	54	46	40	55	53	45	32′17–69
B...............	48	64	50	72	65	54	63	63	54	4′<u>5278</u>–
C...............	45	44	47	52	40	50	48	52	54	–<u>521</u>

highest down to (but not including) a T value of 54. When these numbers have been written they are followed with a dash. The number of the scale with the lowest T score is written next followed by the numbers of successively higher scale values until a T of 46 is reached. Numbers of scales having T values of 46 to 54 inclusive are not written. Finally, a prime is placed after the number of the last of the high scales that has a T value of 70 or more.

Consider next the profile represented by B in Table 1. The code for this is 4′<u>5278</u>–. In this case, the underlining indicates that the four scales are equal or proceed in a sequence differing by only one point. There are no scale values below a T score of 46 so no values appear to the right of the dash.

Example C in Table 1 presents still another possibility. The code for these data is –<u>521</u>. The code shows Mf to be the lowest point with Hs and D equal or within one point of each other.

Finally, if the ? or the L has a T value greater than or equal to 70 or if the F has a T value greater than or equal to 80, a capital X is placed after the code to indicate the probable invalidity of the profile. (The K score, if it is used at all, is assumed to have been used in obtaining the T values themselves.)

For filing coded profiles a card index is prepared with blank 3 by 5 index cards having five tab positions. On nine of these index cards having the extreme left tab, the numbers 1 to 9 are printed. Behind each of these nine cards are placed eight cards, with index tabs in the second from the left position carrying the eight possible pairs of digits. For example, behind the index card with 1 there will be index cards 12, 13, 14, 15, 16, 17, 18, 19. (An 11 is not a possible combination.) The index to this point requires 81 index cards. For further separation seven cards with middle tabs could be placed behind each of the 72 second position tab cards. For example, behind the 12 card there would be cards marked 123, 124, 125, 126, 127, 128, 129. If the file were extended, still more tabular cards could be inserted. These would have fourth position tabs and carry four numbers. Behind the 123 card would be placed 1234, 1235, 1236, 1237, 1238, 1239. Such index subdivision would require a very large number of tabular cards and no ordinary file of profiles will need such complete subdivision. Our experience indicates that it is best to complete the second position cards and insert only a few of the third or fourth position cards to separate larger packs of code cards as they accumulate. The degree of fineness in subdivision by index cards will then depend upon the frequency of certain rough groups of coded profile types.

To prepare codes for filing, the code is written in the upper left corner of lined 3 by 5 cards. The name, sex, and other identification referring to the original profile are placed in the upper right corner. Other data may be written on the lower faces of the cards. Finally the cards are filed in the prepared index. A code such as 4–21 would be placed behind the index card marked 4. Filing is done only with reference to the numbers to the left of the dash. Cards with no coded high or low point are coded "–" only and placed behind a first position tab index card marked "–." Cards with only low points may be similarly placed after serial arrangement in terms of the low-point code, or if research on low points is intended, a separate index file should be prepared as described above except that the index numbers should be preceded by a "–." When such a low-point file is used, all coded profiles having both low and high coded scales should be recorded on a "low" as well as a "high" card. On the "low" card the code can be written backwards. For example, the first code of Table 1 would be written –69;32'17 on the "low file" card. These low file cards should be indexed exclusively with reference to the low points. They are at once identifiable by the semicolon as duplicate cards with a high-point file card.

As soon as a number of profiles have been coded and filed, one has various data available. The number of code cards behind each first position index card shows the frequency of occurrence of each scale as a high point. Similarly the number of cards behind each of the second position tab cards shows the frequency of all the combinations of two high points. Other such possibilities for profile analysis are apparent. Frequency tables of these types as found among the MMPI normative cases will soon be published [307, 308 (see III, 15)] to afford a comparison with data observed elsewhere.

One may wish to select out of a file all the available profiles that are similar to a particular example. To do this the referent profile is first coded. The index will at once yield any identically coded profiles. Usually, because of the great variety of profile shapes and elevations, there will be few if any such identical codes. One may next write variants of the referent code making any changes he feels will not materially affect the basic pattern. Each variant is checked in the index until such concessions to variation have provided as many cases as seem reasonably similar.

To serve as an example, the mild psychoneurosis averaged profile as given by Gough [234 (see VI, 38)] has the code 132'6478–. This code indicates that the typical mild psychoneurosis profile is characterized by two plateaus of higher values. The triad Hs, D, and Hy are at 70 or above and another four scales, Pd, Pa, Pt, and Sc, are nearly equal at a lower level. There were no scales below 46.

In matching this profile one may set up criteria permitting variation enough to obtain reasonably similar profiles until the differences become experimentally intolerable.

To further illustrate, a file of 681 "normal" profiles yields eight with codes beginning 123, four with 132, and three with 231. Some of these have several of the four scales, 6, 7, 8, or 9, and most have some low scales. The 15 cases probably represent the best available group of profiles among these normals that could be considered at all comparable to Gough's "mild neurotics." The averaged profile, however, may have partly obscured the patterning of the curves on neurotic patients. If a summary of the code types from which the averages were obtained was available, it might be possible to extend the search for similar profiles more widely.

In using the above system there is place for one more scale that could be called 0. This would greatly extend the number of classes, but profiles without the extra scale (or profiles disregarding any one of the scales) can be matched with similar ones by writing their codes (the number assignments to the scales should never be changed) assuming the missing scale to have any acceptable position in the code. For example, most MMPI profiles of the normative groups do not have Mf items. Codes on these will never have the number 5. Suppose such a profile to be represented by the code 46–. One may look for similar profiles among an indexed assortment of profiles that do have the Mf under the 46– and variants with other scales but always omitting 5. This would force any matched profile to have an Mf between 45 and 55. On the other hand, one may wish to disregard the value of Mf. In this case one could also look under 546–, 456–, 465–, and variants using other scales among the high points. For such profile matching the low points may be disregarded or of course they may be specified in any desired way.

In summary, an MMPI profile coding system that provides an approach to pattern-intensity analysis is presented. The codes retain much of the original information but effect a simplification that seems a good compromise with too great diversity at one extreme and oversimplification with loss of information at the other. The coded profiles may be indexed and filed. The file provides an immediate reference for profile elevation and shape frequencies among given classes of subjects.

ARTICLE 13 *An Extension of Hathaway's MMPI Profile Coding System*

THE method of coding MMPI profiles for classification developed by Hathaway [296 (see III, 12)] has proved to be very helpful in interpretation of profiles and useful for research. In work with neuropsychiatric patients, however, where many scores lie above 70, it is often desirable to indicate the amount of elevation more accurately. Similarly it is often helpful to know the lowest scores in such profiles even though they may lie between 46 and 54 ; these are not coded in the original method.

Accordingly in the extended profile coding method all scale digits are used and each profile code will contain nine digits (ten if 0 is used for Si [177 (see IV, 19)]). The basic method is followed in that the highest score appears first and the others follow in descending order. It differs in that there is no reversal for the low scores since the middle scores are included and there is no break in the coding.

The advantages of this method are that the lowest scale always appears in the code and is easier to find since it will always be the last digit at the right of the code. If the codes are being filed by lowest scales they do not have to be rewritten. The method outlined by Hathaway for filing the high scores is followed except that in this instance the duplicate cards will be arranged with the digits reading from right to left. It is also somewhat easier to check the codes developed by this method.

In order to indicate the amount of elevation more accurately the following symbols are used : all scores 90 or over will be followed by °, 80 to 89 by ″, 70 to 79 by ′, 60 to 69 by –, 50 to 59 by /, 40 to 49 by :, and 30 to 39 by #. All scores below 30 then will appear to the right of #. All these symbols appear on standard typewriters and can be easily made by hand.

In the clinic when we speak of a "starred" profile we know that there are some scores 90 or over; a "double prime" profile means that some scores are in the 80's; a "prime" profile will indicate one in which some scores are in the 70's.

As in the original method all scores lying within one point of one another will be underlined.

The code in the original method was followed by an X if ? or L was 70 or more, or if F was 80 or more. In the extended method the sign of the invalidating scale follows the code instead of an X. For example, if the L score is 73 the code will be followed by an L. An elevation of K to 70 or more may be similarly indicated.

If it is necessary to distinguish the extended code from the original method the extended code may be enclosed in parentheses.

130

Examples of the extended coding method are given in Table 1. It will be seen that from any such code all MMPI profiles with scores lying between 99 and 20 can always be reconstructed on the basis of the code alone to an accuracy of five points for any scale. Ordinarily the accuracy will be within two or three points.

A comparison of the original and the extended methods of coding is made in Table 2, with code examples in Table 3.

Table 1. Hypothetical Profile Data and Extended Codes

Case	Hs (1)	D (2)	Hy (3)	Pd (4)	Mf (5)	Pa (6)	Pt (7)	Sc (8)	Ma (9)	Code
A........	74	86	75	79	55	69	92	95	46	(87°2″431′6–5/9)
B........	65	82	63	50	49	46	55	57	29	(2″ ′13–874/56:#9)
C........	52	46	51	49	46	47	50	47	54	(9137/4 6825)

Table 2. Summary and Comparison of Original and Extended Methods of Coding

Item	Original	Extended
Code length	Variable: From none up to nine digits.	Constant: Always nine digits (if all scales used).
Code without all scales	It may be impossible to tell whether a given scale has been used or whether it is merely in the uncoded range between T scores 46 to 54.	If a scale (such as 5 which was not used in the *Atlas* or 0 which is not routinely scored by all workers) is not in the profile, it is immediately apparent from the code.
Code order	Variable and inconsistent: 1. From highest to lowest for scores above T = 54. 2. Scores between T = 46 to T = 54 not coded. 3. From *lowest* to *highest* for scores below T = 46.	Constant: Always from highest to lowest in a natural sequence throughout the range of scores.
Position of highest scale	Variable or indeterminate: 1. Will be the first digit if the T score is over 54. 2. If it falls in the T-score range 46–54 and any other scale also falls in this range, the high scale cannot be determined. 3. If the highest scale is below 46, it will be the *last* digit in the code.	Constant: Always the first digit in the code.
Position of lowest scale	Variable or indeterminate: 1. Will be the last digit if all T scores in profile are over 54. 2. Will be the first digit if all T scores in profile are under 46. 3. If it falls in the T-score range 46–54 and any other scale also falls in this range, the low scale cannot be determined. 4. It will be the last digit if it is the only scale below 46. 5. It will be the next to last digit if two scales are below 46, etc.	Constant: Always the last digit in the code (increasingly important since work on low points has begun — e.g., Cantor [110] and Sutton [578]).

Table 2 — continued

Item	Original	Extended
Elevation indication	Four unequal classes: 1. ≧ 70 2. 55–69 3. 46–54 4. <46	Eight standard classes: 1. ≧90 2. 80–89 3. 70–79 4. 60–69 5. 50–59 6. 40–49 7. 30–39 8. <30
Reproducibility of profile from code	Only crude reconstruction is possible for most profiles; some cannot be reproduced at all.	All profiles with scores between 20 and 99 can be reproduced absolutely to an accuracy of five T-score points; usually an accuracy of two to three points is obtained.

Table 3. Code Examples

			MMPI Scores							
Hs	D	Hy	Pd	Mf	Pa	Pt	Sc	Ma	Original Code	Extended Code
50	50	51	53	47	46	47	49	54	–	94 312/8 576
70	62	75	59	50	48	52	53	55	31′249–	31′2–49875/6
49	39	50	53	47	45	40	42	54	–2786	94 3/15687:2
48	52	50	56	47	46	52	53	54	4–	498273/156
49	46	48	60	49	52	48	54	50	4–	4–869/15372
48	77	50	54	45	68	75	72	59	278′69–5	278′6–943/15
40	91	49	39	35	68	75	72	61	278′69–541	2°″78′69–/31:45

G. S. WELSH

ARTICLE 14 *Some Practical Uses of MMPI Profile Coding*

A METHOD of coding MMPI profiles has been developed by Welsh [617 (see III, 13)] following the original work of Hathaway [296 (III, 12)]. The purpose of such coding is, first, to reduce the T scores of the MMPI scales to a form which is more easily handled and, second, to emphasize the configurational aspects of the profile.

The primary utility of such codes lies in the ease with which profiles can be treated. Codes can be filed as suggested by Hathaway, and the data are then in a convenient form for tabulation with regard to the frequency of particular profile configurations. A pool is available for profile-matching purposes in which the degree of similarity can be specified. While this could be done from the profiles as drawn on the recording sheet, it is apparent that it would be infinitely more difficult and time consuming. If, for example, the clinician were interested in profiles with a peak on the neurotic triad in which $Hs > D > Hy$, he could sort a stack of MMPI records and pull out those with this particular shape at a great expenditure of time. With a file of coded cases, on the other hand, he can immediately locate all profiles with a 123 code and quickly count the number of cases available.

Another use of the code lies in ease of communication. The oral reporting of a list of T scores takes some time and is even then in an awkward form which must be drawn into a profile before it is of any practical use. The code digits with their elevation symbols, however, can be given in a matter of seconds and in a form which is useful immediately. It should be remembered that from the extended code itself the MMPI profile can be reconstructed with very little loss of accuracy in terms of T scores if it is desired to present the profile in graphic form.

The code also offers a shorthand way for clinicians to speak of particular profile configurations. Thus, if we have a profile of a conversion hysteric that shows an elevation of the neurotic triad into the 70's with Hy higher than Hs and both higher than D and with Si as the lowest score lying in the extroverted end of the scale, this fact can be expressed quite simply as "312 prime with 0 down."

For the computation of tetrachoric correlations which might be used in factor or cluster analysis, the code may be conveniently utilized. A red pencil line is drawn through the fifth and sixth place digits (if ten scales are used), separating the scales into a high and low group. The frequencies required for calculation of the tetrachoric r can easily be obtained by assortment of the code cards thus divided. The method has, in addition to convenience, an emphasis on the relative position of the

133

scales and the configurational aspect of the profiles which might not appear in the use of T scores for this purpose.

The above examples illustrate the first purpose of MMPI coding, the reduction of T scores to a convenient and usable form. To exemplify the second purpose, emphasis of the profile configuration, data published in an article by Andersen [20] will be used. These data were T scores on successive administrations of the MMPI to a psychiatric patient following lobotomy. As they stand, any profile configurations are difficult to discern. If they are drawn as a set of profiles on a recording sheet, it is almost impossible to follow the individual profiles in the confused welter of lines; even the use of differently colored pencils does not help much. If they are drawn as a series of profiles, six separate sheets will be needed and the advantages of simultaneous visualization will be lost.

Table 1. Andersen's Data in Coded Form

Test	Code
Preoperative	2̲7̲8°4̲3̲5̲1̲"6'0–9 FK?̲L̲/
1st postoperative	8°7"245'106–93 F?̲L̲/K
2nd postoperative	27°8"4̲5̲ 60'1̲3̲–/9 F?̲L̲/K
3rd postoperative	28°4̲7̲1"5̲6̲0̲'3–9 FK?̲L̲/
4th postoperative	2°47"8̲0̲5̲6̲'13–9 F?̲L̲/K
5th postoperative	24°'"78'5360–19 KF?̲L̲/
Average	2°874"5̲1̲'6̲0̲3–9 FK?̲L̲/

Let us look at Table 1 where the data are presented in code form. The scores of the validating scales have been coded and placed at the end of the profile code. The salient features of each of the six profiles with regard to both configuration and elevation are at once apparent, and a simultaneous comparison of the profiles is possible. A single scale such as depression can be traced by following the position of the digit 2 in the successive codes. We see that it remains consistently in first place with the exception of the first postoperative test where schizophrenia, 8, appears first and the 2 has moved to third place. It is also seen from the codes that D is quite consistently high (in the 90's), since it is followed by the elevation symbol ° in all but one case. In a similar manner the place of Pd, both with regard to position among the scales and in terms of elevation, may be followed by observing the code digit 4.

It is particularly important, however, to note that relationships may emerge which are not easily anticipated either in the table of T scores or in the graphic profile forms. In these particular data it can be seen that, although there is considerable variation in elevation and some shifts in scale position, the basic personality structure (as revealed by this test) remains essentially the same. This does not support the author's contention that there was "a progressive change from a typically schizophrenic profile through a typically psychopathic profile." D, Sc, Pt, and Pd occupy the first four positions in all the codes and Ma is the last scale in all but one of the codes. Also, the several scales do not differ greatly from their averages, which have been computed from Andersen's data. The average T scores are as follows: ?, 50.0; L, 50.0; K, 51.3; F, 55.6; Hs, 70.5; D, 98.1; Hy, 66.8; Pd, 83.3; Mf, 74.8; Pa,

69.8; Pt, 86.3; Sc, 87.1; Ma, 52.8; Si, 69.6. Although there is a trend for Pd to rise in the last three profiles, the profiles are by no means typically psychopathic.

It is of interest to note that the average ranks of the scales on the six profiles are Hs, 7.4; D, 1.4; Hy, 8.0; Pd, 3.2; Mf, 5.2; Pa, 6.9; Pt, 2.7; Sc, 3.0; Ma, 9.8; Si, 7.2. The code of these ranks would be 2784560139, which is very similar to the code of the average T scores. This latter code may be termed a 2 star 874 double prime with 9 low. It might be said here parenthetically that it has been found best to include the first four scales and the last scale in selecting profiles for similarity.

Table 2. Profile Codes of Rubin's Data

Diagnostic Term	N	Code
Psychotic (schizophrenia)	33	8<u>24</u>–<u>71</u> 6<u>9</u>3/5 F–?LK
Psychoneurotic (anxiety state, hysteria. hypochondriasis, neurasthenia, reactive depression, mixed neuropsychiatric)	28	24 <u>731</u>–8695 <u>KF</u> <u>?L</u>/
Chronic alcoholic (without psychosis)...	8	42–<u>318</u>/<u>97</u> <u>56</u> KFL?/
Psychopathic	24	48<u>372</u>–<u>1596</u> <u>F</u>KL?/

In an article by Rubin [509] (this paper has been discussed by Aaronson and Welsh [1]) an analysis of variance technique was used to show that no statistically significant differences existed between average scale scores for four diagnostic groups. Yet, if these data are coded as in Table 2, it will be apparent that there are real configurational differences between the groups. The schizophrenic code shows the peak score on Sc with the typical elevated F and lowered K. The psychoneurotic and the alcoholic groups are differentiated by the reversal of the position of D and Pd as well as by the much higher place of Pt in the neurotic group. The alcoholic and the psychopath groups both show Pd as the peak score, but D is clearly lower and Sc much higher in the psychopath group.

The writer feels that if series of MMPI profiles either for individuals or for groups are coded and placed in tabular form, the data will be presented in a manner economical of space and easily grasped; also, relationships and interpretive features which are not readily apparent in ordinary presentation might then be discovered.

To summarize, MMPI coding is of value in reducing the T scores to a form that may be handled conveniently. The code is useful in filing data and in locating cases for research or clinical use. Ease and economy in communication result from the use of coding. The placing of codes in tabular form may disclose relationships which are not easily seen in usual methods of presentation.

ARTICLE 15 *Psychiatric Implications of Code Types*

THE MMPI was particularly designed to provide an estimate of symptomatic syndromes commonly recognized among psychiatric patients. Two facts should be borne in mind in MMPI work: (1) The nine clinical scales were derived at least in part from the general descriptive background of Kraepelinian terminology as modified and applied in clinical practice. The scales were not expected to measure pure traits or represent discrete etiological or prognostic entities. (2) Nearly all patients seen in a diagnostic clinic will show a mixture of such diagnostic patterns; and, as a rule, a final diagnosis is a compromise between the strength of the diagnostic syndromes as estimated from the patient's symptoms and, on the other hand, the meanings of those symptoms in a patient's environment. For example, a very large number of schizophrenic patients are deeply depressed. Seen with reference only to the strength of the symptom pattern, the depression often will appear more important than the schizoid characteristics. Since, however, the schizoid components are less responsive to treatment and generally virulent in their disabling character, such a patient will be classed as schizophrenic rather than some type of depression.

The MMPI data are not adequate as a basis for evaluation of the meaning of the symptoms in the patient's environmental adjustment; and, for that reason, among others, the MMPI profile does not directly provide a diagnosis with the majority of patients. The profile must always be evaluated by the clinician in terms of his concepts of the prognosis and the extent to which the particular symptoms lead to incapacitation.

MMPI scales show very considerable variability from one testing to another; often this variability occurs within a matter of hours. For personality factors subject to therapy or to diurnal variation it should be obvious that this would be so. As an example, a clinically significant depression may disappear almost in minutes where it has represented a reaction to some environmental stress that is suddenly relieved. The sensitivity of the paranoid person is also often variable depending upon his conceptual view of his environment. With explanation of what to him were puzzling, disturbing, or threatening social factors, he may change from a highly suspicious and defensive individual into an open, warm, and friendly one (although he will probably be susceptible to new suspicions). To a large extent, repeated MMPI profiles will follow these changes. They also follow the shifting patterns of symptomatology as the patient progresses through therapy. At times the disappearance of

136

a depression may be accompanied by the appearance of a definitely antisocial or psychopathic pattern of symptoms. Again, a hypomanic patient may shift to a depression; and all patients tend to obtain more and more normal appearing profiles as they get better. It should also, in this connection, be kept in mind that the various specific symptoms of a disorder are not equal in their disabling characteristics. Of two paranoid persons equally distorted in their thinking, one may be dangerously specialized and thus be considered committable; the other may be so generalized that he is not effectively dangerous and can remain free although he is known as a "crank" or reclusive misogynist.

The MMPI also provides a number of checks upon the attitude of the patient as he takes the inventory and upon the validity of his item responses. Four scales are commonly used in this area; and while they are by no means infallible, interpretation of the validity scales is an absolute requirement to proper use of the whole inventory. Obviously a subject who answers the items of the inventory with the knowledge that the data may be used to his disadvantage will tend to react differently from what he would do if he were answering the items in a completely permissive and nonthreatening setting. Not infrequently, subjects will be defensive in what would seem to be an ideal setting for them to be frank. This is especially likely with paranoid individuals who can distort, on occasion, the most unthreatening surroundings to the extent that they make every effort to conceal any response that might appear undesirable. Unfortunately, these varying attitudes with which a subject may take the test are not simple over-all effects. For example, a patient may be extremely defensive about any possible physical symptom that he thinks he has, yet be entirely frank and lacking in defenses regarding psychological symptoms. More often, the reverse of this is true. There is an unknown number of such variables in test-taking attitude that must be considered by the clinician in his use of the MMPI. Every effort should be made to ensure confidence from the subject and to promise him security about the uses that may be made of the individual item responses and the profile obtained.

From the foregoing it should be clear that adequate use of the MMPI can only be achieved by persons with extensive clinical experience and particular training with the inventory itself.

The clinical scales were originally derived from contrasting item data on various psychopathic hospital diagnostic groups and assumed normal samples. The hospital diagnoses probably represented current psychiatric practice in diagnosis. The "normal" persons were mostly adults between the ages of 20 and 45 who said they were not under the care of a physician at the time of testing. They were asked to take the test while they waited in a general hospital clinic after bringing in a patient or while they were visiting a patient. They seemed to be a good cross-sectional group of the general population since norms derived from them have proved to be reasonably satisfactory.

The current research by sophisticated users of the MMPI emphasizes three things: First, the shape of the total profile is of greater significance than the elevation of single scores. To get the most out of this instrument, the clinician must treat the data in a *configural* rather than an *atomistic* fashion. Second, there is an increasing tendency to *start with the test*, i.e., to arrange or sort patients on the basis of the test results and *then* to examine these "test-similar" patients for resemblances in history, symptoms, dynamics, course, and diagnosis. This approach seems to be more fruitful and more in harmony with actual clinical practice than the traditional "validation" study which proceeds by asking the psychologist for his guesses to compare with the psychiatrist's diagnostic opinion. Third, we have become increasingly interested in those correlates of the profile which are not strictly "psychiatric," such as the normal, everyday traits and tendencies that will be readily noted and named by a person's acquaintances.

The material which follows reflects these three lines of thinking. It must be emphasized that the *following is in no sense a rigorous documented summary of statistical findings or published research.*

It is not the individual scale that we must evaluate in using the MMPI profile, but rather the pattern afforded by the whole group of scales including the validity indicators. There is an indefinitely large number of patterns possible; and, although one may often feel he has seen some given pattern a number of times before, there are in reality almost no exact duplicates.

To make patterns useful a two-digit coding system has been applied. Although this method discards much of the information it does reduce the possible number of different profiles to a practicable size.

One should get into the habit of using the code to talk about curves, instead of talking about the psychiatric category names at the top of the profile sheet. It is worst to talk about the "schizophrenia" key; it is better to talk about the Sc key; it is best to talk about *scale 8*. That, of course, helps one to start with the test and then look at the people, instead of trying to guess the diagnosis.

It is greatly desirable to avoid the psychiatric implication when working with more or less "normal" populations, and it is preferable to refer to curves by code even in a hospital setting. It is all very well to say, "Well, we won't talk about the psychiatry of it," but the clinician's mind is such that if he talks about the "schizophrenia" key he cannot help thinking about schizophrenia, whereas if he talks about the 87's or the 23's, then he can set up relatively fresh associations with the significance of those numbers.

The first thing of interest about codes is the frequency of various code types among "normals" and general "abnormals" (the latter all inpatients but of varying diagnoses). Tables 1 through 4 present comparative data. From these figures one may check the probability of a code to the second high point.

It is difficult to make general statements as to what clinically characterizes the cases with a given code because the frequencies are so small. For example, the commonest two-digit high-point code among normal males is 94. (A peak on Ma and a secondary peak on Pd.) But to say it is the commonest is not saying much. In terms of its actual occurrence, it is found in only 4.3 per cent of the subjects, since there are so many curve possibilities. This means that to have 10 such normal males to scrutinize clinically, a sample of 233 normal males is needed. The problem of getting enough cases in order to be able to say anything with confidence, at the same time getting the code fairly detailed as to configuration, is a very difficult one. That we face this problem is understandable in view of the complexity of human behavior. One could hardly expect to describe persons usefully with a restricted terminology such as is often offered for clinical generalization. We feel that the number of described categories should always approach the limit of the clinician's ability to remember and generally assimilate.

The sexes are quite similar as to the relative incidence of various code types, except for D. Among normal women there are nearly twice as many codes with D as the peak (code 2′ . . . or ′2 . . .) as there are among normal men even though there are separate norms for the T scores of the two sexes.

The most common peak score among normals is Ma. That is true for either sex. Eighteen per cent of the males and 13 per cent of the females have the Ma score as the highest (code 9′ . . . or ′9 . . .).

There are certain code types or configurations that appear much more often among abnormals than normals and hence are more worthy of attention. That is, they are indicative of pathology in the probability sense because they rarely occur in the normal population. For instance, whereas Ma is the commonest normal peak, a combination of Ma and Sc, or Sc and Ma, as the *top two* scores (code 98 or 89) is rare and occurs more frequently in abnormals. The combination of D and Pd, that is, a 24 or 42, is even more a comparative characteristic of the sick. The 27 pattern, D and Pt, occurs twelve times as often in the sick male as it does in the well. (Note, we are here considering the *patterns* regardless of how high they are.) Sometimes the trends seem more striking if one includes elevation. Thus, pattern 27 occurs with D equal to or greater than 70 twenty-five times as frequently among the sick as among the well. The combination of Pd and Sc is more common among the sick, but Sc and Pd in that order are not particularly more common. The pattern 87 is eight times as frequent in the sick as in the well. As a matter of fact, with either of these two scores equal to or greater than 70, the pattern 87 did not occur once among 258 male normals!

There are some code types which appear more often among normals than abnormals. The code 3− is six times as frequent among normals. Interestingly, the combination 64 is more frequent among normals than abnormals. This trend is reversed as the T scores go above 70. A profile where only Ma is coded is ten times as frequent among normals as it is among abnormals. The manics, some alcoholics, and a few aberrant conduct disorders that one wonders about diagnostically are the only abnormals with 9−. When the Ma key is 70 or above (if it is alone in the code) it would be three times as frequently found among normal persons as it would among abnormals if there were the same number of normals and abnormals in the total population.

The next thing to do with the codes, after determining how often they occur, is to study characteristics of code types in the hospital population. Cutting across diagnosis, one considers all the patients who have a 13 or 27, or whatever it might be, and asks what kinds of features they show. Take the 12's and 21's for instance. As a preliminary study, we have classified the incidence of symptoms in terms of three levels: things that are found in the majority of these cases, things that are found in one third to one half, and things found in one fifth to one third.

The actual absolute values of those fractions are practically meaningless. It is only the *relative* probabilities of symptoms that make any real difference because to say that they are found in the records of these people means really that the psychiatrist, when he wrote up the summary, was struck by it and put it in. If it

Table 1. Relative Frequencies of High-Point Codes of 710 Male Psychiatric Unit Inpatients

High-Point Code	70 or Over	Total	High-Point Code	70 or Over	Total	High-Point Code	70 or Over	Total
?.........	8	21	36........	0	1	72........	26	27
-ᵃ........	0	13	37........	0	1	73........	0	0
1/.........	0	0	38........	0	3	74........	3	4
12........	26	27	39........	0	2	76........	1	3
13........	41	43				78........	14	17
14........	9	10	4.........	0	5	79........	1	2
16........	0	1	41........	4	5			
17........	4	4	42........	22	29	8.........	0	0
18........	8	9	43........	11	17	81........	7	8
19........	4	6	46........	9	11	82........	11	12
			47........	7	10	83........	2	3
2.........	0	2	48........	27	33	84........	8	13
21........	44	47	49........	11	21	86........	6	8
23........	23	27				87........	23	23
24........	9	17	6.........	0	0	89........	10	11
26........	7	8	61........	0	0			
27........	66	70	62........	4	6	9.........	2	8
28........	3	14	63........	0	1	91........	3	4
29........	2	2	64........	2	5	92........	2	7
			67........	3	3	93........	1	6
3.........	0	3	68........	7	7	94........	11	12
31........	16	19	69........	1	3	96........	3	3
32........	4	9				97........	1	1
34........	3	4	7.........	0	0	98........	15	15
			71........	4	4			

Table 2. Relative Frequencies of High-Point Codes of 1053 Female Psychiatric Unit Inpatients

High-Point Code	70 or Over	Total	High-Point Code	70 or Over	Total	High-Point Code	70 or Over	Total
?.........	35	64	36........	3	5	72........	18	21
-ᵃ........	0	18	37........	6	6	73........	3	3
1.........	0	2	38........	4	7	74........	1	2
12........	14	18	39........	7	7	76........	3	4
13........	68	75				78........	9	12
14........	3	5	4.........	1	4	79........	0	0
16........	2	4	41........	4	9			
17........	1	1	42........	15	25	8.........	0	1
18........	1	2	43........	16	24	81........	6	7
19........	1	2	46........	22	26	82........	21	21
			47........	6	7	83........	5	6
2.........	1	8	48........	22	28	84........	9	14
21........	33	37	49........	12	18	86........	15	18
23........	49	56				87........	20	20
24........	18	22	6.........	0	3	89........	4	8
26........	20	21	61........	3	5			
27........	81	85	62........	9	14	9.........	1	7
28........	25	25	63........	8	10	91........	2	4
29........	0	3	64........	14	14	92........	1	3
			67........	5	7	93........	4	7
3.........	2	2	68........	16	18	94........	24	27
31........	65	82	69........	3	4	96........	8	16
32........	29	34				97........	3	5
34........	13	20	7.........	0	1	98........	15	18
			71........	1	1			

ᵃ Includes cases with no high point above 54 and those with tied high points.

Table 3. Relative Frequencies of High-Point Codes of 258 Adult Male Minnesota Normals

High-Point Code	70 or Over	Total	High-Point Code	70 or Over	Total	High-Point Code	70 or Over	Total
?	1	10	36	0	0	72	2	3
-ᵃ	0	61	37	0	0	73	0	1
			38	0	3	74	0	0
1	0	3	39	0	1	76	0	0
12	2	7				78	2	3
13	6	9	4	0	7	79	0	3
14	1	1	41	0	1			
16	0	0	42	0	2	8	0	1
17	1	1	43	1	9	81	0	3
18	1	4	46	0	0	82	0	2
19	0	2	47	0	1	83	0	0
			48	2	5	84	0	3
2	0	5	49	2	5	86	0	2
21	1	2				87	0	1
23	1	3	6	0	3	89	1	1
24	1	1	61	0	1			
26	1	2	62	0	4	9	2	24
27	1	2	63	0	1	91	0	0
28	0	0	64	0	6	92	0	1
29	0	2	67	0	2	93	0	2
			68	1	1	94	5	11
3	0	5	69	0	2	96	2	2
31	0	4				97	1	3
32	1	2	7	0	4	98	1	2
34	0	3	71	0	3			

Table 4. Relative Frequencies of High-Point Codes of 360 Adult Female Minnesota Normals

High-Point Code	70 or Over	Total	High-Point Code	70 or Over	Total	High-Point Code	70 or Over	Total
?	1	16	36	1	2	72	0	6
-ᵃ	0	93	37	0	2	73	1	2
			38	0	2	74	0	1
1	0	2	39	0	0	76	1	2
12	1	4				78	4	5
13	3	14	4	0	13	79	1	1
14	3	6	41	0	0			
16	2	0	42	0	2	8	0	3
17	1	4	43	0	4	81	2	2
18	0	0	46	1	4	82	1	2
19	0	1	47	1	2	83	0	2
			48	0	1	84	0	3
2	0	9	49	1	4	86	0	2
21	2	9				87	1	4
23	1	6	6	0	10	89	1	4
24	0	4	61	1	1			
26	0	3	62	0	3	9	1	27
27	7	12	63	0	0	91	0	3
28	0	1	64	1	2	92	1	1
29	0	1	67	0	2	93	0	2
			68	2	4	94	2	8
3	0	5	69	1	4	96	1	2
31	3	11				97	1	1
32	0	2	7	0	4	98	0	3
34	0	3	71	0	2			

ᵃ Includes cases with no high point above 54 and those with tied high points.

happens in a third of the cases as counted by reading the charts, it might happen to two thirds of them in actuality.

Classifying codes by the first two digits and neglecting their order (i.e., lumping 13 and 31 curves together) leads to twenty-eight theoretically possible code types (excluding noncoded and single-digit cases and neglecting Mf throughout). Many of these occur too rarely to be susceptible of meaningful statistical treatment (and are, correspondingly, less important clinically). In other cases, the results exhibit a confusing sex difference, or such slight or inconsistent trends that they cannot be profitably presented here. The following nine forms are each rather common and also manifest some apparent homogeneity and consistency in the clinical pictures presented.

Code Types 12 and 21

The patients with 12 and 21 had, in the majority of cases, pain, regardless of formal diagnosis. Some of the people were called schizophrenics or even psychopaths. Pain, depression, irritability, shyness and seclusiveness, and somatic concern were to be expected. Somatic concern was distinguished from conversion. These people had anxiety, worry, or rumination about the state of their bodies.

Two thirds of these patients received a formal diagnosis of psychoneurosis, chiefly somatic (hypochondriasis, hysteria) and some "mixed." The remaining third were split between schizophrenia and manic-depression. This code practically excluded psychopathic personality and conduct disorders generally.

Code Types 23 and 32

For the 23's and 32's we had so few males in our sample that we analyzed tallies only for females, and the only thing that showed up in the majority of them was depression. Showing up in a strong minority were weakness, apathy, and agitation or tenseness.

Diagnostically, these cases were about equally likely to be psychotic (manic-depressive depression and involutionals — almost never schizophrenics or paranoid states, never manics) or psychoneurotic (scattered over subtypes, although conversion hysteria was very rare here). As in the preceding group, psychopathy was contraindicated by this code type. This tended definitely to be a "female" curve, and the diagnostic trends just mentioned did not hold among our small male sample.

Code Types 27 and 72

In the majority 27's and 72's, that is, those with a D and Pt combination, had depression; they were described as tense or nervous; and for a third to a half, a strong minority, we found anxiety, insomnia, and undue sensitiveness.

Psychosis had a slight edge over psychoneurosis in both sexes. By far the commonest psychotic diagnosis for these cases was depression (manic-depressive or involutional). Schizophrenia occurred but was rare. The modal neurotic diagnosis in both sexes was reactive depression with obsessive-compulsive neurosis running closely behind. Mixed neurosis and hypochondriasis were unlikely and conversion hysteria was definitely contraindicated. Psychopathy was also very improbable, except if sociologically defined (i.e., some of these patients commit antisocial acts on a neurotic basis).

Code Types 28 and 82

For the majority of 28's and 82's one can expect depression, anxiety, or agitation; and in a strong minority, hysterical tendencies (usually, however, excluding pain). There was a collection of hysterical phenomena here like conversion, paralyses, blindness, etc., but rarely pain. We found the pre-illness personality described as unsociable. There was "mental loss" in the sense that the patient complained he could not concentrate, or there was psychometric evidence of deficit, or he said he was confused, or others said he was becoming inefficient in carrying on his activities. These cases are suspicious or sensitive, and hypochondriacal. Heredity, defined here rather crudely simply as psychosis in siblings or parents, tended to be unfavorable in these individuals.

A majority of these patients were psychotic diagnostically, actually more often psychotic depressions than schizophrenias, the latter forming a strong minority. Almost all the neurotics in this group fell into one of two categories — psychoneurosis mixed or, less frequently, reactive depression. Hysteria did not occur and hypochondriasis was extremely unlikely. These patients were not psychopaths.

Code Types 31 and 13

The 31 and 13 code has become known as the "conversion V" or "hysteroid valley" with D beginning below the two somatic variables. In the majority, two things appeared: pain, and some symptoms involving eating. Other kinds of conversion also occur, of course. The eating problem might appear as actual anorexia or hysterical vomiting, or the person complained of discomfort after eating, or he ate too much. Also the 13's and 31's tended to complain of pain in different places than the 12's and 21's. The former got pain in the head very commonly and in the arm, back, or legs, the eyes hurt, the neck hurt, etc.; while the 12's and 21's preferred the viscera of the trunk, especially the lower bowel and the like. When the hysterical valley cases *did* have inner pain, it occurred higher up in the body cavity, e.g., precordial pain.

A sizable minority of the 31 and 13 cases were described by the examiner as sociable and extroverted. This socially oriented hysterical personality, which of course is not found in all people with conversion, did characterize them relatively more than it did hypochondriacs, obsessives, and anxiety states. Also marked in a sizable minority of 13 and 31 cases was objection to psychiatric study. They came into the hospital for their sore back; now they were being processed for this "mind" business, and they did not like it a bit.

The overwhelming majority of these cases were neurotics, the very small proportion of psychotics and psychopaths being atypical of their class. The modal diagnosis was conversion hysteria which had given to the 31 configuration the name "hysteroid valley" or "conversion V" formed by the dip of the D score below both of the somatic variables Hs and Hy. This is a more characteristically feminine configuration and in males suggests a socially oriented, passive, dependent utilization of somatization to achieve neurotic ends.

Code Types 64 and 46

Surprisingly, no trait or symptom showed up to characterize the majority of 64's and 46's. But in a sizable minority depression, irritability, nervousness, introversion, suspiciousness, judgment defect, and alcoholism appeared.

About half of these patients were "conduct disorder" cases, behavior problems, criminals, and psychopaths of various kinds. Approximately one third were psychotic, chiefly schizophrenia (most commonly paranoid) and a few paranoid states or paranoid involutional psychoses. This curve argues against straight manic-depressive psychosis and against schizophrenia of the hebephrenic form. The minority of psychoneurotics in this group seemed to have reality-based, or psychopathic, or situational elements; obsessional and somatization features, deep inner conflicts, and anxieties were lacking.

Code Types 68 and 86

The 68's and 86's had only one characteristic appearing in the majority: paranoid delusions. In a strong minority there were four characteristics: depression, apathy, irritability, and withdrawal. As might be expected, the majority of these cases were psychotic; three fifths were found to occur with psychosis, chiefly schizophrenia, with a strong minority of paranoid states. (About half of the entire set of 68's were either schizophrenic or paranoid.) The neurotics were scattered with a slight piling up on the "dysphoric" end (i.e., neurotic depression, anxiety, adult maladjustment) rather than at the point of "satisfactory" somatic outlet. A minority showed conduct disorders although they were not of the pure Pd (asocial, amoral) variety.

Code Types 78 and 87

Among the 78's and 87's two things showed up in the majority: depression and introversion; and in a strong minority: withdrawal, apathy, nervousness, worry, and irritableness. Incidentally, the 78's and 87's were significantly younger than the other code groups, at least in our hospital sample.

These cases split about evenly between neurosis and psychosis, the former having a slight preponderance. A small minority were psychopaths. The neurotics were mainly depressions, psychasthenics, or "mixed," with very few somatizing forms. All kinds of psychotics seemed about equally likely, except for mania.

Code Types 49 and 94

The 94's and 49's shared little with any of the preceding groups. In the majority they were overactive; and in a strong minority, irritable, violent, talkative, extroverted, ambitious, and energetic.

Psychoneurosis (except for a very rare severe "anxiety state," possibly misdiagnosed) can be excluded in a curve of this sort. Three fourths of the cases were psychotics, and these were practically all manics. The exceptions were paranoid states, schizophrenia, and delirium tremens. A strong minority were psychopaths.

✦

ARTICLE 16 *Common Characteristics Associated with Frequent MMPI Profile Types*

PSYCHOLOGICAL tests which yield scores on more than one trait present problems of interpretation since there is usually no simple formula for combining the series of scores to make interpretive judgments. A "one-trait-at-a-time" technique of interpretation is inadequate, for this discrete approach fails to take into account the fact that the interpretation of one score may be modified by the score on a second scale. Thus a clinician should not attempt to evaluate 4 M, an A on aviator, or a low score on Block Design without taking into account the other scores of the test concerned as well as other data that may be available on the client. The interpretation of the results of multi-score tests has been facilitated by the use of profiles which quickly suggest the scores on which an individual is abnormally high or low. Out of experience with profiles the clinician develops the habit of looking for a certain pattern to answer specific questions or of making his discriminating or diagnostic statements on the basis of the pattern he detects. A particular pattern may be generally accepted and validated among many clinicians or it may be a more or less unformulated result of the clinician's own experience with a certain group of clients.

Profiling and the subsequent interpretation of differences between scores is deceiving when it fails to emphasize the unreliability of these differences. The reliability of the difference between scores on two scales decreases with an increase of correlation between the scales and decreases with lower reliability of the scales themselves. This source of error is particularly important with multi-score personality tests whose scales are of relatively low reliability and, with the exception of scales derived by factor analytic techniques, of high intercorrelation. These considerations of the significance of differences are applicable not only to scores on questionnaires but also to the indices derived from such unstructured tests as the Rorschach. The low reliability of differences implies that we must seek some method of identifying patterns which takes into account the fact that, while the true scores of several individuals may follow the same pattern, their obtained scores will vary within a certain range of patterns.

The MMPI yields scores on nine clinical and four validating scales. With the earliest publication [304] the authors recommended that interpretation should be based on the profile pattern rather than individual scores. There are two methods

145

of arriving at statements concerning the implication of a certain pattern. Schmidt [528 (see VI, 39)], Gough [234 (VI, 38)], Hovey [330 (VI, 40)], Guthrie [272 (VI, 41)], and others have found certain profile patterns associated with diagnostic groups. An alternative method is grouping patients according to similar profiles and studying the groups to find common features of persons having a given profile pattern. Hathaway [296 (III, 12)] has proposed grouping profiles by the two highest clinical scales. Welsh [617 (III, 13)] has introduced a modification of this classification system which is somewhat easier to handle.

Most studies concerned with patterns of psychometric results have grouped patients according to some nontest criterion and sought common patterns. Few have used the other technique of seeking the characteristics of persons who show a certain pattern of test results. Such research would seem desirable inasmuch as it constitutes a duplication of the experience of a clinician who, when confronted with a test profile, must rely on his experience to develop an assessment of the client based upon the pattern of that particular profile.

Following the latter procedure Hathaway and Meehl have published an atlas [307] of short case histories and MMPI data on 968 patients. The order of presentation is arranged so that patients are presented consecutively according to their profile type. The authors did not offer summaries of the outstanding features of patients with similar profiles because they felt that "we might have missed many points, emphasized wrong ones, and in general communicated a mixture of truth with our own possibly false summaries of a kind of experience that could hardly be adequately organized or tabulated, let alone statistically validated." While a certain validity must be conceded to their argument, they are asserting in effect that all they can communicate to users of the test is the uninterpreted results from past patients. If experience with the test gives anything it should give some suggestion of the implications of an elevation of scale A in a configuration of elevations and depressions of scales B, C, etc. To be more specific, if one reads the 12 (Hs D) cases in the *Atlas* one gathers the impression of extensive variation within the group. This great variation is reduced if one eliminates from consideration those with L scores above 60, the point at which a profile is of dubious validity. The remaining cases appear sufficiently homogeneous to warrant certain summarizing statements.

Procedure

This study is concerned with the characteristics of persons giving essentially similar MMPI profile patterns. The data were made available by a specialist in internal medicine who used this test with many of his patients. He took a history of the patient with a careful list of current complaints and recorded his impressions of the patient before administering the test. Subsequent data regarding the patient could, of course, be contaminated by the test results.

The profiles of 1104 patients were coded according to Hathaway's system and grouped according to the profile patterns 12, 13, etc. The files of patients of each profile group, where numbers permitted, were studied in an attempt to develop a summary of the most frequently appearing physical and psychological symptoms and the course of the disorders.

After the descriptions were obtained, the answer sheets of each group were subjected to an item analysis to discover those items which differed significantly from

Hathaway's original standardization group and from a random sample of the total population of this study. The purpose of this analysis was to discover those items which differentiated the group in question not only from people in general but from other patients. It was predicted that many of the items identified would be those which appeared on the two identifying scales. Even so, these and others which might appear should serve to elucidate the characteristics of the groups concerned.

Some discussion should be included at this point concerning the nature of this sample. These were private patients who chose to come to this particular physician. He selected for testing those he felt had complications in part attributable to emotional factors. The incidence of various code types in this population, particularly those with a high Hy scale, is different from that of other populations such as mental hospitals. Indeed, some of the sorts of patients encountered in this study are rarely seen in psychological clinics. Test results from diverse sources should serve to increase perspective on the various scales and consequently interpretive skill with the test.

Results

Data were available on 365 men and 739 women, a total of 1104 patients. The distribution of code types is shown in Table 1. It can be seen that every type except 8–, 81, and 83 appeared in this population although many types are so infrequent as to preclude the possibility of any study. The 1–, 2–, etc. groups are those whose profiles had only one scale above a T score of 54. In the coding of these profiles Mf, or 5, was not used since this scale has been found to have limited clinical value. There follow brief summaries of common features of frequently occurring types.

Table 1. Distribution of MMPI Profile Types of 1104 Patients (the Highest Scale Is Given on the Ordinate, the Second Highest on the Abscissa)

Scale	1–, etc.*	1 (Hs)	2 (D)	3 (Hy)	4 (Pd)	6 (Pa)	7 (Pt)	8 (Sc)	9 (Ma)	Total
1 (Hs)	1		53	60	4	4	11	3	6	142
2 (D)	14	64		140	25	19	55	7	8	332
3 (Hy)	40	112	89		45	49	10	11	25	381
4 (Pd)	1	8	17	20		16	6	10	9	87
6 (Pa)	6	5	9	16	6		3	7	3	55
7 (Pt)	1	6	12	1	1	3		3	1	28
8 (Sc)	0	0	3	0	4	3	11		2	23
9 (Ma)	7	10	3	10	11	6	5	4		56

* The first column is of those profiles having only one T score above 54. Thus a profile with only Hs above 54 would be coded 1–.

12 (Hs D) and 13 (Hs Hy) Profiles. These two groups are described together because their differences are slight. These patients presented numerous complaints with a strong emphasis on abdominal distress and backaches. There was little demonstrable physical pathology. Their distress appeared to be only moderate but their histories showed a high frequency of visits over a protracted period of time with symptomatic relief usually short-lived. Little could be learned concerning the emotional factors in the background of these patients for they concentrated upon their aches and pains and were relatively insightless concerning their personal adjustment. The impression was gained that these patients, more than any other group, had learned to live with and to use their complaints to such an extent that they were difficult patients to treat. Few showed marked changes for better or worse over periods of several years but they did show brief reductions of symptoms over short periods of a month or more.

By way of differences the 12 group reported more feelings of anxiety and tension than the 13 group. The differences between the men and women within this group are in accord with a trend that appeared in all the groups. Men with profiles similar to those of women placed less emphasis on their emotional difficulties and more emphasis on their physical symptoms. This is probably a function of our culture in which it is more acceptable for women to admit their worries and fears than it is for men. These differences between the men and women of this population become more apparent in the following 21 and 23 groups.

The results of the item analyses show that these patients obtain their elevated scores primarily from the enumeration of their symptoms. They picture themselves in terms of their symptoms and do not admit with significant frequency any items which relate to emotional problems.

21 (D Hs) and 23 (D Hy) Profiles. The male patients of this group showed one or the other of two symptom pictures. They complained of marked epigastric distress or they complained of tension and depression. Nothing was found in their profiles to differentiate these two groups. In contrast to the preceding group there was a more marked concentration of symptoms in the upper gastrointestinal tract with few who presented multiple aches and pains. These patients resembled the ulcer syndrome described by Alexander [r4]; they were competitive and industrious but immature and dependent. Though they dreaded increased responsibilities they sought promotions in their jobs. In spite of their difficulties they had maintained their normal level of efficiency. Very few of these patients had demonstrable physical pathology. When no pathology was demonstrable about one half of them did not return for further treatment. There were no data to explain whether they responded favorably to reassurance or went to other physicians who would not emphasize the emotional etiology of their disorders.

The females of this group gave a much more varied set of physical complaints than the men with a slight emphasis on epigastric distress. Their complaints centered predominantly about their feelings of tension and depression. They emphasized a loss of initiative, dysphoria, and occasional attacks of dizziness and fear. The interview materials indicated that these patients accepted a chronic level of maladjustment at which others would have been strongly motivated to seek help. Consequently, with their lack of motivation to improve, they showed a poor response to treatment.

The item analysis produced items which told of a loss of self-confidence, lack of efficiency, and brooding. The remaining items suggest a subtle rigidity of outlook and sensitiveness, an inability to feel comfortable with other people. The 21's showed items which told of poor health and of aches and pains. No items of this sort appeared in the 23 results.

27 (D Pt) Profiles. This was the most homogeneous group found in this study. These patients did not stress their physical complaints. One half of them were seriously depressed. With the rest there were strong symptoms of depression warranting such diagnostic terms as effort syndrome, fatigue, and exhaustion. Psychasthenic trends of rigidity and excessive worry were frequent among the men. The item analysis further clarified the picture of this group, yielding items which described them as unhappy with themselves and uncomfortable with others. They complained of a marked loss of efficiency and initiative, brooding, and loss of self-confidence. Although they are visiting a physician they do not present physical complaints. Contrary to expectation, these depressed patients did not respond well to treatment. Nor was there evidence of "spontaneous recoveries" as is so frequent with mild depressive disorders. For the most part their condition remained stable over protracted periods of time.

31 (Hy Hs) Profiles. As might be expected from the discussion of the significance of slight differences between highly correlated scales, there are few outstanding differences between the patients having 31 patterns and those having 13 patterns. The complaints of these patients were of the sort that arise secondary to protracted periods of mild tension. They include headaches, backaches, pains in the chest, and abdominal distress. Conversion hysteria was exceedingly rare in the entire population on which this study was based so that it is not surprising that there was only one instance of it in this group. Few of these patients were incapacitated by their symptoms. They appeared on interview to have a lengthy history of insecurity and immaturity and a tendency to develop symptoms when stresses increased. In contrast to those whose highest scale was D, these patients placed little stress on the discomforts of their current emotional state and in contrast to those whose highest scale was Hs, they showed greater specificity of physical complaint and presented disorders which were of a somewhat more episodic nature. They differed significantly on items which told of aches and pains and on subtle items suggestive of a hysterical lack of self-criticism.

32 (Hy D) Profiles. This group proved difficult to study because fewer than half of them returned for further treatment following the administration of the test. There was no way to discover whether reassurance had alleviated their wide variety of mild complaints or whether they changed physicians to avoid discussing their personal adjustment. Those who continued contacts showed a history of changing symptoms of neither increasing nor decreasing severity. Although the D scale was elevated there was little evidence of depressive trends.

The item analysis produced a small number of items telling of concern for their health. The remaining items were of the Hy-subtle variety which give a picture of an individual who verbalizes strict conformity to approved behavior patterns. They deny unacceptable impulses and ideas and any feeling of social inadequacy. These data together with those obtained from interviews suggest an insightless, nonintrospective person who is very resistant to psychotherapy.

34 (Hy Pd) and 36 (Hy Pa) Patterns. There is a marked predominance of women showing these profile patterns, outnumbering the men more than four to one. Their presenting physical complaints were numerous. None were of acute onset or incapacitating. On interview they concentrated on their symptoms and minimized emotional factors. A check of the items on the test revealed that much of their elevated profile came from the so-called zero items. These are items which deny shortcomings present in everyone. They are not so naive as the L scale items but rather, on face validity considerations, suggest a superficial outlook on life with an inability to recognize the shortcomings of either themselves or their friends. It is the cumulation of these items that reveals the patient's overly perfect attitudes toward himself and others. With such a personality picture, little was achieved in treatment.

It should be pointed out that none of these patients showed either frank asocial psychopathic or paranoid features. However, the interpersonal relations of this group were tenuous and many expressed a well-rationalized hostility toward members of their immediate family.

Validation of These Results

It is important in such a study as this to question the validity of the results. Another internist made available the profiles and histories of sixty-six of his patients. These histories were studied and four predictions were made of the profile type. An estimate of the best one could do by chance was made using the four code types with the highest frequency in the first group studied. These were 23, 21, 12, 13 for the men and 23, 31, 32, and 36 for the women. A profile was considered correctly identified if one of the four estimates was correct. The results showed forty estimates correct which is an improvement over chance of twenty-seven correct, significant at the .01 level. This is an optimal estimate, for it is a test of what the author has learned about MMPI profiles rather than what he has succeeded in communicating.

Summary

1. The MMPI profiles of 1104 patients visiting a specialist in internal medicine were coded according to Hathaway's system and grouped according to the two highest scales.

2. The histories of each group were studied to discover common characteristics. Results are presented for those having profile patterns of 12, 13, 21, 23, 27, 31, 32, 34, and 36.

3. A validation study with a different population gave results supporting the validity of these descriptions.

4. These results were obtained on the population described. They are probably not completely applicable to populations which are markedly different.

ARTICLE 17 *Adjectives Associated with Various MMPI Codes*

THE MMPI scales were derived from the study of psychopathological groups and it remains an empirical question whether these scales can be meaningfully applied throughout the range of personality adjustment. This study was designed to provide evidence on this question.

A check list of adjectives was modified from one developed by Hathaway and Meehl [308] by deleting 36 items and including 15 words from Cattell [r32]. The check list and instructions are shown in Table 1. Table 2 shows the comparison with the original set of adjectives devised by Hathaway and Meehl.

The MMPI, the adjective check list, a personal data blank, and a secret ballot (see X, 62) were administered to 206 undergraduate women at Stanford University. The girls resided in six dormitories and constituted practically 100 per cent samples of these residences. Each girl was also asked to complete the adjective check list on one other girl assigned to her at random. Occasionally exchanges had to be made when some girl denied knowing the one whose name she received. With few exceptions, these girls had been residing in the same small residence groups for eight months.

The mean number of adjectives checked by the girls when describing themselves was 47.6 out of a total of 140. The standard deviation was slightly more than 15 adjectives. When the group was split into two groups of 100 and 106 subjects each, on the basis of residence, the correlation between the number of checks each adjective received was .98.

The MMPI scores for each girl were coded by the extended system [617 (III, 13)] and groups were formed on the basis of these codes. An analysis of the adjective check list for girls in these various MMPI code groups was made to establish, first of all, whether, when "normal" people are grouped solely according to their MMPI profiles, they seem to be characterized or to characterize themselves in any consistent fashion on a check list of adjectives. If they do, then it would seem that the scales are measuring factors which have meaning in the population being studied. Secondly, of course, it was felt that a list of adjectives which are known to characterize people scoring high on certain scales would be of value to the psychologist who would like to use the test in schools, colleges, or industrial settings.

Table 1. Adjective List

Please check the words in this list that you feel characterize the person named above. Do not debate too long over any particular word; you may check as few or as many words as seem appropriate.

honest	generous	eccentric	gloomy
dishonest	tight-fisted	flattering	laughterful
self-denying	easygoing	self-centered	frivolous
selfish	mature	lively	serious
loyal	infantile	˙ggressive	high-strung
fickle	clear-thinking	inflexible	relaxed
fair-minded	incoherent	adaptable	impulsive
partial	independent	hostile	deliberate
reliable	dependent	friendly	emotional
undependable	wise	jealous	unemotional
persevering	foolish	ruthless	irritable
quitting	polished	kind	good-tempered
orderly	rough	shrewd	unself-controlled
disorderly	interests wide	naive	self-controlled
conscientious	interests nar-	clever	contented
practical	row	conceited	grateful
unrealistic	self-effacing	self-dissatisfied	thankless
worrying	shows off	self-confident	softhearted
decisive	argumentative	self-distrusting	hardhearted
indecisive	talkative	energetic	cynical
enterprising	quiet	apathetic	idealistic
shiftless	boastful	enthusiastic	popular
many physical	modest	versatile	unpopular
complaints	arrogant	submissive	suspicious
neurotic	humble	sensitive	trustful
depressed	pugnacious	poised	impatient
cheerful	peaceable	awkward	curious
moody	thoughtful (a	sophisticated	inarticulate
balanced	thinker)	shy	likes drinking
absent-minded	reasonable	adventurous	religious
alert	affected	timid	worldly
seclusive	natural	aloof	rebellious
sociable (mixes	logical	affectionate	conventional
well)	aesthetic interests	sentimental	individualistic
frank	courageous	hardheaded	dreamy
secretive	cowardly	cooperative	easily bored

On the pages that follow, fifteen different MMPI profile codes will be discussed. Due to the small N's which result from coding the profiles of only 206 subjects, it was necessary, for the most part, to group the adjective check lists primarily in terms of the single MMPI high point, although there are a few combinations of first and second high points with sufficiently large N's to warrant analysis. In a few cases, low-point codes were studied, principally when they occurred with high frequency or when the behavior of an MMPI scale at the low end was of special interest. In all cases the adjective lists by and about each code group were compared with the lists from the total population minus that subgroup.

The resulting lists of significant adjectives for each code group studied include all adjectives significant at or beyond the 10 per cent level of probability. (In each table of adjectives, the following symbols are used: $p < .001$: †; $p < .01$: °°°; $p < .02$: °°; $p < .05$: °.) It was felt that, with the small N's involved, a too rigorous

Table 2. Comparison of the Present Adjective List with the List Devised by Hathaway and Meehl

Number of items common to both lists.. 125

Items eliminated from the Hathaway-Meehl list.....................................   36

conscienceless	acquisitive	assertive	sensuous
placid	languid	tough	ascetic
facing life	temperate	simple-hearted	uninquiring
evasive	dissatisfied	sociable (forward)	verbal
emotionally intem-	intuitive	responsive	habit-bound
perate	physical strength	frigid	labile
exhibitionistic	and endurance	home and family	reverent
taciturn	amorous	interests	political (national
mulish	pious	obstructive	interest)
defensive	settling down	mirthless	wandering

Items appearing only in the present list.......................................   15

moody	self-centered	clever
shows off	dreamy	popular
quiet	easily bored	unpopular
thoughtful	lively	impatient
flattering	aggressive	religious

Total number of items in the present list....................................... 140

level of significance would undoubtedly obscure a large number of real differences. While there is one chance in ten that some of the unstarred adjectives on the lists appear through the action of sampling errors alone, it is suggested that where they are compatible with the adjectives achieving higher levels of significance or with clinical expectation, they should be tentatively accepted as belonging to the list; where there is no supporting evidence for them, they should probably be attributed to chance factors.

The High 2's (N = 16)

According to the MMPI *Manual* [305], "a high D score indicates poor morale of the emotional type with a feeling of uselessness and inability to assume a normal optimism with regard to the future." Hathaway found high 2 persons characterized as "worrying, frank, generous, modest, sensitive, sentimental, verbal, emotional, and aesthetic." Gough's early list of adjectives [598], derived from clinical experience and theoretical expectation, emphasizes "depression, dejection, discouragement, subjective distress." Scale 2 probably poses fewer difficulties in interpretation than any other MMPI scale and it has received little attention in the literature on nonclinical populations. An interesting, though inconclusive, study by Patten [472] showed that nine college students judged to be "deficient" in written expression had a mean 2 score 13 points higher than seven students judged to be "excessive." Patten concludes that "a mild to severe depression pattern accompanies paucity in written expression while a mild manic tendency accompanies prolixity." In another part of the present study (see X, 62), it was noted that the "most sensitive" group had a 2 score 10 points above the mean, while the most likable girls and the best conversationalists had significantly lower 2 scores.

On the adjective check list (see Table 3), the high 2 persons describe themselves by a combination of generally unhappy, unpleasant, and critical adjectives while they characteristically avoid adjectives which might apply to happy, hopeful, and

Table 3. High 2 Profile Code [a]

Others' Descriptions		Self-Descriptions	
More Frequently Checked	Less Frequently Checked	More Frequently Checked	Less Frequently Checked
Shy°°°	Energetic°°°	Indecisive†	Lively†
	Sociable°°°	Affected†	Decisive°°°
	Kind°°	Aloof†	Cheerful°°°
	Peaceable°°	Self-dissatisfied°°°	Independent°°°
	Self-denying°	Moody°°°	Self-confident°°°
	Laughterful°	Quiet°°°	Poised°°°
	Relaxed°	Neurotic°°	Laughterful°°°
	Curious°	Self-distrusting°°	Contented°°°
	Self-confident	Shy°°	Practical°°
	Cooperative	Worrying°	Aggressive°°
	Cheerful	Secretive°	Friendly°°
	Independent	Unself-controlled°	Talkative°
	Courageous	Selfish	Courageous°
	Flattering	Unrealistic	Energetic°
	Frank	Depressed	Relaxed°
		Infantile	Popular°
		Dependent	Curious°
		Emotional	Worldly°
		Easily bored	Enterprising
			Alert
			Sociable
			Natural
			Logical
			Adaptable
			Adventurous
			Cooperative
			Interests wide

[a] The symbols used in this and the following tables are the following: p < .001: †; p < .01: °°°; p < .02: °°; p < .05: °.

optimistic people. However, the Stanford girls with high 2's are described by their acquaintances with the single word "shy" at a statistically significant level. They tend less commonly to be described by acquaintances with the more positive, pleasant adjectives suggesting self-confidence, cheerfulness, and effective functioning. It seems possible that the failure to obtain a long list of words commonly checked might be a result of some reluctance on the part of college women to check unfavorable adjectives on their acquaintances, except that this tendency does not hold true with all the code groups. Perhaps a more logical explanation is that these girls with a peak on 2 are less well known by their associates than most of the others, are perhaps less offensive in a group because their poor morale tends to elicit sympathy and tolerance rather than hostility. In any event, the adjectives suggest that the group is frankly and thoroughly self-dissatisfied and self-critical and that apparently they are not conspicuous and are relatively inoffensive to their associates, being noteworthy more for their failure to display characteristics than for any, except shyness, that they do display.

The self-checks of the women with this code are particularly noteworthy when we realize that virtually none of the group had scores above T = 70. Even when the evaluation is relatively modest, then, a peak on 2 apparently reveals a significant degree of self-dissatisfaction and self-criticism. It is perhaps this fact that makes the presence of a high 2 score a favorable sign for therapy [291, 276], i.e., the client is powerfully motivated to change himself. The large number of significant self-checks and the small number of checks by others are also consistent with the view that 2 is a "mood scale," that at the time of testing these people were somewhat depressed but are not necessarily consistently so. However, they are apparently rarely cheerful, laughterful, sociable, or relaxed.

The High 3's (N = 25)

Scale 3 was based on patients who developed conversion-type hysteria symptoms and the *Manual* suggests that persons scoring high on this scale are *likely* "to become overtly hysterical and solve problems . . . by the development of symptoms." Hathaway [308] points out that the scale includes "a set of items which seem to express an overcompensatory rejection of the possibility that the subject is capable of being neurotic." In his study, high 3 persons were described as "frank, talkative, enthusiastic, sociable, adventurous, affectionate and worrying." Gough's list emphasizes the need for social approval, amenability to group ideas, courtesy, naiveté, immaturity, and lack of insight. Cottle [146] offers a somewhat different interpretation: "A score above average on the Hy scale seems to indicate a lack of self-confidence for normals. It represents a tendency to overreact, to overanticipate a situation, to overplan for it. This individual makes more plans than are needed. Such a person will sound off fairly readily and calm down quickly afterwards." Brower [84] found a correlation of —.65 between the 3 score and Wechsler-Bellevue scores among college undergraduates, and Daly [162] has reported that women scoring high on 3 liked artistic activities but disliked clerical work. Art majors have been reported to have higher scores on L and 3 [488]. Unsuccessful practice teachers had significantly higher 3 scores than successful ones in a study by Michaelis and Tyler [443]. In another part of the present study (see X, 62), it was noted that the most likable Stanford girls had significantly lower 3 scores than the total group.

The list of significant adjectives in the present study for the high 3's (see Table 4) is short but confirms some of the expectations for this scale. A lack of insight is implicit in the absence of any overlap between the self and peer descriptions. A need to see themselves in a favorable light is suggested by the fact that all the words with which they describe themselves are culturally approved while all the

Table 4. High 3 Profile Code

Others' Descriptions		Self-Descriptions	
More Frequently Checked	Less Frequently Checked	More Frequently Checked	Less Frequently Checked
Many physical complaints°°°	Partial°°	Trustful°°°	Emotional°°°
Flattering°	Energetic	Friendly°°	Unrealistic°
Irritable	Undependable	Alert°	Boastful°
Religious	Interests narrow	Loyal	Shy°
	Clever	Practical	Suspicious°
	Sophisticated		Jealous
	Dreamy		Conceited
			Hardheaded
			Irritable

ones they reject as characterizing themselves are generally considered unfavorable. Certainly there is nothing in the list to support Cottle's idea of a conscious lack of self-confidence or of a tendency to overplan. It seems probable that Cottle based this latter notion largely on a study of pilot error, but others [138, 570] have found no positive relationship between the 3 score and errors attributable to overanticipation. Cook and Wherry [138] found a negative Hy loading on such a factor among submarine personnel.

To their peers, the high 3's at Stanford seem to have many physical complaints, to be irritable, flattering, lacking in sophistication, energy, and dependability. The presence of physical complaints certainly substantiates one basic aspect of scale 3; it should be noted, however, that they do not perceive themselves as having physical complaints. Daly's finding with respect to their interests may be interpretable in terms of a sort of dilettantism among these girls, i.e., clerical work is hard, unglamorous, lacking in prestige, while artistic interests may be quite the opposite; the latter are therefore more acceptable to people who lack energy, are undependable, have physical complaints, and desire social approval.

The High 13's and 31's (N = 9)

The small number of 1's made it impossible to analyze this scale separately, but by taking only the 13's and adding the 31's we obtain a small but apparently quite homogeneous group, for a large number of adjectives prove significant, especially among the ratings by others. Furthermore, scales 1 and 3 are closely related, since the latter also contain a substantial number of physical complaint items. Together with 2, they are frequently referred to as the "neurotic triad" of the MMPI.

The present rater list (see Table 5) proves to contain most of those adjectives

Table 5. High 31 and 13 Profile Codes

Others' Descriptions		Self-Descriptions	
More Frequently Checked	Less Frequently Checked	More Frequently Checked	Less Frequently Checked
Eccentric†	Energetic°	Partial°°°	Orderly°
Apathetic†	Enterprising	Affectionate°	Serious°
Many physical complaints°°°	Adaptable	Thoughtful	Conventional°
Indecisive°°°	Conscientious		Aggressive
Dependent°°°	Versatile		Contented
Neurotic°°			
Secretive°°			
High-strung°°			
Selfish°			
Seclusive°			
Idealistic°			
Flattering			
Self-centered			
Hostile			
Self-distrusting			
Serious			
Emotional			
Irritable			
Unself-controlled			

which describe the 3's alone, but they are overpowered, in a sense, by other factors which must be contributed by the 1 component. The result is a much less attractive group than the 3 alone, although the latter portrait was not a particularly favorable one. Some of the adjectives would not ordinarily fit the hysteroid, e.g., "apathetic," "seclusive," "eccentric," "hostile." However, these adjectives are not inappropriate clinically for many hypochondriacs. Gough's list of interpretive words [598] includes, for 1, "pessimistic, dour, and dispirited." These are compatible with many of the present list which emphasizes physical complaints, lack of drive or energy, egocentricity, and a generally neurotic picture. These findings substantiate the Hathaway-Meehl observation that 1 is closely related to the older diagnostic category of neurasthenia and the findings that high 1 scores tend to indicate a neurotic rather than psychotic process in psychiatric patients.

It is important to realize that only one of the 1 scores in this group reached $T = 70$ while the mean value was 63.5, and that, in all probability, virtually none of the girls would warrant a diagnosis of hypochondriasis. In spite of not being fully developed hypochondriacs, however, they show a very clear-cut personality pattern, a finding which should remind psychologists that scale 1 must not be validated or interpreted merely in terms of the presence of a large number of complaints about health.

A word should be said about 31 and 13 profiles as the "conversion V," i.e., scale 2, is lower than the other two of the neurotic triad. This has been described as the typical psychosomatic profile. In the present group of college women, there are probably factors which interfere with the development of effective conversions and successful psychosomatic conditions, a fact which may partially account for the grossly neurotic personality picture they present to their acquaintances. Studying the patients of a general physician, Guthrie [274 (see III, 16)] found the 31's were rarely incapacitated by their physical symptoms, placed little stress on the discomforts of their current emotional state, and had a history of insecurity and immaturity. Hawkes [313] found that a group of students with scales 1, 2, and 3 above $T = 70$ had significantly lower ratings on "fitness of vocational objective" and showed less social participation. The results of the adjective study with this group suggest a degree of personal maladjustment which is compatible with the findings of these investigators.

Finally, the differences in the adjective lists for the 3's alone compared with this group of 13's and 31's suggest that, contrary to opinions expressed by some observers, the two scales are not measuring the same factor. A similar conclusion was reached by Tyler and Michaelis [443], who obtained intercorrelations on scales 1, 2, and 3 of .50, .32, and .16 in a nonclinical group. Among the Stanford women, the presence of both 3 and 1 is associated with a different personality picture than obtains with 3 alone. The factors do not, however, oppose one another but seem rather to complement and reinforce.

The High 4's (N = 26)

According to the *Manual*, "the Pd scale measures the similarity of the subject to a group of persons whose main difficulty lies in their absence of deep emotional response, their inability to profit from experience, and their disregard of social mores. . . . Their most frequent digressions from the social mores are lying, stealing, alcohol or drug addiction and sexual immorality." In his adjective study, Hathaway found them characterized as "sociable, frank, talkative, adventurous, individualistic and fond of drinking." Gough's clinical list [598] emphasizes irresponsibility, undependability, individualism, tactlessness, egocentricity, and "deficiencies in ability to calculate their own stimulus value." Gough [240] has elsewhere offered a theory of psychopathy which is based on a lack of role-playing ability, an incapacity to judge one's behavior from the viewpoint of others, to identify with others or share their outlook.

Much of the literature on underachievers indicates a tendency for 4 (and usually 9) to be elevated, or to be the primary peak, in underachieving students [76, 455]. Williamson [653] found student political leaders had higher 4 and 6 scores than any other student activity leaders, and Norman [465] found 4 higher in sociology and psychology majors than in students of other subjects. He interpreted this in terms of their concern for social ills and their interest in social change.

Table 6. High 4 Profile Code

Others' Descriptions		Self-Descriptions	
More Frequently Checked	Less Frequently Checked	More Frequently Checked	Less Frequently Checked
Incoherent†	Practical°	Dishonest°°	Adaptable†
Moody°°°	Self-controlled°	Lively°	Friendly†
Partial°	Conventional°	Clever°	Practical°°°
Sociable°	Cheerful	Cynical°	Peaceable°°°
Frivolous°	Hardheaded	Worldly°	Kind°°°
Arrogant		Apathetic	Natural°
		Dreamy	Easily bored°
			Honest
			Serious
			Affectionate
			Self-controlled

While few adjectives in the present study are identical with those found by Hathaway or the ones suggested by Gough, there is a general similarity in the way the high 4 girls are perceived by their associates (see Table 6). It is interesting, however, that they are seen in a less favorable light than we might expect since, as Hathaway points out, "although sometimes dangerous to themselves or others, these persons are commonly likeable and intelligent." It may be that the favorable impression which these people often make on superficial acquaintanceship is not maintained among persons who know them well or with whom they must live, as in a college residence hall. It is also surprising that their self-characterizations are not more generally favorable. Indeed, they are the only group in the present study who saw themselves as dishonest. Perhaps their ability to check some rather unfavorable adjectives reflects a certain lack of concern with or real understanding of the opinions of others. This hypothesis is substantiated by the failure to check any adjectives which indicate self-dissatisfaction or concern. The contrast between the type of unfavorable adjective chosen by the high 2's and the ones checked by this group is very striking.

There may be some support for Gough's idea of role-playing deficiency, for the peer descriptions give the impression that these high 4's are not well understood, and there is a certain lack of coherence in their self-characterizations. In working with some college students who have high 4 scores, the author has been impressed frequently with their concern that they didn't know how they were "supposed to act" in certain situations and that they frequently felt they were being dishonest, or "phony." Neither of these observations, however, seems to be accompanied by any feelings of guilt or concern for other people; the students seem rather to be complaining about the effort or trouble involved in knowing how one should act and then doing it.

It is probably not without significance that adjectives which convey strong affect are not checked by the high 4's, since clinically they are characterized by the superficial nature of their feelings. The lists, however, do not include some adjectives which ordinarily are associated with the amoral-asocial psychopaths, e.g., undependable, impulsive, rebellious. It is possible that the rigorous selective policies applied to college women, especially in terms of consistent and effective academic achievement, tend to eliminate the seriously inadequate psychopaths. If this is true, it is certainly important for counselors to keep in mind that college women with peaks on 4 will not ordinarily show the defiant and undisciplined behavior ordinarily predicted from such peaks.

The High 34's and 43's (N = 11)

This code combination yields a very short list of adjectives which does not clearly reveal the interaction of the two scales involved (see Table 7). While the code is not especially common, college women who do have this code are not judged to be different from the college population in general, except for being

Table 7. High 34 and 43 Profile Code

Others' Descriptions		Self-Descriptions	
More Frequently Checked	Less Frequently Checked	More Frequently Checked	Less Frequently Checked
Impatient°	Conventional	Incoherent°°	Sensitive°°°
	Dependent	Talkative°	Affectionate°°
	Peaceable	Energetic°	Aesthetic interests
	Relaxed	Reasonable	Shy
		Frivolous	Irritable
			Dreamy

impatient, and less dependent, peaceable, relaxed, and conventional. The adjectives listed under others' descriptions seem to show more of the 4 than of the 3. In contrast, the self-chosen adjectives show both components: there is the lack of emotional sensitivity of the 4 and some reflection of the hysteroid's need to see herself in a favorable light. If we consider certain words which were checked by every one of the 11 in the group or none of them (but which were not statistically significant), this fact appears more clearly: all of them saw themselves as having wide interests and being loyal and conscientious; none of them said they were conceited, self-distrusting, suspicious, or rebellious. Guthrie [274 (see III, 16)] has emphasized the 34's "superficial outlook on life with an inability to recognize the shortcomings of either themselves or their friends." The present study in no sense contradicts this observation.

One may speculate that the high 4's inability to form warm personal attachments, her shallowness of affect, and some of her unconventionality and impulsiveness remain in the 34's and 43's, but that the 3 factor ameliorates these to a degree.

The High 5's (N = 15)

Scale 5 "measures the tendency toward masculinity or femininity of interest pattern," according to the *Manual*. "A high score indicates a deviation of the basic interest pattern in the direction of the opposite sex." Items for the scale were chosen by contrasting the responses of males and females and the responses of masculine with feminine males. Thus the scale was principally directed toward detecting femininity in males, particularly the possibility of overt or repressed homosexuality. The clinical significance of the scale on women has not been adequately investigated, although Hathaway says "with females the Mf scale seems useful as a measure of dominance-submission."

In his adjective study, Hathaway found that low 5 males and high 5 females were called "easy-going, adventurous, relaxed, and having physical strength and endurance." In the present study, the lack of femininity which is a theoretical expectation in this group is implicit but subtle (see Table 8). These girls described themselves as rough, deliberate, and unemotional — characteristics which might be more frequently attributed to the male. This tendency is supported by their rejection of adjectives which might be considered highly typical of the feminine sex, e.g., polished, peaceable, aesthetic interests, kind, affectionate, sentimental, emotional, idealistic. The characterizations by acquaintances do not point to any gross masculinity but again may suggest a certain lack of interest in being feminine. The girls are not seen as polished, sensitive, poised, or worldly, and they

Table 8. High 5 Profile Code

Others' Descriptions		Self-Descriptions	
More Frequently Checked	Less Frequently Checked	More Frequently Checked	Less Frequently Checked
Unrealistic°	Dreamy°	Shiftless°°°	Interests wide°°°
Natural°	Polished	Incoherent°	Popular°°°
Rebellious°	Sensitive	Unemotional°	Lively°°
Indecisive	Poised	Rough	Kind°°
	Worldly	Deliberate	Good-tempered°°
			Alert°
			Polished°
			Talkative°
			Peaceable°
			Aesthetic interests°
			Affectionate°
			Sentimental°
			Emotional°
			Idealistic°
			Clever
			Serious

are seen as natural and rebellious. A certain tomboyishness may thus be present in these girls but the adjectives do not seem to support the characterization of high Mf women by Gough as "driving, vigorous, and determined." Indeed, the presence of adjectives like indecisive, shiftless, and incoherent seems to suggest just the opposite. It may be that in a culture of middle- and upper-class college women, the girl who lacks typically feminine interests is seen by her friends as unrealistic and may be frequently conflicted (indecisive, perhaps relatively inarticulate), and incoherent. In any event, the presence of so many significant differences between this group and its peers would suggest that the 5 elevation in women cannot be interpreted simply as an interest in the objects or materials which commonly are attractive to males without recognizing that deeper personality differences are also present. It is certainly correct to say that the interests of the high 5's do differ from those of women in general. Daly [162], for example, found women with high 5 scores tended to score high on the mechanical, computational, and scientific scales of the Kuder, and to dislike reading and literary pursuits. Nevertheless, there appear to be broader psychological or personality differences between the high 5 girls and their peers. There is no evidence, however, that the scale points to "abnormal sexual interest," as described by Fry [209].

The Low 5's (N = 68)

This is the largest code group in the entire population of this study. Furthermore, as a negative (low) code on a scale intended principally to measure femininity-masculinity of interest, it might not be expected to yield a very distinguishing list of adjectives.

The literature contains little research on the low Mf in females, though Hathaway and Meehl comment: "It is a clinical impression that low Mf scores in females represent an almost masochistic passivity." They found high 5 males and low 5 females were described as sensitive and idealistic. In his factor analysis, Tyler [598] obtained one factor with a positive loading on 1 and a negative loading on 5 which he interpreted as indicating "the association of conventional femininity with a distinct tendency toward physical complaints." The peer descriptions in this investigation do not yield a very clear-cut portrait of the low 5's, and they certainly do not substantiate the suggestions in the literature (see Table 9). The *in*frequency of checks for "energetic" is highly significant, but this is not a very powerful indication of passivity. Moreover, the other adjectives suggest a generally effective person — decisive, worldly, versatile, not undependable or disorderly or shy. The self-checks, on the other hand, do rather strongly indicate a self-dissatisfied, self-distrusting person who apparently does not perceive that her defenses effectively conceal many of the shortcomings she seems to feel she possesses. The number of direct contradictions between the self check list and the peer check lists is rather surprising, especially in view of the fact that the self-perceptions are the ones which tend to be unfavorable.

In any event, the following conclusions seem justified: (1) The low 5's are not simply the opposite of the high 5's; (2) though they are self-critical, there is no convincing evidence of a masochistic passivity in this population; the low 5's are apparently much more effective personalities than they realize. It appears that further understanding of the scale may await a more detailed study, perhaps taking into consideration the high points of these low Mf profiles, or analyzing them in terms of their relative deviancy.

The High 6's (N = 24)

Scale 6 was based, according to the *Manual*, on "a group of clinic patients characterized by suspiciousness, oversensitivity, and delusions of persecution, with or without expansive egotism." In his adjective study, Hathaway found persons with high 6 scores characterized as "worrying, sensitive, emotional, soft-hearted, and kind." Clinically, people with high 6 scores have often seemed to be rather critical of others and easily hurt by criticism of themselves; aggressive, moody, and skeptical [598].

The list of significant adjectives in the present study provides no straightforward confirmation of these clinical impressions and previous findings (see Table 10). The

Table 9. Low 5 Profile Code

Others' Descriptions		Self-Descriptions	
More Frequently Checked	Less Frequently Checked	More Frequently Checked	Less Frequently Checked
Worldly°	Energetic†	Self-distrusting†	Balanced°°°
Decisive	Rough°°	Self-dissatisfied°°°	Practical°°
Versatile	Undependable°	Sensitive°°°	Independent°°
Popular	Disorderly°	Neurotic°°	Relaxed°°
	Shy°	Moody°°	Decisive°
	Unrealistic	Unrealistic°	Modest°
		Polished°	Good-tempered°
		Talkative°	Loyal
		Aesthetic interests°	Contented
		Shy°	
		Sentimental°	
		Indecisive	
		Naive	

list is as interesting as it is difficult to interpret. Others see high 6's as either more mature or more infantile than the average college woman, for example; and they describe themselves as both sociable and arrogant, shy and timid. It would appear that either the scale is selecting two distinct groups of people or the high 6's are principally characterized by conflicting, contrasting, and inconsistent behavior. There is a subset of adjectives in this list which may reflect one aspect of the paranoid personality which sometimes impresses one clinically: affected, shrewd, clever, hardhearted, arrogant, ruthless, unemotional.

To investigate this group further, the adjective check lists supplied by peers were distributed into four groups according to whether the high 6's were called "mature," "infantile," both, or neither. Table 11 contains these data and provides emphasis for the importance of considering secondary peaks in the profiles. For example, the 67's have an almost 100 per cent chance of being called mature or neither mature nor infantile. If a high 6 girl was called infantile, there are nearly four chances in five that her secondary peak was on 1, 8, or 9. In general, then, the association of 7 or 3 with a 6 peak contributes to an impression of maturity; the associa-

Table 10. High 6 Profile Code

Others' Descriptions		Self-Descriptions	
More Frequently Checked	Less Frequently Checked	More Frequently Checked	Less Frequently Checked
Shrewd°°°	Grateful°	Arrogant†	Easily bored°
Hardhearted°°°	Rebellious	Shy†	Practical
Infantile°°		Affected°°°	
or		Naive°°°	
Mature°		Sociable°°	
Affected°		Conventional°	
Clever°		Persevering°	
Submissive		Ruthless°	
Poised		Timid°	
High-strung		Fickle	
		Unrealistic	
		Boastful	
		Submissive	
		Unemotional	
		Contented	

tion of 1, 8, or 9 is more likely to call forth the adjective infantile. In only two cases were both adjectives checked for the same girl.

It may be well to refer to some of the data involving 6 presented in another part of this study (see X, 62). In this group of high 6's fall one third of the best leaders one fourth of the most aggressive girls, and one fourth of the most sociable girls On the other hand, the mean 6 score of the most shy, the most naive, and the most easily hurt girls was 59; the mean 6 score of the most aggressive girls was 50. It has been noted also that the incidence of primary elevations on 6 rises through adolescence and then tapers off in the adult population.

To synthesize all these data is virtually impossible. A more detailed study of the scale with a larger population seems indicated. Perhaps to a greater extent than with other scales, the meaning of the 6 peak is dependent upon its absolute magnitude and upon the secondary peaks of the MMPI profile. These high 6 girls

Table 11. Distribution of High 6 Codes in Terms of Descriptions of Mature and Infantile on the Adjective Check List

Code	"Mature"	"Infantile"	Neither	Both	Total
61........	0	1.0	0	0	1.0
62........	.5[a]	.5	0	0	1.0
63........	3.0	0	1.5	0	4.5
64........	1.5	0	0	.5	2.0
65........	1.0	0	.5	0	1.5
67........	5.0	.5	0	0	5.5
68........	1.0	.5	.5	1.0	3.0
69........	1.0	1.5	2.5	.5	5.5
Total ...13.0		4.0	5.0	2.0	24.0
Pa means..63.2		62.7	64.0	59.0	62.9

[a] Those codes where the secondary peaks were equal or within one T score of each other were divided between the two codes.

are confused about themselves, yet not depressed or self-dissatisfied. Indeed, there are no 62's in the group at all. There is an emotional coldness about the group; though they may be easily hurt, one suspects that he who produces the hurt may be made somehow to suffer more. If this is true, it is quite compatible with the clinically paranoid personality. The idea that they are aggressive, in the usual sense, does not appear substantiated in this group. When the entire MMPI profile is low, then a peak on 6 may be associated with aggressiveness or leadership among college women, but otherwise they apparently give the appearance of submissiveness and see themselves as shy, timid, and submissive. On the other hand, a person who is shrewd, clever, persevering, hardhearted, and ruthless may display a more subtle form of aggressiveness — a circuitous rather than frontal attack.

Table 12. Low 6 Profile Code

Others' Descriptions		Self-Descriptions	
More Frequently Checked	Less Frequently Checked	More Frequently Checked	Less Frequently Checked
Self-distrusting†	Cheerful●●●	Secretive†	Sentimental●●●
Humble●●	Unemotional●●	Rough†	
Self-dissatisfied●●	Aggressive●	Hardhearted†	
Idealistic●●	Adaptable●	Inflexible●●●	
Inflexible●	High-strung●	Modest●●	
Awkward●	Sociable	Shrewd●	
Shy●	Laughterful	Cooperative●	
Deliberate●	Worldly	Rebellious●	
Rough		Self-effacing	
Seclusive		Arrogant	
Thoughtful		Aggressive	
Timid		Relaxed	
		Cynical	

The Low 6's (N = 14)

The low 6's were studied because they occur with considerable frequency and because of the impression held by some clinicians that under certain circumstances those with very low 6 scores seem quite as paranoid as those with very high ones. Hathaway, for example, reports that "some clinicians have felt that a Pa scale value below a T of 45 on a person who is known to be a behavior problem is almost as indicative of paranoid mentation as is a high score." In his study, he found persons with lowest 6 to be characterized as "cheerful, facing life, and self-distrusting." Morgan [455] found that his underachieving males had 6 as one of the two lowest points on their MMPI profiles more often than their achieving classmates. Gough and Pemberton [261 (see V, 36)] found that a 6 score >50 <56 was a good "sign" for differentiating good from poor practice teachers, thereby indicating that low 6 scores (as well as very high ones) were undesirable.

The women in this study whose codes end in 6 are seen by others as rather inept socially (rough, awkward, shy, seclusive, not sociable), self-dissatisfied and humble, deliberate and inflexible, not cheerful or laughterful (see Table 12). There are almost no contradictions in this picture they present to others. In their self-characterizations, however, there are some contradictions; they see themselves as modest and self-effacing, yet arrogant and aggressive; as cynical and rebellious, yet co-operative. They make no mention of self-dissatisfaction, and they call themselves secretive, shrewd, inflexible, hardhearted, unsentimental.

It will be apparent already that there is no sharp contrast between the high and low 6's. Indeed, although there is not a great deal of overlap in the word lists, the general picture presented by the two extremes of 6 girls is markedly similar. The principal difference seems to lie in the relative lack of social interest or skill among the low 6's; they are seen as rough, awkward, shy, timid, and unsociable, while their high 6 peers are seen as poised, clever, affected, in some cases mature. With this exception, however, the lists seem to convey a similar picture of coldness, rigidity, shrewdness, inflexibility.

The High 7's (N = 20)

The psychasthenia scale was developed on psychiatric patients troubled by phobias or compulsive behavior. In the *Manual*, Hathaway says, "Frequently a psychasthenic tendency may be manifested merely in a mild depression, excessive worry, lack of confidence, or inability to concentrate." In his adjective study, persons with higher scores on 7 tended to be called "worrying, peaceable, sensitive, sentimental, individualistic, and high-strung." In a college population, persons with high 7 scores seem generally self-critical, self-doubting, indecisive, and may experience difficulty in concentrating on their studies. Gough's list describes 7 as indicating persons who are apprehensive, tense, hesitant, insecure, self-conscious, anxious, and suffering feelings of inadequacy.

Cottle [146] feels scale 7 "has little meaning by itself," though it does suggest to him a "worry wart." However, Bier [60 (see X, 65)] found the 7 scale gave the best discrimination of all scales between well and poorly adjusted male college students. Elsewhere in the present study (see X, 62), it was noted that the most shy and most sensitive girls had higher mean scores on 7 while the most athletic and most aggressive had lower means.

The findings of the present study are in general agreement with most of the foregoing (see Table 13). Girls with peaks on 7 are seen by their peers as dependent, quiet, kind, and trustful and they do not impress people as being enterprising, energetic, aggressive, friendly, clever, or independent. As we might expect, they paint a darker picture of themselves: gloomy and depressed, irritable, unpopular, many physical complaints, absent-minded, etc. It is interesting that, though seen by others as trustful, they regard themselves as suspicious and not loyal. A comparison of the adjectives which describe the high 2's reveals the large common element in these two groups, especially in terms of their self-perceptions. The principal difference lies in the fact that the high 2's are clearly more depressed, and give more purely affective responses.

The High 8's (N = 11)

"The Sc scale measures the similarity of the subject's responses to those of patients who are characterized by bizarre and unusual thoughts or behavior," the *Manual* states. Adjectives commonly checked for persons with high Sc scores are "worrying, frank, kind, courageous, and with aesthetic interests," according to Hathaway's study. To Cottle [146], the high Sc students seem "to avoid reality by day-

Table 13. High 7 Profile Code

Others' Descriptions		Self-Descriptions	
More Frequently Checked	Less Frequently Checked	More Frequently Checked	Less Frequently Checked
Dependent°°	Self-centered°°	Indecisive†	Easygoing†
Kind°	Idealistic°°	Many physical	Clear-thinking°
Trustful°	Alert°	complaints†	Independent°
Quiet	Independent°	Depressed°°°	Aggressive°
	Individualistic°	Softhearted°°°	Self-confident°
	Enterprising	Dreamy°°°	Loyal
	Aggressive	Easily bored°°	Alert
	Friendly	Sentimental°	Shows off
	Clever	Gloomy°	Lively
	Energetic	Irritable°	Adaptable
	Impatient	Suspicious°	Worldly
		Absent-minded	
		Dependent	
		Emotional	
		Unpopular	

Table 14. High 8 Profile Code

Others' Descriptions		Self-Descriptions	
More Frequently Checked	Less Frequently Checked	More Frequently Checked	Less Frequently Checked
Apathetic°°°	Mature	Pugnacious†	Loyal°°°
Worldly°°°	Talkative	Eccentric°°°	Persevering
Undependable°	Self-confident	Conceited°°°	
Orderly°	Sensitive	Rebellious°°°	
Seclusive°		Boastful°°	
Wise°		Easily bored°	
Humble°		Selfish	
Aesthetic interests°		Aesthetic interests	
Adaptable°		Hostile	
Sophisticated°		Serious	
Secretive			
Clear-thinking			
Peaceable			
Courageous			
Serious			
Grateful			

dreaming and fantasy." Gough feels they are "bashful, withdrawn, oversensitive, secretive, cautious, diffident, resigned." Norman [465] found students majoring in chemistry, mathematics, and physics had low mean 8 scores and suggested that these fields "represented a unique reality" which might not appeal to those with high 8.

The present study produces a list of adjectives which is more in line with the clinical impressions and theoretical expectations (which determine Gough's [598] list) than with the descriptions which Hathaway's study elicited (see Table 14). It seems to clarify the meaning of the schizophrenic scale within the normal ranges. The schizoid tendency to withdraw is suggested by words like seclusive, secretive, apathetic. Perhaps because of this tendency, the high 8's tend to be perceived as serious, wise, clear-thinking, and sophisticated. They are humble, peaceable, grateful; have aesthetic interests; but are undependable and not mature.

Apparently, however, those with high 8 scores see themselves somewhat differently: they check pugnacious, hostile, and rebellious; selfish, conceited, and boastful; and describe themselves as eccentric and moody. It may be that what is perceived by others merely as secretive and seclusive behavior is recognized by the high 8's themselves as hostility and negativism. It is difficult to rationalize their self-styled boastfulness and conceit with others' perceptions of humility and an absence of self-confidence or talkativeness, unless perhaps they are boastful in fantasy only. Finally, the lack of overlap between the adjectives significant for the high 7's and high 8's is interesting in view of the high correlation between these scales in most studies. This finding would seem to suggest that, though the factors measured by these two scales may tend to go together, they are not identical factors, or that when one is clearly primary, the descriptions and self-perceptions of the subjects differ considerably.

The High 9's (N = 52)

The MMPI *Manual* says of the 9 scale that it "measures the personality factor characteristic of persons with marked overproductivity in thought and action." It also contains the interesting observation that "a principal difficulty in the development of the scale was the differentiation of clinically hypomanic patients from normal persons who are merely ambitious, vigorous and full of plans." Hathaway and Meehl [308] comment that a relatively high 9 score "is an asset to an individual who wishes to be extrovertive and active" and that the determining factor between the normal and the abnormal in this area is often the person's ability to finish what he starts. In their study, Meehl and Hathaway found high 9 persons described as sociable, enthusiastic, frank, likes drinking, and idealistic. Gough's clinical list includes confident, hypersensitive, not persistent, aggressive, charming, expansive, irritable, impatient.

The adjectives which are associated with 9 peaks in the present research are generally compatible with the lists cited above although the emphasis is different (see Table 15). The high 9 girls are seen by their peers as egocentric (selfish, self-centered), as exhibitionistic (boastful, shows off); as infantile and awkward; but simultaneously they are given credit for being energetic, enterprising, and even persevering. It seems possible that women may appreciate the hypomanic characteristics in their fellow coeds less than they might in males; at any rate the present list is less uniformly favorable than the Hathaway-Meehl list. The self-checks point to an optimistic, outgoing, independent, self-confident person who seems generally pleased with herself, though she is not entirely without insight into some of her shortcomings. To the extent that this population is representative, the 9 peak appears to be associated with a college woman who may be relatively effective in accomplishing things but whose adolescent immaturity often tires other people so that her popularity is not high. Clinically, it has sometimes seemed that persons with high 9 scores might do better in work which provides numerous relatively superficial contacts as opposed to fewer but closer associations.

The Low 9's (N = 18)

The hypothesis which led to a study of the low 9's was that they should display an absence of those characteristics which proved descriptive of the high 9's. Clinically, it seems that a large incidence of low 9 scores occurs among students who come for counseling and that these students are sometimes quite difficult to help. It therefore is important to learn what the low hypomania score may mean.

Table 15. High 9 Profile Code

Others' Descriptions		Self-Descriptions	
More Frequently Checked	Less Frequently Checked	More Frequently Checked	Less Frequently Checked
Shows off†	Peaceable†	Enterprising†	Reliable†
Boastful†	Honest°	Jealous†	Dependent°°°
Infantile°°°	Loyal°	Polished°°°	Indecisive°
Idealistic°°	Seclusive°	Courageous°°°	Seclusive°
Selfish°	Mature°	Aggressive°°°	Generous°
Self-centered°	Unself-controlled°	Self-confident°°°	Clear-thinking°
Energetic°	Popular°	Energetic°°°	Sensitive°
Persevering	Aesthetic interests	Popular°°°	Partial
Enterprising		Self-controlled°°	Unrealistic
Inflexible		Sophisticated°°	Quiet
Awkward		Decisive°	Shy
		Sociable (mixes well)°	Conventional
		Independent°	
		Peaceable°	
		Flattering°	
		Enthusiastic°	
		Affectionate°	
		Relaxed°	
		Good-tempered°	
		Contented°	
		Worldly°	
		Practical	
		Natural	
		Aesthetic interests	
		Adaptable	
		Versatile	
		Poised	
		Laughterful	
		Curious	
		Individualistic	

It appears from the adjective list that the hypothesis is supported (see Table 16). Low 9's are seen as seclusive, quiet, modest, humble, and conventional, as lacking various hypomanic traits, and as unpopular, good-tempered, and having narrow interests. To some extent, the adjective findings are suggestive of a lack of drive or strong motivational forces, which may account for the difficulty in helping such students by means of counseling.

The findings with respect to low 9 indicate that the hypomania scale is a continuum, a fact which is apparently not equally true of the paranoia or of the interest (Mf) scale in women.

Table 16. Low 9 Profile Code

Others' Descriptions		Self-Descriptions	
More Frequently Checked	Less Frequently Checked	More Frequently Checked	Less Frequently Checked
Quiet•••	Sociable•	Unpopular	Sociable•••
Seclusive•	Talkative•	Interests narrow•	Interests wide•••
Modest•	Lively•	Good-tempered	Lively•••
Conventional•	Aggressive		Energetic•••
Humble	Self-confident		Laughterful•••
	Adventurous		Polished••
	Affectionate		Talkative••
	Frivolous		Natural••
	Self-controlled		Adventurous••
			Enterprising•
			Aggressive•
			Versatile•
			Self-denying
			Practical
			Shows off
			Self-distrusting
			Relaxed
			Grateful
			Popular
			Suspicious

The 93's (N = 14)

Clinically, one might expect those persons scoring highest on 9 and next highest on 3 to be characterized by a marked lack of insight, considerable egotism, boastfulness, sociability, aggressiveness, and energy. Even a superficial glance at the adjective list (see Table 17) will serve to substantiate some of these predictions. Not a single adjective checked by this group as descriptive of themselves is even faintly unfavorable and the only overlap between self and peer descriptions is an agreement that the 93's are flattering and not moody. The impression they make on others is summarized by adjectives such as dishonest, shows off, boastful, and flattering.

The general interaction of these two scales might be interpreted as follows: the self-confidence, aggressiveness, and enthusiasm of the 9 are strongly present; as a result, the lack of energy and presence of many physical complaints of the 3 have disappeared. However, in place of the easygoing sociability of the 9 we get the hysteroid's need for acceptance and approval with the result that the 93 tries to appear what she is not and is quite unsuccessful in doing so. The 9, of course, is a highly social creature, but in a sense she seems willing to settle for the presence of other people while the 93 apparently requires also undivided attention and constant approval.

When the peaks on these two scales are very modest, the result should be a person who is fairly effective in interpersonal relationships; three of the most likable and three of the best leaders have 93 profile codes. As the elevations rise, however, it is apparently very difficult for the 93's to achieve their goals in interpersonal relationships; thus three of the girls who do not fit in their groups, three of the most aggressive girls, and two each of the most tense and least mature girls have 93 codes. This is especially true as the 3 rises in the absolute sense.

Table 17. High 93 Code

Others' Descriptions		Self-Descriptions	
More Frequently Checked	Less Frequently Checked	More Frequently Checked	Less Frequently Checked
Dishonest°°°	Loyal†	Flattering†	Dreamy°°
Flattering°°	Honest°	Poised°°°	Unrealistic°
Boastful°	Partial	Practical°	Moody
Self-centered°	Moody	Cheerful°	Easily bored
Sophisticated°	Interests wide	Sociable°	
Shows off	Natural	Polished°	
Arrogant	Popular	Courageous°	
Suspicious		Self-confident°	
		Energetic°	
		Adventurous°	
		Contented°	
		Popular°	
		Interests wide°	
		Loyal	
		Orderly	
		Enterprising	
		Alert	
		Generous	
		Peaceable	
		Reasonable	
		Lively	
		Aggressive	
		Adaptable	
		Affectionate	
		Laughterful	
		Good-tempered	
		Grateful	

The 98's (N = 12)

This code was studied because it occurs with significant frequency among college women and represents a problem in interpretation. The high 9, obviously, is an essentially outgoing or extratensive individual. The high 8, both theoretically and empirically, is somewhat withdrawn, seclusive, and secretive. It seems worth while to attempt an investigation of what happens when these two traits predominate together in a profile. From a glance at the adjective list for this group (see Table 18), it appears that whatever happens when these two scales are combined in a college woman's profile, it is a relatively unsatisfactory adjustment. The descriptive words chosen by peers for this group are much less favorable than those for either the 9's or 8's alone. On the other hand, the self-chosen adjectives suggest that perhaps subjectively the 98's are more at peace with themselves than the 8's as a group.

Although the 9 predominates in this code, the self-chosen adjectives show more overlap with the lists for the high 8's; the peer-checks, however, clearly emphasize the hypomanic's boastfulness and egocentricity. The suggestion is that a secondary peak on 8 alters rather drastically the behavioral significance of the primary elevation on 9. Some additional clues as to the significance of this combination may be obtained by reviewing the data on ballot nominations (see X, 62). Girls with a 98 code were mentioned twice as most independent, most shy, not fitting into the group, immature, and least interested in dating. They were mentioned once each as naive, career minded, and most athletic. They are not mentioned at all in any of the other categories. The presence of the 8, then, appeared effectively to destroy the sociability and self-confidence and optimism of the 9 but without quite bringing the seclusiveness of the 8 or the impression she gives of being wise, clear-thinking, sophisticated, courageous, and serious. The 98's, however, are free of the inner hostility which is so striking in the high 8's (pugnacious, hostile, rebellious); perhaps instead, she is gloomy, relaxed, not worrying, not sensitive. The 98 may be psychologically a little "tougher"; she is basically more independent than the high 8, and therefore limits her social participation more by choice than from fear. She is thus a little more flexible and though she may not be particularly effective in interpersonal relationships, she can tolerate a greater variety of them.

Table 18. High 98 Profile Code

Others' Descriptions		Self-Descriptions	
More Frequently Checked	Less Frequently Checked	More Frequently Checked	Less Frequently Checked
Infantile†	Courageous°°	Secretive°°°	Sensitive°°°
Boastful°°°	High-strung	Eccentric°°	Frank°
Unemotional°		Polished	Dependent°
Idealistic°°		Thoughtful	Reasonable°
Fickle		Courageous	Likes drinking°
Persevering		Gloomy	Selfish
Thoughtful		Relaxed	Worrying
Self-centered		Inarticulate	Clear-thinking
Self-dissatisfied			

Discussion

We have studied a number of different MMPI profile codes by examining the adjectives by which college women obtaining them are described or describe themselves. In many cases, the length, consistency, and agreement with theoretical expectation or clinical impression of the resulting adjective lists have been surprising in view of the small groups in some of the codes. It appears that within this "normal" population, a particular profile peak ordinarily has a significant meaning with respect to an individual's personality. It also suggests that adjectives such as made up the list in this study are employed with a stability and uniformity which may not be fully appreciated. The findings of the adjective study seem to substantiate the statement by Daniels and Hunter [163] which their own data did not justify: "In contrast to a rather common interpretation of the MMPI that a score below 70 does not indicate a significant personality deviation, it is believed that any individual deviation from the mean T score, either positive or negative, is indicative of a certain tendency toward behavior in that direction, and that extremes such as a critical T-score are not necessary for the instrument to have definite meaning and application in the industrial field."

The success with which the profile codes led to distinguishing lists of adjectives certainly casts doubt on the conclusion of Wheeler, *et al.* [634 (see IV, 28)], on the basis of their factor analysis, that "refined differential diagnosis or the formulation of dynamic personality descriptions on the basis of MMPI profiles is a questionable procedure." Even if the four factors they obtained did account for all the variance, the possible combinations of these factors would leave considerable room for personality evaluations. In passing, there appears to the author some question of the value of factor analyses of a single test when the meaning of the scales in the population used has not been adequately studied; it would represent more of a contribution to include in the matrix other data which might clarify the meanings of the factors isolated.

To provide an objective index of the extent to which the empirically derived lists of adjectives in this study corresponded with theoretical expectation, three clinical psychologists were asked to match the obtained adjectives with the profile codes. Allowance was made in the scoring for identities in the lists, so that there were only 10 necessary pairings. Of these, two of the clinicians matched five correctly ($p < .003$) and one matched three correctly ($p < .06$). Most common mispairings were designating the list for the 7's as the 2's, calling the 2's the 8's, and low 6's the high 6's, and the high 5's the 98's. Only the list for the low 9's was correctly identified by all three clinicians, and none found the correct lists for the 4's, the 34's and 43's, or the high and low 5's. The superiority of the matchings over chance suggests that many of the lists obtained accord with expectations, but that others of them apparently suggest behavioral descriptions not previously associated with the scales concerned.

One interesting aspect of the adjective lists in this study is their suggestion of a continuum of insight along which the MMPI scales might be located, and perhaps even some objective index of insight in terms of the identities between self and peer checks. The lists might easily lend themselves to other investigations in accordance with a particular theoretical concept, e.g., ego-strength, self-acceptance, which might then be related to MMPI scales and codes.

Finally, it should be emphasized that the present study was designed to produce, if possible, practical findings that might enhance the usefulness of the MMPI with college students; its failure to delve into many interesting theoretical questions, or to attempt to relate the test scores of college students to psychoanalytic or other personality theories, does not mean that such questions are not deemed important or that the MMPI could not be profitably studied in terms of such personality theories. As the test achieves wider use and greater acceptance with nonclinical populations, such theoretical studies will become more necessary and more feasible.

✦──

ARTICLE 18 *MMPI Profiles and Interview Behavior*

THIS study is an attempt to discover whether there are any particular profile patterns on the card form of the MMPI which characterize male counselees who may be difficult for inexperienced counselors to deal with as well as to obtain more descriptive information regarding profile patterns in general for a student population.

Procedure

The first step was to read case notes in the files of the Student Counseling Center and to note descriptive phrases and other data on key-sort cards. Since it was desired to obtain a representative sample of students coming to a counseling center, students were included who had taken the MMPI but who never had a counseling conference. At times the number of new counselees was so great that appointments had to be made well in advance; hence, tests were often assigned by an intake interviewer before a counseling conference. Including these profiles has an important implication in the analysis of results as will be noted later.

To eliminate any possible bias, the MMPI profiles had been pulled from the folders before the author read the cases. No interpretations of the meaning of the phrases used by the counselors in describing the behavior of the counselees were made by the author at the time of reading the notes. Profiles and other data were thus obtained for 1080 male students.

After the key-sort cards had been punched for the data included on them, the profile codes were entered on the cards. The coding system used was that reported by Hathaway and Meehl [307]. That is, all scales with T scores above 54 were coded high and arranged in order according to magnitude and underlined when they were within one point of each other. The code numbers ranged from 0 to 9 as described by Hathaway and Monachesi [312]. The scales with T scores of 45 or less were coded low, with a maximum, in this study, of two being coded low except in cases where there were ties in which case the first 3 low scales were included.

The following tabulations for each of the ten scales were then made:

1. The frequency of being coded highest or of being tied for highest.

2. The frequency of being coded in the highest 1, 2, or 3 places. This is somewhat of a departure from the practice of Hathaway. Often only 2 or 3 T scores separate the highest point from the third highest, and consequently it is the opinion of the author

173

that significant data may be lost if only the first two high points are reported. Furthermore such small differences are well within the range of the probable error of measurement.

3. The frequency of being coded lowest or being tied for lowest.

4. The frequency of being coded in the lowest 1, 2, or 3 places.

5. The frequency of appearance of each scale with every other scale in the highest 2 or 3 places. Since only pairs of scales were included in this tabulation only those profiles could be used in which at least 2 scales were coded above 54, hence the N for this distribution was reduced to 967.

These frequency distributions provide, then, a standard of comparison for subgroups selected on the basis of various criteria. Three subgroups were selected as representing counselees who might pose problems of rapport for the relatively inexperienced counselor.

These subgroups will be labeled as follows:

A. Aggressive: 50 students variously described as defiant, argumentative, cocky, snobbish, aggressive, resistant, opinionated, or belligerent.

B. Shy: 45 students described as shy, retiring, or withdrawn.

C. Nonresponsive: 52 students described as nonresponsive, nonverbal, or apathetic.

The frequencies of occurrence of the various high points, low points, and pairs of high points were determined for each subgroup in the same categories as for the total group. The numbers in the subgroups were reduced to 47, 43, and 45, respectively, when pairs of scales were tabulated. Using the percentage frequency of occurrence for the total group in each category as a standard of reference, then, it is possible to determine whether the percentage of occurrence of a scale or pair of scales was significantly more or less frequent in any of the subgroups.

The significance of differences between the total group and the subgroups was tested by Yule's formula [r175] for comparing a total group with a subgroup:

$$e^2 = \frac{p_0 q_0}{n_1 + n_2} \cdot \frac{n_2}{n_1}$$

The subscript $_0$ refers to the total group, $_1$ to the subgroup, and $_2$ to the total minus the subgroup.

Factors in Interpretation

Before discussing the results certain things about the data should be pointed out that in some cases may have reduced the differences between the subgroups and the total.

A skillful counselor is often prepared for certain behavior manifestations and when he sees signs of them he handles the counselee in such a manner that the behavior is never actually manifested. He may note a tendency to be belligerent and quickly orient his counseling to overcome the apparent belligerency. Hence, if successful, he would not label the the counselee as belligerent. The size of the subgroups is determined to some extent, then, by the skillfulness of the counselors.

Counselors often omit items in their case notes which may be important for a study of this sort. This may be due to negligence or to a notion that it is not necessary to list things that will be readily recognized in a second conference. This factor of omission will likewise diminish the size of groups positively identified according to a particular characteristic.

Another factor which limits the size of the subgroups relative to the total is that mentioned previously, namely, the inclusion of profiles for students who came to the counseling center but had no interviews.

These factors, when operating, should not detract from positive results in describing individuals who are categorized in regard to certain behavior characteristics in the counseling situation. They do, however, prevent the sort of analysis made by Hathaway and Monachesi in predicting juvenile delinquency [312, p. 126–129, Table 15].

Another factor that might be thought to influence the data in the opposite direction from the above is the fact that in most cases the MMPI profile was in the counselee's folder at the time of the interview. The author does not believe that this factor, except in the case of the Si scale, invalidates the results. The chief reason for this conclusion is that at no time, in case conferences, clinics, or seminars, did any counselor offer any interpretation of MMPI profiles at all remotely related to the findings of this study. It should be noted that the cases extend back over a period of eight years and in the earlier days, at least, few, if any, hypotheses had been formulated regarding profiles of "normal" populations such as university students. Furthermore, several of the counselors believed that the MMPI was a waste of time and only included it in a test battery for counselees because the author indicated a desire to obtain MMPI data.

One exception to the above was the Si scale [177 (see IV, 19 and 20)]. Since this scale had been derived from a student population and since hypotheses could be developed quite easily and were developed in relation to university students, the judgment of a counselor could have been easily affected by his knowledge of this score. Hence, results involving the Si scale, although reported, must be interpreted with extreme caution.

Results

In order to save space the following tables include results for those scales or profile types for which the differences between the subgroups and the total group divided by e was 2+.

Table 1 shows the frequency of occurrence of the various high and low points and pairs of high points for the aggressive group with the corresponding frequencies for the total group and the critical ratios.

In reading this table one may note that scale 4 (Pd) was coded highest and appeared among the first three high points significantly more frequently (according to the author's definition of significance) for the subgroup than for the total. The same was true for scale 9 (Ma). Furthermore the scales 4 and 9 occurred more frequently as a pair coded high for the subgroup aggressive. It is interesting to note, although this article is not the place to discuss it in detail, that these two scales, 4 and 9, were also found by Hathaway and Monachesi to be strong predictors of delinquency. The relative infrequency of scale 5 (Mf) being found coded highest in the aggressive group may indicate that this group tends to be rather masculine and further analysis might show scale 5 to be an inhibitor similar to scale 2 having a negative influence for delinquency as reported by Hathaway and Monachesi. The percentages for the

Table 1. Percentage of Counselees Labeled Aggressive in the Various Code Classes Compared with the Total Group

Code Class	Percentage of Total Group	Percentage of Aggressive Group	CR between 1st and 2nd Columns
Single scales			
4 highest or tied.....	9	18	2.31
4 highest 1, 2, or 3..	25	42	2.88
5 highest or tied....	24	10	2.37
7 lowest 1, 2, or 3...	5	14	3.00
9 highest or tied....	21	34	2.32
9 highest 1, 2, or 3...	39	56	2.54
Pairs, high			
13	7	15	2.07
29	4	13	2.97
49	12	23	2.53
48	7	16	2.46

other categories are too small to be considered reliable even though the statistic would indicate so.

Table 2 shows the data in the same way for the group labeled shy. The 0 scale (Si) alone and in combination characterizes this group very significantly, but as was said previously the counselors may have been biased by knowing this score when judging the counselee's behavior. Clinically, however, one would expect these results since the scale 0 is supposed to measure introversion. Scale 7 (Pt), however, is quite significant for this group. In the last two or three years the staff of counselors had become aware of difficulties in dealing with cases with this scale coded high. However, the hypothesis developed was that such profiles indicated extremely indecisive persons. It was not recognized that those labeled shy or withdrawn would have this scale coded high. The increase in percentage of profiles with no codings below 46 may be an artifact caused by the tendency for elevated 0 scale scores. Table V, page xxviii of the *Atlas* [307], shows the distribution of low points for 2805 University of Wisconsin male students when 0 was not included as one of the scales. Thirty-six per cent of this group had no low point coded under the circumstances, which compares favorably with the 33 per cent in Table 2.

Table 3 shows the data in the same way for the group labeled nonresponsive. Here scale 7 (Pt), coded high, stands out especially as characteristic of this group, but with a deficiency of elevated 5 (Mf). Scale 5, it will be recalled, was also infrequently coded high for the aggressive group. This re-emphasizes the desirability of investigating further the possible effect of scale 5 upon scales 4 and 9 and upon scale 7 in relation to the sort of behavior being studied here. Scale 6 (Pa) occurred in the high coding significantly. This would appear reasonable if nonresponsiveness is considered in some cases to be the result of defensiveness.

Summary

In conclusion, it appears that those counseling cases found to be difficult to deal with because they were aggressive or opinionated were characterized by having

Table 2. Percentage of Counselees Labeled Shy in the Various Code Classes Compared with the Total Group

Code Class	Percentage of Total Group	Percentage of Shy Group	CR
Single scales			
0 highest or tied....	2	9	3.50
0 highest 1, 2, or 3..	8	29	5.38
0 lowest or tied....	40	18	3.10
0 lowest 1, 2, or 3..	48	24	3.29
6 highest or tied....	4	11	2.50
7 highest or tied....	36	53	2.46
None coded low....	20	33	2.24
Pairs, high			
02	1	5	2.22
04	4	15	4.69
05	3	9	2.22
06	1	5	2.86
16	0.8	5	3.08
46	3	12	3.33
59	12	0	2.50

Table 3. Percentage of Counselees Labled Nonresponsive in the Various Code Classes Compared with the Total Group

Code Class	Percentage of Total Group	Percentage of Nonresponsive Group	CR
Single scales			
5 highest or tied...	24	10	2.41
5 highest 1, 2, or 3..	43	29	2.09
6 highest or tied....	04	10	2.31
6 highest 1, 2, or 3..	13	23	2.22
7 highest 1, 2, or 3..	36	52	2.46
Pairs			
35	13	00	2.60
46	03	11	3.08
68	02	09	3.04
69	02	07	2.27

MMPI profiles with scales 4 and 9 elevated but with a deficiency of scale 5 coded high.

The shy group was best characterized as having scales 0 and 7 coded high with a deficiency of 0 in the low codes.

The nonresponsive group was best characterized by having scales 6 and 7 coded high with an absence of scale 5 coded high. The nonresponsive group may be a more mixed group than the other two. Scale 7 being elevated in groups B and C and scale 5 being lacking in the high codes of both A and C would indicate an overlap.

SECTION IV   New Scales

AT THE time of its original publication, the MMPI was scored on approximately 300 of the 550 items. The remaining items could of course have simply been omitted, as was done in the AGO's military form TC-8b. The tentative stage of its development and the likelihood of the need for additional scales, however, were recognized by the authors and, for the most part, the MMPI was administered with the 250-item research pool routinely included. Since the time of publication, over 100 additional scales have been devised for the instrument, according to a survey made for a forthcoming handbook of the MMPI by the present editors. Clearly, there is an important question posed by this development which has as yet been unanswered. In the utilization of a multivariate personality instrument, is it economical and efficient to continue indefinitely developing a new scale for each new practical problem posed by society or can the test constructor settle upon a significantly smaller subset of scales which will satisfy all these requirements?

The problem posed here seems to be one for which factor analytic methods could provide a useful solution. Such an analysis could deal with the alternative ways of specifying the relationships obtained by empirical scale construction. According to the test authors, the MMPI scales were developed "to provide an estimate of symptomatic syndromes commonly recognized among psychiatric patients" [308 (see III, 15)]. Factor analyses of the intercorrelations among these scales could perhaps provide a smaller subset of scales which would reproduce these intercorrelations. Whether this would be any advantage depends upon the magnitude of the intercorrelations themselves. If they prove to be small, then little would be gained, since each scale would be serving largely an independent function, presumably equally important with every other one. If the correlations prove to be large, however, considerable economy could be gained. Since the scales were originally constructed against a set of theoretical constructs developed to account for observations within the psychiatric domain, refinements within the MMPI scales could have important implications for psychiatric nosology. The studies of Wheeler, Little, and Lehner (article 28) and of Welsh (article 29) in this section deal directly with these questions.

The original question posed about the continual development of new scales has not yet been answered, however. In fact, the factor analytic work to date has merely led to more scales. In dealing with a different but related question of prediction versus analysis, Hathaway and Monachesi [312] discussed the two alternatives of constructing a new MMPI scale for proneness to delinquency or using existing clinical scales. In deciding to use the latter approach they pointed out the need for analytic differentiation between delinquents whose difficulties may be determined on a neurotic basis and those whose difficulties are psychotic or psychopathic. Although a composite prediction scale could conceivably give proper weight to each of these delinquency-prone groups, it would provide no information about these important differences among them. Good analytic scales can make this differentiation; Hathaway and Monachesi offer considerable evidence that existing analytic scales can also do the prediction job. If we apply their philosophy and observations to the present question, the answer would seem to be to apply existing scales and the patterns found among them to the new problem. If no useful variance resides in the present scales, then and only then construct a new scale. Such pattern analyses using the original MMPI scales are dealt with in subsequent sections. In this section, some of the new scales are described.

At the time the MMPI was being constructed in the late thirties, the empirical scale construction methods were a distinct innovation. By now the method of item selection and verification employed in the original MMPI work is well known and widely used. However, scales continue to appear based upon pooled judgments or often even single author opinions. For example, the scale labeled Manifest Anxiety and developed on the former basis by Taylor [587] has only moderate relationship to ratings and judgments of manifest anxiety level [379, 325, 334]. Perhaps it is surprising that it should have any valid relationship to its descriptive label at all. The fact that it correlates very highly (.92) with scale 7 (Pt) and is seriously affected by K-factor variance ($-.74$) in a sample of neuropsychiatric patients [79] makes it of little use in the practical setting of the psychiatric center. Its success in separating subjects for psychological experiments is encouraging and indicates that better separations could probably be obtained by using the entire MMPI battery.

Steps have now been taken in the experimental applications of the Taylor scale to minimize the K-factor distortions through the forced-choice format [314]. It remains for future developments to determine whether the whole MMPI should be so converted. One of the most important drawbacks now is the relatively high difficulty level of the instructions and procedures of the forced-choice technique. In the many clinical settings where the MMPI format is appropriate, the forced-choice forms may prove to be too confusing and difficult.

In this section, a number of different techniques which have been utilized to develop scales for the MMPI are illustrated. For the most part, the method used by Hathaway and McKinley of contrasting a criterion group with a large general normative group has not been followed. Drake, in developing scale 0 (Si) (article 19), and Gough the Pr (prejudice) scale (article 23), used groups formed on the basis of other tests. Gough in article 20 describes the St (status) scale constructed from contrasting groups at the extremes of rated socioeconomic status. In article 22, Wiener describes the refinement of the empirical MMPI scales into obvious and subtle subscales on the basis of composite clinical judgment. Gough, McClosky, and Meehl utilized peer nominations from high school and college groups to form extremes in social dominance to develop their Do scale (article 24). Contrasting clinical groups furnish the basis for item selection in the development by Williams of the Ca (caudality) scale (article 25), and by Cuadra of the Cn (control) scale (article 27). Barron makes a direct attack on the problem of prediction by selecting the groups he uses to build his Es (ego-strength) scale on the basis of outcome under psychotherapy (article 26).

In the last article in this section, Meehl raises some cogent questions about the standard methods of item selection and combination in the usual cumulative scales in the MMPI. He also outlines a method for using the variance furnished by taking item patterns into consideration. His initial suggestions and empirical findings have been extended and generalized by Horst [r77], but no application of the methods to the MMPI has been published. H. L. Williams (in a personal communication) has applied the configural method to pairs of items in scale 6 (Pa), obtaining excellent separation by means of this nonlinear scale on the original groups. However, the separation shrank rapidly on successive cross-validation groups. He attributes some of this error function to the fact that each item was allowed to operate in more than one pair, thus enhancing the effect of any sampling error operating in a given item. His analysis did not allow non-Pa items to enter into consideration either. It awaits future research to determine whether configural patterns can be used most efficiently at the item combination level, or between more stable refined scales of the usual cumulative kind.

The articles in this section came from the following sources: article 19 from L. E. Drake, A social I.E. scale for the MMPI, *Journal of Applied Psychology*, 1946, 30, 51–54; article 20 from L. E. Drake and W. B. Thiede, Further validation of the social I.E. scale for the MMPI, *Journal of Educational Research*, 1948, 41, 551–556; article 21 from H. G. Gough, A new dimension of status: I. Development of a personality scale, *American Sociological Review*, 1948, 13, 401–409; article 22 from D. N. Wiener, Subtle and obvious keys for the MMPI, *Journal of Consulting Psychology*, 1948, 12, 164–170; article 23 from H. G. Gough, Studies of social intolerance: II. A personality scale for anti-Semitism, *Journal of Social Psychology*, 1951, 33, 247–255; article 24 from H. G. Gough, H. McClosky, and P. E. Meehl, A personality scale for dominance, *Journal of Abnormal and Social Psychology*, 1951, 46, 360–366; article 25 from H. L. Williams, The development of a caudality scale for the MMPI, *Journal of Clinical Psychology*, 1952, 8, 293–297; article 26 from F. Barron, An ego-strength scale which predicts response to psychotherapy, *Journal of Consulting Psychology*, 1953, 17, 327–333; article 27 from C. A. Cuadra, A psychometric investigation of control factors in psychological adjustment, Ph.D. dissertation, University of California, 1953; article 28 from W. M. Wheeler, K. B. Little, and G. F. J. Lehner, The internal structure of the MMPI, *Journal of Consulting Psychology*, 1951, 15, 134–141; article 29 is an original manuscript prepared for this volume; and article 30 from P. E. Meehl, Configural scoring, *Journal of Consulting Psychology*, 1950, 14, 165–171. We are indebted to the authors and to the publishers of the journals for permission to reproduce these articles in this form.

ARTICLE 19 *Scale 0 (Social Introversion)*

THE Minnesota T-S-E Inventory [r54] has been used as a part of the standard battery of tests administered to students in the guidance program at the University of Wisconsin for over a year. The inventory has yielded data that have been useful in counseling students. Since, however, the Minnesota Multiphasic Personality Inventory [300 (see II, 5)] is also a part of the standard battery and since many items of the latter resemble items in the former, it was thought desirable to try to devise keys to score theMMPI to yield data now obtained by means of the T-S-E Inventory. This report is limited to results obtained for a social I.E. scale. Scales for thinking and emotional introversion-extroversion are not yet ready for publication.

Procedure

An item analysis of the MMPI was made by contrasting the percentage responses of two groups of students to the items. One group consisted of 50 students who obtained centile ranks of 65 and above on the T-S-E Inventory when scored for social introversion-extroversion. The second group consisted of 50 students who obtained centile ranks below 35 on the T-S-E Inventory. The students were all females because of the small male population in the university, but the scale was validated with a male population as will be shown later. There was no other factor used in the selection of cases except that three cases were not included because the L scores on the MMPI were quite high.

Items were selected for the key which showed a difference between the percentage responses of the upper and lower groups of at least twice the standard error of the difference. Some significant items, however, were eliminated because there was an extremely high or extremely low frequency of response for both upper and lower groups.

After the item selection had been completed a new group of MMPI record sheets were scored with the obtained key for purposes of validation. These record sheets contained the responses of a group of female students who cleared through the testing office after the group of students who provided the data for the item analyses. The scores obtained with the new key were next correlated with the social I.E. scores obtained on the T-S-E Inventory. The key was then used for scoring all available record sheets for male students, providing there were T-S-E scores also available, and these scores were correlated with the T-S-E scores.

Finally, norms were established by scoring all available MMPI record sheets.

181

The norms are reported in terms of T scores obtained in the customary way, namely:

$$T = 50 + \frac{10\,(X_1 - M)}{SD}$$

where X_1 is the raw score, M the mean, and SD the standard deviation of the raw scores for the normative group.

Results

The items for this key are listed in Table 1 according to the way they are designated on the MMPI record sheets. The raw score is obtained by counting one point for every cell on the record sheet having an X corresponding to the key and one point for every cell which is blank corresponding to a 0 on the key. The cells containing question marks are not counted [420 (see II, 6)].

Table 1. Scoring Key for Social I.E.

Item No.	Scoring Direction	Item No.	Scoring Direction	Item No.	Scoring Direction	Item No.	Scoring Direction	Item No.	Scoring Direction
A36	X	D50	X	E36	X	F8	X	H18	0
A37	X	D53	X	E38	X	F9	X	H51	X
A38	X	D54	X	E43	X	F30	0	H52	X
B6	X	E18	X	E44	X	F31	X	I21	0
B22	X	E23	X	E46	X	F34	X	I25	X
C20	X	E26	X	E47	X	F36	X	I26	X
C25	X	E27	X	E49	X	F41	X	I27	X
C48	0	E28	X	E52	X	F45	X	I28	X
C55	X	E29	X	E55	X	G18	X	I29	X
D2	0	E30	X	F2	X	G24	0	I38	X
D34	0	E32	X	F3	X	G35	X	I41	X
D35	0	E33	X	F4	X	G42	0	J24	0
D37	0	E34	X	F5	X	H2	X	J32	0
D45	0	E35	X	F6	X	H12	0	J33	X

Table 2. The T Scores for the Social I.E. Scale

Raw Score	T Score	Raw Score	T Score	Raw Score	T Score	Raw Score	T Score
70	97	52	79	34	61	16	41
69	96	51	78	33	60	15	40
68	95	50	77	32	58	14	39
67	94	49	76	31	56	13	38
66	93	48	75	30	55	12	37
65	92	47	74	29	54	11	36
64	91	46	73	28	53	10	35
63	90	45	72	27	52	9	34
62	89	44	71	26	51	8	33
61	88	43	70	25	50	7	32
60	87	42	69	24	49	6	30
59	86	41	68	23	48	5	29
58	85	40	67	22	47	4	28
57	84	39	66	21	46	3	27
56	83	38	65	20	45	2	26
55	82	37	64	19	44	1	25
54	81	36	63	18	43		
53	80	35	62	17	42		

Twenty-eight of the items on this key have not been used on any keys reported by Hathaway and McKinley.

Record sheets for 87 female students were then scored with this key and the scores were correlated with the social I.E. scores on the T-S-E. The resulting coefficient of correlation was —.72. The coefficient was negative because the key for the MMPI was constructed so that a high score would indicate introversion whereas on the T-S-E a low score indicates introversion.

Record sheets for 81 men students were likewise scored and the scores correlated with social I.E. scores on the T-S-E. The resulting coefficient was —.71. Hence the key was used for both male and female students in obtaining norms.

Table 2 gives the T scores for this scale based upon records for 350 female students and 193 male students. Separate norms were computed for males and females, but they were so similar, differing by only 2 from raw score 0 to 6 and being identical for most of the range, that the tables were combined for both sexes.

Summary

1. Using the social I.E. scores on the Minnesota T-S-E Inventory for a group of female students as a criterion, an item analysis of the MMPI was made.

2. The derived key appears to have equally good validity for both male and female students.

3. An attempt is being made to derive thinking and emotional I.E. scales in a similar way.

ARTICLE 20 *Further Validation of Scale 0 (Si)*

A GROUP of 594 female students who came to the University of Wisconsin Student Counseling Center for assistance and for whom the information was complete provided the data for this study. Only females were included because the data were collected from students who were in the university during the period of 1944 and 1945 and it was thought that the male students in residence at that time might be atypical due to the war. Foreign students, veterans, and married students were excluded because they were also assumed to be atypical.

Each student filled out a detailed information blank which included items regarding high school and college extracurricular activities. The activities were grouped into six categories as follows: Literary, Dramatics, Debating, Music and Art, Athletics, and Student Government. A score of one was assigned to each area in which the student indicated she participated regardless of the amount of participation in that area. An error may be involved in this since it is not known whether the categories are equivalent in relation to I.E. However, it is apparent that the error would be increased if the total number of activities participated in was used as a score rather than the number of types of activities since this would increase the effect of these inequalities if they exist. The ratings, then, for activity participation ranged from zero to six. All the students took the MMPI (card-sorting form) as a part of the testing for counseling purposes.

Results

Since the size of the community in which a person has lived most of his life might have some relationship to social I.E., it was thought desirable to study this factor first. Hence the students were classified according to the following population groups: farm to 2499; 2500 to 9999; 10,000 to 99,999; 100,000 and up.

The chi square test was applied to a contingency table to determine whether the students participating in 0 or 1, 2, 3, 4, and 5 or 6 types of high school activities are proportionately distributed in each population group. The resulting chi square with 12 degrees of freedom gives $p(\chi^2 > 30.5) = 0.001$ indicating highly significant differences between population groups with respect to activity participation. Hence it was deemed necessary to make separate analyses for the four population groups even though the χ^2 for a contingency table made up of population groups with respect to Si scores with 24 degrees of freedom gives $p(\chi^2 > 27.2) = 0.30$.

However, if a separate analysis is made for each of the population groups in terms of the five quantities of activity participation listed above, the numbers in some categories as distributed are rather small. Hence the cases were combined in each population group to make two categories as follows: (1) those who participated in 0, 1, or 2 types of high school activities; and (2) those who participated in 4, 5, or 6 types of activities. Those who listed three types of activities were omitted since the means of the population groups ranged from 2.6 to 3.4.

Table 1 shows the Si scores for the four population groups as divided into the two categories and the t-test results for the significance of the difference between means.

Table 1. Comparison of Si Scores for High School Activity Groups

Group	Students Reporting 0, 1, or 2 Types of Activity			Students Reporting 4, 5, and 6 Types of Activity			Differences			
	Mean	SD	N	Mean	SD	N	M_{diff}	t	df	p
Farm–2499	57.850	10.800	40	49.711	11.101	52	8.139	11.558	90	<.0005
2500–9999	54.730	10.690	26	48.533	10.363	45	6.197	7.659	69	<.0005
10,000–99,999 ..	55.943	11.337	70	45.724	8.383	58	10.219	18.058	126	<.0005
100,000–over ...	52.093	9.165	86	47.667	9.313	45	4.426	7.863	129	<.0005

In every case the differences are highly significant — at less than the 0.05 of 1 per cent level of confidence. The mean score on the Si scale of the students who participated in 4, 5, or 6 activities is in the direction of extroversion (low scores indicate extroversion) and the mean for those participating in 0, 1, or 2 activities is in the direction of introversion. The percentage of students participating in 4, 5, or 6 types of activities who reach or exceed the mean for students who participate in 0, 1, or 2 types of activities for each population group is as follows: Group I, 23 per cent; Group II, 28 per cent; Group III, 15 per cent; and Group IV, 22 per cent.

Since freshman women are not permitted to participate in major activities it was necessary to omit all students so classified in the study of the relationship of Si and college activity participation. This left 283 cases for study. The chi square test was applied as before to a contingency table made up of the number of types of activity participation with respect to the size of the town in which the student said she had spent most of her life. The resulting chi square with 6 degrees of freedom gives $p(\chi^2 > 8.8) = 0.19$. Applying the same test to a table made up of size of town with respect to Si scores with 12 degrees of freedom gives $p(\chi^2 > 14.25) = 0.29$. Since the differences cannot be assumed to be significant, the group of 283 students was studied without regard to the size of the home community.

The mean number of types of activities participated in by these students while in the university was 0.94. The comparison was made, then, between those students who participated in no activities and those who participated in two or more types of activities. Table 2 shows the result of the comparison.

The difference in means is 4.981, yielding a t of 10.349 which with 192 degrees of freedom gives p < 0.0005. The difference is highly significant with the activity-

Table 2. Comparison of Si Scores for University Activity Groups

Group	Mean	SD	N
Students reporting no activities.............................	53.153	11.025	124
Students reporting two or more types of activities............	48.171	8.920	70

participation group deviating toward the extrovert end of the scale. Only 28 per cent of this group reach or exceed the mean Si score for the nonparticipating group in the introverted direction.

✦

ARTICLE 21 *A Scale for a Personality Dimension of Socioeconomic Status (St)*

IT IS generally recognized among social psychologists that the position occupied by an individual in the social hierarchy is one of the most important variables determining his behavior. Thus, attitudes toward political and economic change [r33], and toward governmental regulations [r120] have been shown to be closely related to class identification. Child-rearing practices seem to follow class lines more closely than color lines [r43], and the language development of children reveals a marked relationship to socioeconomic status [r104]. School achievement correlates positively with socioeconomic status [r63].

Personality factors have also been shown to covary with status. Maddy found children from professional families to be more dominant, extroverted, and emotionally stable, whereas children from semiskilled families had more worries [r109]. The characteristic conflicts of middle-class male children, and the neurotic outcomes toward which they are predisposed, have been analyzed by Green [r65]. Davis has contributed an excellent discussion of the effect of class position on socialization [r42], and stresses the differences in aggressiveness, as do others [r119]. Verbal behavior also appears to have status implications [r133]. A brief summary of some of the more important class differences may be found in a recent volume by Sorokin [r151].

The conclusion appears justified that social status has fairly clear influences on personality and behavior. As Murphy says, the social classes show distinct psychological cleavage, or discontinuity, and these cleavages are reflected in personality structure [r126]. The personality factors relating to status levels will not, of course, include all personality traits. Most persons in any society will have certain modal traits in common, certain other traits in common with only a specific group, and finally certain purely individual traits [r99]. If these may be called general, group, and specific traits, those relating to socioeconomic status would be classified as group traits.

In spite of the findings of the studies cited, and many more unmentioned, it may justifiably be said that the implications of the social status concept for sociology and social psychology have scarcely been realized. Except for the defining indices of class membership, and certain very general characteristics which pertain to such

187

membership, little is actually known about socioeconomic status and personality structure. What is needed is empirically derived information sufficiently systematic and exact to permit the inference of certain group traits from the fact of class membership. It is felt that the interrelations between status and personality are imperative enough to make possible such specific inferences; the contention is that once an individual has been assigned to a status level, it may be asserted with known probability that he will possess the group traits common to that level.

The point may perhaps be clarified by reference to the field of psychopathology. In the case of the psychiatric diagnostic entities, such as hysteria, there are a number of behaviors (symptoms) which are characteristically interrelated. Some of these, in general those which have been identified for the longest time, are more or less defining; that is, a minimum of certain such symptoms will suffice for the assignation of the subject to the class hysteria. Other symptoms, in general those which have most recently been identified, are not usually accepted as defining or diagnostic, but are considered as corroborative factors. For example, a paralyzed arm with negative neurological findings, etc., in a subject for whom the paralysis could serve as a respectable resolution of a serious conflict, might well be called an instance of hysteria. If, in addition, the patient displayed a seeming lack of concern over his disability, maintained a cheerful but rather unrealistic optimism about himself and others, and resisted quite strongly the suggestion that any of his problems had any psychogenic components, our confidence in the diagnosis would be enhanced.

Even if these latter features were not investigated, the psychopathologist would feel quite comfortable in asserting that such traits, as well as others, would be found more often than not if the original diagnosis was accurate. Thus, there are a number of traits included within the class designated hysteria, and once a subject has been assigned to this class according to certain identifying properties, the presence of other related traits may safely be inferred. The general argument could, of course, be more clearly established by recourse to disease entities in organic medicine where the appropriate properties have been clearly delineated. However, it is felt that psychopathological concepts, being based almost entirely on behavioral observations, are more similar to sociological concepts, such as status position, and hence more enlightening.

The objection could now be raised that psychopathological concepts may indeed permit the inferring of other attributes once some have been demonstrated, but that such concepts are fundamentally different from sociological concepts, which do not possess this characteristic. Concepts of the former type have a very slight social reference, and are primarily defined by the very clusterings of behavior which are being discussed. Gross questions, such as deviancy or nondeviancy, have a large social reference, but the more precise question of a diagnosis is dependent upon the organization and interrelationship of a number of personality factors. In the case of sociological concepts, the bases for classification are much more largely in the responses of others, stimulated by quite manifest cues, and are not primarily related to factors of personality structure. It is understood that all the classifications depend, basically, upon the responses of others. However, in hysteria, the emphasis is on what the patient does, whereas in status the emphasis is on what *others* do. In short, a person is assigned to the psychiatric class hysteria only after certain characteristics have been discovered in his personality structure; a person is assigned to the class high socioeconomic status by the presence of various economic and social facts. The assigning in the first case is made only after intensive study of the individual by experts; in the second case it is made easily and quickly by peers.

The fact that there is a sociological difference in the processes by which persons are classified in the two cases mentioned above must be admitted. However, it does not necessarily follow that the value of the concepts in both cases, that of indicating concomitant properties which will be found in conjunction with certain defining properties in some given degree, must be different. There seems to be good reason to believe, on the other hand, that certain personality characteristics are related to socioeconomic status and that once a subject is properly classified according to the usual indices of status, these personality aspects are discoverable.

Sociologists in general have been aware of such psychological factors as being common to primary groups, and other membership groups, but have not, apparently, been so clearly aware of them in relation to reference groups. Cantril, for example, states that studies attempting to show personality trait differences between liberals and conservatives have not resulted in any "unequivocally positive conclusions" [r31]. The failure to find such differences is probably not so much due to an absence of personality factors associated with reference group identification as to the tendency to use personality scales which were devised with completely different measurement problems in view. If the aim is to discover personality factors associated with sociological categories, scales designed to detect neuroticism, maladjustment, etc., are not the method of choice. A better technique is the systematic analysis of a large number of factors, either items of verbal behavior or of personal history, to select those which will reliably discriminate the criterion group. If such a procedure does yield a set of personality variables, then it may be said that the distinguished factors are the ones characteristic of the group studied.

The remainder of this paper will be concerned with an investigation such as this. A set of items will be presented which contain no reference whatsoever to socioeconomic status, and yet constitute reliable predictors of status. These items form a scale, which may be called a new dimension of status because it has not previously been recognized that certain personality factors are so characteristically aligned with status.

Method

The basic technique in this study was the individual analysis of a large number of personality inventory items to select those which would reliably separate high- and low-status persons. The pool of items was drawn from the MMPI [303], providing 550 items for consideration. This test is particularly useful for an investigation such as this, inasmuch as it offers internal checks on the accuracy of response [235], and does not depend upon the subject's self-evaluations [433 (see I, 1)]. These advantages stem from the rigorous empiricism employed in the test's construction, which will not be discussed.

All these variables, as well as a number of others, were considered in relationship to socioeconomic status. The other variables compared were the Maslow Security-Insecurity Inventory [r112], IQ, and three-year high school grade average. Socioeconomic status itself was ascertained by means of the Sims Score Cards [r149]. The conception of status utilized in this study was that developed in an earlier paper by the writer, namely, "as a prestige variable dependent upon social and economic factors, which are not configurated in any constant manner" [r63]. The use of a scale score as an index of such a variable would appear thoroughly justifiable in light of the discussions of Lundberg [r102] and Chapin [r34].

Results

The sample upon which the study was based consisted of 223 high school seniors (90 boys and 133 girls) from a Minnesota community of about 25,000 population. The means and standard deviations for this group on each of the variables studied are given in Table 1. It will be noted that most of the personality inventory means are expressed in T-score units; that is, a mean of 50 and a standard deviation of 10 represent the norms.

Inspection of Table 1 reveals rather pronounced elevations of means on the Pd, Pa, Pt, Sc, and Ma subtests of the MMPI, over one half of a standard deviation in each case. This may reflect the inapplicability of adult norms to such a group, or it may indicate an actual trend in the present group. Not enough research on students has been done with the MMPI to answer this question, but it is highly unlikely that the entire elevation would be due to an artifact of the norms. The grade average is somewhat above a C average, where 2.00 represents C and 3.00 B. The status mean is just below the 7th rank in the scale from zero to ten suggested by Sims [r149] and would be placed in the "high" category.

The item analyses were based upon two subsamples of 38 each, 20 girls and 18 boys, representing the high and low ends of the status continuum respectively. These cases were selected in order to restrict the subsamples to subjects falling beyond one standard deviation above or below the mean; the addition of more cases would have added persons who were not clearly high or low status, according to the group norms. Table 2 gives the summary statistics for these two subsamples, as well as differences between the means and significance tests. It can be seen that the two samples were quite well matched on a number of factors, although no attempt was made to equate them except for sex. The only significant differences are those on IQ and grade average, both in favor of the high-status group, and of course on status, the selection variable. These results, incidentally, confirm the statement made previously, that differences between sociologically categorized groups are difficult to establish when personality measures designed for other purposes are used. None of the thirteen personality factors shows a significant difference.

Item analysis was carried out by comparing the percentages in each of the two subsamples giving a "true" response to each question. The differences between the two percentages were evaluated by means of the phi coefficients [r86], and those items differentiating at the .01 or .02 levels were retained. These items, the direction of scoring for high status, and their critical ratios are given in Table 3.

Inspection of these items suggests that they may be grouped under five general categories: (1) literary-esthetic attitudes, items 78, 126, 149, and 204; (2) social poise, security, confidence in self and others, items 136, 138, 180, 229, 237, 267, 280, 304, 452, and 521; (3) denial of fears and anxieties, items 213, 352, 365, 388, 448, and 480; (4) "broad-minded," "emancipated," and "frank" attitudes toward moral, religious, and sexual matters, items 118, 199, 249, 297, 314, 324, 378, 427, 430, 441, and 488; and (5) positive, dogmatic, "self-righteous" opinions, items 289, 491, 513.

Table 1. Means and Standard Deviations for Several Measures on the Criterion Groups

Group	Secur.-Insec.	Otis IQ	Grade Average	Status	L[a]	F[a]	K	Hs	D	Hy	Pd	Mf	Pa	Pt	Sc	Ma
Total (N = 223)																
Mean	50.0	103.4	2.3	16.4	3.9	6.2	51.3	52.3	53.5	53.4	59.0	…	55.4	58.7	60.2	57.0
SD	10.0	10.7	0.7	5.4	2.3	4.1	7.9	9.5	10.5	8.8	11.4	…	10.3	11.3	12.4	11.2
MMPI Code: 8-4796231 FK/L																
Girls (N = 133)																
Mean	50.4	102.6	2.4	16.3	4.1	5.7	50.9	50.3	51.8	52.3	57.0	53.5	55.0	56.7	57.4	55.6
SD	10.1	10.3	0.7	5.4	2.2	3.9	7.8	8.4	9.0	8.9	11.1	9.5	9.8	9.5	10.0	11.3
MMPI Code: 847 965321/ FKL/																
Boys (N = 90)																
Mean	49.6	104.3	2.1	16.6	3.7	6.9	51.7	55.0	55.6	55.0	61.6	55.6	56.1	61.3	64.0	58.9
SD	9.9	11.2	0.6	5.4	2.4	4.3	8.0	10.2	12.0	8.5	11.3	10.3	11.0	12.8	14.2	10.7
MMPI Code: 847-965213 FK/L																

[a] Raw scores.

Table 2. Means, Standard Deviations, Mean Differences, and t Values for Several Measures on Two Status Samples (18 Males and 20 Females in Each Group)

Group	Secur.-Insec.	Otis IQ	Grade Average	Status	L[a]	F[a]	K	Hs	D	Hy	Pd	Mf_M	Mf_F	Pa	Pt	Sc	Ma
High status																	
Mean	47.4	109.3	2.5	24.8	3.6	5.3	53.9	52.4	52.7	55.3	59.3	58.8	53.2	55.6	60.0	59.3	59.1
SD	9.7	12.0	0.8	1.0	2.2	4.0	8.8	7.5	11.1	8.2	9.9	10.1	10.3	9.9	10.9	10.5	11.6
MMPI Code: 7489 63 21/ FK/L																	
Low status																	
Mean	49.8	99.1	2.0	9.8	4.5	6.3	51.1	51.2	54.0	52.8	58.0	53.9	57.2	56.3	61.5	63.3	57.2
SD	9.8	9.6	0.5	1.8	2.2	3.6	6.0	10.9	11.7	7.8	11.2	11.9	10.5	13.5	12.3	16.0	10.6
MMPI Code: 87-49②231 FLK/																	
Diff	-2.4	10.1	0.5	15.0	-1.0	-1.1	2.8	1.2	-1.3	2.5	1.4	4.9	-4.0	-0.7	-1.5	-4.0	1.9
t[b]	1.04	4.02	3.46	42.92	1.85	1.19	1.60	0.56	0.49	1.35	0.56	1.31	1.17	0.27	0.56	1.28	0.74

[a] Raw scores
[b] A t value of 2.58 is significant at the .01 level, and of 1.96 at the .05 level.

These groupings have been qualitatively derived, and it is possible that formal mathematical analysis might reveal different clusters; nevertheless, the categories listed do seem to possess internal consistency and meaningfulness.

It is probably not surprising to find sets of items relating to social skills and to lack of worry and fears appearing. Upper class persons lead a more secure existence in many ways, and also have more opportunities to develop poise and proper social behavior. On the other hand, the apparent paradox of urbane, liberated attitudes

Table 3. Personality Inventory Items Significantly Differentiating between High- and Low-Status High School Students

Item Number in MMPI Group Form	Item	Answer by High-Status Group	Critical Ratio
78.	I like poetry.	true	3.226
118.	In school I was sometimes sent to the principal for cutting up	true	3.034
126.	I like dramatics.	true	2.624
136.	I commonly wonder what hidden reason another person may have for doing something nice for me.	false	2.807
138.	Criticism or scolding hurts me terribly.	false	2.572
149.	I used to keep a diary.	true	2.598
180.	I find it hard to make talk when I meet new people.	false	3.077
199.	Children should be taught all the main facts of sex.	true	3.426
204.	I would like to be a journalist.	true	3.653
213.	In walking I am very careful to step over sidewalk cracks.	false	2.737
229.	I should like to belong to several clubs or lodges.	true	2.798
237.	My relatives are nearly all in sympathy with me.	true	2.746
249.	I believe there is a Devil and a Hell in after life.	false	2.746
267.	When in a group of people I have trouble thinking of the right things to talk about.	false	2.964
280.	Most people make friends because friends are likely to be useful to them	false	2.528
289.	I am always disgusted with the law when a criminal is freed through the arguments of a smart lawyer.	true	2.546
297.	I wish I were not bothered by thoughts about sex.	false	3.391
304.	In school I found it very hard to talk before the class.	false	2.807
314.	Once in a while I think of things too bad to talk about.	false	3.226
324.	I have never been in love with anyone.	false	2.580
352.	I have been afraid of things or people that I knew could not hurt me.	false	3.426
365.	I feel uneasy indoors.	false	2.615
378.	I do not like to see women smoke.	false	2.781
388.	I am afraid to be alone in the dark.	false	2.816
427.	I am embarrassed by dirty stories.	false	2.703
430.	I am attracted by members of the opposite sex.	true	2.493
441.	I like tall women.	true	3.260
448.	I am bothered by people outside, on streetcars, in stores, etc., watching me.	false	3.304
452.	I like to poke fun at people.	true	2.528
480.	I am often afraid of the dark.	false	2.816
488.	I pray several times every week.	false	3.025
491.	I have no patience with people who believe there is only one true religion	true	2.833
513.	I think Lincoln was greater than Washington.	true	2.485
521.	In a group of people I would not be embarrassed to be called upon to start a discussion or give an opinion about something I know well.	true	3.679

coadunated with a sort of pompous and rigid dogmatism may not have been so obvious. Such contradictions in the status folkways may underlie the inconsistent behavior which high-status persons often display in regard to social and political affairs. Further implications of the items will be developed in a later paper.

These 34 items were then assembled as a scale, and the original group of 223 test papers were rescored on this basis. The obtained mean was 17.43, and the standard deviation 4.783; for the girls alone, the values were 17.496 and 5.058, respectively, and for the boys 17.354 and 4.440. The corrected split half reliability for the total group was .739, with a standard error of .065. The test-retest correlation for a smaller sample of 101 students was .869, standard error .100. This latter value may be taken as a better index of reliability, according to Chapin's discussion [r34], and also falls above the value of .80 which he suggests as a lower limit for reliability. It appears, then, that these items do show enough consistency to be considered as a scale.

The validity of the scale is determined by the degree to which it will predict its criterion, socioeconomic status as measured by an objective index. For the original group of 223 students the correlation between St (status) and the Sims Score Cards was .676, standard error .07; for girls only the correlation was .708, SE .09, and for the boys the correlation was .634, SE .11. These correlations are again in the optimum range recommended by Chapin for validity coefficients [r34]. For the two subsamples used in the item analysis, the means and standard deviations were 22.79 and 3.27 for the high-status group, and 12.53 and 3.38 for the low; the mean difference was 10.26, and the t ratio of this difference was 13.26.

The St scale was next administered to a new high school class of 263 students (140 boys, 123 girls), and was compared with a different index of socioeconomic status, the American Home Scale [r89]. The latter scale was used in order to determine whether the St scale was capable of predicting socioeconomic status as meas-

Table 4. T-Score Conversion Table Based upon
486 High School Seniors (256 Girls, 230 Boys) [a]

Raw Score	T Score	Raw Score	T Score
34	86	16	46
33	84	15	44
32	82	14	42
31	80	13	40
30	78	12	38
29	75	11	35
28	73	10	33
27	71	9	31
26	69	8	29
25	66	7	27
24	64	6	24
23	62	5	22
22	60	4	20
21	58	3	18
20	55	2	15
19	53	1	13
18	51	0	11
17	49		

[a] High scores refer to high status, low scores to low status.

ured by other scales than the Sims. The correlation between St and AHS for the entire group was .500, SE .06; for the girls only, .512, SE .09; and for the boys only, .490, SE .08. These results indicate that the St scale has validity which is not limited entirely to the population and specific measurements from which it was derived.

The St scale may be used as a separate test, in which case the 34 items are presented to the subject with two alternatives (true or false), and he is instructed to choose whichever is more applicable; or, it may be used in conventional MMPI testing by merely constructing an additional scoring plate using the item numbers provided in Table 3. In either case, the norms given in Table 4 may be used. These norms are based entirely upon a sample of senior high school students from a small midwestern city and may not be appropriate for other populations. Users of the scale should observe proper cautions, especially in regard to adult populations.

Summary

The development of a new kind of scale for socioeconomic status has been described. This scale consists entirely of items drawn from a personality inventory, and contains no overt references to status whatsoever. Inspection of the items suggests that they fall into five general groups: literary-esthetic attitudes; social poise, security, confidence in self and others; denial of fears and anxieties; "broadminded," "emancipated," and "frank" attitudes toward moral, religious, and sexual matters; and positive, dogmatic, and self-righteous opinions. The tested reliability of the scale as a whole appeared to be satisfactory, and its validity in the original and in a test sample was demonstrated.

These results tend to substantiate the argument advanced in the first part of this paper. There are certain personality factors characteristically related to sociological categories; once these personality factors have been empirically isolated they may be presumed to be present in some degree among persons assignable to the class according to some other defining property. The argument is not in favor of an Aristotelian dichotomy, or even for a typology as ordinarily understood. The personality traits which can be demonstrated to align themselves with status are not the only traits which will be possessed by an individual classified with reference to status; as indicated above, there will be general, group, and specific traits in each case. It is the task of empirical analysis to establish the particular cluster of personality factors related to a given sociologically defined category.

D. N. WIENER

◆ ————————————————————————————

ARTICLE 22 *Subtle and Obvious Keys for the MMPI*

IN A recent article [441 (see I, 2)], Meehl and Hathaway described the need for and the development of a scale to indicate test-taking attitudes and their effect upon scores obtained on structured personality inventories. Their conclusions were that there was a conscious or unconscious tendency of subjects to present a picture of themselves that has a considerable influence upon their personality test scores; that this tendency might be to place them in an overly favorable or unfavorable light; and that the present "validity" scales of the MMPI did not seem to be sufficiently subtle to detect this test-taking attitude. They developed a K scale for the inventory to detect the influence of these test-taking attitudes and to improve the discrimination of the test between normal and abnormal populations [306 (see II, 11)].

While the K scale was being considered and developed, colleagues and the present author were developing the concept of relatively subtle and obvious keys for the scales of the MMPI on the same grounds as those given by Meehl and Hathaway. It was felt that the development of such keys on individual scales of the MMPI would yield more information and be of more practical usefulness than an over-all validity scale, such as L, N, G, and finally K, developed by Hathaway and Meehl.

The main problem of the counselor working with a relatively normal population in a broad counseling situation, as differentiated from the clinical psychologist working with a seriously disturbed group, is to distinguish nondisabling personality factors that characterize counselees as do aptitude and interest test results. The seriously disturbed group can probably be distinguished by a test consisting of items obviously indicating deviate personality characteristics, since the extreme deviates are probably largely unaware of the significance of their symptoms and are usually frank in their test answers. Screening devices developed for the military services and for private industry, which consist largely and obviously of deviate items, probably owe their success to this fact.

Extremely deviate individuals, then, can be picked out by a test consisting of obvious items. To help the counselor working with a normal population, however, a much more subtle test is required which will both distinguish the extreme deviates and differentiate among the characteristics of a normal population. These two functions of a personality test appeared to be best served by developing both subtle and obvious keys.

195

Method

In the experimental development of subtle and obvious keys for a personality test, the MMPI was used because it was available for a large, relatively normal population, because it was felt to have the most extensive and useful validation of any personality test, and because it uses generally accepted categories of personality characteristics. In addition it had the unique feature of validity measures designed to indicate, on a limited basis, test-taking attitudes. After extensive experience with it, however, it was felt that when it was used with a relatively normal population, one that was functioning relatively successfully in society, certain important aspects of personality were masked because of its validation in terms of abnormal groups. The most obvious items distinguished these abnormal groups from the normal, whereas it appears that the more subtle items should have the greater validity in distinguishing the personality characteristics of normal groups.

To develop subtle and obvious keys, Harmon and the present author divided all items of the MMPI into two groups, those to which significant responses were relatively easy to detect as indicating emotional disturbance, and those to which they were relatively difficult to detect. By use of several criteria, the items for each scale were sorted into these two categories. All F-scale items that also appeared in other scales were automatically assigned to the "obvious" category because by definition they seldom occur in a normal population. In addition, those items for which a blank response (no check on the answer sheet) was scored in a significant direction were assigned to the subtle keys. Pooled judgments of the raters were then used to sort the other items into the two categories with no attempt made to equalize the number of items in each group. There were more obvious items than subtle. The keys thus developed were used to rescore the test sheets of a representative sampling of 100 cases of the original male norm group for the MMPI. T scores were developed and assigned to subtle and obvious item counts on the same basis as for the total scale T scores.

Tabulation tables for the raw scores on the subtle and obvious keys (hereafter referred to as S and O) indicated a positive skew for most of the O-item distributions of the norm group; relatively few individuals in the normal population answered the obvious items in a significant direction. It seemed probable that significant answers to these O items were most characteristic of an institutionalized population. The S items were distributed in a relatively normal manner.

An additional check on the validity of the selection of items for the keys was the frequency of their occurrence among the responses of a normal population. Frequencies of responses in a significant direction to items of the O and S keys for five MMPI scales are indicated in Table 1 for 139 normal Minnesota males (from unpublished data by Hathaway). For all five scales the S items were answered in a significant direction approximately twice or more as frequently as the O items. In addition, for 65 of the 110 items in the S keys for these five scales, the "significant" direction for scoring reversed the expectation of Hathaway and McKinley when they included these items in the MMPI, whereas only 8 out of the 146 O items scored in a reverse direction from the original authors' expectation.

It can thus be seen that the bases used to select items for the S and O keys for five scales of the MMPI yielded O items which were answered relatively infrequently in a significant direction by a normal population compared with S items,

and S items whose significant answers were in a reverse direction from the expectation of both the original authors of the MMPI and the authors of the present keys.

The attempt was originally made to develop S and O keys for all scales of the
MMPI, but the results for Sc, Pt, Mf, and Hs were almost uniformly negative. Hs
consisted almost entirely of obvious items. Pt and Sc by definition also consisted of
extremely deviate items which were therefore obvious, and Mf probably has too low
validity as a scale to yield positive results.

Table 1. Average Frequencies of Significant Responses in the Normal Male Population to Items
in Subtle and Obvious Keys of the MMPI

Scale	Responses per 100 Cases	
	Obvious	Subtle
D	19	48
Hy	13	41
Pd	20	38
Pa	10	32
Ma	23	38
Mean	17	39

Correlations among Subtle and Obvious Keys, Hs, and K

Table 2 indicates the intercorrelations among S and O keys, and correlations
with Hs, which is really an O scale. In general, these intercorrelations show the
O keys highly correlated with each other positively, and uncorrelated with the S
keys; while the S keys show low positive correlations with each other. Considered
only as a rough index of relationship, the average intercorrelation among the O keys
is +.60, the average correlation of the O with the S keys is —.15, and the average
intercorrelation among the S keys is +.21.

Correlations between O minus S scores and the K scale of the MMPI are shown
below (N = 152):

$$\begin{array}{ll} \text{Hy....} \ -.78 & \text{Pd....} \ -.64 \\ \text{D.....} \ -.72 & \text{Pa....} \ -.60 \\ & \text{Ma....} \ -.47 \end{array}$$

Table 2. Correlations between Obvious and Subtle Keys of the MMPI

	Hs	D-O	D-S	Hy-O	Hy-S	Pd-O	Pd-S	Pa-O	Pa-S	Ma-O
D-O	.64									
D-S	.05	—.20								
Hy-O	.88	.78	—.24							
Hy-S	—.45	—.48	.51	—.46						
Pd-O	.51	.68	—.52	.61	—.58					
Pd-S	—.09	—.05	.19	.29	.36	.04				
Pa-O	.48	.61	—.07	.58	—.21	.64	.08			
Pa-S	—.21	—.18	.45	—.14	.59	—.12	.14	.10		
Ma-O	.41	.51	—.11	.45	—.68	.61	—.14	.56	—.29	
Ma-S	—.18	—.26	—.17	—.10	—.06	.22	.22	.19	—.17	.24

The uniformly high negative correlations that exist suggest the strong appearance of a test-taking attitude in each of the five scales, and the close relationship between S responses and the K score.

Relationships with Lie Scores, Ability, Psychological Sophistication, and Neuropsychiatric Diagnosis

Table 3 suggests relationships between S and O, and the Lie scale, intelligence, psychological sophistication, and neuropsychiatric diagnosis. These studies are meant only to suggest certain relationships and have not been subjected to rigid statistical analysis. The group with high scores on the Lie scale (9 items plus) of the MMPI was higher on the S keys of all five scales than on the O keys, and was also, in four cases out of five, higher on the S keys than was the low Lie (0 and 1 items) scale group. For the group with low Lie scores, the 0 scores were for all scales approximately equal to or higher than the S scores.

Individuals of high ability (intelligence T score above 60 on the Unit Scales of Aptitudes or the Otis S-A Test, and some college work) have approximately equal O and S scores, whereas individuals of low ability (T score below 40, and less than a ninth-grade education) have generally higher O scores than S, and higher O scores than the high-ability group.

MMPI profiles of a psychologically sophisticated group, as indicated by study in the ASTP psychology training program, showed a clear-cut distinction between S and O keys, with S much higher than O whether the group was giving "honest" results or was attempting to "fake good." With this psychologically sophisticated group it appeared to make little difference whether the test was taken "honestly" or "faked good"; in either case, O items were successfully avoided, whereas S items yielded average and above average T scores. Very few O items were answered in

Table 3. Means and Medians of Various Groups on Subtle-Obvious
Keys of the MMPI (S and O in T Scores)

Group	N	Criteria	D		Hy		Pd		Pa		Ma	
			O	S	O	S	O	S	O	S	O	S
Lie												
High scores	45	9 L items +	57	64	57	67	47	60	46	57	46	53
Low scores	50	0 & 1 L items	61	42	58	50	56	52	48	51	57	58
Ability												
High scores	40	Intell. scores 60+, plus some college	56	54	58	59	59	53	57	57	50	53
Low scores	29	Intell. scores below 40, less than 9th grade	67	55	68	53	57	59	59	49	60	59
Psychological sophistication												
"Honest" test results [a]	53	ASTP students, fall 1943	40	58	42	64	42	56	39	54	42	58
"Fake good" test results [a]	53	Same	37	61	41	64	40	58	39	60	44	62
Neuropsychiatric diagnosis												
No diagnosis, high profile [a]	12	One or more T scores above 70	69	48	54	51	63	56	53	57	56	58
Diagnosis, high profile [a]	12	Same	69	52	76	49	56	52	52	56	66	51

[a] Median scores; all others are means.

a significant direction; the raw-score mean for the group was approximately 2.5 on D-O, 1.0 on Hy-O, 2.5 on Pd-O, 0 on Pa-O, and 3.5 on Ma-O.

To generalize from a very limited number of cases, there is a possibility that individuals without neuropsychiatric diagnoses but with high MMPI profiles (one or more T scores above 70) are somewhat higher than on the S keys and somewhat lower on the O keys than a group with neuropsychiatric diagnoses and with high MMPI profiles.

S-O Differences between Successful and Unsuccessful Students and Trainees

The practical significance of the S and O keys was tested by their application to the MMPI answer sheets of groups of successful and unsuccessful veterans in school and in on-the-job training. These veterans had previously been studied to determine what factors in the counseling procedures differentiated between success and failure in training. Very few tests or case history factors did differentiate for any vocational groups; the MMPI showed consistent but generally insignificant differences favoring the emotional stability of the successful group. Generally, success was defined as having been in school or on-the-job training successfully for six months or more and still being there at the time of the study, whereas failure was defined as having left school or on-the-job training prior to completion.

The results of S and O as well as of the total scores were studied for 50 successful and 50 unsuccessful cases chosen at random. Table 4 indicates the results. The O

Table 4. Significance of Differences between Successful and Unsuccessful Groups on Subtle, Obvious, and Total Scales of the MMPI (N = 50 Each for the Successful (S) and Unsuccessful (U) Groups) [a]

Group	Mean	SD	SE_M	CR	Group	Mean	SD	SE_M	CR
D-O					Pd-T				
S	54.00	13.75	1.94		S	51.90	10.60	1.50	
U	62.40	18.85	2.67	2.55°°	U	55.20	11.80	1.67	1.47
D-S					Pa-O				
S	51.50	10.55	1.49		S	47.00	11.55	1.63	
U	50.50	10.75	1.52	−.47	U	53.30	13.70	1.94	2.49°°
D-T					Pa-S				
S	54.40	12.65	1.75		S	54.00	8.30	1.17	
U	60.50	16.70	2.36	2.07°°	U	51.40	12.15	1.72	−1.26
Hy-O					Pa-T				
S	55.20	12.05	1.70		S	50.90	8.80	1.24	
U	62.80	14.85	2.10	2.81°°	U	52.80	11.65	1.65	.92
Hy-S					Ma-O				
S	55.20	8.75	1.24		S	51.50	12.05	1.70	
U	52.70	8.95	1.27	−1.41	U	56.90	13.10	1.85	2.15°°
Hy-T					Ma-S				
S	56.50	10.35	1.46		S	55.90	11.35	1.61	
U	58.50	12.50	1.77	.87	U	55.50	9.05	1.28	−.20
Pd-O					Ma-T				
S	50.40	11.10	1.57		S	55.40	10.45	1.48	
U	55.50	10.25	1.45	2.39°°	U	58.90	11.30	1.60	1.61
Pd-S									
S	54.00	8.75	1.24						
U	52.40	10.35	1.46	−.84					

[a] °indicates significance at the .05 level; °°significance at the .01 level.

Table 5. Subtle and Obvious Keys for the MMPI

Obvious				Subtle			
Item No.		Scoring Direction		Item No.		Scoring Direction	
Card Form	Booklet Form	Card Form	Booklet Form	Card Form	Booklet Form	Card Form	Booklet Form
Depression (D)							
B12	2	F	X	B31	5	T	X
F39	8	F	X	J51	30	F	X
C17	9	F	X	G31	39	F	O
B18	18	F	X	D22	58	F	O
I27	32	T	X	G37	64	F	O
A6	36	F	X	I4	80	F	O
F44	41	T	X	C33	89	F	O
B28	43	T	X	D18	98	F	X
A24	46	F	X	B8	130	T	O
A2	51	F	X	G32	145	F	O
E24	52	T	X	A4	155	F	X
E36	57	F	X	A3	160	F	O
F36	67	T	X	B4	191	F	O
F38	88	F	X	B6	193	T	O
D10	95	F	X	C48	208	F	O
G7	104	T	X	C31	233	F	O
G12	107	F	X	B36	241	F	O
A23	122	F	X	G25	248	F	O
H43	131	F	X	B3	263	F	O
F34	138	T	X	G18	296	F	X
I37	142	T	X				
B30	152	F	X				
A1	153	F	X				
A18	154	F	X				
F51	158	T	X				
B2	159	T	X				
A27	178	F	X				
H55	182	T	X				
A40	189	T	X				
E41	207	F	X				
A8	242	F	X				
F42	259	T	X				
G38	270	F	X				
D49	271	F	O				
G23	272	F	X				
J50	285	F	X				
A15	23	T	X				
I34	290	T	X				
I39	86	T	X				
F45	236	T	X				
Hysteria (Hy)							
A1	153	F	X	A3	160	F	O
A2	51	F	X	A10	190	F	X
A5	163	F	X	B40	279	F	O
A11	44	T	X	C25	147	F	O
A12	114	T	X	C33	89	F	O
A15	23	T	X	C42	6	F	O
A16	175	F	X	C43	12	F	X
A17	174	F	X	D38	141	F	X
A31	274	F	X	D44	289	F	X

200

Table 5 — continued

	Obvious				Subtle		
Item No.		Scoring Direction		Item No.		Scoring Direction	
Card Form	Booklet Form	Card Form	Booklet Form	Card Form	Booklet Form	Card Form	Booklet Form
A32	188............	F	X	D48	71............	F	X
A40	189............	T	X	D52	93............	F	O
A42	192............	F	X	D54	124............	F	O
A44	103............	F	X	E3	26............	F	X
A45	186............	T	X	E23	292............	F	O
A46	243............	F	X	E43	267............	F	O
A55	7............	F	X	E44	180............	F	O
B1	47............	T	X	E53	265............	F	O
B9	55............	F	X	E54	253............	T	O
B10	230............	F	X	F5	201............	F	O
B11	10............	T	X	F7	170............	F	X
B12	2............	F	X	F9	172............	F	O
B27	3............	F	X	F25	162............	F	O
B28	43............	T	X	F33	129............	F	O
B48	137............	F	X	G29	234............	F	O
C17	9............	F	X	G40	213............	F	O
C51	179............	T	X	G50	109............	F	O
F39	8............	F	X	H10	136............	F	O
F49	76............	T	X	J51	30............	F	X
G12	107............	F	X				
G21	238............	T	X				
H54	128............	F	X				
I27	32............	T	X				

Paranoia (Pa)

A22	326............	T	X	A9	299............	T	X
A36	281............	F	X	B54	327............	F	X
E12	294............	F	X	D33	157............	T	X
E37	24............	T	X	D35	111............	F	X
F10	317............	T	X	D46	319............	F	O
F35	305............	T	X	D50	117............	F	O
F51	158............	T	X	D52	93............	F	O
G6	338............	T	X	D53	316............	F	O
G9	202............	T	X	D54	124............	F	O
G34	341............	T	X	D55	313............	F	O
G52	347............	F	X	G12	107............	F	X
G53	35............	T	X	G16	268............	F	X
G54	110............	T	X	G50	109............	F	O
G55	16............	T	X	H9	348............	F	X
H3	284............	T	X	H26	127............	T	X
H4	123............	T	X	H49	365............	T	X
H6	293............	T	X	J41	15............	T	O
H7	275............	T	X				
H8	291............	T	X				
H11	121............	T	X				
H14	151............	T	X				
H16	364............	T	X				
H25	27............	T	X				

Hypomania (Ma)

A19	156............	T	X	B37	11............	T	X
A20	194............	T	X	C6	21............	T	X

Table 5 — continued

Obvious				Subtle			
Item No.		Scoring Direction		Item No.		Scoring Direction	
Card Form	Booklet Form	Card Form	Booklet Form	Card Form	Booklet Form	Card Form	Booklet Form
A21	251	T	X	C27	148	F	O
A22	22	T	X	C31	233	T	X
A37	119	F	X	D7	101	F	X
B3	263	T	X	D26	232	T	X
B40	279	T	X	D34	143	T	X
B50	212	T	X	D44	289	F	X
C3	226	T	X	D49	271	T	X
C24	59	T	X	E31	181	T	X
D33	157	T	X	E43	267	F	O
D35	111	F	X	E44	180	F	O
E1	298	T	X	E48	240	T	X
E7	250	T	X	F8	171	F	O
E11	277	T	X	F14	222	T	X
E15	167	T	X	G16	268	T	O
G19	100	T	X	G26	228	T	O
G20	266	T	X	G30	134	T	O
G21	238	T	X	G37	64	T	X
G47	97	T	X	G50	109	T	X
H19	73	T	X	H26	127	T	X
I34	13	T	X	H47	166	F	O
J54	120	F	X	J44	105	F	X

Psychopathic Deviate (Pd)

Obvious				Subtle			
B42	215	T	X	A4	155	F	X
B47	42	T	X	B51	235	F	X
B48	137	F	X	B55	96	F	X
B49	216	T	X	C6	21	T	X
B52	224	T	X	C7	237	F	X
B53	245	T	X	C12	239	T	X
C47	20	F	X	C35	173	F	X
D30	118	T	X	D2	231	F	O
D32	38	T	X	D38	141	F	X
E12	294	F	X	D44	289	F	X
E17	37	F	X	D51	183	F	O
E37	24	T	X	E43	267	F	O
E46	91	F	X	E44	180	F	O
E50	94	T	X	F5	201	F	O
F36	67	T	X	F7	170	F	X
F39	8	F	X	F8	171	F	O
F50	106	T	X	G18	296	F	X
G4	61	T	X	G25	248	F	O
G12	107	F	X	G30	134	F	X
G53	35	T	X	H26	127	T	X
G54	110	T	X	I13	102	T	X
G55	16	T	X	I26	82	F	O
H3	284	T	X				
H12	33	T	X				
H31	287	F	X				
I12	84	T	X				
I27	32	T	X				
I30	244	T	X				

Table 6. T Scores for Subtle and Obvious Keys

Raw Score	D O	D S	Hy O	Hy S	Pd O	Pd S	Pa O	Pa S	Ma O	Ma S
0	31	9	38	24	34	18	39	27	28	14
1	34	13	41	26	37	22	44	31	32	18
2	37	17	44	28	40	26	49	35	36	22
3	40	21	47	30	43	30	54	39	40	26
4	43	25	50	32	46	33	59	43	44	30
5	46	29	52	35	49	37	64	47	48	34
6	49	33	55	37	52	41	69	52	52	38
7	52	37	58	39	55	45	74	56	55	42
8	55	41	60	41	58	48	79	60	59	46
9	58	45	63	44	61	52	84	64	63	50
10	61	49	66	46	64	56	89	68	67	54
11	64	53	68	48	67	60	94	72	71	58
12	67	57	71	50	70	63	99	76	75	62
13	70	61	74	53	73	67	104	80	79	66
14	73	65	76	55	76	71	109	84	83	70
15	76	69	79	57	79	75	114	88	87	74
16	80	73	82	59	82	79			91	78
17	83	77	84	62	85	82			95	82
18	86	81	87	64	88	86			98	86
19	89	85	90	66	91	90			102	90
20	92	89	92	68	94	94			106	94
21	95		95	71	97	97			110	98
22	98		98	73	100	101			114	102
23	101		100	75	103	105			118	106
24	104		103	77	107	109			122	110
25	107		106	79	110	112			126	114
26	110		109	81						
27	113			83						
28	116									
29	119									
30	121									

keys (see Table 5) in all cases showed a significantly higher score for the unsuccessful as compared with the successful group, the S keys (see Table 5) indicated insignificantly higher results for the successful group, and total scale results yielded differences in between the results of O and S keys, insignificantly (with one exception) favoring emotional stability in the successful group (for T-score distribution, see Table 6).

In most counseling situations where work is done with a relatively normal population, it is probable that the present MMPI total scale scores will largely fail to differentiate between successful and unsuccessful counselees because the total score represents a compromise between two fairly well differentiated aspects of each scale. Apparently elevation on the S keys tends to indicate, or at least does not counter-indicate, success in school or on-the-job training. Conversely, elevation on the O keys tends to predict failure. Results of total scale scores alone obscure this difference in function of S and O items in the MMPI.

Summary and Conclusions

1. New scales are needed for personality tests to indicate test-taking attitudes which might place the counselee in an overly favorable or unfavorable light.

2. Items in personality tests may be considered on a continuum from obviousness to subtlety. The O items differentiate best between abnormal and relatively normal groups; S items probably work best in measuring the personality characteristics of normal individuals.

3. Counselors working with a normal population would be served best by a personality test performing both as a screen for extreme deviates and as an indicator of personality characteristics of normal individuals.

4. S and O keys for the MMPI were developed for five scales of the MMPI, D, Hy, Pd, Pa, and Ma. T scores were developed from a sampling of the original male norm group of the inventory.

5. In general, O keys are highly correlated with each other and have no correlation with S keys; S keys have a low positive correlation with each other. There is a high negative correlation between O minus S and K, indicating the considerable weighting of K with S items.

6. There is some very limited evidence that high Lie scale scores are associated with higher S than O scores, whereas the converse is true for low Lie scores; that individuals of high ability have equal O and S scores, while those of low ability have higher O than S scores; that psychologically sophisticated individuals almost completely avoid significant O responses and have much higher S scores; that high MMPI profiles without neuropsychiatric diagnoses show higher S scores and lower O scores than high profiles with neuropsychiatric diagnoses.

7. While total scale scores on the MMPI failed to differentiate significantly between successful and unsuccessful students and on-the-job trainees, O keys were significantly higher than the S for the unsuccessful group. The S keys were insignificantly lower, and the total scale scores were between the two.

8. A word of caution: The S and O keys are not presented in final form or for indiscriminate use. Their proper use is predicated upon the recognition by counselors that extensive prior experience with and understanding of the MMPI are required. Furthermore, only subjective clinical observations indicate their significance on each of the five scales considered independently. However, the objective evidence indicates that the O and S scores are distributed, and associated with the factors studied, in an approximately similar manner for each of the scales. They seem to have the same meaning and to perform the same functions for each scale.

9. It is probable that the use of S and O keys in counseling a relatively normal population will increase appreciably the usefulness of the MMPI in predicting vocational and educational success as well as in distinguishing test-taking attitudes of importance in the therapeutic process. More specific statements regarding the significance of S and O keys for the MMPI will be possible upon the completion of further research into the validity of the original item selection method, the differentiating power of S and O keys among abnormal groups, and the predictive value of S and O for therapeutic success.

ARTICLE 23 *A Personality Scale for Anti-Semitic Prejudice (Pr)*

IT IS a matter of common observation that certain beliefs and attitudes tend to go together, and that others seem to be incompatible. For example, persons who feel that the government should play a more active role in preventing depressions and controlling inflations are frequently also in favor of greater rights and powers being granted to labor unions. On the other hand, persons who believe strongly in the tradition of individual enterprise and profit are frequently opposed to proposals such as those for national health and medical programs and those for governmental regional development programs such as the T.V.A.

In recent years psychologists have been studying these attitude clusters, particularly with respect to the question "What accounts for the *positive* relation of Attitude x to Attitudes m, n, and o, and its *negative* relation to Attitudes q, r, and s?" The evidence so far suggests, but does not prove, that only attitudes which are harmonious with the total personality are retained. It appears that, to some extent, highly specific attitudes of a person can be quite accurately predicted merely from knowing in a general way "what kind of a person he is."

This kind of thinking at once raises the question of whether a set of predictors might not be found which would identify the persons holding, or tending to hold, Attitude x, but which would contain no overt reference whatsoever to the actual content of this attitude. Many of the psychological and sociological correlates of anti-Semitism listed in the first paper in this series [246], and in the work of other writers [r61, r95], provide clues for possible starting points. Many of these previously enumerated correlates, however, involve indices and measurements which are difficult and time consuming to obtain, or which, on the other hand, hint at the issues being considered through the inclusion of material conventionally known to be related to ethnic beliefs.

Previous work with the MMPI [303] has revealed that quite useful scales for the prediction of socioeconomic status [236 (IV, 21), 242] and academic achievement [241] could be developed, and this fact suggested that a similar analysis with respect to ethnic attitudes might yield a number of items which would bear no apparent relationship to the continuum being studied, but which would nevertheless constitute reliable predictors of it. Furthermore, it was found in the previous studies that inspection of the items themselves added appreciably to an understanding of the psychological dimensions considered, in addition to any usefulness attaching to the scales as such. It was accordingly decided to carry out an item analysis of the MMPI to determine whether an "anti-Semitism" scale might not be developed.

The first step in the present study was the administration of the Levinson-Sanford anti-Semitism scale [r95] to a class of 271 high school seniors in a midwestern community of about 25,000 population. From this class the 40 highest scoring students (22 boys, 18 girls), and the 40 lowest scoring students (22 boys, 18 girls) were chosen for special consideration. The summary statistics for these two criterion subsamples are presented in Tables 1 and 2.

The two subsamples are differentiated on 13 of the 24 factors on which they were compared. The high (more anti-Semitic) subjects have lower MMPI K scores, suggestive of less forethought and prudence in response to personal inquiry, have slightly higher D, F, and Pd scores, are higher on Sc and Si [177 (IV, 19), 244] and are lower on the St [236 (IV, 21)] scale. These differences give the impression of a person with a somewhat injudicious and disgruntled manner, given to impulsive and poorly controlled social behavior, characterized by unusual and extreme complaints, inadequately poised, socially timid, uncertain of self and particularly of social skills, and harassed by fears and doubts concerning his own worth, capability, and integrity. A complete MMPI profile analysis would specify a great deal more than this, of course, but an indication has been given of the kinds of remarks that would be made.

Other differences are these: it appears that the more prejudiced students come from poorer homes, have fewer material advantages, are more undemocratic and ethnocentric, are less intelligent, are markedly inferior in academic achievement, and tend to have "objective" status scores in excess of their "subjective" status scores. This AHS-St index was found in an earlier study [242] to be related to indications of vertical mobility; that is, students with AHS relatively higher than St gave signs of potential *downward* social mobility, and those with St in excess of AHS gave indications of *upward* social mobility. The observed mean difference on AHS-St thus suggests that the more prejudiced students are potentially the more downwardly mobile students, and may therefore, perhaps, be assumed to be more dissatisfied with and more resentful of the present world.

This finding, obviously, ties in with much current sociological thinking concerning the importance of economic hopes and ambitions in producing reactions of tolerance and intolerance. The functioning of the AHS-St index is such that students getting higher scores are not necessarily those who recognize the possibility of a drop in status, or who manifestly expect to decline in economic standing from their parents' level, but are, rather, those whose actual anticipations justify such a prediction for them. The discrepancy score then serves to identify students whose declared expectations for adult life are greater, equal to, or less than other students of equivalent "objective" status. The prejudiced students in the present comparison have AHS-St indices betokening this curtailment and restriction of life expectations, and, by inference, the associated psychological overtones of feelings of resentment and victimization.

The responses of these two subsamples (40 vs. 40) to each of the 550 items in the MMPI were next tabulated and each item discriminating at or beyond the .05

Table 1. T-Score Means, Standard Deviations, and Codes of Criterion Groups and Differences and t Values between Groups (N = 22 Males and 18 Females in Each Group)

Group	L[a]	F[a]	K	Hs	D	Hy	Pa	Mf_M	Mf_F	Pa	Pt	Sc	Ma	Si
High scorers														
Mean	3.5	8.2	48.8	50.7	55.4	50.7	62.4	50.6	55.9	55.2	58.2	62.6	59.7	57.1
SD	2.3	3.7	8.3	7.6	10.4	6.4	7.8	8.8	10.2	10.5	10.1	11.1	9.5	9.3
						MMPI Code: 84-97026 31 F-/KL								
Low scorers														
Mean	3.4	4.1	55.3	50.5	51.4	53.4	58.1	54.8	50.7	54.2	54.7	56.8	57.4	51.7
SD	1.7	2.5	9.9	5.4	7.4	6.4	8.4	9.5	9.3	7.6	8.9	9.0	10.6	10.2
						MMPI Code: 498 763 021/ KF/L								
Diff	0.1	4.1	-6.5	0.2	4.0	-2.7	4.3	-4.1	5.2	0.9	3.5	5.8	2.3	5.3
t	0.11	5.75	3.16	0.13	1.95	1.84	2.31	1.46	1.31	0.44	1.51	2.54	1.01	2.42

[a] Raw scores are used instead of T scores.

Table 2. Means, Standard Deviations, Mean Differences, and t Values of Additional Measures on Criterion Groups (N = 22 Males and 18 Females in Each Group)

Group	Ac Scale (MMPI)	St Scale (MMPI)	Secur.-Insec.	Amer. Home Scale	Anti-Sem.	E-F Scale	Otis IQ	HPR	AHS-St_1[a]	AHS-St_2[b]
High scorers										
Mean	49.5	46.3	50.9	48.2	262.9	168.2	98.2	1.8	51.9	49.8
SD	9.5	8.0	10.8	8.6	21.0	22.2	10.5	0.6	10.1	11.2
Low scorers										
Mean	50.7	57.4	48.2	53.6	93.9	126.5	111.1	2.5	46.3	52.5
SD	9.8	9.3	11.2	11.9	19.6	20.0	10.7	0.6	10.9	10.9
Diff	-1.2	-11.0	2.7	-5.5	169.1	41.7	-12.9	-0.7	5.6	-2.7
t	0.56	5.63	1.10	2.33	36.80	8.72	5.36	4.79	2.34	1.06

[a] The difference between AHS and St with sign considered; the tabled figures have been converted to T scores.
[b] The difference between AHS and St taken without regard to sign; the tabled figures have been converted to T scores.

level was retained. Forty-seven items appeared in this analysis. These 47 items were then given to a new senior class of 263 students, who had also taken the Levinson-Sanford anti-Semitism scale, and two new criterion subsamples of 38 each (19 boys, 19 girls) were chosen. Comparison of the summary statistics for the two new subsamples revealed significant mean differences essentially similar to those found for the first criterion samples. Two additional variables, number of extracurricular activities and political and economic conservatism [246], were considered in the second class, with the less tolerant students being less participant and more conservative. The item analysis of the original 47 items left 32 which retained their differentiating power in the new situation. These items, the "prejudiced" direction of response, and the critical ratios for each analysis are listed in Table 3.

An inspection of these items suggests a number of factors as characteristic of the more prejudiced students. One of these factors seems to be anti-intellectuality. The less tolerant subjects do not like poetry, and do not like science, and one might infer an antipathy to systematic and logical analysis of human behavior, and a distrust of intellectuals, theorists, and "long-hairs." The MMPI does not include many items referring to literary and aesthetic interests, but one expects to find the more prejudiced subjects aligned with philistinism and anti-intellectuality throughout.

A second cluster of items refers to a pervading sense of pessimism and lack of hope and confidence in the future. The high scorers doubt whether they will be very successful in life, feel that the future is too unsure for making serious plans, and in general appear to be dispirited and dour concerning the future.

Closely related to these attitudes are feelings of cynicism, distrust, doubt, and suspicion. The high scorers feel that other people cannot be trusted, that others will prey upon them and exploit them, and that notions such as rectitude, probity, and so forth, are in fact mere façades and fictions. There is a brooding, doubting, and apprehensive quality to their conceptions, and they are unable to put confidence in others. Tendencies such as these would also suggest a basic lack of self-regard and a basic distrust of self-integrity. It is as if the high scorers, feeling unable to accept themselves, were unable to credit the motives and behavior of others.

This basically cynical cast seems to carry over, furthermore, into a diffuse misanthropy and querulousness. The more prejudiced students not only appear to doubt others, but they also appear to resent them and to dislike them. There is a tendency to debunk and discredit the abilities and achievements of others, to deflate and to disrespect them.

Another item cluster bespeaks a rather hostile and bitter outlook on the part of the more prejudiced, which ramifies into a destructiveness as exemplified in the item "Sometimes I feel as if I must injure either myself or someone else." This is a rather transparent expression of aggression, and emphasizes the emotional basis of the intolerant person's animosities, as opposed to a rational or intellectual one.

A seventh cluster of items betokens a repining, grumbling, and discontented evaluation of their current status by the more prejudiced students. The high scorers are resentful of the way in which others respond to them, and complain of the unfairness and injustice of their difficulties. They state that they have had more than their share of things to worry about, that they have often been punished without cause, that others are jealous of their good ideas, and that most people inwardly dislike putting themselves out to help others.

Table 3. Personality Inventory Items Which Discriminate between High and Low Scorers on an anti-Semitism Attitude Scale in Two High School Senior Classes (40 vs. 40 in the First Class, 38 vs. 38 in the Second)

MMPI Group Form Item No.	Item	"Prejudiced" Response	Critical Ratio A	B
47.	Once a week or oftener I feel suddenly hot all over, without apparent cause	true	2.77	1.88
78.	I like poetry	false	2.51	1.91
84.	These days I find it hard not to give up hope of amounting to something	true	2.70	2.40
93.	I think most people would lie to get ahead	true	2.31	1.95
106.	Much of the time I feel as if I have done something wrong or evil	true	3.52	2.38
117.	Most people are honest chiefly through fear of being caught	true	2.31	2.17
124.	Most people will use somewhat unfair means to gain profit or an advantage rather than to lose it	true	2.50	3.19
136.	I commonly wonder what hidden reason another person may have for doing something nice for me	true	3.03	2.79
139.	Sometimes I feel as if I must injure either myself or someone else	true	3.90	3.10
157.	I feel that I have often been punished without cause	true	2.71	1.64
171.	It makes me uncomfortable to put on a stunt at a party even when others are doing the same sort of thing	true	3.58	1.91
176.	I do not have a great fear of snakes	false	2.51	2.12
186.	I frequently notice my hand shakes when I try to do something	true	3.52	2.12
221.	I like science	false	2.26	2.09
250.	I don't blame anyone for trying to grab everything he can get in this world	true	2.42	1.73
280.	Most people make friends because friends are likely to be useful to them	true	4.31	4.47
304.	In school I found it very hard to talk before the class	true	3.58	2.76
307.	I refuse to play some games because I am not good at them	true	3.27	1.84
313.	The man who provides temptation by leaving valuable property unprotected is about as much to blame for its theft as the one who steals it	true	3.32	3.34
319.	Most people inwardly dislike putting themselves out to help other people	true	3.40	3.27
323.	I have had very peculiar and strange experiences	true	3.02	1.63
338.	I have certainly had more than my share of things to worry about	true	3.02	3.00
349.	I have strange and peculiar thoughts	true	2.67	1.84
373.	I feel sure that there is only one true religion	true	2.65	2.88
395.	The future is too uncertain for a person to make serious plans	true	3.32	2.07
406.	I have often met people who were supposed to be experts who were no better than I	true	2.68	3.70
411.	It makes me feel like a failure when I hear of the success of someone I know well	true	2.98	2.62
435.	Usually I would prefer to work with women	true	2.61	1.95
437.	It is all right to get around the law if you don't actually break it	true	4.08	3.70
469.	I have often found people jealous of my good ideas just because they had not thought of them first	true	2.74	2.12
485.	When a man is with a woman he is usually thinking about things related to her sex	true	2.48	2.73
543.	Several times a week I feel as if something dreadful is about to happen	true	3.01	1.85

209

An eighth cluster presages a rigid, somewhat dogmatic style of thinking. The evidence is not as clear-cut as that advanced by Frenkel-Brunswik and Sanford [r61] for categorical thinking, but the inflexibility is obvious in statements such as "I feel sure that there is only one true religion."

There seem to be signs of a lack of poise and self-assurance too. The less tolerant subjects found it very hard to talk before the class in school, feel uncomfortable in putting on a stunt at a party, and refuse to play some games because they are not good at them.

A final cluster seems to suggest an underlying perplexity, an ominous fearfulness, and feelings of estrangement and isolation which have mystifying and frightening consequences. The more prejudiced subjects state that they have had strange and peculiar experiences, that they have strange and peculiar thoughts, that they frequently feel as if something dreadful is about to happen, and that they usually feel as if they have done something wrong or evil.

The over-all picture which emerges from these item clusters is one of a harassed, tormented, resentful, peevish, querulous, constricted, disillusioned, embittered, distrustful, rancorous, apprehensive, and somewhat bewildered person. The syndrome is almost paranoid in its intensity, but is not equatable to paranoia for it lacks the excessive circumstantiality and self-deluding aspects of the latter. Nevertheless, it is clear that a set of characteristics such as those listed must be quasi- or near-pathological in its distorting and incapacitating implications for personality. All the tendencies mentioned are socially isolating in varying degrees and would be expected to interfere with and impair the efficiency of social interaction and response.

Attention is now turned from considering the items as clues to the psychology of anti-Semitism to their possible use as a scale or measuring instrument. The corrected split half reliability for the Pr ("prejudice") scale on a sample of 770 students was .79, SE .04. This compares favorably with the reliabilities reported for other MMPI scales [see 303]; test-retest reliability was not obtained, but experience with other scales would suggest that it would be higher [see 236]. The correlation of Pr with the Levinson-Sanford anti-Semitism scale was .49, SE .06, in the first senior class, and .45, SE .06, in the second. Its correlation with the E-F scale was .46, SE .06, in the first class, and .43, SE .06, in the second. The Pr scale was also checked against the Purdue Attitude Scale toward Jews in a third senior class of 231 students, with a resulting correlation of —.28, SE .07 (high scores on the Purdue scale indi-

Table 4. T-Conversion Table for Pr, Based on 1078 High School
Students (528 Males and 550 Females)

Raw	T	Raw	T	Raw	T	Raw	T
32	83	23	67	15	53	7	39
31	81	22	65	14	51	6	37
30	79	21	63	13	49	5	35
29	78	20	62	12	47	4	33
28	76	19	60	11	46	3	31
27	74	18	58	10	44	2	30
26	72	17	56	9	42	1	28
25	71	16	55	8	40	0	26
24	69						

cate favorable attitudes). This correlation is appreciably lower than the first two, which may be as much a result of the lower validity of the Purdue scale [246] as of the decline of validity of the Pr scale as it is extended to new samples.

The final step in the present study was to prepare a T-conversion table for the Pr scale, as indicated in Table 4. This table is based on a sample of 1078 high school students from several different communities, and may be considered a fairly dependable basis for estimating the frequency of various Pr scores in comparable samples.

In summary, an item analysis of the MMPI in two different high school senior classes using the Levinson-Sanford anti-Semitism scale as a criterion yielded 32 items, each of which significantly differentiated the criterion subsamples in both classes. These items were strongly suggestive of certain personality trends on the part of both the more and the less prejudiced students. The 32 items were also considered as a scale, which appeared to be sufficiently reliable and valid to be used as a measuring instrument in its own right.

H. G. GOUGH, H. McCLOSKY, AND P. E. MEEHL

✦

ARTICLE 24 *A Personality Scale for Dominance (Do)*

THE present study is part of a project concerned with political behavior and, especially, political participation. The purpose of the larger project is to investigate the validity of certain ideas of political scientists, political leaders, and citizens about the nature and operation of the democratic process, and to discover how realistically they take into account the facts of political life in our country. These ideas usually presuppose a developed sense of *participation, awareness,* and *responsibility* among both the leaders and the governed of the American body politic. In the light of such "mass society" developments as urbanization, the enormous increases in population, the increasing complexity of social living, the growing emphasis on specialization, and the vast extension of governmental functions, it becomes of increasing importance to determine the character of political participation, awareness, and responsibility, how they develop, how they may be influenced, and how they manifest themselves.

The general plan of the project will be described in other publications, but it is pertinent to outline briefly the research setting for the present study, and the manner in which it fits into the program. The basic research problem is to discover and specify the various factors — sociological, psychological, and so forth — which underlie and relate to political participation. The variable of participation is treated as a criterion, and the task is to ascertain what other factors are related to it. Participation is assumed to be a function of factors $x_1, x_2, x_3 \ldots x_n,$ and the goal of the research is the identification and description of these factors. We are, of course, concerned with "prediction" mainly in the statistical sense, since our chief aim is the exploration of causal factors of participation .

Preliminary theoretical analysis suggested that factors such as "awareness," sense of responsibility, socioeconomic status, sense of community identification, feelings of bewilderment and confusion, intellectuality, dominance, and so forth might play a part, and attention was accordingly directed to techniques for assessing these variables.

In translating this kind of thinking into an actual research program, the first task is to obtain a clearly defined and tangible criterion and then to find reliable methods for evaluating the predictor variables and for relating them to the criterion.

We considered dominance to be a particularly important dimension in relation to political participation, and the decision was therefore made to construct a new

212

personality scale which would embody elements not present in extant devices, and which would, furthermore, correlate closely with group ratings on dominance.

Development of the Scale

The technique utilized in constructing the dominance scale was one which might be called the "peer group nomination technique," as distinguished from a strictly sociometric procedure. Subjects were not asked to choose the group member they would most or least prefer to see in some specified role, but were asked to nominate the members of their group whom they considered to be most and least dominant. A number of different groups cooperated in carrying out this phase of the study, including one fraternity and one sorority at the University of Minnesota, and several classes in social science at North High School in Minneapolis. Approximately 100 students were included in the college sample, and 124 were in the high school sample.

Each student participating in the study was given a personal data sheet calling for routine information, for dominance selections, and for dominance self-ratings. Instructions were included defining the dimension of dominance. It was an interesting observation that none of the students seemed to feel a need for this specification, and many stated that they could have completed the choices and ratings equally well without any guide other than the trait name itself. This fact is mentioned in support of the contention that the concept "dominance," for all its complexities, is a functioning term in the vocabularies of unsophisticated persons, a term which they apply in their everyday evaluations.

That these judgments, furthermore, are not merely fortuitous or idiosyncratic is established by the concordance in ratings to be reported shortly, and further documented by the repetitive validity of a number of subtle personality test items in the two groups. In short, the concept "dominance" appears to have both empirical content and social relevance. Whether or not it has significance in regard to the broader questions of political participation remains to be seen.

The directions for the nomination section are reproduced below:

The dominant person tends to be the "stronger" in face-to-face personal situations, for instance, with friends, salespeople, etc. He is able to influence others, to gain their automatic respect, and if necessary to control them. He is not readily intimidated or defeated, and his own feelings in most face-to-face situations seem to be feelings of safety, security, personal rightness, and self-confidence. Such people are often described by others as "forceful," "masterful," "strong," "confident," "authoritative," and "sure of himself."

People with *low* dominance are submissive. They appear and feel weaker in face-to-face contacts. They find it hard to assert themselves, to stand up for their rights and opinions, and are more easily influenced and intimidated by others. When a dominant and submissive person come into conflict, the dominant one gets his way.

There are three things to be especially careful about in rating dominance:

1. Do *not* assume that "dominance" means domineering or "autocratic." While most domineering people are dominant, not all dominant people are domineering. Dominant people do not necessarily become leaders, or go out of their way to control and influence others. But whether they do or not, they create this effect of masterful self-assurance and others are often influenced by them. They may be very fair and

reasonable: they may not want to lead people; yet still this basic dominance shows through.

2. Please rate on the basis of the person's *actual behavior*, not on the basis of how you think he would like to act, or how he fancies himself in his daydreams, etc. We want to know how dominant he is in actual behavior.

3. Remember that some people get into positions of prestige and power and thus control others, even though they may not be particularly dominant, for instance, because they are very bright, or have much money, etc. Do not confuse this with the *personal trait* of dominance, which we are asking you to judge.

Following this set of instructions, the high school students were asked to list the names of the five most dominant and the five least dominant in that particular classroom. (All ratings were taken in social science classes so that no student voted, or was voted upon, more than once.) In the college samples, students were asked to list the ten most and the ten least dominant members of the fraternity or sorority to which they belonged. The self-rating section utilized the graphic-rating technique with a four-inch scale calibrated in half-inch intervals.

In order to select the criterion groups for the item analyses, weights of plus 1 for each "most dominant" choice, and of minus 1 for each "least dominant" choice, were assigned. Adding these weights gave a "score" to each subject, on the basis of which rankings and selections were made. There was a broad range of scores in each group, indicating that certain students were clearly seen as dominant and others just as distinctly seen as submissive. The self-ratings did not show the same spread of scores, for, as might be expected, not very many subjects were willing to rate themselves as "submissive." There was a noticeable piling up of scores, nevertheless, at the middle, at the most dominant extreme, and the least dominant extreme, in that order. The correlation between the group- and self-ratings in the college sample was .421, SE .14, and in the high school sample .441, SE .09.

Prior to obtaining the nominations in each group, we administered a questionnaire consisting of some 150 items which were especially written to assess the dominance factor, as it was then conceptualized by the writers. In the college group, subsamples composed of the 25 most and the 25 least dominant students were selected (13 females, 12 males in each subsample) for the item analysis. In this total group there was no question of whether males or females were most dominant, as the rankings were made separately for the fraternity and for the sorority, and the extreme cases were pooled for the subsequent analysis. In the high school group, subsamples of 25 at each extreme were chosen (12 females, 13 males in each). The ratings here did indicate a slight tendency toward greater dominance for males.

A number of college students had taken the MMPI [303] as part of a routine testing procedure at other times, and on the basis of those records, which were available to us, the responses of 16 more and 16 less dominant college students (8 females, 8 males) were studied. Approximately 100 items from the MMPI showed promise in discriminating these two subsamples, and these items were, accordingly, administered to the high school classes a few days after the previously mentioned questionnaire. Each of the criterion subgroups for this second analysis included 12 females and 12 males.

From the two item analyses in each of the two groups (high school and college) a total of 60 items was retained, all of which revealed differentiating power in both samples. Thirty-two of these items were drawn from the specially written pool, and 28 from the MMPI. The items are listed below, with responses scored for "dominance":

1. A person does not need to worry about other people if only he looks after himself. (Disagree) 2. When I work on a committee I like to take charge of things. (Agree) 3. I enjoy planning things, and deciding what each person should do. (Agree) 4. I'm not the type to be a political leader. (Disagree) 5. People seem naturally to turn to me when decisions have to be made. (Agree) 6. I would be a good leader of people. (Agree) 7. I have a natural talent for influencing people. (Agree) 8. I like to give orders and get things moving. (Agree) 9. I hate to have to tell others what to do. (Disagree) 10. I think I would enjoy having authority over other people. (Agree) 11. I would rather not have very much responsibility for other people. (Disagree) 12. I doubt whether I would make a good leader. (Disagree) 13. Disobedience to any government is never justified. (Disagree) 14. I think I am usually a leader in my group. (Agree) 15. Every citizen should take the time to find out about national affairs, even if it means giving up some personal pleasure. (Agree)

16. There are times when I act like a coward. (Agree) 17. People should not have to pay taxes for the schools if they do not have children. (Disagree) 18. I am embarrassed with people I do not know well. (Disagree) 19. When the community makes a decision, it is up to a person to help carry it out, even if he had been against it. (Agree) 20. I would be willing to give money myself in order to right a wrong, even though I was not mixed up in it in the first place. (Agree) 21. School teachers complain a lot about their pay, but it seems to me they get as much as they deserve. (Disagree) 22. In a group, I usually take the responsibility for getting people introduced. (Agree) 23. I am a better talker than listener. (Agree) 24. I would rather have people dislike me than have them look down on me. (Agree) 25. I would be willing to describe myself as a pretty "strong" personality. (Agree) 26. We should cut down on our use of oil, if necessary, so that there will be plenty left for the people fifty or a hundred years from now. (Agree) 27. I dislike to have to talk in front of a group of people. (Disagree) 28. I must admit I am a pretty fair talker. (Agree) 29. We ought to let Europe get out of its own mess; it made its bed, let it lie in it. (Disagree) 30. I must admit I try to see what others think before I take a stand. (Disagree)

31. When prices are high you can't blame a person for getting all he can while the getting is good. (Disagree) 32. I can honestly say that I do not really mind paying my taxes because I feel that's one of the things I can do for what I get from the community. (Agree) 33. I find it hard to keep my mind on a task or job. (Disagree) 34. I have not lived the right kind of life. (Disagree) 35. I sometimes keep on at a thing until others lose patience with me. (Agree) 36. I am easily downed in an argument. (Disagree) 37. I am certainly lacking in self-confidence. (Disagree) 38. I do many things which I regret afterwards (I regret things more or more often than others seem to). (Disagree) 39. I frequently notice my hand shakes when I try to do something. (Disagree) 40. I very much like hunting. (Disagree) 41. My parents have often objected to the kind of people I went around with. (Disagree) 42. I should like to belong to several clubs or lodges. (Agree) 43. I never worry about my looks. (Disagree) 44. I believe there is a Devil and a Hell in afterlife. (Disagree) 45. I don't blame anyone for trying to grab everything he can get in this world. (Disagree)

46. Sometimes at elections I vote for men about whom I know very little. (Agree) 47. When in a group of people I have trouble thinking of the right things to talk

about. (Disagree) 48. Something exciting will almost always pull me out of it when I am feeling low. (Disagree) 49. When I leave home I do not worry about whether the door is locked and the windows closed. (Agree) 50. In school I found it very hard to talk before the class. (Disagree) 51. I usually have to stop and think before I act even in trifling matters. (Disagree) 52. I have more trouble concentrating than others seem to have. (Disagree) 53. I have sometimes stayed away from another person because I feared doing or saying something that I might regret afterwards. (Agree) 54. The future is too uncertain for a person to make serious plans. (Disagree) 55. I played hooky from school quite often as a youngster. (Disagree) 56. I have strong political opinions. (Agree) 57. Christ performed miracles such as changing water into wine. (Disagree) 58. I practically never blush. (Agree) 59. A large number of people are guilty of bad sexual conduct. (Disagree) 60. The one to whom I was most attached and whom I most admired as a child was a woman (mother, sister, aunt, or other woman). (Disagree)

Inspection of these items reveals some interesting trends. It would appear that no more than half are immediately obvious, in the sense that they deal explicitly with matters of superordination, control, strength, and ascendancy. A few of the items are quite subtle, in the sense that they would not ordinarily be thought of as correlates of dominance (e.g., "Sometimes at elections I vote for men about whom I know very little," answered "Agree"), and one or two actually seem to work "backwards," (e.g., "I sometimes act like a coward," answered "Agree").

A careful reading of the items suggests a number of characterizations of the subjective side of the dominant personality. The factor which is implied by the largest number of items appears to be one of poise and self-assurance. The dominant personality maintains a high level of self-confidence, does not seem to be plagued by self-doubts or equivocations, and therefore appears freer to behave in an unencumbered and straightforward manner. The impression given is one of resoluteness and vigorous optimism. Closely related to this is another suggested factor of resourcefulness and efficiency. The dominant personality appears to move forward in a realistic, task-oriented fashion and manifests feelings of adequacy in meeting whatever obstacles may be encountered.

There is also a certain element of perseverance, or even doggedness, implied. The dominant subjects admit to working on at things even when others become impatient with them, etc., and in general give evidence of strong completion-needs.

The dominant subjects indicate what might be called a "dutiful" sense of morality. They agree that people should pay school taxes even if they have no children, that everyone must get behind a community decision regardless of previous sentiments on the issue, that we should curtail our own use of oil in order to preserve a fair share for future generations, and state that they would be willing to give money to right a wrong which was no particular concern of theirs. Dominant persons, as so visualized, would be expected to take active roles in getting group members to accept the collective responsibilities of the group. They would be the ones who would insist on distributed sacrifices and obligations in carrying out group projects.

Trends such as these might also suggest an element of rigidity and inflexibility, but it appears on closer investigation to be not so much a matter of rigidity in the ordinary sense of routinization of method and procedure, as an unyieldingness in the area of goals and values. The dominant personality would show adaptiveness in relation to means and techniques, but less in respect to aims and purposes.

The high scorers would also seem to be characterized by a rather deep-seated seriousness. This does not imply solemnity or pomposity, but would appear to reflect a basic acceptance of self and a consequent disinclination to treat fundamental needs, satisfactions, and dissatisfactions in a light or trivial manner. Thus, the dominant subjects deny that something exciting will almost always pull them out of a low mood, agree that they have strong political opinions, and deny that they never worry about their physical appearance. There is almost a compulsive need to face reality. (For example, the high scorers admit that they sometimes vote for unknown candidates at an election, and that they sometimes act in a cowardly manner, even though the latter description would probably not be applied to their behavior by friends and acquaintances.) Similar tendencies might account for the denial of certain conventionally accepted religious beliefs by the dominant subjects.

It should be emphasized at this point that the authors are merely elaborating some of the impressions and inferences which they have obtained from a consideration of the items listed above. These speculations are not offered as conclusions, or as demonstrated findings, but as hypotheses for further investigation.

The next consideration in the development of the dominance scale was the question of reliability. The only evidence so far observed on this point comes from a coefficient based on the Kuder-Richardson formula No. 21, of .79 for the combined distribution of the two original samples.

On the more important question of validity, the evidence cited in Table 1 may be offered. The number of cases in the two subsamples for each group is rather small, an unavoidable limitation because not all the subjects in both groups were exposed to all the items finally selected to make up the 60-item scale. It can be seen, nevertheless, that for the cases scored on the total scale, the discrimination between most and least dominant subsamples was very good. With the exception of two cases in the college samples, and four in the high school samples, the two distributions are nonoverlapping. The percentage of correct sortings which would be achieved with a cutting score of 36 in the college sample would be 94, and a cutting score of 39 in the high school sample would correctly classify 92 per cent of the cases. Validation in samples beyond the two already reported has not as yet been carried out.

The correlation between scores on the dominant scale and the dominance ratings was .599, SE .14, in the college sample, and .687, SE .09, in the high school group. The coefficient between self-ratings and the personality scale was .520, SE .14, in the college group, and .555, SE .09, for the high school.

The high school had a system of volunteer social service activities, participation in which gave "points" to the student. Thirty-four of the high school students had acquired social service points, and 89 had not. The biserial r between this dichotomy and scores on the dominance scale was .33.

Another comparison was made between dominance measures and social status, as defined by an objective inventory [r64]. The correlation of the Home Index with the dominance scale was .352, with the nominations .266, and with self-ratings .302, SE .09 throughout. (These comparisons were made only in the high school group.)

For the total 60-item dominance scale, the means and standard deviations were

Table 1. Distribution of Raw Scores on the Dominance Scale for Each of the Two Subsamples ("Most" and "Least" Dominant) in the Two Criterion Groups

Score	College Group M	College Group L	High School Group M	High School Group L
53–54	2			
51–52	2		1	
49–50	1		2	
47–48	3		5	
45–46	2		2	
43–44	3		1	
41–42	1		6	
39–40	0	2	3	
37–38	0	2	2	1
35–36	0	0	1	2
33–34	0	0	0	0
31–32	1	6	0	3
29–30	1	1	0	5
27–28		2	1	0
25–26		0		1
23–24		1		5
21–22		1		2
19–20		0		2
17–18		1		2
15–16				0
13–14				1
N	16	16	24	24
Mean	45.31	30.50	42.83	26.12
SD	6.47	5.93	5.32	6.28

37.06 and 8.47, and 34.11 and 8.06, for the total college and high school samples respectively.

The 28 items drawn from the MMPI were also considered separately. In the college group, correlation of the 28-item scale with the group ratings was .524, and with self-ratings .651, SE .14 throughout. In the high school sample the MMPI dominance scale correlated .597, SE .09, with nominations, and .411, SE .09, with self-ratings.

The distributions of raw scores on the MMPI portion of the dominance scale for the college and high school samples, and for two additional samples, are presented in Table 2. The decline in average dominance scores from the older to the younger age groups may be remarked (the F test is significant beyond the .01 level). Two equally likely (not necessarily exclusive) explanations can be advanced for this trend. It may actually be a matter of age and maturity, etc., or it may be that the more ambitious and capable (and hence more dominant) students are more likely to move on to twelfth grade and college from the earlier high school years. T scores for this MMPI dominance "scale" have not been provided because of the highly selected nature of the samples studied. Workers who care to use the scale, however, may compute tentative conversion tables from the data given in the last column of Table 2.

The present study has certain serious limitations in light of the broader purposes for which it was carried out. The most important of these is that the larger research project is being conducted entirely with adults, and the present scale has been

Table 2. Distribution of Raw Scores on the 28 Items of the Dominance Scale
Taken from the MMPI

Score	Criterion Groups		Additional Samples		Total
	College	High School	High School	Ninth Grade	
28............					
27............					
26............		1			1
25............	1	1			2
24............	1				1
23............	6				6
22............	4	3	6	3	16
21............	1	7	5		13
20............	5	6	11	5	27
19............	3	9	14	7	33
18............	8	13	14	13	48
17............	8	10	29	17	64
16............	2	15	24	24	65
15............	4	7	23	32	66
14............	1	11	29	32	73
13............	1	15	30	21	67
12............	2	7	28	17	54
11............	2	5	27	15	49
10............		5	21	17	43
9............		5	9	11	25
8............			6	2	8
7............			4	2	6
6............	1	1	1	1	4
5............		2	1	1	4
4............					
3............				1	1
2............					
1............					
0............					
N	50	123	282	221	676
Mean	18.08	15.47	14.20	13.98	14.64
SD	3.84	3.89	3.50	3.17	3.70

developed on the basis of the responses of adolescents only. The extent to which this disparity will obscure and prejudice results when the scale is used on the adult population cannot be predicted, but it may be assumed that some distortion will occur. For one thing, it seems unlikely on the basis of casual observation that the rather stern morality of the dominant adolescents considered here will prevail to the same degree among adults.

In spite of these manifest limitations the authors would conclude that the dominance scale in its present form is a useful measuring instrument and should yield dependable results for the specification of group trends in most situations.

Summary

Dominance is one of the dimensions that would appear to be of importance in the psychology of political participation. It was accordingly decided to attempt the construction of a dominance scale which would reliably predict group judgments of dominance and which would incorporate a wider and more significant range of item content than has been true of previous scales.

A final 60-item scale was evolved which included 28 items from the MMPI and 32 original items. This scale correlated to the extent of .599 and .687 with group ratings on dominance, and appeared to be sufficiently reliable for group interpretation.

The implication of a number of item clusters for personality analysis was discussed, and certain limitations of the scale were recognized.

ARTICLE 25 *A Caudality Scale for the MMPI (Ca)*

RECENT studies have demonstrated that in order for the clinical psychologist to measure adequately the psychometric effects of brain damage, he must consider not only gross signs of deficit, but also such matters as the location of the lesion [r8, r9, 21 (see VIII, 53), 208]. Andersen in his study of the "laterality" dimension has demonstrated that the psychologist can offer assistance in localization. Andersen and Hanvik [21 (see VIII, 53)] and Friedman [208] have shown that patients with focal lesions in the frontal lobes can be discriminated from those with parietal lesions by use of the MMPI. Friedman [208] developed a parietal-frontal scale with which he achieved remarkable differentiation between the two groups. The present study is concerned with a cross-validation of Friedman's work and the development of a "caudality" (Ca) scale which is believed to have somewhat more general application than the original parietal-frontal scale.

The Group

The subjects used were 116 male patients supplied by the neurological and neurosurgical staffs of four hospitals in Minnesota. The age of the patients ranged from 17 to 64 years; the mean age was 36.35 years, and the SD 11.53 years. Comparison with population statistics showed that there were no statistically significant differences between the occupational classification of the group and that for the general population [r180]. Educational data were not available on many patients.

All patients had suffered focal cerebral damage confined to one brain hemisphere as far as could be determined. The focal nature of the damage was verified through surgical procedure except in the case of several gunshot wounds where authentication was made by means of X-ray demonstration of retained metallic foreign bodies. Although surgical diagnosis is probably one of the best criteria for localization, there is still room for doubt since there are the possibilities of *contrecoup* damage, distortion of other regions by expansion of the lesion, or unreported damage such as that incurred by concussion. In addition, a number of cases suffered lesions which extended beyond a single lobe. These were recorded as frontal, parietal, or temporal after consultation with members of the neurological and neurosurgical staffs of the several hospitals. These factors would tend to attenuate rather than exaggerate differential results, however, and within the limits of the conclusions drawn from the study, the criteria seem reasonably adequate.

221

The total sample of 116 cases was treated in several subgroups. In addition to Friedman's original group of 56 cases (28 frontal and 28 parietal), 20 frontal, 20 parietal, and 20 temporal patients were obtained for cross-validation purposes. All these subgroups were evenly divided in terms of laterality (i.e., dominant and non-dominant hemisphere damage). With regard to the statistics mentioned above for the total sample, there were no significant differences between the subgroups.

Procedure

The study is concerned entirely with personality changes associated with focal brain damage. The test used is the MMPI which has been described in detail elsewhere [305]. Profile differences between frontal and nonfrontal cases, as well as rather detailed analyses of profile patterns, will be considered in a later paper. It can be said, however, that when analysis of variance was used to hold constant the laterality variable, the results in the parietal-frontal cross-validation sample tended to confirm the earlier observations of Friedman, and Andersen and Hanvik. Although there was evidence of considerable regression toward the mean, the cases with parietal damage did show significant elevations on the D and Pt scales when compared with the composite frontal profile which was rather flat, with an elevation of Sc. In addition, the mean temporal profile based upon 20 cases was not significantly different from the mean parietal profile, but could be distinguished, statistically, from the composite frontal profile. However, like the profiles of frontal patients, temporal cases tended to produce secondary elevations on the Sc scale. As Friedman observed, there were no significant differences associated with laterality of the lesion, although there was a trend toward higher scores on the psychotic variables in relation to dominant hemisphere damage.

By a comparison of the frequency of responses in the significant direction in his frontal and parietal samples, Friedman succeeded in developing a parietal-frontal scale which differentiated them with high validity. However, in his relatively small cross-validation sample, the discrimination, although still statistically significant, involved considerably more overlap. The present cross-validation included three procedures. The first was a determination of the effectiveness of the Friedman scale on the new sample of 40 frontal and parietal cases. The other two involve item analysis, and include a modification of the method of "Double Cross-Validation" suggested by Katzell [r125].

When the original Friedman scale was applied to the cross-validation sample (20 frontal and 20 parietal cases), using the raw score cutting point of eleven recommended by him, it failed to identify 25 per cent of the cases. Chi square applied to this problem, scoring tallies as hits or misses, is significant at the .01 level.

In order to study the behavior of individual items, rather extensive item analysis was undertaken. First, the total frontal-parietal group of 96 cases was divided into two equal subgroups (A and B), with 48 frontal and 48 parietal cases in each. The percentage of significant responses to a particular item in the two diagnostic groups was then compared, using phi coefficients. Items were selected for further study which separated frontal from parietal cases with the rather liberal probability criterion of .10. Items selected at this level in group A were further studied in group B and vice versa. A final scale was constructed of items which held up in the opposite group at the .05 level or better. This procedure differs from that recommended by

Mosier, *et al.* [r125], in that selection of items for the final scale is not based upon product probabilities [r103].

The resulting scale contained twenty items, 56 per cent of which appear in the original Friedman scale. It has a disadvantage in terms of reliability in that it contains so few items.

An alternative approach to item selection is to combine both subgroups into one sample, and select a final scale using a fairly stringent significance criterion. This was done in the present case, and items were accepted which discriminated the frontal and parietal groups at a confidence level of .02 or better. A scale of thirty-three items resulted, 44 per cent of which overlapped with the Friedman scale, and 48 per cent with the scale developed by modified double cross-validation.

Since the mean profile for temporal patients was very similar to that observed in relation to parietal damage, it seemed appropriate to apply the several scales to the temporal group in order to study their respective validities. Technically, it will be impossible to demonstrate entirely adequate cross-validation since a third frontal group is not available. However, if the raw score cutting points used in the parietal-frontal studies successfully discriminate the temporal group from the combined frontal sample, it seems relatively safe to argue that the scales are valid predictors of caudality.

Results

When the 20 temporal cases and 48 frontal cases are distributed on the original Friedman scale, there are 9 frontal and 9 temporal patients misclassified. Chi square applied to this data is significant beyond the .01 level, but when the temporal cases are considered alone, with a raw score cutting line between 11 and 12, the sorting is almost at chance. Since this scale held up remarkably well on parietal-frontal cross-validation, the present result suggests that it is tapping behavior specifically associated with parietal and frontal involvement, and that it is not valid for predicting temporal damage.

The 20-item scale separates the two groups with six errors in the temporal and six in the frontal sample. Chi square is significant beyond the .001 level. The 33-item scale misses eight frontal and six temporal patients. Chi square is again significant beyond the .001 level. These results indicate that the 20-item scale performs somewhat better than the others in both the parietal-frontal and temporal-frontal problems. However, it is only slightly more valid than the 33-item scale.

It is interesting and important that the three scales without great item overlap each discriminate the criterion with high validity. This suggests that certain personality variables are associated with focal lesions in two different areas, and that these traits are not defined strictly by one set of empirically derived items. Since there were advantages in both the scale developed by modified double cross-validation and the one based upon analysis of the total frontal and parietal sample, and since their respective validities seemed about equally high, the two were combined into a single final scale which will now be designated the Ca (Caudality) scale. Listed below are the thirty-seven items, and the direction they are to be scored to predict a nonfrontal lesion:

A-5. I do not tire quickly. (F) Hy, Hs. A-7. I do not dread seeing a doctor about a sickness or injury. (F) A-8. I believe I am no more nervous than most others.

(F) D. A-24. My judgment is better than it ever was. (F) D. A-28. I am greatly bothered by forgetting where I put things. (T) A-32. I can read a long while without tiring my eyes. (F) Hy, Hs. A-40. I feel weak all over much of the time. (T) D, Pt, Hs, Hy. A-48. I have numbness in one or more regions of my skin. (T) Sc, Hs. A-52. I practically never blush. (F) B-2. I cannot understand what I read as well as I used to. (T) D, Sc, Pt. C-12. I have been disappointed in love. (T) Pd, Mf. C-25. I have often lost out on things because I couldn't make up my mind soon enough. (T) Hy. C-50. I am very strongly attracted by members of my own sex. (F) Mf. D-55. The man who provides temptation by leaving valuable property unprotected is about as much to blame for its theft as the one who steals it. (T) Pa. E-9. When someone does me a wrong I feel I should pay him back if I can, just for the principle of the thing. (T) Mf. E-30. I enjoy the excitement of a crowd. (F) E-36. I am a good mixer. (F) D. E-44. I find it hard to make talk when I meet new people. (T) Hy, Ma, Pd, K. E-50. I do many things which I regret afterwards. (I regret things more or more often than others seem to.) (T)

F-37. I am usually calm and not easily upset. (F) F-39. My daily life is full of things that keep me interested. (F) D, Sc, Pt, Hy, Pd. F-45. I brood a great deal. (T) D. F-49. Most of the time I feel blue. (T) Sc, Pt, Hy. G-6. I have certainly had more than my share of things to worry about. (T) Pa. G-31. At times I feel like smashing things. (T) D, K. G-36. I usually have to stop and think before I act even in trifling matters. (T) Pt. H-5. Sometimes I am sure that other people can tell what I am thinking. (T) H-29. I must admit that I have at times been worried beyond reason over something that really did not matter. (T) H-55. I am afraid of losing my mind. (T) D, Sc, Pt. I-15. My plans have frequently seemed so full of difficulties that I have had to give them up. (T) I-32. I am inclined to take things hard. (T) Pt. I-37. I certainly feel useless at times. (T) D, Pt. I-41. I shrink from facing a crisis or diffi-culty. (T) J-9. I sometimes feel that I am about to go to pieces. (T) J-13. I feel tired a good deal of the time. (T) J-17. I think Lincoln was greater than Washington. (F)

When the entire sample of 116 cases is distributed against the final Ca scale, using a cutting line at the gross median (raw score 11), 12 parietal and 10 frontal cases are misclassified. This is an error of 22 per cent. With the same cutting score, the scale fails to identify 6 of the patients with temporal involvement.

In order that this scale could be compared with other MMPI scales, raw scores were converted to T scores, based on the frontal distribution. The T-score equiva-lents are presented in Table 1. The mean raw score of nonfrontal patients is equiv-alent to a T score of 70.

It is apparent from a study of the list above that the new scale reflects rather diffuse symptomatology. The items contribute to ten scales on the MMPI, with greatest overlap on D, Pt, Hy, and Sc.

The Pearson correlations between the original MMPI scales (plus Si) and scores on the Ca scale over the frontal-parietal sample of 96 cases were computed. Al-though the Friedman scale correlated highest with D, the present scale correlates most with Pt (r equals .82). The scale correlates significantly with ten MMPI vari-ables, and is negatively correlated with K.

Conclusions

The results of the study indicate that the conclusions of Andersen and Hanvik, and later Friedman, were to a considerable extent justified. Patients with lesions in the parietal region respond to the MMPI in such a way as to suggest anxiety, de-

Table 1. T-Score Equivalents for Raw Scores on the Ca (Caudality) Scale

Raw Score	Z	T	Raw Score	Z	T
37	6.86	119	18	2.33	73
36	6.62	116	17	2.09	71
35	6.38	114	16	1.86	69
34	6.14	111	15	1.61	66
33	5.90	109	14	1.38	64
32	5.66	107	13	1.14	61
31	5.43	104	12	.90	59
30	5.19	102	11	.67	57
29	4.95	100	10	.43	54
28	4.71	97	9	.18	52
27	4.47	95	8	−.05	50
26	4.23	92	7	−.28	47
25	4.00	90	6	−.52	45
24	3.76	88	5	−.76	42
23	3.52	85	4	−1.00	40
22	3.28	83	3	−1.24	38
21	3.05	80	2	−1.47	35
20	2.80	78	1	−1.71	33
19	2.57	76	0	−1.95	30

pression, guilt, introversion, feelings of inadequacy, worry about the future, and somatic concern. Although frontal lobe patients exhibit schizoid trends, their MMPI behavior is characterized primarily by denial of anxiety or worry, and attitudes of acceptance, affability, and self-confidence, with rather low levels of aspiration. In addition it is seen that patients with lesions in the temporal lobe tend to respond much like parietal cases, except that like the frontal group, they show peculiar thought processes. We can conclude then that the differential MMPI behavior noted here is associated with caudality in the broad sense, rather than specifically parietal-frontal localization.

In addition, the results imply that the reactions associated with parietal and temporal damage are secondary to the frustration and stress imposed by disablement. Frontal patients, on the other hand, whether because of the "silent" character of frontal lobe lesions, or because of loss of necessary fiber tracts, fail to react with anxiety.

✦————————————————————————————————————

ARTICLE 26 *An Ego-Strength Scale Which Predicts Response to Psychotherapy*

THIS paper reports the development and cross-validation of a scale which was originally designed to predict the response of psychoneurotic patients to psychotherapy. Consideration of the scale content and its correlates, however, suggests that a somewhat broader psychological interpretation be placed upon it, making it useful as an assessment device in any situation where some estimate of adaptability and personal resourcefulness is wanted. It appears to measure the various aspects of effective personal functioning which are usually subsumed under the term "ego-strength."

The scale consists of 68 items from the MMPI, selected from the total pool of 550 items on the basis of significant correlation with rated improvement in 33 psychoneurotic patients who had been treated for six months in a psychiatric clinic. The test responses of the patients were obtained before psychotherapy began, so that the scale, so far as logic of construction is concerned, is designed to predict whether or not after about six months of therapy the patient will have improved.

The sample of 33 patients was divided into two groups: 17 patients who were judged to have clearly improved, and 16 patients who were judged to be unimproved. Although the sample is small, the cases were intensively studied, and two skilled judges who had thoroughly acquainted themselves with the course of the therapy (although not themselves involved in it otherwise) were in considerable agreement (r of .91) in their independent ratings of degree of improvement. While one would not ordinarily base scale development on a sample of this size, it was reasoned here that a small number of well-studied cases who were classified with high reliability, and, as collateral evidence indicated [42], with high accuracy as well, would serve better than the practical alternative, which was to get a large sample in which the therapist's rating of outcome was accepted uncritically.

When the improved and unimproved groups were scored on this 68-item scale, the mean of the improved group proved to be 52.7, that of the unimproved group 29.1, a difference which is significant well beyond the .01 level (t of 10.3). The odd-even reliability of the scale in a clinic population of 126 patients is .76. Test-retest reliability after three months in a sample of 30 cases is .72.

The 68 items of the scale are presented below, arranged in groups according to

226

the kinds of psychological homogeneities which, in the judgment of the writer, are involved in the item content. The improved direction of response is given in parentheses after each item. The item numbering is taken from the booklet form of the MMPI.

Physical functioning and physiological stability. 153. During the past few years I have been well most of the time. (T) 51. I am in just as good physical health as most of my friends. (T) 174. I have never had a fainting spell. (T) 189. I feel weak all over much of the time. (F) 187. My hands have not become clumsy or awkward. (T) 34. I have a cough most of the time. (F) 2. I have a good appetite. (T) 14. I have diarrhea once a month or more. (F) 341. At times I hear so well it bothers me. (F) 36. I seldom worry about my health. (T) 43. My sleep is fitful and disturbed. (F)

Psychasthenia and seclusiveness. 384. I feel unable to tell anyone all about myself. (F) 489. I feel sympathetic towards people who tend to hang on to their griefs and troubles. (F) 236. I brood a great deal. (F) 217. I frequently find myself worrying about something. (F) 100. I have met problems so full of possibilities that I have been unable to make up my mind about them. (F) 234. I get mad easily and then get over it soon. (T) 270. When I leave home, I do not worry about whether the door is locked and the windows closed. (T) 359. Sometimes some unimportant thought will run through my mind and bother me for days. (F) 344. Often I cross the street in order not to meet someone I see. (F) 241. I dream frequently about things that are best kept to myself. (F)

Attitudes toward religion. 95. I go to church almost every week. (T) 488. I pray several times every week. (F) 483. Christ performed miracles such as changing water into wine. (F) 58. Everything is turning out just like the prophets of the Bible said it would. (F) 420. I have had some very unusual religious experiences. (F) 209. I believe my sins are unpardonable. (F)

Moral posture. 410. I would certainly enjoy beating a crook at his own game. (T) 181. When I get bored, I like to stir up some excitement. (T) 94. I do many things which I regret afterwards (I regret things more or more often than others seem to). (F) 253. I can be friendly with people who do things which I consider wrong. (T) 109. Some people are so bossy that I feel like doing the opposite of what they request, even though I know they are right. (T) 208. I like to flirt. (T) 430. I am attracted by members of the opposite sex. (T) 548. I never attend a sexy show if I can avoid it. (F) 231. I like to talk about sex. (T) 378. I do not like to see women smoke. (F) 355. Sometimes I enjoy hurting persons I love. (T)

Sense of reality. 33. I have had very peculiar and strange experiences. (F) 349. I have strange and peculiar thoughts. (F) 251. I have had blank spells in which my activities were interrupted and I did not know what was going on around me. (F) 48. When I am with people, I am bothered by hearing very queer things. (F) 22. At times I have fits of laughing and crying that I cannot control. (F) 192. I have had no difficulty in keeping my balance in walking. (T) 62. Parts of my body often have feelings like burning, tingling, crawling, or like "going to sleep." (F) 541. My skin seems to be unusually sensitive to touch. (F)

Personal adequacy, ability to cope. 389. My plans have frequently seemed so full of difficulties that I have had to give them up. (F) 82. I am easily downed in an argument. (F) 32. I find it hard to keep my mind on a task or job. (F) 244. My way of doing things is apt to be misunderstood by others. (F) 555. I sometimes feel that I am about to go to pieces. (F) 544. I feel tired a good deal of the time. (F) 261. If I were an artist, I would like to draw flowers. (F) 554. If I were an artist, I would like to draw children. (F) 132. I like collecting flowers or growing house plants. (F) 140. I like to cook. (F) 380. When someone says silly or ignorant things about something I know, I try to set him right. (T)

Phobias, infantile anxieties. 367. I am not afraid of fire. (T) 525. I am made nervous by certain animals. (F) 510. Dirt frightens or disgusts me. (F) 494. I am afraid of finding myself in a closet or small closed place. (F) 559. I have often been frightened in the middle of the night. (F)

Miscellaneous. 221. I like science. (T) 513. I think Lincoln was greater than Washington. (T) 561. I very much like horseback riding. (F) 458. The man who had most to do with me when I was a child (such as my father, stepfather, etc.) was very strict with me. (T) 421. One or more members of my family is very nervous. (T) 515. In my home we have always had the ordinary necessities (such as enough food, clothing, etc.). (T)

The pretherapy characteristics of patients who improve in therapy, as compared with those who do not improve, might be summarized as follows:

Improved: (a) good physical functioning; (b) spontaneity, ability to share emotional experiences; (c) conventional church membership, but nonfundamentalist and undogmatic in religious beliefs; (d) permissive morality; (e) good contact with reality; (f) feelings of personal adequacy and vitality; (g) physical courage and lack of fear.

Unimproved: (a) many and chronic physical ailments; (b) broodiness, inhibition, a strong need for emotional seclusion, worrisomeness; (c) intense religious experiences, belief in prayer, miracles, the Bible; (d) repressive and punitive morality; (e) dissociation and ego-alienation; (f) confusion, submissiveness, chronic fatigue; (g) phobias and infantile anxieties.

From an inspection of these differences, one might easily be led to envy the mental salubrity of psychoneurotic patients who are about to improve. Their actual mental distress, however, has been detailed in case material presented in two previous reports [42, 45 (see IX, 57)], and will not be repeated here. What the group comparison really reveals, of course, is the *dimension* on which the improved and unimproved groups differed. Had the improved patients been compared with an exceptionally healthy nonclinic group of subjects, the same items might well have emerged as descriptive of the difference between the groups, but with the characteristic responses of the improved patients being exactly opposite to those listed above. In other words, the nature of the criterion behavior determines the nature of the dimension which the item analysis will reveal, but the question of the strength of that variable in the criterion groups must be answered separately.

In this case, it is suggested that what is being measured is a general factor of capacity for personality integration, or ego-strength. The greater vividness of psychopathology often tends to obscure the ego-synthetic or constructive forces in the behavior of a psychologically disturbed individual, so that a prognostic evaluation is generally more difficult to make than a diagnostic evaluation. Nevertheless, in spite of the saliency of psychopathology in the clinical picture, it may be presumed that the patient has certain latent strengths which will gradually show themselves, particularly as the psychological crisis which brings him to therapy subsides. What the item content of the prediction scale seems to indicate is that these strengths are of the sort that are generally ascribed to a well-functioning ego, and that it is latent ego-strength which is the most important determinant (within the patient) of response to brief psychotherapy.

Such an interpretation would, of course, have relatively little warrant without supporting evidence from other samples. The obvious next step is to inquire into the relation of the scale to other measures in new populations.

Correlates of the Prediction Scale

In this further inquiry, one clinic sample and two nonclinic samples were studied. The clinic sample consisted of 77 women and 50 men who were seen for diagnostic studies on the psychology service at the Langley Porter Clinic during a given term of work. The nonclinic samples consisted of 160 male air force officers and 40 male graduate students.

The first step was to obtain adjective descriptions, by objective and skilled observers, of high and low scorers on the prediction scale. This was made possible by administering the MMPI to graduate students who were participating in intensive three-day psychological assessments being conducted at the Institute of Personality Assessment and Research, University of California, Berkeley. Following the assessment periods, the staff members of the Institute filled out an adjective check list with the purpose of describing each one of the subjects in the assessment, on the basis of the subject's socially observable behavior in situational procedures, interviews, and informal social interaction. A composite staff impression was thus assembled.

The 10 highest and 10 lowest scorers on the psychotherapy prediction scale were then compared by item-analyzing the composite adjective list for the two groups. The adjectives which showed a statistically significant difference (.05 level) between high and low scorers are listed below. (The staff observers were, of course, in ignorance of the test scores of the subjects.) The adjectives checked more frequently about high-scoring subjects were alert, adventurous, determined, independent, initiative, outspoken, persistent, reliable, resourceful, responsible. The adjectives checked more frequently about low-scoring subjects were affected, dependent, effeminate, mannerly, mild. The general impression conveyed is of greater resourcefulness, vitality, and self-direction in the high scorers, and effeminacy, inhibition, and affectation in the low scorers. This picture is supported by staff ratings of these same subjects on a number of psychological variables which it was thought could be inferred from social behavior in the assessment setting. The psychotherapy prediction scale correlated significantly with vitality (.38), which was defined simply as "general energy level," and with drive (.41), defined as "persistence, resolution, perseverance, *directed* energy." In addition, the scale showed low but positive correlation with several other variables descriptive of effective functioning. These are self-confidence (.24), poise (.24), and breadth of interest (.25). Significant negative correlations are with submissiveness (−.40), effeminacy (−.34), and intraceptiveness (−.34). As in the adjective descriptions, the high scorers on the scale emerge as more adequate physically, more at ease socially, and somewhat broader culturally. Low-scoring men are effeminate, submissive, and inclined to turn inwards rather than to be emotionally outgoing.

The relationship of the prediction scale to intelligence was next investigated. Among the functions of the ego, as described by psychoanalytic writers and summarized by Fenichel [r56], are perceiving, planning, synthesizing, and, in general, bringing the subject into an adaptive relationship to reality. Ego-determined behavior is what we are accustomed to call *intelligent* behavior. Any scale which purports to measure ego-strength should be positively correlated with standardized measures of intelligence.

In the sample on which the scale was developed, its correlation with Wechsler-Bellevue IQ is .44. In the air force officer sample, the scale correlates .36 with total score on the Primary Mental Abilities Test, and .47 with the intellectual efficiency scale of the California Psychological Inventory. In that same sample it correlates .48 with the potential success scale developed at the Institute of Personality Assessment and Research against a criterion consisting of faculty ratings of the probable professional success of the doctoral candidates studied. In the graduate student sample itself, the psychotherapy prediction scale correlates .39 with intelligence as measured by the Miller Analogies Test. Further, in the latter sample it correlates .52 with the intellectual efficiency scale. Thus it relates to general intelligence, as measured by a variety of tests, even in highly restricted ranges of intelligence. Certainly the ego-strength interpretation of the scale is supported.

The scale also is related to tolerance and lack of ethnic prejudice. In the standardization sample it correlates —.47 with the ethnocentrism (E) scale of Form 60 of the University of California Public Opinion Study Questionnaire. In the graduate student sample it correlates —.35 with the prejudice scale [246] of the MMPI, and —.46 with the E scale. Its correlation with the E scale in the air force officer sample is —.23, and its correlation with the tolerance scale of the CPI in that sample is .42.

Again, these findings lend some weight to the notion that what is being measured is general excellence of ego-functioning. The authors of *The Authoritarian Personality* [r3], in their successful search for the character defects which accompany ethnocentrism, found that high scorers on the E scale show "lack of differentiation of the ego." This is manifested among clinic patients [388], in "a narrow range of experience, emotionally and intellectually," together with "rigidity and constriction," "stereotyped thinking," and so on. All these things are thus, by inference, negatively related to scores on the psychotherapy prediction scale.

The relationship of the scale to the diagnostic and validity scales of the MMPI was determined in both the graduate student sample and the diagnostic study cases. The results are shown in Table 1. Surprisingly high negative correlations are found with most of the measures of psychopathology, averaging in the neighborhood of —.60 with hypochondriasis, depression, hysteria, psychasthenia, and schizophrenia, and around —.50 with paranoia in the clinical samples. What this suggests is that the prediction scale is picking up a general factor of psychopathology in the MMPI, reflecting degree of maladjustment or ego-dysfunction irrespective of differential diagnosis. In other words, it is related to general elevation of the profile, regardless of the pattern.

The correlations are, of course, partly a function of overlap of items (generally scored in the reverse direction) between the prediction scale and the diagnostic scales. The amount of net overlap for each scale is shown in Table 2. The very fact of overlap itself testifies to the character of the scale as a measure of general excellence of ego-functioning, manifested in this instance by absence of chronic psychopathology.

The scale has not yet been put in a T-score form which would be comparable with the profile scores of other MMPI scales. This is principally because no representative sample of normal records has been available to the writer. The raw score means and standard deviations of the samples studied are presented in Table 3, however. The values are fairly consistent in the clinical samples, with somewhat higher means for the graduate students and air force officers.

It would be justifiable, of course, to determine T scores on the basis of the clinic

Table 1. Relationship of the Ego-Strength Scale to Diagnostic and Validity Scales of the MMPI in Clinic and Student Populations

Scale	Male Clinic Patients (N = 50)	Male Graduate Students (N = 36)	Female Clinic Patients (N = 77)
F	−.49	−.36	−.47
K	.31	.31	.31
Hs	−.62	−.67	−.63
D	−.60	−.53	−.67
Hy	−.39	−.61	−.63
Pd	−.48	−.07	−.34
Mf	−.04	−.43	.07
Pa	−.62	−.07	−.49
Pt	−.71	−.54	−.71
Sc	−.55	−.44	−.64
Ma	−.04	−.33	−.21

Table 2. Item Overlap of the Ego-Strength Scale and MMPI Diagnostic Scales

Scale	Items Scored in Same Direction	Items Scored in Opposite Direction	Net Overlap
Hs	None	2, 43, 51, 62, 153, 189, 192	Seven items, scored opposite
D	58, 241	2, 32, 36, 43, 51, 153, 189, 208, 236, 270	Eight items, scored opposite
Hy	253	2, 32, 43, 51, 109, 153, 174, 189, 192, 234	Nine items, scored opposite
Pd	82	32, 33, 94, 231, 244	Four items, scored opposite
Pa	None	109, 341	Two items, scored opposite
Pt	None	22, 32, 36, 94, 189, 217, 344, 349, 359	Nine items, scored opposite
Sc	None	22, 187, 192, 241, 251, 349	Six items, scored opposite
Ma	109, 181	22, 100, 251	One item, scored opposite

Table 3. Ego-Strength Scale Statistics

Sample	N	Range	Mean	SD
Standardization sample	33	15–62	41.94	13.30
1st cross-validation sample [a]	53	26–58	40.10	7.62
2nd cross-validation sample	52	23–60	41.04	8.18
3rd cross-validation sample	46	22–61	42.06	9.32
Clinic diagnostic cases	127	23–60	41.97	7.36
VA mental hygiene clinic patients	52	22–59	41.79	7.38
I.P.A.R. graduate students	40	37–60	50.92	5.62
Air force officers	160	38–60	52.73	4.05

[a] Scores on the abbreviated scale are prorated for length of scale.

samples alone, provided that the scale is to be interpreted solely as a psychotherapy prognosis scale for use in an outpatient clinic. In Table 4, a chart is given for conversion of raw scores into T scores when the scale is used only for such prediction purposes rather than as a measure of ego-strength in the general population.

Cross-Validation of the Scale as a Prediction Instrument

The prediction scale was tested on three new samples of psychotherapy patients, in order to see whether it was doing the job for which it was designed. The patients were psychoneurotic, the psychotherapy was brief (very close to six months in all cases), and the clinical setting was similar to that in which the scale was developed. All the patients took the MMPI at the beginning of therapy, and all were rated as to degree of improvement at some date following termination of therapy. The three cross-validating samples are described below:

Table 4. Conversion Table for Use of Ego-Strength Scale in Clinic Samples

Raw Score	T Score	Raw Score	T Score	Raw Score	T Score	Raw Score	T Score
22	25	34	42	46	57	58	72
23	27	35	43	47	58	59	73
24	29	36	44	48	59	60	74
25	30	37	45	49	60	61	75
26	32	38	47	50	62	62	76
27	33	39	48	51	63	63	78
28	34	40	49	52	64	64	79
29	36	41	50	53	65	65	80
30	37	42	52	54	67	66	82
31	38	43	53	55	68	67	83
32	39	44	54	56	69	68	85
33	40	45	56	57	70		

1. Fifty-three patients who were given psychotherapy because of delayed recovery from injury or physical disease. Ratings of improvement were made by expert judges (who had not taken part in the therapy) on the basis of terminal interviews. At a final rating conference, these 53 patients were ranked in terms of degree of improvement. This sample of patients had been studied some six years earlier by Harris and Christiansen [292], who showed that patterns of test scores on both the Rorschach and the MMPI were predictive of improvement. The same pretherapy MMPI's were now scored on the prognosis scale. Only 39 items of the 68 could be used, however, as these patients had been given a shortened form of the MMPI, containing only the items which make up the clinical and validity scales of the test. The correlation with terminal rating is .42.

2. Fifty-two patients who had received brief psychotherapy during the preceding five years at the Langley Porter Clinic. The sample was obtained by asking therapists who had worked at the clinic during that period of time to nominate patients whom they remembered as clear examples of exceptional improvement, complete lack of improvement, and moderate improvement. The latter group consisted of 27 patients, while the two extreme groups numbered 9 and 16 respectively. The degree of relationship between pretherapy prognosis scale scores and this

trichotomy, as determined by computation of eta, is .54. The means were as follows: unimproved, 32.75; improved, 43.07; exceptional improvement, 49.66.

3. Forty-six patients who were part of the current patient load on the psychiatric service of a general hospital. All these patients had had approximately six months of psychotherapy at the time the rating was obtained. Ratings were made by the therapists themselves, on a 9-point scale of improvement. The correlation with pretherapy prognosis scale scores is .38.

These correlation coefficients are of about the magnitude that one would expect for a scale which is giving a valid measure of patient variables related to outcome of psychotherapy. It is reasonable that there should remain considerable unaccounted-for variance, quite apart from whatever error variance is contributed by the fallible criterion and predictor measure; for there are many important determinants of outcome of therapy besides the personality of the patient. The personality of the therapist, for example, is also important; and, in addition, there is a subtle inter-actional factor which results from the combination of a particular patient with a particular therapist, which is not infrequently the crucial determinant of outcome in a given case. Then there are, of course, life-situational variables outside of the therapy, affecting both patient and therapist, individually or jointly. It seems safe to say that no standardized test is likely to achieve any very high order of correlation with therapeutic outcomes. At the same time, the effort to construct measures of the different sources of variance tends to advance the research problem somewhat, and to make new questions answerable. If the scale presented here continues to prove effective upon further investigation, it opens the way to an inquiry into the effect of the therapist's personality, intelligence, and social attitudes upon therapeutic results, with the effect of patient variables held constant. Beyond that question, of course, lies the more difficult problem of measuring interactional effects, and their unique influence on the therapeutic relationship.

Summary and Conclusions

To recapitulate: an MMPI scale was developed for the purpose of predicting response to psychotherapy, and upon inspection of its item content and its personality and intelligence test correlates it was interpreted as being essentially a measure of ego-strength. It is here proposed that the scale be known as the ego-strength scale of the MMPI, and that the conventional abbreviation for it should be Es.

The relationship of the scale scores to therapeutic outcomes in several cross-validating samples led to the conclusion that a significant determinant of personality change in psychotherapy is strength of the ego before therapy begins. Among the characteristics which are collectively referred to as ego-strength are physiological stability and good health, a strong sense of reality, feelings of personal adequacy and vitality, permissive morality, lack of ethnic prejudice, emotional outgoingness and spontaneity, and intelligence.

Since the patients who seek psychotherapy are almost invariably in some sort of psychological difficulty, it must be evident that these characteristics are usually not salient features of the clinical picture at first contact. The evidence suggests, however, that such strengths are latent in the personality, and that they emerge as therapy progresses. By implication, it seems probable that the kind of personal crisis which brings the person of good ego-strength to the clinic is more situation-linked and less characterologically based (i.e., less chronic) than the personal difficulties of the person with poor ego-strength.

The scale should be useful both as a research instrument and as an additional clinical indicator on the MMPI. The present writer would suggest, however, that considerable caution should be exercised in the clinical use of the scale. Certainly it should not serve as the basis for categorical recommendations to treat or not to treat certain patients; the grounds for such action in a clinic should properly involve values as well as facts, and in any event the kind of crude measuring device presented here represents a fairly low order of "fact." Any prognostic assertions made on the basis of this scale should be quite tentative, and probably should be accompanied by a visual image of the kinds of scatter plots which may give rise to correlations in the general neighborhood of .45.

As a research instrument, the scale should prove useful in giving some assessment of the role of "patient variables" in determining the complex outcome which is involved in response to psychotherapy. It may also be of some value in assessing the kind of change that occurs in therapy. One may ask, for example, whether there is actually an enhancement of ego-strength as a consequence of therapy, and get an answer by comparing pretherapy with post-therapy scores on the scale. Or one might inquire whether the therapy itself is causing the change for the better in patients who improve; evidence on the issue might be obtained by setting up a research design which would use as a control group a sample of patients who are matched with the therapy sample in terms both of Es scores and of present need for psychotherapy, but who differ in that they do not receive psychotherapy.

In addition, the scale may be useful as an assessment device quite apart from the clinical situation. Its correlates with personality variables in normal samples are similar to the pattern of relationships seen in clinic samples, and in general it seems to be measuring constructive forces in the personality. Thus it may serve as a predictor in any situation in which an estimate of personal adaptability and resourcefulness is called for.

C. A. CUADRA

ARTICLE 27 *A Scale for Control in Psychological Adjustment (Cn)*

IT IS a rather puzzling if commonplace fact that some persons are better able to function as responsible adults than are others. This is of interest to psychology not only as a datum concerning individual differences but also because psychologists are sometimes called upon to make judgments and predictions about a given individual's capacity to function with and without psychiatric intervention.

There are two main ways of accounting for the aforementioned variability in psychological adjustment. It can be argued that this reflects the varying severity of the problems with which individuals must cope. The "war neuroses," for example, are often held as examples of "normal" reaction to extreme stress and, at times, insoluble problems. Yet here, too, it has been noted that individuals vary in their capacity to withstand what appears to the observer to be the same kind of stressful situation, and many psychologists feel that some as-yet-unidentified intrapsychic factors may account for this variation in psychological stability. They would hold that "maladjusted" persons are not simply those persons with more numerous and difficult environmental problems, but rather are individuals whose characteristic devices and means for solving problems are not so effective as those of others. These devices (usually called "defense mechanisms") have been systematically investigated by many workers.

Psychologists have attempted to develop psychometric instruments suitable for assessing and, if possible, quantifying, inter-individual variation in adjustment. One main deterrent to success in this enterprise, however, has seemed to be the lack of good criterion measures. If one is interested in saying something about the disabling effect of a psychiatric disorder, for example, should the criterion consist of the judgment of clinical psychologists, psychiatrists' diagnoses, self-ratings of the patient, test protocols, or the opinions of family and friends of the patient? May severity of the disorder be inferred from the patient's work record or from the length of psychiatric treatment necessary for rehabilitation, or should the criterion reflect all these in some combination?

Another reason for our difficulties in predicting and accurately evaluating the extent of psychological disability may lie in the inherent limitations of testing instruments themselves. For most accolades by adherents of a particular test reported on in the psychological literature there are rebuttals, critiques, and often harangues pointing up, more or less correctly, the inadequacies of the particular instrument for certain purposes. Results found to hold for a particular sample of individuals are attenuated or may wholly disappear when new samples are tested. Sometimes this has led to a search for more stable criteria against which to validate judgments based on test protocols. This has been the case, for example, with the Stanford-Binet Intelligence Test. Since teachers' judgments, the original criteria of Binet, were recognized as being themselves only indirect and somewhat undependable estimates of intelligence, attention has increasingly been directed toward the reliable prediction of those psychological characteristics which are, either by definition or common agreement, held to represent important aspects of intelligence itself.

Another response to negative results with a particular test has been an increased interest in reorganizing the methods of scoring and interpreting the protocols. This has usually been the case whenever the criterion itself is felt to be unassailable, as for example with those who attempt to compute formulas, ratios, and indices to diagnose "schizophrenia" without calling into question the validity of the concept. The basic assumption involved here is that with a knowledge of the proper weighting to give the test variables it should be possible to predict the criterion in question with a high degree of accuracy. Whether a given test elicits the kind and range of responses necessary for such predictions is, of course, an empirical question, and there can hardly be any quarrel with studies which attempt to discover the limits of applicability of a given test instrument.

Given the hypothesis that there are some sources of information in our testing instruments as yet untapped, there are several ways of approaching their discovery. One may seek by elaborate statistical manipulation to find within test data clues to stable and important dimensions of personality. For example, factor analytic studies by Cook and Wherry [138], Cottle [144], Tyler [598], Welsh [622], and others have indicated that there may be psychologically meaningful dimensions which cut across the usual scoring categories of the MMPI, a fact which is of immediate importance to the research about to be described. No doubt there have been similar findings for other tests. One difficulty in putting the results of such an approach to any immediate practical use stems in part from the relative independence of a factor analytic solution from nontest criteria, e.g., psychiatrists' diagnoses. Since there are a great number of possible factorial solutions for a given correlation matrix, the problem is not solved when factors are derived. They must still be identified and, ultimately, tied to what Brunswik [r26] calls "distal" variables, i.e., external criteria.

Another approach, the one which will be followed in the present research, uses the method of contrasted groups. Here, individuals who are felt to represent the two extremes on some variable, e.g., "social responsibility," are tested and an attempt is made to tease out from the resulting sources indices, "signs," or, in the cases of the "structured" personality tests, items which differentiate the two groups. There is still, of course, the necessity for validating the resulting items or scales in groups other than that from which they were first derived and it is here that many such attempts have been stymied. For example, the "N" (normality) scale developed by Meehl [435] from MMPI data was found to have good discriminating power with groups similar to those upon which the scale was developed; on a more heterogeneous group, however, and on a selected group, college students, the discrimination diminished to the point of little practical utility. One problem which the latter finding raises, that of general versus special norms, will be discussed later.

The dimension, aspect, or factor with which the present research is concerned has to do with psychological control, or, conversely, psychiatric incapacitation. The importance of ascertaining the extent of psychological disability hardly needs elaborate justification. Knowledge of the severity of illness is essential not only in determining the kind of treatment but also in determining the locale of treatment, i.e., whether it must be carried on only in a hospital setting or whether the patient is able to function sufficiently well to carry on most of his ordinary activities.

The problem has some intriguing theoretical aspects also. Why is it, we may ask, that some persons whose test protocols suggest disabling abnormality are not so disabled, while others with equally or even less alarming protocols cannot function in the community and must be hospitalized for their own protection or that of others? To say simply that the test is inadequate may beg the question; we have not yet explored the possibilities and limitations of many of the most frequently used testing instruments. To say that a certain number of false positives and test misses is inevitable reflects a complacency out of keeping with the goals of clinical psychology. If we are to reduce the probability of error in our psychometric instruments and in the inferences we make from them, it is necessary to pay attention to "test misses" and to the aspects of personality which may account for them.

The particular personality aspect of interest here has been described as control, ego-strength, integration, intactness, stability, and, with a rather negative connotation, rigidity. What seems to be common to most of these terms is their reference to a single behavioral fact, namely, that the individual to whom the term is applied has not experienced a psychiatric breakdown in the face of acute or chronic stress. He is, in a sense, able to "roll with the punch." For some investigators this resiliency is easily identifiable: those persons who are not psychiatric patients have it and those who are, do not. For others, "control" has been described as one function of a postulated intrapsychic structure. The difficulty with such a formulation, as with all formulations of relatively nonaccessible or highly inferential data, is that arguments in this area are almost impossible to resolve, except — and all too often — by fiat.

Perhaps the most reasonable demand that may be made of scientific investigators is that their methods and procedures be clearly detailed and that their criteria, whether external and palpable, or subjective and highly inferential, be made explicit. In the present study the criterion of severity of disorder will be a somewhat gross one, but from the social-psychological standpoint a most important one, namely, the necessity for confinement on a locked psychiatric ward. Wright [r174] has stated the position well: "A satisfying definition of mental or nervous illness or disorder has never been made, nor have 'wellness' or 'normality' been adequately defined. It has been said many times, in more or less earnestness, and with more or less thoughtfulness, that the only workable definition of a psychosis is that which one has if he is behind locked doors in an asylum; and of a neurosis, that which one has if he goes to see a psychiatrist."

The earliest directly relevant study on this general problem was done by Humm and Wadsworth [r81], who constructed a "normality" or "braking" scale based on Rosanoff's [r138] theory of temperament. Briefly, the theory holds that there are three major components tending toward abnormality as manifested in full-blown psychiatric conditions. These components, held to be present also in lesser degrees among so-called normal individuals, are the *antisocial* component, the *cyclothymic* component, and the *chaotic sexuality* component. Rosanoff postulates a fourth factor, which is the "normality" or "controlling" factor of temperament. Relatively independent of the three abnormal components, this normality factor if present in sufficient quantity acts to suppress any blatant outbursts due to excesses in any of the abnormal components.

The scale measuring the "normal" component of personality consists of 38 items selected empirically by contrasting workers who were considered adjusted to their jobs with a heterogeneous group of patients committed to state hospitals. Critical evaluation of the scale, and for that matter the test as a whole, is difficult, since the reports in the literature tend to be rather incomplete. The fact that some of the test components are known to correlate rather highly together (correlations of as high as .8 having been reported) indicates that the components are not factorially pure and raises the possibility that the "control" scale is not independent of the other components. Inspection of the items on the scale seems to reinforce this possibility, since the majority of the items are scored for "normality" when they are answered in the direction that a naive person would consider the more normal. It should be evident that if a person is going to say psychiatrically "bad" things about himself, thus earning high scores on some of the abnormal component scales, he is hardly likely to give the psychiatrically "good" responses on the normality scale. Even if this were so, however, mere differentiation of a heterogeneous group of abnormals from normal persons cannot in itself substantiate the contention that the scale measures control, since there are numerous other uncontrolled variables which might also account for the differentiation.

Meehl, working with the MMPI, developed a "normality" (N) scale by contrasting a number of normal persons having "abnormal" profiles with mental patients having similar profiles. Since the present study is in some ways closely patterned after the Meehl study, it will be expedient to describe the latter in some detail in order to point up the similarities and differences.

The first step in the N-scale research was the selection of a group of cases with profiles showing deviation that would ordinarily be labeled "abnormal," in spite of the fact that the subjects were apparently free from incapacitating psychiatric involvement. An "abnormal" profile was arbitrarily defined as one in which there was an elevation ($T = 70$) on any of the three scales of the neurotic triad: hypochondriasis, depression, and hysteria. It was immediately apparent that any systematic effort to avoid cases in which some other scale was elevated would have reduced the number of cases available beyond a workable limit, so this was not attempted. Each of these profiles was then matched as closely as possible with that of a "true" abnormal for eight clinical scales of the MMPI, most attention being paid to the three scales of the neurotic triad.

In spite of the inspection of over 400 profiles, it was impossible to make an extremely close match for each "abnormal" profile, especially since age, too, was roughly equated. The differences between the two groups were significant at the .05

level (or greater) on six of the eight scales, the greatest difference occurring on the psychasthenia (Pt) scale. This was felt to be one possible explanation for the high correlation later found between the derived N scale, and Pt. Meehl raised the question, however, of how such a systematic trend could arise as a result of the matching process unless there were some factor in or associated with the Pt scale which contributes to normality in the presence of elevated scores on the neurotic triad. The factor, he finally concluded, was allied with a tendency to say psychiatrically "bad" things about the self, a kind of nonclinical psychasthenia.

Application of the N scale to new groups showed continued discrimination for many of them except in the case of college students and college graduates, for whom Meehl suggested that separate norms might be needed. The implication was clear that the kind of verbal behavior considered "normal" for the college groups might well not be what was originally considered normal on the basis of the large and heterogeneous MMPI standardization group.

In a further effort to isolate and control some of the factors which might be confounding MMPI personality evaluations, McKinley, Hathaway, and Meehl [424 (II, 11)] collaborated in developing the K scale. The emphasis was no longer on "control" but rather was focused on the influence of a hypothesized "test-taking attitude." The search for such a factor was, of course, a retreat from the era of naive optimism in which it was assumed that influence of the testee's attitude could be averted by the simple expedient of asking for his cooperation. There can be no argument with the contention that a person's verbal behavior is of interest and predictive significance in its own right, without regard for its veridicality. To proceed from this undeniable fact, however, to the assertion that empirical establishment of scoring keys does not allow test-taking attitude to function follows neither the laws of logic nor the facts of human behavior. The studies which led to the development of the K scale represent one effort to fill this lacuna.

The K-scale research resulted in the development of a preliminary 22-item scale measuring, it seemed, a tendency to avoid saying psychiatrically "bad" things about oneself. Since the N scale seemed to measure a tendency toward admitting psychiatrically "bad" things about oneself, it was not surprising that the K scale should correlate approximately —.70 with N, nor was it entirely unexpected that 7 of the 22 original K items should also appear on the N scale but scored in the opposite direction. The fact that these two scales, derived on quite different groups, should lead to virtually the same attitudinal factor is of considerable interest. Another fact, however, namely that K was highly correlated with many of the clinical scales, again raised the question whether what was being measured was a transient and independent attitudinal factor attributable to the testing situation or an ingrained personality characteristic relating to the individual's self-concept.

There are theoretical and empirical grounds for debating the merits of the K scale. The items were derived by an item analysis of the responses of fifty patients in a psychopathic hospital, the diagnoses on whom were mostly "psychopathic personality, alcoholism, and allied descriptive terms indicating behavior disorders rather than neuroses." The assumption was made that persons with such diagnoses were more likely to be defensive in taking a personality test than most cases of psychoneurosis. This assumption can be questioned, in view of the findings reported by Benton [53 (see VII, 44)], Capwell [112], Gough [234 (see VI, 38)], and

Monachesi [450] that there is a strong and fairly uniform tendency for behavior disorder cases to have elevated scores on Pd and Ma, both of which are negatively correlated with K in normals as well as abnormals.

Experimental evidence on the effectiveness of use of the K corrections is also conflicting. Rubin [509] reported that the K scale weakened the discriminating power of some of the other scales. His conclusions, however, appear to be contradicted by the data he presents. Jeffrey [345] used interviews and questionnaires in order to get more intimate data on responses to the K items. The data did not support either the notion that K measures test-taking attitude or the hypothesis that some sort of verbal-semantic distortion is involved. She concluded that her data were consistent with the assumption that K measures a deeply rooted attitude toward the self. This view has also been expressed by Gough, who rejects the contention that K measures only a transient and isolated reaction toward the testing situation.

Because of the conflicting evidence on the meaning and usefulness of the K corrections, it was decided not to use K-corrected scores in the present study. There was, therefore, a strong a priori possibility that the investigation to be described might result merely in a duplicate K scale. The results, however, did not bear out this possibility.

In order to control the factor of motivation toward the test as well as toward psychiatric treatment, it was required that all the subjects of the research have voluntarily applied for psychiatric treatment. Although it cannot be assumed that all such persons are willing and able to give revealing information about themselves, the imposition of this requirement seemed the most satisfactory alternative to use of the K scale, whose meaning is still in dispute.

Wiener [642 (IV, 22)] developed subtests of "subtle" and "obvious" items for some of the MMPI scales and compared the responses of hospitalized and non-hospitalized schizophrenics [644]. His researches led him to the conclusion that a "control" factor may be expressed in the tendency for "successful," i.e., nonhospitalized persons, to avoid the more deviate, obvious items in responding to the test. Since he did not equate his groups for over-all profile elevation, however, it should follow that his "unsuccessful" group, having more elevated profiles, would answer more of the obviously pathologic items.

Benarick, Guthrie, and Snyder [51], working only with the schizophrenia (Sc) scale, isolated a set of items which seemed to differentiate psychotics from those nonpsychotics who showed abnormally elevated Sc scores. While this kind of discrimination is somewhat afield from the central problem of our research, which is to assess severity of disorder regardless of diagnostic category, Benarick's findings are of interest in that they seem to confirm Wiener's conclusion that the more disturbed patients answer the more glaringly pathological items in a psychiatrically significant manner.

The writer recently carried out a brief survey in which clinicians with various degrees of experience with the MMPI were asked to identify from among the records of twenty psychiatric patients those ten records of patients on a locked psychiatric ward. The sortings did not differ significantly from chance. To be sure, this is a very difficult discrimination to demand and it would be unreasonable to expect any great accuracy in making such specific judgments and predictions without other information about the patients. However, the fact that clinicians occasionally do and must make judgments of the severity of a patient's illness in part on the basis of one or more psychometric instruments argues for research aimed at improving our predictive accuracy.

The research to be described was undertaken in order to discover intra-test factors which might make more reliable our judgments about the degree of incapacitation exhibited by a patient. While it was intended for the most part as an exploratory study, it was expected to shed some light on the questions raised by Wiener, Benarick, and others with respect to whether the disturbed but not hospitalized persons were actually answering a different and less malignant subset of items on the MMPI.

The basic plan was to compare two very closely test-matched groups differing mainly in severity of psychiatric illness. It was expected that in the broad sample of verbal behavior elicited in the MMPI there would be found responses which would differentiate the two groups, and that analysis of the differentiating responses as a group would serve as a springboard for further research into the kinds of psychological factors the presence of which makes possible the individual's continued social adjustment.

There were, to be sure, some more specific expectations as to the kind of items which might emerge. The hypothesis was advanced that normal persons who achieved elevated profiles were answering somewhat different subsets of items than were being answered by abnormals with similar profiles. It was supposed that whereas the normals were answering items indicative of anxiety and apprehension, the abnormals would be answering items suggestive of loss of realistic appraisal of the self and of the environment. Since both of these kinds of items may appear on a single scale, the meaning of an elevation on a given scale is in and of itself somewhat ambiguous. The goal of the present study is to attempt to identify those subsets of items which differentiate groups with similar profiles but dissimilar adequacies of adjustment.

The "Criterion Abnormals"

The first step was to select a group of persons who, after having been examined by psychiatrists, psychologists, or psychiatric social workers, were regarded as such a risk to themselves or to others that it was felt necessary to hospitalize them. Every clinician recognizes, of course, that the criteria for inclusion in such a group are vague, ill-defined, and variable. By no means do we find every individual who might be dangerous to himself and others in a hospital (or a jail); similarly there may be found in psychiatric hospitals patients who are no more a risk than many of their unconfined brethren. This can be at times as much a function of hospital policy and of accessibility of other community resources as it is of variability in the criteria used in judging severity of illness. Diagnosis is, to be sure, of some aid in identifying severely disturbed persons, there being more likelihood of finding in a psychiatric hospital a patient diagnosed "psychotic" than one diagnosed "neurotic." This is not enough, however; a severe psychoneurosis can be just as incapacitating as some psychotic conditions.

The possibility was considered, in the early phases of the present research, that one criterion for determining severity of illness might be the need for intensive somatic therapy, e.g., insulin or electric shock, the notion being that this kind of therapy tends to be used when the patient is so disturbed that effective communication cannot be maintained. Unfortunately this is not universally the case. Often the decision to administer these treatments is related more to the training and convictions of the individual physicians than it is to the degree of social incapacitation exhibited by the patient.

It was decided, finally, to accept as the working criterion of severity of illness the simple fact of hospitalization, regardless of diagnosis and regardless of the kind of therapy received. Such a criterion involves, of course, an overgeneralization, but the error is in the direction of making it more difficult for any psychometric instrument to differentiate this group from a "normal" group, in which there might well be some persons who are by no means psychiatrically well.

The institution from which the hospitalized cases were drawn was the Langley Porter Clinic in San Francisco. From their file of inpatients were taken the first 30 cases, 15 of each sex, which met the following criteria: The patients had to be between the ages of 19 and 26, must have completed at least one semester of college, and were required to have applied voluntarily for psychiatric treatment. These restrictions were imposed in order to control to some degree such factors as age, intelligence, socioeconomic status, and motivation, operation of which had been reported as tending to vitiate the results of other researches.

In addition to these criteria relating to the patients themselves were some concerned with their test protocols. Since the object was to discover as many differentiating test items as possible, only those profiles were accepted wherein the subject had been given the full 550-item test. Also, profiles showing a very large number (more than 40) of unanswered items were excluded. The fairly large number of records which were rejected on the latter basis suggests that the height of the Cannot Say score may be a good diagnostic clue; this was not pursued further, however, being only tangential to the purposes of the present research.

The attempt was made to avoid including cases where the tests had been given months before or after admission. An arbitrary cutting point was established at 21 days either before or after hospitalization, but more than 95 per cent of the cases finally accepted were found to have been tested either shortly before or within 15 days following admission.

The reasons for limiting the number of records selected to 30 were practical ones. As each restriction was imposed, the number of cases available was sharply reduced. The 30 cases which survived the selection process represented the gleanings from a 3½-year period of inpatient admissions. While the reliability of data obtained from this small number of cases cannot be as high as would be desirable, the rigorous and multiple criteria imposed decrease the a priori possibility that results obtained are contaminated by variables not really relevant to the research.

Some of the data available on the criterion abnormal groups are presented in Tables 1 and 2. It will be noted that for both the males and females the diagnosis most frequently given is schizophrenia. In this respect the criterion abnormals are quite different from the criterion normal group, in which the majority received the diagnosis of psychoneurosis. It is not clear to what extent this is a function of different policies with respect to diagnosis and to what extent it represents sharp differences in the behavior of the two groups.

Table 1. Age, Education, and Other Available Data for the Male Criterion Abnormals

Case No.	Age	Education	Diagnosis	Days between Hospitalization and Testing
1..............	22	14+	Psychoneurosis, mixed	6
2..............	22	14+	Psychoneurosis, mixed	−7 [a]
3..............	21	12½	Schizophrenia, unclassified	7
4..............	25	14+	Schizophrenia, catatonic	4
5..............	19	12½	Schizophrenia, paranoid	7
6..............	20	14	Character neurosis	2
7..............	25	13+	Schizophrenia, paranoid	6
8..............	26	13½	Psychopathic personality without psychosis; pathological sexuality	6
9..............	24	14+	Schizophrenia, paranoid	10
10..............	19	13	Psychoneurosis, mixed	9
11..............	23	14	Character neurosis	15
12..............	18	14	Character neurosis	4
13..............	20	14	Schizophrenia, paranoid	6
14..............	20	13½	Schizophrenia, unclassified	10
15..............	26	14	Schizophrenia, paranoid	−11
Median	22	14		6

[a] The minus sign indicates that testing occurred prior to admission to the hospital.

Table 2. Age, Education, and Other Available Data for the Female Criterion Abnormals

Case No.	Age	Education	Diagnosis	Days between Hospitalization and Testing
16..............	21	14+	Psychoneurosis, mixed	5
17..............	24	14+	Manic-depressive psychosis, manic	21
18..............	21	14+	Schizophrenia, unclassified	10
19..............	22	14+	Psychosis, undifferentiated	−4 [a]
20..............	25	14+	Psychopathic personality without psychosis, mixed type	3
21..............	18	14+	Schizophrenia, paranoid	15
22..............	21	14+	Schizophrenia, paranoid	10
23..............	26	12½	Schizophrenia, paranoid	7
24..............	22	14+	Schizophrenia, paranoid	5
25..............	24	14	Schizophrenia, paranoid	0
26..............	25	12½	Schizophrenia, unclassified	1
27..............	19	12½	Schizophrenia, unclassified	11
28..............	22	12+	(Undiagnosed)	5
29..............	24	12½	Psychoneurosis, mixed	3
30..............	18	13	Psychoneurosis, mixed	12
Median	22	14+		5

[a] The minus sign indicates that testing occurred prior to admission to the hospital.

The "Criterion Normals"

The next step was to select for each of the criterion abnormal profiles a closely matching profile obtained from a person who, although presenting psychiatric complaints, was not so severely disturbed as to warrant hospitalization. These cases were selected from three sources: the outpatient psychiatric clinic of Cowell Memorial

Hospital in Berkeley, and the Veterans Administration mental hygiene clinics in San Francisco and Oakland, California. No individuals were included who had been hospitalized subsequent to testing, insofar as it was possible to determine this fact from the case histories available. The other criteria relating to personal data and test protocols were the same as had been utilized with the criterion abnormal group. Some of the personal data for the criterion normals are presented in Tables 3 and 4.

Criteria for determining the closeness of match of the MMPI profiles included comparable over-all elevation, similar general configuration, and congruence of predominant scale elevations. Use of the Welsh MMPI profile coding system [617 (see III, 13)] which summarizes all these aspects, reduced the matching task to workable proportions. In selecting the records, all nine of the clinical scales were considered, the validating scales being allowed to vary independently. The excep-

Table 3. Age, Education, and Diagnosis for the Male Criterion Normals

Case No.	Age	Education	Diagnosis
1.	22	14+	Psychoneurosis, mixed
2.	24	15½	(None)
3.	24	15+	Psychoneurosis, mixed
4.	25	14	(None)
5.	25	14	(None)
6.	23	12½	Schizophrenia
7.	25	14+	Schizophrenia, paranoid
8.	26	12½	Psychoneurosis (immaturity reaction)
9.	21	12½	Schizophrenia, simple
10.	24	18	Psychoneurosis, bordering on schizophrenia
11.	21	14	Psychoneurosis
12.	25	13	Psychoneurosis, anxiety reaction
13.	21	14+	Conversion hysteria
14.	22	12½	Schizophrenia, paranoid
15.	19	13+	Psychoneurosis, mixed
Median	24	14	

Table 4. Age, Education, and Diagnosis for the Female Criterion Normals

Case No.	Age	Education	Diagnosis
16.	26	13+	(None)
17.	18	12½	Psychoneurosis, mixed
18.	22	15+	Schizophrenia, paranoid, latent
19.	19	13+	(None)
20.	24	16+	Psychoneurosis, mixed
21.	26	15+	Psychoneurosis, mixed
22.	22	15+	Psychoneurosis, mixed
23.	18	12½	Psychoneurosis, mixed
24.	26	16+	Psychoneurosis, mixed
25.	20	15+	(None)
26.	19	13+	(None)
27.	21	15+	(None)
28.	21	15	Psychoneurosis, mixed
29.	27	17+	Psychoneurosis, mixed
30.	23	15+	Simple adult maladjustment
Median	22	15+	

tion here was the Cannot Say score, restrictions on which have already been discussed. Because of the present ambiguity of the K scale, especially in a college population, the matching was based on use of the uncorrected clinical scores.

In spite of the laborious canvassing of more than 4000 records, repeated for each of the criterion abnormal profiles, it was impossible to obtain a perfect match in every case. Certain kinds of profiles do not occur with as great a frequency in a normal or clinic population as they do in a hospital group. Considering, however, that it was necessary to match for all nine of the clinical scales, the similarity between the group means and profile codes is quite good, as can be seen from Table 5.

Table 5. Mean T Scores for the Two Criterion Groups, Sexes Pooled and Separately

Criterion Group	N	?	L	F	K	Hs	D	Hy	Pd	Mf	Pa	Pt	Sc	Ma
Abnormals	30	50.0	51.5	68.0	56.0	62.0	76.0	69.5	72.5	a	69.0	65.0	71.0	61.5
					MMPI Code: 248'36719ª F–KL?									
Normals	30	50.0	47.0	64.0	54.0	61.5	76.0	69.0	72.0	a	69.0	67.5	71.0	62.0
					MMPI Code: 248'36791ª F–K?/L									
Male abnormals	15	50	51	69	56	68	83	74	75	74	73	68	75	63
					MMPI Code: 2"48356'179 F–KL?									
Male normals	15	50	46	64	54	70	82	73	75	71	73	72	75	66
					MMPI Code: 2"48 36751'9 F–K?/L									
Female abnormals	15	50	52	67	56	56	69	65	70	48	65	62	67	60
					MMPI Code: 4'283679–1/5 F–KL?									
Female normals	15	50	47	64	53	53	70	65	69	45	65	63	67	58
					MMPI Code: 2'48367–91/5 F–K?/L									

a The meaningfulness of a T score on the Mf scale for a combined group is open to question. The omission of scale 5 from the code is obvious. The closeness of the matching for each sex considered separately can be seen in the adjacent rows.

It will be noted that the most pronounced difference for both sexes occurs on the L scale, where the abnormals fall approximately one half a standard deviation above the normals. Although the difference does not quite reach the .05 level of statistical significance, it should nevertheless be borne in mind in view of the correlation later found between the derived scale and the L scale. It will be remembered that the validating scales (L, F, and K) did not enter into the matching. The clear similarity of the validating scale scores for the two criterion groups is of considerable interest and supports the view that these scales are by no means independent of the configuration of the clinical scales.

After examination of the paired profiles for closeness of match, the next step was to consider each of the 550 items to see if among them there were any which might serve to differentiate the two criterion groups. The a priori probability of finding such items had, of course, been decreased somewhat by the matching process. An example will make this point clear. If all the items on the depression (D) scale of the MMPI have in common a known positive correlation with the total score on this scale, then in matching individuals on the basis of total score we have also, to a certain extent, matched them in terms of their responses to the particular items which comprise the scale. It would be possible to determine all the item intercorrelations on the various scales for the particular groups involved but the extra precision gained would hardly be worth the laborious computations and statistical manipulations which would be necessary.

The True and False responses given to each of the items were tallied and summed for the two criterion groups. Those items which on inspection showed promise of differentiating the groups were subjected to more exact tests of statistical significance. The differences between the proportions of significant responses in the two criterion groups were expressed in terms of their phi coefficients, using the method described by Jurgensen [r86] and ignoring the correlational factor introduced by the matching procedure. Failure to take into account this factor meant that the significance of the differences between proportions would be underestimated to an unknown degree. However, since the mathematics of item intercorrelation are both very complex and exceedingly time-consuming, it was decided to forgo precise determination of the phi coefficients involved.

The phi coefficient which a proportion must reach for samples of 30 vs. 30 in order to be significant at the .05 level is approximately .253. Thirty-nine items exceeded this figure and of the 30, 12 were significant beyond the .01 level (phi = .333). Some of the items were significant for one sex but not for the other. One item which discriminated well for the males actually worked backwards for the females. In almost every case where the item worked for one sex, it was discovered that the total number of persons who answered the item in a statistically infrequent direction was quite small. For example, one item achieved statistical significance by virtue of the fact that 16 per cent of the criterion normals and 0 per cent of the criterion abnormals answered the item in a particular way. Although it cannot be argued that such an item is spuriously significant, there are nevertheless some good reasons for not wishing to include it in a scale.

Consider for the moment the hypothetical example of a verbal test item a particular answer on which was positively and uniformly indicative of schizophrenia. The diagnostic potentialities of such an would be astounding provided, and here is the point of difficulty, that a sufficiently large number of schizophrenics answer the item in the pathognomonic direction. If they do not, then the item contributes nothing to the scale in most of the instances in which the scale is used.

On these two bases then — discrimination for one sex only and low percentage of response frequency — 7 of the statistically best 39 items were eliminated. In order to lengthen the scale and improve its reliability for the validation procedures to follow, the decision was made to include an additional number of nearly significant items which, although not as differentiating as some of the others, at least had the advantage of discriminating in the same direction for both sexes. The final scale accepted for further study consisted of 50 items, to be described below.

Because the research began with the notion that some such function as psychological "control" might account for the observed psychological resiliency of some persons even under stress, the derived scale was called the "control" scale or more simply the Cn scale. It was not expected at the outset that any items found would exhibit an obvious psychological homogeneity, for we do not yet know all the psychological correlates of the kinds of verbal behavior tapped by the MMPI. The items might well be homogeneous only in the sense that they had all shown promise of effectively differentiating very disturbed persons from those not so seriously ill.

It was quite gratifying, therefore, to find that many of the items "made sense" as a group; this will be elaborated subsequently. The items of the Cn scale are given below, the items being listed according to decreasing differentiating power. The numbers are as given in the manual of directions for the MMPI [305] and after each item is given the more characteristic answer of the criterion normals of the present research.

1.	D22	(False)	18.	D37	(True)	35.	J35	(True)
2.	D19	(False)	19.	H30	(False)	36.	B41	(True)
3.	J44	(True)	20.	F29	(False)	37.	D45	(True)
4.	G1	(True)	21.	G32	(True)	38.	F36	(True)
5.	G30	(True)	22.	E15	(False)	39.	D40	(True)
6.	D1	(False)	23.	J4	(True)	40.	E7	(False)
7.	I29	(True)	24.	A17	(False)	41.	D16	(False)
8.	C42	(True)	25.	E31	(True)	42.	H33	(True)
9.	F45	(True)	26.	F25	(True)	43.	A8	(False)
10.	J51	(True)	27.	C13	(False)	44.	D46	(True)
11.	J48	(True)	28.	E51	(False)	45.	C47	(True)
12.	F22	(False)	29.	D55	(False)	46.	D29	(True)
13.	C1	(False)	30.	B55	(False)	47.	H8	(False)
14.	I4	(False)	31.	I17	(True)	48.	D35	(False)
15.	D36	(True)	32.	J1	(False)	49.	J50	(True)
16.	G21	(True)	33.	D11	(False)	50.	I36	(True)
17.	G18	(True)	34.	G13	(False)			

A scoring key was prepared in which the direction of scoring was that characterizing the criterion normals more than the criterion abnormals. It has already been pointed out that 30 items, constituting 60 per cent of the Cn scale length, are scored for "normality" when answered in the direction that was statistically infrequent in the original Minnesota population. This fact requires some elaboration and explanation. Let us take, for example, the item "It makes me feel like a failure when I hear of the success of someone I know well." The most frequent response to this item for both the criterion abnormals and the criterion normals is False, and this was the answer most frequently given in the original standardization of the MMPI. Nevertheless, since there was a greater (and statistically significant) tendency for the criterion abnormals to give this particular response than for the criterion normals, the opposite response, i.e., True, was scored in the direction of normality on the Cn scale. The consequences of this arrangement are not easy to predict; it was possible that such a scoring scheme might well result in the scale's loss of potency in discriminating between psychiatric patients as a group and "real" normals, i.e., persons who are neither hospitalized patients nor receiving treatment at an outpatient clinic.

This kind of problem is not unique to the present research. It was, in fact, encountered early in the original MMPI studies, where it was found that scales based on differentiation between, say, hypochondriacs and normals were not able to discriminate as well between hypochondriacs and schizophrenics. It was necessary to develop a correction scale to effect the latter differentiation. In the study by Benarick *et al.*, when it was discovered that the Sx (schizophrenia screening scale) items did not work especially well for particular kinds of profiles, it was suggested by the authors that application of the scale not be attempted except for borderline profiles in which the schizophrenia T score was between 65 and 75. Similarly, Meehl's research on the K scale led him to conclude that with respect to over-all profile elevation there were upper and lower limits beyond which deviations on K cannot effectively operate to improve diagnostic efficiency. The foregoing findings suggested that considerable care needed to be exercised in the selection of subjects on whom the validity of the Cn scale was to be investigated.

In order to discover the range of applicability of the Cn scale, it was felt necessary to consider a variety of profiles, beginning with those of the original criterion groups. Differentiation between these groups is a necessary although not sufficient condition to establish the merit of the scale. It is obvious that the method of construction used (selection of discriminating items) will make it inevitable that any such scale will separate the criterion groups. However, the degree of overlap

Table 6. Distribution of Raw Scores on the Cn Scale for the
Two Criterion Groups, Sexes Shown Separately

Scores on Cn	Criterion Normal		Criterion Abnormal	
	Males	Females	Males	Females
45		1		
44				
43	1			
42				
41				
40	1	2		
39	3			
38		1		
37	1	2		
36	1	1		
35	1			
34	2	1		
33	1		1	
32	1	2		
31	1	1		
30	1	1		
29	1			2
28		1	2	1
27		2	1	
26			1	2
25				1
24			2	2
23				2
22			2	
21			2	1
20				
19			1	
18				
17				1
16			1	1
15			1	
14			1	
13				1
12				
11				
10				
9				1

is not predictable in advance, being a function not only of the discriminating power of the individual items but also of their interrelationships.

Table 6 shows the distribution of raw scores on the Cn scale for the two criterion groups, sexes shown separately. Although there is some overlap, the separation can be seen to be quite good, especially for the males. Table 7 compares the means on the Cn scale for the 30 criterion abnormals versus the 30 criterion normals. The mean difference has a critical ratio of 13.05, significant beyond the .001 level.

A more meaningful estimate of the scale's differentiating power on the criterion groups may be obtained by consideration of the differences in score between the paired profiles. It is especially striking that in no case does a given criterion abnormal have a higher Cn score than the criterion normal with whom he was matched.

The content of the Cn scale was examined in order to see whether any psychological meaning or item homogeneity was immediately apparent. There did seem

Table 7. Comparison of Means on the Cn Scale for the 30 Criterion Abnormals and the 30 Criterion Normals

Group	N	Mean	SD	M_{diff}	CR	p
Criterion abnormals	30	22.43	5.47			
				12.40	13.05	<.001
Criterion normals	30	34.83	4.64			

to be such meaning and homogeneity, at least among some of the items. Inspection of the items suggests that a person answering in the indicated direction might be described by acquaintances as rather sophisticated, realistic, somewhat impatient with naive, overly moralistic, and opinionated persons but withal quite aware of his own weaknesses and inwardly sensitive to social criticism. A person answering in the opposite direction would, on the contrary, be described as fairly conventional, moralistic, and disinclined to experiment with and explore the environment about him. Use of each of the adjectives in the above hypothetical descriptions is supported by one or more clusters of items in the Cn scale, and to these some attention may now be directed.

The two most discriminating items on the scale have to do with acceptance of certain religious beliefs. There is another, less potent, item relating to belief in an afterlife, as well as one item attesting to frequent prayer. What is of interest is that all these are answered False by the criterion normals. Whether one subscribes to particular religious beliefs is, it will be agreed, a matter of faith rather than of ironclad logic and unmistakable evidence. The rejection of such beliefs by the criterion normals is suggestive of a certain intellectual sophistication and rebelliousness against authority.

The criterion normals, more frequently than the abnormals, admit to attending sexy shows, to enjoying races or games better when having bet on them, to gambling for small stakes, to having been suspended from school as a youngster for misbehavior, and to indulging in some dangerous enterprises for the thrill and excitement afforded by them. All this is suggestive of a somewhat greater tendency on the part of the criterion normals to explore the various aspects of their environment, even though this may at times involve the risk of social disapproval. It is interesting that assent to each of the items would earn the criterion normals credit toward a (pathological) elevation of the regular MMPI scales, since their answers are in the statistically infrequent direction. One suggestion from this is that such responses may not be so pathognomonic in a college group as they were for the original Minnesota population.

The criterion abnormals, more frequently than do the criterion normals, say they are usually not interested in newspaper articles on crime, do not admit to being cross when not feeling well, and deny ever feeling like swearing, gossiping, or laughing at a dirty joke. Some of these denials of ordinary human "weaknesses" strike one as going beyond conventionality and bordering on unrealistic self-appraisal. This impression is furthered when we note that the criterion abnormals deny experiencing resentment when taken in cleverly by others and do not admit to feeling like a failure when they hear of the success of someone they know well. The question arises: are these persons as a group as unwilling to see malevolent motivation, in others as they are to recognize it in themselves? There is some evidence that this may be true. To the statement "People generally demand more respect for their own rights than they are willing to allow for others," the criterion abnormals answer False, and to the item "Most people inwardly dislike putting themselves out to help other people," they again answer False.

Some of the other suggestions concerning the characteristics and attitudes of the person who answers the Cn scale items in the indicated direction, namely, impatience with overly moralistic and opinionated persons and awareness of imperfections in oneself and others, should be fairly clear from a perusal of the remaining items and it does not seem necessary to justify and elaborate at this time, especially since this subjective examination of the item content is intended only to be suggestive of hypotheses. Rather, we may turn our attention to a consideration of the item composition of the Cn scale and its relation to some of the regular and special MMPI scales.

There are a variety of ways in which the validity of a test can be discovered. The Pearsonian correlational technique is the most precise but it is somewhat inconvenient when a large number of comparisons are to be made and when a high degree of statistical accuracy is not required. One rough and quasi-empirical way of ascertaining the relationship between a number of scales drawing upon a common item pool is to consider the amount of item overlap between the scales. It is, of course, true that item overlap does not necessarily prove covariation; nevertheless the method, like the purely rational examination of the items described in the preceding section, may serve as a preliminary source of hypotheses about the psychological correlates of the Cn scale.

Of the 550 items which appear in the box form of the MMPI, approximately 300 were scored on the standard scales. The other items were retained by the test authors to serve as an item pool to aid in the development of new scales. Noninclusion on the original scales was not because of any psychological irrelevance; it meant simply that these items did not discriminate between normal persons and selected psychiatric diagnostic groups — hypochondriacs, schizophrenics, etc. Later research has shown that many of these items are of value in measuring some of the more "psychological" variables such as repression and anxiety, which are not an exclusive characteristic of any particular diagnostic group (see IV, 29).

Fourteen of the 50 items on the Cn scale do not appear on any of the regular MMPI scales. The remaining 36 items appear on one or more of the scales, as indicated in Table 8. It may be noted that the number of items listed exceeds 36, totaling in fact 56. This is because some of the items appear on as many as four of the standard scales. For example, the item "At times I feel like swearing," answered False, gives the subject one point on the L, K, depression, and hysteria scales. It may also be seen that approximately half of the Cn scale items are scored in the same direction as for the regular scale. To illustrate, of the nine Cn scale items appearing on the depression (D) scale, five are scored in the direction which would give rise to an elevation on D and four are scored in the opposite direction. This suggests that the Cn scale is not simply an indirect measure of depression.

Table 8. Overlap of Cn Scale Items with the
Regular MMPI Scales

Name of Scale	No. of Items	Direction of Scoring	
		Same as on Cn	Opposite to Cn
L	15		4
F	64	2	2
K	30		4
Hypochondriasis	33		
Depression	60	5	4
Hysteria	60	2	3
Psychopathic deviate ..	50	2	2
Masculinity-femininity.	60	3	2
Paranoia	40	2	2
Psychasthenia	48	3	1
Schizophrenia	78	3	2
Hypomania	46	5	3

This may be contrasted with the overlap on the L and K scales. On each of these there appear four items which occur also on the Cn scale. (Actually, one of these items appears on both L and K; thus the total overlap is seven rather than eight.) What is especially striking is that they are all scored in the direction opposite to that for the Cn scale. Since both L and K are felt to measure somewhat different aspects of one psychological characteristic, namely, a tendency to see oneself in a very favorable light and to assume an overly perfect attitude, it seemed possible that persons who achieved high scores on Cn would not exhibit such an attitude. This was borne out by the scale intercorrelations. For the 60 criterion cases, the Cn scale correlates —.60 with L, .48 with F, and —.41 with K. Of interest from the psychological standpoint is the suggestion from this finding that the factor which differentiates hospitalized patients from normal persons may be something akin to degree of realistic self-appraisal, i.e., "insight."

Because comparisons with the regular MMPI scales had proved useful in suggesting possible psychological meanings for the Cn scale, further comparison with certain special scales was undertaken. Since the publication of the MMPI there has been a proliferation of scales and subscales for various purposes. Some, for example those for "dominance" [258 (see IV, 24)] and "social responsibility" [259], have an obvious and general applicability. Others, for example the scale developed by Hanvik [285] for distinguishing functional low-back pain cases from organically based cases, are clearly of limited utility in evaluating most of the profiles with which the clinical psychologist deals. In spite of the low a priori probability that the Cn scale would be related to such variables as the low-back pain scale, a comparison of item content was made for many of them. For most of them the item overlap is very small and the direction of scoring relatively uncorrelated with that of the Cn scale. On several scales, however, the overlap is quite striking and to some of these we may devote more detailed consideration. Table 9 presents the item overlap for a number of special scales.

The special scale on which there is the greatest item overlap is the social respon-

Table 9. Special MMPI Scales on Which There Is a Large Overlap of Items

Name of Scale	No. of Items	Direction of Scoring	
		Same as on Cn	Opposite to Cn
Re (social responsibility) [259] ...	32	0	8
A (first factor) [621]	39	7	0
Px (experimental scale) [624]	34	0	7
Po (experimental scale) [624]	45	5	0
R (second factor) [621]	40	0	4
Sx (schizophrenia screening) [51] ..	20	0	3
Do (dominance) [258]	28	3	0
Nm (neuroticism) [661]	30	3	0
St (social status) [236]	34	3	0
Es (ego-strength) [44]	68	7	3
C (third factor) [624]	40	2	1
Ds (dissimulation) [255]	74	2	1
Lb (low-back pain) [287]	25	4	1
N (normality) [435]	78	4	1
P (fourth factor) [624]	38	3	0
Pg (shock prognosis) [200]	52	2	1
Si (social introversion) [177]	70	4	3

sibility (Re) scale, one fourth of whose items appear on the Cn scale. They are, however, all scored in the opposite direction. Persons achieving high scores on Cn (and thus presumably quite dissimilar to hospitalized patients) tend not to be characterized by the kind of traits, attitudes, or behavior measured by the Re scale. Again, the suggestion based on item overlap is confirmed by the correlation between these scales, —.60 for the sixty criterion cases. This is in some ways a surprising finding and raises the question whether the Re and L scales (on both of which there is considerable overlap with Cn) measure in common some characteristic the presence of which makes more likely the possibility of a psychiatric breakdown. There is some evidence for and against this belief. In Welsh's factorial studies of the MMPI [621 (see IV, 29)], the scale whose factor loadings are most similar to the L scale is the Re scale. On the other hand, Gough has reported correlations of only approximately .20 between these scales. Since the populations upon which these findings were based were quite dissimilar from each other as well as from that of the present study, it is not possible to reconcile them at present.

Abramson [4] used the MMPI to predict the fitness for job responsibilities of twenty-eight officers engaged in scientific research work. One of the more significant findings was that a person showing even moderate elevation on the L score will over-conventionalize his own position. This seems to confirm the impression of most clinical workers that the scale does not merely measure "lying" but rather a rigidity of personality and lack of insight.

A person with a high L score is usually described in psychological reports as one who has achieved psychological stability by excluding from consciousness any "improper" thoughts and from behavior any socially unacceptable, unconventional actions. He would be described by others as high-principled and uncompromising but also, frequently, as conscientious and dependable. This is, it may be noted, not an inappropriate description of a "socially responsible" person. But why should such a person be more likely to become severely psychiatrically ill than a person not so described? Consideration of this question will be postponed at this point in order that we may study some of the relationships between the Cn scale and other special scales.

Another scale on which there is considerable item overlap is that thirty-nine-item A scale developed by Welsh to measure the very powerful first factor which has kept reappearing in various factorial studies. The scale is thought to tap a tendency toward preoccupation with the self, a kind of neurotic self-criticism or "psychic solipsism." Since seven of the thirty-nine A-scale items appear on the Cn scale and are scored without exception in the same direction, it may be that severity of psychiatric illness is to some extent inversely correlated with degree of critical self-concern, a hypothesis that is also consistent with the findings from the overlap on the L and Re scales. The correlation between Cn and the A scale is .53 for the sixty criterion cases.

"Px" and "Po" scales have also been developed by Welsh by contrasting the item frequencies of a group of normals versus a group of hospital and mental hygiene clinic patients. Scores on five factorially derived scales were held constant. The Px items were those answered in an opposite direction in these two groups, whereas the Po items were those answered in the same direction by both groups. There has been no systematic investigation of these scales, but their method of derivation suggests that they measure something akin to concordance with the opinions and statements expressed by the majority of people. The congruence of items between Px, Po, and Cn and the direction of scoring as listed in Table 9 are consistent with an interpretation of the Cn scale as measuring, in part, an awareness of social norms.

The Sx scale, three of whose twenty items appear on the Cn scale, was discussed previously. It will be recalled that the scale was developed by contrasting psychotics and nonpsychotics with equally elevated schizophrenia scores. Again, while the amount of overlap is fairly small, the direction of scoring suggests that persons found "truly" schizophrenic in terms of the Sx scale will be those whose Cn scores are low.

The remaining special MMPI scales listed in Table 9 have so little item overlap with Cn, relative to the scale length, that detailed consideration of them does not seem fruitful.

Summary

The more significant findings and suggestions from the present study may be summarized briefly as follows:

It has been demonstrated that the association between patterns of MMPI scores

and the verbal responses which contribute to these patterns is sufficiently indeterminate that two individuals may achieve virtually identical profiles while answering True or False to quite different subsets of items.

An empirically derived scale for differentiating between psychiatric patients
with different degrees of incapacitation appeared, on the basis of rational analysis
and comparison of item content with other scales, to be positively related to psychological insight, absence of rigidity, and freedom from overconventionality of
behavior.

This study began with a twofold purpose. One aim was to discover whether
there were intra-test factors which might help in making more reliable judgments
about the degree of incapacitation shown by a psychiatric patient. A second goal,
provided the first was realized, was to determine the psychological implications of
whatever differentiating factors emerged.

It seems fairly clear that there are intra-test factors which are related to severity
of psychiatric illness, as indicated by the fact of hospitalization. What is not so
clear is the exact psychological meaning or meanings of these factors. The hypothesis
that one of these factors is related to realistic self-appraisal seems fairly well confirmed by the data from the validation studies. The other explicitly advanced hypotheses received little support.

W. M. WHEELER, K. B. LITTLE, AND G. F. J. LEHNER

ARTICLE 28 *The Internal Structure of the MMPI*

THE MMPI is a widely used diagnostic tool. Many studies have been made concerning its use in various situations and with various types of cases, its relationship to other tests, the reliability and validity of the various scales, and the relationships among the scales as reflected in "patterns" or "profiles" of scores. Little, however, seems to have been done to determine the nature and extent of the interrelationships *among* the various scales of the total test. Information concerning the intercorrelations of the various diagnostic scales is needed. The present study attempts to provide information about scale interrelationships by utilizing a factor analysis approach. An examination of the literature fails to show any factorial study of the scales of the MMPI, although in a study by Cottle [144] a factorial analysis was made of the MMPI in relation to the Strong, Kuder, and Bell inventories.

Another aim of the present study is to appraise statistically the possibility of making dynamic interpretations in terms of different scale scores. If, for example, one factor were found, it would imply that the test measures *degree* of disturbance, not *kind* of disturbance, indicating that the test served mainly as a screening device. If, on the other hand, several different factors should emerge, each fairly closely identified with a scale, the use of the test in its present form for differential or dynamic interpretations would be supported.

Each scale was designed to provide a measure, in terms of a score, of the strength of a certain trend or component in personality make-up. High scores on any of the scales purportedly indicate deviations in terms of which differential diagnoses may be made. Although the MMPI has been described as "the first inventory measuring common specific clinical syndromes, in contrast to the earlier schedules designed for either the more general concept of 'neuroticism' or the special states like 'inferiority'" [525], this assertion has not been tested. In the light of the data to be reported from the present factor analysis study, this statement is questionable — particularly if it implies much emphasis on "specific" clinical syndromes for differential diagnosis.

As a matter of fact, work such as that of Meehl [436 (see V, 31)] and Gough [234 (VI, 38)], who discuss the clustering of scores of certain scales and who speak of the "neurotic scales" (Hs, D, and Hy) and the "psychotic scales" (Pa, Pt, and Sc), also suggests considerable overlap of the various "specific" scales frequently employed for differential diagnoses. The discovery of the "neurotic triad" and the

255

"psychotic triad" in clinical work reinforces the need to make a more detailed study of individual scale loadings and their contribution to total test score variance. Although the authors of the test suggest that interrelationships among scales indicate "the dynamic interrelationships of different clinical syndromes" [303], a more parsimonious interpretation suggests that these relationships indicate the degree of psychological identity of the scales.

Procedure

The MMPI, group form, was administered to 110 neuropsychiatric male patients in a large veterans hospital in Los Angeles, California. These patients ranged in age from 20 to 63, with a mean age of 33. The cases represented a random selection of

Table 1. Amount of Overlap of Scales Due to Common Items

	L	K	F	Hs	D	Hy	Pd	Mf	Pa	Pt	Sc	Ma
L	15	.05	.03	.00	.08	.03	.00	.03	−.04	−.04	−.03	.04
K	1	30	.02	.00	.09	.24	.16	.08	.06	−.05	.02	.08
F	1	1	64	.02	.03	.01	.09	.03	.18	.02	.21	.01
Hs	0	0	1	33	.18	.46	.02	.00	.03	.05	.08	.00
D	2	4	2	8	60	.20	.14	.03	.04	.26	.10	.05
Hy	1	10	1	20	12	60	.18	.06	.08	.13	.12	.00
Pd	0	6	5	1	7	10	50	.02	.18	.12	.16	.08
Mf	1	3	2	0	2	4	1	60	.04	.02	.06	.02
Pa	−1	2	9	1	2	4	8	2	40	.09	.23	.05
Pt	−1	−2	1	2	13	7	6	1	4	48	.25	.06
Sc	−1	1	15	4	8	8	10	4	13	15	78	.18
Ma	2	3	1	0	−3	0	4	1	2	3	11	46

neurotic and psychotic patients (and a few cases in which organic factors were also present) tested at the hospital during the year 1948. A detailed nosological breakdown of the cases was not attempted in view of the usual unreliability of such categorizing. The comparison group consisted of 112 male college students at UCLA.

Although a short 373-item group form was used, all K-scale items were included in the test, thus including all scored items.

To measure the inter-scale relationships of the MMPI, or, more accurately, to investigate the extent to which the scales measure the same personality factor or factors, Thurstone's centroid method of multiple factor analysis was employed. All computations of the Pearsonian correlation coefficients for the two groups were made on the raw scores rather than on the T scores of the scales.

Preliminary to the use of Thurstone's technique in the present investigation, a pilot study was made on two groups of 30 and 53 cases utilizing a statistical technique developed by Gengerelli [r62]. His method suggested that most of the total variance of the MMPI could be explained in terms of the variance of two or three scales. For example, these preliminary studies showed that the correlation between the Sc and Pt scales was above .80, suggesting that the two tests are measuring the same personality variable. The correlational matrix obtained by Cottle [144] shows an r of .84 for these two scales, as well as other correlations reflecting the same type of relationship among various scales.

Since many of the scales contain items also appearing in another scale or scales, the possible effect of overlapping items on the present investigation was considered. Table 1 indicates, above the principal diagonal, the r's among scales based on the amount of item overlap. Below the diagonal are the number of items in common minus those items that are scored in the opposite fashion for the respective scales. The two halves are, of course, merely different representations of the same relationship. Along the principal diagonal (italicized figures) is given the number of items in each scale. This table is presented to indicate the amount of communality any two scales have as a result of identical items. At first glance a correction of the empirical correlations would seem to be indicated. However, the consideration of a correlation coefficient as an index of percentage of common elements, of which physical identity is only one kind, leads to the conclusion that extraction of these would be based on spurious reasoning. In other words, positive item overlap is one way in which the scales are related and should not be interpreted as detracting from empirical relationships based on scores obtained on the scales.

Results

The mean values obtained for each group and the combined groups for each of the MMPI scales are given in Table 2. Cottle's means are listed in Table 3 with the combined data from the present study for comparison. Also presented are the differences between the college and neuropsychiatric means on each scale and the

Table 2. Means, Standard Deviations, and Codes of MMPI Variables on Two Diagnostic Groups, with Differences, SE_{diff}'s, and CR's

Group	L	F	K	Hs	D	Hy	Pd	Mf	Pa	Pt	Sc	Ma
College (N = 112)												
Mean	3.3	4.7	16.4	3.9	19.8	20.7	15.6	27.7	8.9	10.0	10.0	16.9
SD	2.3	3.1	4.7	3.2	5.2	4.3	4.3	4.3	2.7	7.4	6.9	4.4
			MMPI Code: 5–239 46 87/1 KF/L									
Neuropsychiatric (N = 110)												
Mean	5.1	8.6	14.5	11.3	26.5	25.7	21.4	24.7	11.7	16.9	18.5	18.8
SD	2.6	7.1	5.3	7.0	7.6	7.8	5.7	4.8	5.0	10.5	12.3	5.6
			MMPI Code: 2'431 8697–5 F–KL									
Diff	1.8	3.9	1.9	7.4	6.7	5.0	5.8	3.0	2.8	6.9	8.5	1.9
SE_{diff}	.3	1.2	.7	1.2	.9	.9	.6	.6	.5	1.2	1.3	.7
CR [a]	5.45	3.39	2.83	6.27	7.61	5.88	9.21	4.84	5.18	5.85	6.49	2.83

[a] All differences are significant at or beyond the .01 level.

Table 3. Means and Codes of the Composite Group Compared with a College Group

Group	L	F	K	Hs	D	Hy	Pd	Mf	Pa	Pt	Sc	Ma
Composite group (N = 222)	4.2	6.6	15.5	7.6	23.1	23.2	18.4	26.2	10.3	13.4	14.2	17.8
			MMPI Code: 2345–91687 FKL/									
College group, Cottle [144] (N = 400)	3.8	4.0	....	5.5	19.5	21.7	15.3	25.3	9.2	12.4	10.8	17.9
			MMPI Code: 5–39246718 F/L									

critical ratio for this difference. All differences are significant beyond the .01 level of confidence.

As can be seen from these data, the neuropsychiatric group scores significantly above the college group on all scales except K and Mf, where they score significantly below, confirming the value of the test as a general screening device.

The intercorrelations obtained for the 12 scales used (the Cannot Say scale was omitted since no records with a Cannot Say score greater than 25 are included in the present data) are presented in the correlation matrices in Tables 4, 5, and 6.

A comparison of the two groups reveals significant differences for 17 correlations as shown in Table 7. The relevant correlations from Cottle's matrix are also presented.

Two general conclusions can be drawn: Cottle's group tends to fall between our college group and our neuropsychiatric group not only in mean scores but also in terms of the direction of change of relationships among scales; the trend of change of relationships between scales is a consistent one and deserves further investigation to determine its implications. For example, one speculation can be made about the changes in relationships of the Pa scale. Pa has its maximal relationship with Hy in the normal group and with Sc in the neuropsychiatric group. With Cottle's group, which included individuals seeking psychological aid, the relationship of Pa to Sc is between that obtained for the two groups in the present study. These relationships would seem to substantiate the interpretation that paranoid reactions as measured by the items in this scale can be part of two different syndromes, perhaps a neurotic and a psychotic.

A comparison of the correlation coefficients obtained here with the reliability coefficients published for the scales [322] reveals that various pairs of scales show correlations that approximate the reliability coefficients obtained for either of the members of the respective pair. This would seem to indicate that the particular scales in question do not measure different things in spite of the different labels applied to them and in spite of the differentiating functions imputed to them. For example, the correlation between Sc and Pt of .86 from the table of data on the combined groups, if corrected for attenuation on the basis of Holzberg's reliabilities, which are the highest published to date, rises to the improbable figure of 1.08, while the correlation between Hs and D of .73 rises to the value of .99.

In Tables 8, 9, and 10 are presented the factor loadings after rotation for the college group, the neuropsychiatric group, and the two groups combined.

Normal Group. An examination of the data for the normal group indicates that there are two major group factors clearly defined.

The first factor has its maximal loadings on the Sc and Pt scales, showing, respectively, values of .943 and .908. Other positive loadings on this factor are found in Hs, F, Pd, D, and to a slight extent, Mf. In contrast with these positive loadings, we find that the K scale shows a high negative loading of −.630.

An interpretation of this factor in the light of these loadings would suggest that it indicates primarily concern with oneself. The scales which are most heavily loaded, Sc and Pt, are two of the three commonly referred to as the *psychotic* triad, and seem to reflect the encapsulating withdrawal of a schizoid type including excessive concern with compulsive needs. The extremely high negative loading on the K scale would seem to indicate that when this factor is present to a marked

Table 4. Correlations among the Twelve Scales of the MMPI for 112 Male College Students

Scale	L	K	F	Hs	D	Hy	Pd	Mf	Pa	Pt	Sc	Ma
L		.366	.046	−.026	.076	.243	−.102	−.029	.127	−.299	−.334	−.151
K	.366		−.105	−.305	−.068	.499	−.090	−.162	.193	−.587	−.510	−.297
F	.046	−.105		.489	.561	.310	.554	.178	.301	.457	.674	.194
Hs	−.026	−.305	.489		.560	.372	.417	.191	.212	.577	.554	.162
D	.076	−.068	.561	.560		.458	.414	.260	.383	.570	.484	−.272
Hy	.243	.499	.310	.372	.458		.348	.183	.399	.049	.077	−.075
Pd	−.102	−.090	.554	.417	.414	.348		.153	.303	.420	.590	.308
Mf	−.029	−.162	.178	.191	.260	.183	.153		.332	.417	.391	.124
Pa	.127	.193	.301	.212	.383	.399	.303	.332		.234	.304	.014
Pt	−.299	−.587	.457	.577	.570	.049	.420	.417	.234		.821	.181
Sc	−.334	−.510	.674	.554	.484	.077	.590	.391	.304	.821		.348
Ma	−.151	−.297	.194	.162	−.272	−.075	.308	.124	.014	.181	.348	

Table 5. Correlations among the Twelve Scales of the MMPI for 110 Male Neuropsychiatric Patients

Scale	L	K	F	Hs	D	Hy	Pd	Mf	Pa	Pt	Sc	Ma
L		.302	−.097	.138	.027	.134	−.121	−.085	.028	−.285	−.194	−.162
K	.302		−.404	−.201	−.185	.138	−.383	−.190	−.261	−.655	−.550	−.451
F	−.097	−.404		.334	.154	.021	.507	.300	.690	.536	.764	.411
Hs	.138	−.201	.334		.680	.759	.405	.258	.477	.523	.516	.271
D	.027	−.185	.154	.680		.690	.453	.346	.346	.635	.469	.038
Hy	.134	.138	.021	.759	.690		.298	.257	.299	.344	.222	.075
Pd	−.121	−.383	.507	.405	.453	.298		.297	.615	.590	.604	.515
Mf	−.085	−.190	.300	.258	.346	.257	.297		.457	.344	.325	.184
Pa	.028	−.261	.690	.477	.346	.299	.615	.457		.538	.703	.436
Pt	−.285	−.655	.536	.523	.635	.344	.590	.344	.538		.857	.461
Sc	−.194	−.550	.764	.516	.469	.222	.604	.325	.703	.857		.539
Ma	−.162	−.451	.411	.271	.038	.075	.515	.184	.436	.461	.539	

Table 6. Correlations among the Twelve Scales of the MMPI for Male College Students and Male Neuropsychiatric Patients Combined

Scale	L	K	F	Hs	D	Hy	Pd	Mf	Pa	Pt	Sc	Ma
L		.241	.070	.262	.226	.274	.081	−.162	.169	−.130	−.066	−.078
K	.241		−.343	−.282	−.205	.162	−.315	−.109	−.163	−.639	−.546	−.408
F	.070	−.343		.471	.360	.195	.580	.118	.657	.566	.775	.383
Hs	.262	−.282	.471		.728	.730	.566	.002	.519	.607	.618	.299
D	.226	−.205	.360	.728		.683	.565	.119	.451	.672	.565	.025
Hy	.274	.162	.195	.730	.683		.435	.082	.408	.357	.307	.099
Pd	.081	−.315	.580	.566	.565	.435		.041	.591	.606	.670	.468
Mf	−.162	−.109	.118	.002	.119	.082	.041		.254	.218	.173	.088
Pa	.169	−.163	.657	.519	.451	.408	.591	.254		.516	.660	.347
Pt	−.130	−.639	.566	.607	.672	.357	.606	.218	.516		.864	.398
Sc	−.066	−.546	.775	.618	.565	.307	.670	.173	.660	.864		.504
Ma	−.078	−.408	.383	.299	.025	.099	.468	.088	.347	.398	.504	

degree in an individual, the usual ego-defensive mechanisms are held in abeyance and the person now tends to show himself in the worst possible light.

The second major factor has its maximal loadings on Hy (with a value of .780) and, interestingly enough, on K (with a value of .578). Other significant loadings on this factor occur on scales D, Pa, F, Pd, L, and Hs. This factor seems to reflect, on the basis of these loadings, the *neurotic* picture of adjustment. The high positive loading of K for this factor, as compared with the high negative loading of K for Factor I, implies that the ego-defenses are intact. Perhaps one of these ego-defensive

Table 7. Significant [a] Changes in Scale Relationships
from College to Neuropsychiatric Subjects

r	College	NP	Diff	Cottle's Data
KF	−.105	−.404	−.299	...
KHy	.499	.138	−.361	...
KPd	−.090	−.383	−.293	...
KPa	.193	−.261	−.454	...
FD	.561	.154	−.407	.344
FHy	.310	.021	−.289	.159
FPa	.301	.690	.389	.206
HsHy	.372	.759	.387	.588
HsPa	.212	.477	.265	.183
DHy	.458	.690	.232	.415
DMa	−.272	.038	.310	−.083
HyPt	.049	.344	.295	.182
PdPa	.303	.615	.312	.329
PaPt	.234	.538	.304	.363
PaSc	.304	.703	.399	.415
PaMa	.014	.436	.422	.112
PtMa	.181	.461	.280	.357

[a] To compute the significance of differences between correlations, they were transformed to z values. All differences given in the table were significant at or beyond the .05 level.

mechanisms is indicated by the positive loading of .510 on the Pa scale. This suggests that the paranoid projections serve more as a neurotic defense *in the normal group* than as a component in the schizoid pattern indicated in Factor I. We shall see in a moment that the Pa scale disappears from Factor II in the neuropsychiatric group and has a loading in Factor I.

The third factor found in the normal group has its only significant loadings on Mf and Pa, reflecting the masculinity-femininity variable and its possible relationship to paranoia — a relationship often stressed in psychoanalytic theory.

The fourth factor has significant loading on D (.595) and Ma (−.595), indicating a bipolar relationship between these two scales. This apparently indicates a dimension of mood independent of the schizoid and neurotic patterns reflected in Factors I and II.

Since scales D, F, and Pd have significant loadings on both Factors I and II, we may infer that the kinds of reactions typified by these scales are parts of both the schizoid and neurotic pattern.

Neuropsychiatric Group. The analysis of the data for the neuropsychiatric group also indicates two major factors. Factor I again has its maximal loadings on Pt

Table 8. Factor Loadings after Rotation for the
College Group (N = 112)

Scale	I	II	III	IV	h²
L	...	.351	...	...	.242
K	−.630	.578	...	...	.740
F	.590	.450	...	...	.592
Hs	.627	.345	...	...	.538
D	.503	.530	...	.595	.894
Hy	...	.780	...	...	.615
Pd	.556	.425	...	...	.581
Mf	.358	...	.538	...	.441
Pa	...	.510	.339	...	.413
Pt	.908	...	...	...	.926
Sc	.943	...	...	...	.914
Ma	...	...	...	−.595	.452

Table 9. Factor Loadings after Rotation for the
Neuropsychiatric Group (N = 110)

Scale	I	II	III	IV	h²
L	...	...	...		.234
K	−.702	...	...		.643
F	.668	...	.458		.700
Hs	.529	.740	...		.873
D	.481	.648	...		.741
Hy	...	.845	...		.771
Pd	.700	...	...		.551
Mf	.381	...	...		.338
Pa	.632	...	.591		.780
Pt	.936	...	...		.944
Sc	.925	...	...		.878
Ma	.620	...	...		.494

Table 10. Factor Loadings after Rotation for the Combined
College and Neuropsychiatric Groups (N = 222)

Scale	I	II	III	IV	h²
L	...	.469	...	...	.307
K	−.670	...	...	...	.633
F	.688	...	.467	...	.707
Hs	.600	.640	...	...	.786
D	.554	.680	...	...	.820
Hy	...	.789	...	...	.747
Pd	.682	...	...	.416	.718
Mf	...	...	...	...	.119
Pa	.602	...	.560	...	.728
Pt	.936	...	...	...	.940
Sc	.931	...	...	...	.907
Ma	.550	...	...	...	.392

(.936) and Sc (.925). Other significant positive loadings are found on Pd, F, Pa,
Ma, Hs, D, and Mf, with a substantial negative loading for K of −.702.

A comparison of these loadings with those found in Factor I for the normal
group shows considerable similarity. For example, Pt, Sc, and K show very similar

loadings. The differences which appear are primarily on two scales: the Hs scale has a lower loading on the "psychotic" factor for the neuropsychiatric group than it does for the group of college males, reflecting evidently the differences in defenses between these two groups; the other difference concerns the loadings of Pa. In the neuropsychiatric group the Pa scale has its heaviest loading on the same factor as the "psychotic" scales, whereas in the college group its heaviest loading is on the same factor as the "neurotic" scales.

An examination of Factor II — the "neurotic" factor — for the neuropsychiatric group indicates that it has its maximal loadings on only three scales: Hy (.845), Hs (.740), and D (.648). Comparing these loadings with those obtained for the college group, we see that the Hs scale has a minimal loading (.345) for the normals, whereas in the neuropsychiatric group it has a loading of .740 — the second highest loading for this factor. It is interesting to note further that in the neuropsychiatric group the K scale has no loading on the neurotic factor, while in the normal group it has the second highest loading, indicating perhaps that in hospital patients the usual neurotic manifestations are accompanied by less of the type of "defensiveness" that K represents. It is well to remember, also, that the loadings of the neurotic triad for the hospital group may have been determined by different items of the same scales than the loadings of the neurotic triad in the normal group. A future item analysis may indicate that the loadings of the neurotic triad for the hospital group represent something quite different from that in the normal group, perhaps a second "psychotic" factor. One must recognize the danger of accepting the present scale titles for interpretation of factors without careful examination of the scale items contributing to the present loadings.

The third factor obtained for the neuropsychiatric group has loadings on only two scales, Pa (.591) and F (458). Pa is common to both the normal and the neuropsychiatric group, with F replacing Mf in the hospital group.

A fourth factor was obtained for the neuropsychiatric group, but it disappeared in the process of rotation.

Combined Group. The factors presented by combining the two groups are much as would be expected from the data obtained in the analysis of the two separate groups. The first factor again has its major scale loadings on Pt (.936) and Sc (.931), with the other values in general falling between those obtained for the separate groups.

The Mf scale, however, shows some peculiar behavior. It will be noticed that in the combined group its communality for the first four factors drops to a value of .119. The meaning of this drop is not clear. It may be that this reflects a curvilinear relationship between Mf and some of the other scales in the more heterogeneous population.

Summary and Conclusion

The results from the present factor analysis of the MMPI seem to indicate that the ambitious goal of measuring specific clinical syndromes has not been completely achieved. The test permits diagnosis mainly in terms of "neurotic" or "psychotic," but not in terms of *type* of neurosis or psychosis or other more specific category. The results do, however, substantiate the use of the MMPI for distinguishing between neurotic and psychotic syndromes. These two syndromes are here defined by their maximal loadings on the Hy and Sc scales, respectively.

Present findings would indicate that refined differential diagnosis or the formulation of dynamic personality descriptions on the basis of MMPI profiles is a questionable procedure. Present results are in accord with such as those reported by Schmidt [528 (see VI, 39)], Gough [234 (VI, 38)], and Benton and Probst [56], who found that specific score profiles on the various scales do not permit differentiation among the patients in various psychiatric categories, though differentiation can be made between normal and abnormal persons.

ARTICLE 29 *Factor Dimensions A and R*

Factor Analytic Background

A NUMBER of factor analytic studies of the MMPI have now appeared. The populations utilized have included both men and women, college and noncollege, psychiatric and normal subjects. For the most part the nine original clinical scales have been used although in some instances one or more of the validity scales were also included. And in at least one study [598], Drake's Si scale [177 (see IV, 19)] and five of Gough's social scales [236 (see IV, 21), 247 (IV, 23), 241, 259, 258 (IV, 24)] supplemented the regular scales.

Borko [673] has reviewed the following studies: Abrams [2], Cook and Wherry [138], Cottle [144], Little [395], Stout [571], Tyler [598], Wheeler, Little, and Lehner [634], and Winne [660]. In almost all the studies there is essential agreement as to the loadings of two factors although the interpretations and the name assigned to these factors vary. One factor (usually the first) shows very high loadings on scale 7 (Pt) and scale 8 (Sc) with negative loading on K whenever it is used. A second factor shows fairly high loadings on the neurotic triad, especially scale 3 (Hy) and scale 2 (D), with negative loading frequently appearing on scale 9 (Ma).

Unpublished factor studies have been carried out by the present writer on three different populations: 66 VA neuropsychiatric hospital patients, 60 medical ward patients from a VA general medical and surgical hospital, and 100 VA mental hygiene clinic outpatients. All three studies confirm very clearly the factor loading patterns outlined above.

In the present writer's studies as well as in those of others referred to above, however, there has been practically no general agreement as to third and fourth factor patterns when these were extracted.

The remarkable similarity of loadings on these two factors has appeared despite the varying populations employed. Up to this time no attempt has been made to explore systematically the dimensions which may underlie these factors. This paper describes the development and use of two new scales which have been especially designed to make possible an accurate estimate of subjects' positions on these two factors. These scales will be described in detail below.

A Scale of "General Maladjustment"

A previous attempt to assess a general dimension underlying the MMPI clinical scales had been carried out in 1947 at the Minneapolis VA hospital by John Pearson,

Roland Peek, and the present writer. These writers had argued that if any one item appeared on a number of scales it might be related to some general dimension which underlay the scales on which it appeared. To this end a series of items were assembled, all scored in the same direction on three or more clinical scales. A subsequent thirty-four-item revision was carried out using scale 0 (Si) in place of scale 5 (Mf) on the basis of the content of the items as well as the nature of the intercorrelations between the clinical scales and scale 0.

Inspection of the content led to the scale being called Gm for "general maladjustment" or "general malaise." For example, one item is scored on six scales (2, 3, 4, 7, 8, 0), "I find it hard to keep my mind on a task or job"; another, "My daily life is full of things that keep me interested," is scored on five scales (2, 3, 4, 7, 8). Six

Table 1. Item Contribution to Gm of the MMPI Scales
and Their Correlations with Gm in a Sample
of Neuropsychiatric Patients

Scale	Item Overlap	Percentage of Scale	Gm r
1 (Hs)	12	36	.87
2 (D)	17	28	.60
3 (Hy)	16	26	.67
4 (Pd)	12	24	.60
5 (Mf)	0	0	.31
6 (Pa)	9	23	.91
7 (Pt)	14	29	.75
8 (Sc)	20	26	.91
9 (Ma)	8	17	.60
0 (Si)	5	21	.67
K			−.60
L			−.31
F			.81
Total	113		

items appear on four scales and the remaining items in Gm are scored on three. In Table 1 may be seen (a) the number of item overlaps with each scale, (b) these overlaps expressed as a percentage of the scale length, and (c) the correlation of each scale with Gm in a population of sixty-six VA neuropsychiatric hospital patients. It is of interest to note that the mean of the overlap percentages is 25.6; thus, about one fourth of the items on a given scale will be Gm items common to at least two other scales.

The economical advantage of general scales may be argued by considering the item overlap of certain scales. In the three scales 2 (D), 7 (Pt), and 8 (Sc) we find the following relations: 2 and 7 have thirteen items in common, 2 and 8 have eight, and 7 and 8 have fifteen. Indeed, six of these items are common to all three scales. It may well be possible, then, to measure the configuration exemplified by the 278 profile code (see Section III of this book) by a briefer scale rather than the three overlapping scales presently employed.

"Pure" Scales

Along with Gm, a series of keys was developed by eliminating all the positive item overlap from each clinical scale. For example, a "pure" or "prime" key for scale

1 (Hs) was obtained by eliminating not only the twelve Gm items but also all the items overlapping with one other scale. Since there are twelve of these latter items, the thirty-three-item Hs scale reduces to a nine-item "pure" scale. The convention has been adopted of referring to these scoring keys as prime scales and using a prime mark after the designation of such scales to indicate this, i.e., Hs' or 1'. The reader may recall that only 366 of the 550 items on the MMPI are scored and, of these scored items, only 136 are scored primely — that is, uniquely on only one of the nine original scales.

By the use of prime scales it is possible to overcome the objections raised by some factor analysts who point out the difficulty of interpreting the meaning of factors obtained from the intercorrelations of scales with overlapping items. This problem was noted by Wheeler *et al.* [634 (see IV, 28)] but they decided to carry out their analysis using the full-length scales.

A Cluster Analysis

In a previously reported study [688] by the present writer a cluster analysis [r162] on a population of 150 male patients in a VA general medical and surgical hospital was carried out using scores on the Gm scale and the nine prime clinical scales. In general, two dimensions seemed to account for most of the common variance; the first domain showed highest loadings on Gm, 7', and 8' while the second had a high positive loading on 2' and the highest negative loading on 9'.

Special scales were then developed from Gm, 2', and 9' and intercorrelated with the prime scales now including K' and 0'; this matrix was subjected to a regular Thurstone centroid analysis. The special scales were developed in the hope that longer and more statistically stable scales would provide a more adequate measure of the factor dimensions.

Development of Special Scales

The general method followed in developing these special scales is a variant of the internal consistency method. Two groups of subjects scoring at opposite extremes on a scale were identified and used to carry out an item analysis of all 550 items in the MMPI. Retained on a final scale were items which showed the maximum difference in frequency of response in a given direction by the two extreme groups. For example, the 150 hospital patients (sample I) who had been scored on Gm were separated into two groups: an upper group of 10 per cent (15 subjects) which had received the highest scores on Gm, and a bottom group falling at the lowest 10 per cent of the distribution of Gm scores.

A second population of 137 male patients seen at a VA mental hygiene clinic (sample II) were also scored on Gm and the upper and lower 10 per cent (14 subjects in each group) used. All items which showed extreme differences — for example, fourteen upper subjects and two lower subjects responding in a given direction — were considered. The final scale, called A, consisted of thirty-nine items which showed at least a 75 per cent separation in both samples. Actually some of the items showed absolute separation, all the subjects in one group and none in the other responding in a given direction. It is apparent that the size of the extreme group and the separation requirements met are considerably more stringent than those usually advocated [r176] in this general type of procedure.

A similar method was followed in developing a scale from 2', subsequently called R, and one from 9' called M. That is, an item analysis of all 550 items using the extreme groups of both samples on 2' and on 9' was carried out. Each of these scales contains forty items and the level of separation, although not so marked as in A, was above 60 per cent for all items.

Table 2 presents the results of the factoring of the matrix with the special scales. The success of the A scale as a dimension can be gauged by the loading of .99 on factor I with inconsequential loadings on II and III. The R scale seems to be the best measure of the second dimension although its loadings are not so striking as

Table 2. Unrotated Centroid Factor Loadings and Communalities of MMPI Scales (Male VA General Medical and Surgical Hospital Patients, N = 150)

Scale	I	II	III	h²
K'	−86	13	28	83
1' (Hs')	56	18	08	35
2' (D')	−36	39	−45	49
3' (Hy')	−62	46	31	69
4' (Pd')	60	13	08	39
5' (Mf')	19	38	35	30
6' (Pa')	−16	34	18	17
7' (Pt')	87	05	−12	77
8' (Sc')	85	02	07	72
9' (Ma')	56	−52	26	65
0' (Si')	52	24	−34	44
A	99	11	−02	98
Gm	81	49	09	90
Ja	90	23	00	87
M	84	−45	−12	92
R	−22	88	−24	87

those obtained with A. R shows a loading of .88 on factor II and −.22 on I. With its loadings the M scale lies between the other two special scales. In addition to Gm, described above, from which A was derived, Table 2 shows a scale called Ja. This is a rationally derived scale of anxiety developed by consensus of ten judges [620 (see V, 32)].

The loadings on the prime MMPI scales again support the configuration obtained in all the previous factor studies with full-length scales. On factor I the highest positive loadings are seen on 7' and 8' with an equally high negative loading on K'. For II the greatest positive loading occurs on 3'; 9' shows the greatest negative value. It should be noted that the communalities of the special scales satisfactorily account for practically all the common variance, but the clinical scales, with the exception of K', 7', and 8', show a good deal of unique variance.

Further work has been carried out with this matrix in extracting a fourth factor and deriving scales to measure the third and fourth factors. But since these scales have not yet been adequately explored, they will not be reported here.

Structural Aspects of A and R

Some clue as to the nature of the dimensions assessed by the specially derived scales may be inferred from the configuration of loadings exhibited in Table 2.

Further help in interpretation may be obtained from an examination of the nature of the items of A and R. It should be noted that all the items in A are scored if answered True with the exception of item 20. Every one of the R items is answered False.

The A scale consists solely of "X" items, i.e., items in which the response is opposite to that of the majority of the standardizing Minnesota normals. The R scale, on the other hand, contains twenty-five "X" and fifteen "0" items; in these latter items credit is earned on a scale for an answer in the *same* direction as the majority of the normal group. The reader should consult the *Manual* [305, pp. 8–9] and Meehl and Hathaway [441 (see I, 2)] if the distinction between the "X" and "0" response direction scoring and its meaning are not absolutely clear to him.

Since all the items save one in scale A are answered True and every one of the items in R is answered False, it may be thought that there is merely some response set at work. This is, however, belied by the actual intercorrelations between A and R since in most samples the r's are close to zero (see Table 8). The negative correlations found in some samples, though, would support such a view. Evidence that there must be more than a response set at work is found in a study by Kooser [369]. He administered the 79 items comprising A and R as a separate scale to over 300 college undergraduates. The scores on A and on R for a subsample of 100 were correlated with the total number of the 79 items which had been answered True. The corrected r's are as follows: A = .04 and R = −.13. These values do not differ from each other and both are approximately zero. Thus, the evidence supports the view that subjects who had many "true" responses were no more likely to be high on A than on R.

Content of A Scale

Although the content of the A scale is relatively homogeneous as compared with most of the regular MMPI scales, it is possible to group the items into content clusters. These are listed below. Following each item is the overlap with regular scales in code terms (see Section III on coding).

The first cluster includes ten items which all seem to be related to thinking and thought processes:

1. I find it hard to keep my mind on a task or job. (2, 3, 4, 7, 8, 0) 2. I have more trouble concentrating than others seem to have. (7, 8) 3. At periods my mind seems to work more slowly than usual. (K [scored on K if answered False]) 4. When in a group of people I have trouble thinking of the right things to talk about. (0, K, 3, 4, 9 [scored on K, 3, 4, 9 if answered False]) 5. I have often lost out on things because I couldn't make up my mind soon enough. (0, 3 [scored on 3 if answered False]) 6. I usually have to stop and think before I act even in trifling matters. (7) 7. I have several times had a change of heart about my life work. (Unscored) 8. Sometimes some unimportant thought will run through my mind and bother me for days. (7, 0 [scored on 0 if answered False]) 9. I am apt to take disappointments so keenly that I can't put them out of my mind. (Unscored) 10. I do many things which I regret afterwards (I regret things more or more often than others seem to). (4, 7)

The first two items relate to trouble in concentrating while slowness and difficulty in mentation are stressed in items 3 and 4. The subject admits excessive doubt and indecision in 5, 6, and 7. Obsessive thinking and rumination are seen in the last three items.

A second cluster consists of items referring to negative emotional tone and dysphoria:

11. I feel anxiety about something or someone almost all the time. (7) 12. I must admit that I have at times been worried beyond reason over something that really did not matter. (Unscored) 13. I wish I could get over worrying about things I have said that may have injured other people's feelings. (Unscored) 14. I worry quite a bit over possible misfortunes. (Unscored) 15. I brood a great deal. (2, 0) 16. I have often felt guilty because I have pretended to feel more sorry about something than I really was. (Unscored) 17. Even when I am with people I feel lonely much of the time. (6, 7, 8) 18. I wish I could be as happy as others seem to be. (2, 4, 7, 0) 19. Most of the time I feel blue. (3, 7, 8) 20. I very seldom have spells of the blues. (Answered False) (Unscored)

The first four items clearly express anxiety and worry, with the added flavor in item 13 of rumination, which is somewhat similar to items in the first cluster. Broodiness, guilt, and loneliness are admitted in items 15, 16, and 17, with rumination again noted in 16. The last three items deal with feelings of unhappiness. It is of particular interest to note that item 20 is both the logical and psychological opposite of 19. This consistency is not found in one pair of items on the second factor scale R.

A third cluster deals with lack of energy and pessimism:

21. Life is a strain for me much of the time. (7, 8) 22. I feel tired a good deal of the time. (Unscored) 23. I have had periods of days, weeks, or months when I couldn't take care of things because I couldn't "get going." (2, 7, 8) 24. I have difficulty in starting to do things. (2, 8) 25. My plans have frequently seemed so full of difficulties that I have had to give them up. (Unscored) 26. I have sometimes felt that difficulties were piling up so high that I could not overcome them. (K [scored on K if answered False]) 27. Often, even though everything is going fine for me, I feel that I don't care about anything. (Unscored)

The first two items indicate directly a lack of energy while 23 and 24 seem to refer to an inability to mobilize one's resources. The subject shows pessimistic feelings in the last three items and admits in 25 and 26 his inability to cope with difficulties.

A fourth cluster of items may be labeled personal sensitivity:

28. I have often felt that strangers were looking at me critically. (5, 0) 29. I am apt to pass up something I want to do because others feel that I am not going about it in the right way. (Unscored) 30. It makes me feel like a failure when I hear of the success of someone I know well. (0) 31. Often I cross the street in order not to meet someone I see. (7) 32. People often disappoint me. (0, K [scored on K if answered False]) 33. I feel unable to tell anyone all about myself. (Unscored) 34. I am easily embarrassed. (7, 0) 35. Criticism or scolding hurts me terribly. (2, 0, K [scored on K if answered False]) 36. At times I think that I am no good at all. (Unscored)

In item 28 a direct and in item 29 an indirect criticism affect the subject. In item 30, again, an unfavorable comparison with others is implied. While personal inferiority is admitted in 31 it must be noted that the subject apparently feels he has reason to be sensitive since item 32 indicates that people disappoint him. Thus the inability to confide admitted in 33 is consistent with the implied mistrust of others seen in this cluster. Items 34 and 35 deal directly with personal sensitivity and the last item reflects the pessimistic tenor of cluster three.

A final and smaller cluster refers to somewhat more malignant mentation:

37. I sometimes feel that I am about to go to pieces. (Unscored) 38. I often feel as if things were not real. (8) 39. I have a daydream life about which I do not tell other people. (Unscored)

Item 37 is akin to the fear of losing one's mind often expressed by psychiatric patients. It is of interest to note that item 38 which implies psychotic dissociation is the only pure Sc item appearing in this key. The last item may refer to fantasy of a personal nature.

A summary of the item overlap and a general indication of the correlation with clinical scales may be seen in Table 3.

Table 3. Item Overlap of Factor Scales A and R with Regular MMPI Scales and Rounded Average r's for Representative Samples (Items Scored Oppositely on the Scale Are Enclosed in Parentheses)

Scale	A Item Overlap		r_A	R Item Overlap		r_R
L			−.25			.30
F			.55	2 (1)		−.10
K	(5)		−.70	4		.35
1 (Hs)			.30	3		.20
2 (D)	6		.60	10		.30
3 (Hy)	2 (2)		.20	4		.30
4 (Pd)	3 (1)		.40			−.05
5 (Mf)	1	M	.30	5 (3)	M	.15
		F	−.10		F	.00
6 (Pa)	1		.50	2		.05
7 (Pt)	13		.75			.05
8 (Sc)	8		.60	1 (2)		.00
9 (Ma)	(1)		.35	(2)		−.40
0 (Si)	10 (1)		.60	9		.40
Unscored on above scales	15			9		

Content of R Scale

The content of the R scale is much more varied than that of the A scale and yet a certain consistency can be traced through the rational clustering which has been attempted below. Following each item are the code numbers of the regular scales in which these items also occur. Remember that all items on R are scored if answered False.

A cluster of eight items relates to health and physical symptoms:

1. I am in just as good physical health as most of my friends. (1, 2, 3) 2. I am about as able to work as I ever was. (1, 2, 3) 3. I do not worry about catching diseases. (2) 4. I do not often notice my ears ringing or buzzing. (1, 6, 8, 0) 5. I have had no difficulty starting or holding my urine. (0) 6. Sometimes, when embarrassed, I break out in a sweat which annoys me greatly. (2) 7. I have never had a fit or

convulsion. (2) 8. I have had periods in which I carried on activities without knowing later what I had been doing. (F, 8, 9 [scored on F, 8, and 9 if answered True])

In items 1 and 2 there is a denial of health and ability plus an admission of worry about health; in items 4 and 5 physical symptoms are admitted but in item 6 either the symptom or the concern about it is denied. Items 7 and 8 are particularly interesting since they seem to be logical opposites: if item 7 is answered False it implies that the subject *has* had a convulsion and should therefore answer True to item 8 (this is the scored direction for scales F, 8, and 9) but the high R person denies this.

A second cluster refers to emotionality, violence, and activity:

9. Once in a while I feel hate toward members of my family whom I usually love. (5, 8) 10. Some of my family have quick tempers. (Unscored) 11. My mother or father often made me obey even when I thought that it was unreasonable. (6) 12. At times I am full of energy. (K, F, 2) 13. I was fond of excitement when I was young (or in childhood). (Unscored) 14. I am often sorry because I am so cross and grouchy. (Unscored) 15. At times I feel like smashing things. (K, 2) 16. At times I feel like picking a fist fight with someone. (2)

In the first three items (9, 10, and 11) the subject denies hate, temper, and unrea-sonableness in his family; the negative emotion implied in item 9 is admitted by a True answer for scales 5 (Mf) and 8 (Sc). In the next two items feelings of energy and fondness of excitement are denied. In item 14 the subject either denies that he ever feels cross or that he is sorry for feeling cross. Direct physical and personal violence are disclaimed in items 15 and 16.

A third cluster deals with reactions to other people in a social situation:

17. I enjoy the excitement of a crowd. (0) 18. My worries seem to disappear when I get into a crowd of lively friends. (0) 19. I enjoy social gatherings just to be with people. (0) 20. I try to remember good stories to pass them on to other people. (0)

It is of interest to note that all four items are scored on social introversion, scale 0 (see IV, 19 and 20). In items 17 and 18 the subject again denies enjoyment as previously noted in the second cluster (item 13). The subject in all four items denies that he is stimulated by other people or that he responds socially to them.

A fourth cluster of items relates to social dominance, feelings of personal adequacy, and personal appearance:

21. If given the chance I would make a good leader of people. (0) 22. I have often met people who were supposed to be experts who were no better than I. (K) 23. I frequently find it necessary to stand up for what I think is right. (F, 5) 24. I am often inclined to go out of my way to win a point with someone who has opposed me. (Unscored) 25. I like to let people know where I stand on things. (K) 26. I do not blame a person for taking advantage of someone who lays himself open to it. (2, 9 [scored on 9 if answered True]) 27. I would like to wear expensive clothes. (Unscored) 28. I am very careful about my manner of dress. (Unscored)

Unaggressiveness and a lack of social dominance are clearly implied in the first five items while in item 26 the subject even denies blaming another person who may have been aggressive. Lack of interest in dress and personal appearance is seen in the last two items. Here the high R person disagrees with the Minnesota normals in not liking expensive clothes but is in agreement with them in denying carefulness in dress.

A fifth cluster of items all refer to personal and vocational interests:

29. I enjoy detective or mystery stories. (3) 30. I like to read newspaper articles on crime. (3) 31. I like to flirt. (2, 0) 32. I am fascinated by fire. (Unscored) 33. I like to attend lectures on serious subjects. (Unscored) 34. I like science. (5) 35. I like mechanics magazines. (5) 36. I like repairing a door latch. (Unscored) 37. I think I would like the work of a building contractor. (5) 38. I think I would like the kind of work a forest ranger does. (5) 39. I like dramatics. (0, 5 [scored on 5 if answered True]) 40. I like to cook. (5 [scored on 5 if answered True])

The first four items seem to reflect a denial of basic, id-like impulses related to hostility and sexuality. This trend was presaged in the second cluster. In items 34 and 35 the subject denies interest even in intellectual pursuits. Nor does he enjoy mechanical and manual activities: 35, 36, 37. Despite the subject's asociality as inferred from cluster three, in item 38 he denies that he would like the solitary work of a forest ranger. Unlike the scale 5 direction the R person does not like dramatics or cooking.

The item overlap is summarized in Table 3 and average intercorrelations of R with the regular scales are presented.

Item Overlap

For A the greatest overlap, thirteen items, and the highest correlation, .75, both occur on scale 7 (Pt). Of these thirteen, four are 7' items. The K scale shows a high negative correlation, —.70, although the two scales have only five items in common. Despite the fact that Gm was the basis for the derivation of A only five of the original thirty-four Gm items survived. Of further interest is the group of fifteen items on A which are unscored on the clinical scales, scale 0 (Si), or the validity scales. These fifteen items represent 38 per cent of the total scale length of A. It is therefore impossible to score for this factor scale on "short-form" records. The prudent MMPI researcher will recognize the folly of saving a few minutes by administering an abbreviated test.

The greatest item overlap for R is found on scale 2 (D) with ten items. But the correlation of R and 2, .30, is no higher than that of scale 3 (Hy) which shares only four items with R. The highest positive correlation is obtained on scale 0 (Si), .40, with a nine-item overlap, while an equally high negative r, —.40, may be seen on scale 9 (Ma) with two oppositely scored items. Seven of the ten items overlapping with scale 2 are 2' items. Of the nine scale 0 (Si) items, seven are 0'. The Gm scale contributes three items to R and nine are unscored on other scales.

Additional meaning of the A and R scales in terms of item overlap may be gained from Table 4. All the special MMPI scales which are included in this volume are listed here together with cross references for the reader's convenience.

Profile Configuration

A different approach to an understanding of the A and R scales is that of profile configuration (see Sections V and VI). A group of 250 K-corrected profiles obtained from the 150 subjects of sample I and 100 of the subjects in sample II were coded

Table 4. Item Overlap of Factor Scales A and R with Special
MMPI Scales Referred to in the Present Volume (Items Scored
Oppositely on the Scale are Enclosed in Parentheses)

Scale	Reference	A	R
G	I, 2	15	2 (2)
Ds	I, 4	3	
Cn	IV, 27	7	(4)
Pr	IV, 23	1	1 (1)
Ca	IV, 25	8	1 (1)
Do	IV, 24	(5)	
Obvious	IV, 22		
D		6	6
Hy		2	2
Pd		3	
Pa		1	1
Ma			(1)
Subtle	IV, 22		
D			4
Hy		(2)	2
Pd		(1)	
Pa			1
Ma		(1)	(1)
Es	IV, 26	(9)	1 (3)
St	IV, 21	(2)	(1)
Gm	IV, 29	5	3
Ja	V, 32	7	(1)
Lb	VIII, 55	1 (2)	4
At	IX, 56	10	(1)
Pg	IX, 61	5	(2)

and arrayed according to frequently appearing codes. The four groups were (a) all codes in which the first three digits were some combination of 2 (D), 7 (Pt), and 8 (Sc), i.e., 278, 287, 728, 782, 827, and 872; (b) 1 (Hs) and 3 (Hy) codes, i.e., the code had 1 or 3 as the first or second digit: 13, 31, 21, 12, 83, 38, etc.; (c) 4 (Pd) and 9 (Ma) codes with analogous combinations as in (b); and (d) all codes which did not fall into one of the three preceding patterns. For convenience these four groups will be referred to as: 278, 1 and 3, 4 and 9, and "other." The respective N's are 45, 70, 56, and 79.

These three commonly observed types of profile configurations were chosen on the basis of the different psychological properties characterizing them. The 278's display directly anxiety and depressive features. The 13's exhibit somatization and conversion symptoms rather than consciously experienced and directly expressed anxiety. The 49's are the "acting out" character and behavior disorders.

A distribution of the A and R scores was plotted with A on the vertical axis and R on the horizontal axis. This was done separately for the four groups and for the total population. The total scatter plot was cut at approximately the medians and divided into quadrants. For an A score of 15 the split was actually 54/46; for an R score of 17, a 46/54 division was obtained. Each of the four group scatter plots was divided at the same level and the number of cases falling in each quadrant determined. These frequencies were converted to corrected percentages to make comparison easier and are presented in Table 5.

There is a marked tendency for the 278 group to score high on A and to fall into

Table 5. Corrected Proportions and Frequencies of Four Code Groups Falling into Quadrants Determined by Plotting A against R

	I $A \geq 15$ & $R < 17$		II $A \geq 15$ & $R \geq 17$		$A \geq 15$	
	%	f	%	f	%	f
278	33.9	17	49.1	22	83.0	39
13	6.2	7	17.4	12	23.6	19
49	37.4	23	7.3	4	44.7	27
Other	27.8	25	30.6	24	58.4	49
Total	25.0	72	25.0	62	50.0	134

	III $A < 15$ & $R < 17$		IV $A < 15$ & $R \geq 17$		$A < 15$	
	%	f	%	f	%	f
278	8.3	4	8.6	2	16.9	6
13	25.1	18	51.4	33	76.5	51
49	37.0	21	18.4	8	55.4	29
Other	26.0	21	15.6	9	41.6	30
Total	25.0	64	25.0	52	50.0	116

	$R < 17$		$R \geq 17$		Total	
	%	f	%	f	%	f
278	42.2	21	57.7	24	99.9	45
13	31.3	25	68.8	45	100.1	70
49	74.4	44	25.7	12	100.1	56
Other	53.8	46	46.2	33	100.0	79
Total	50.0	136	50.0	114		250

quadrant II (high A, high R). It is clear that the 13's score low on A and cluster in quadrant IV (low A, high R). The 49's do not seem to differ much on A but they fall strikingly low on R. Thus it is apparent that the two factor scales may be related to profile configuration.

Further evidence for the relation of A and R to scales salient in the profile may be seen in detailed consideration of the codes that could not be classified as one of the three common configurations. In Table 6 the number of times a scale appeared in a code is listed for the four quadrants. Although three-digit codes had been used, the total frequency is greater than 237 ($3 \times N$ (79)) since in many cases there were ties for the first, second, or third positions. The frequencies are also expressed as percentages of the total frequency for each scale.

Here again we find scales 2, 7, and 8 much more common above the median of A. Scales 2 and 7 predominate in quadrant II (high A, high R) but scale 8 is more frequent in I (high A, low R). Scale 6 is almost as frequent as 8 in this quadrant but 6 is more frequent than 8 in III (low A, low R). Three scales, 6, 8, and 9, fall more often below the median of R. This is strikingly so in the case of scale 9 where all of the eleven instances fall below the cutting score on R.

It is of interest to note that scale 3 is no longer predominant in IV (low A, high R) but is actually more common in II. Apparently when this scale is not in a 13 type profile, it is actually more common in II along with 2 and 7. This deficiency in IV may also be noted in the case of scale 1 but it seems to be equally distributed over the remaining quadrants.

In pursuing the relation of scales 6 and 8 it was found that there were in the 1 and 3, 4 and 9, and the "others" groups fourteen cases of codes in which both 6 and 8 appeared. Half of these occurred in quadrant I and the rest were equally distributed. Thus when these scales occur together they are related both to A and to R.

Table 6. Frequency of Occurrence of Scales in Codes
for "Others" Group (N = 79)

	I A ≥ 15 & R < 17		II A ≥ 15 & R ≥ 17		A ≥ 15	
	%	f	%	f	%	f
1	28.6	12	30.9	13	59.5	25
2	31.4	16	45.1	23	76.5	39
3	20.8	5	33.4	8	54.2	13
4	33.4	6	22.2	4	55.6	10
5	23.5	4	23.5	4	47.0	8
6	40.0	6	13.3	2	53.3	8
7	35.8	14	43.6	17	79.4	31
8	44.2	19	18.6	8	62.8	27
9	54.5	6	0.0	0	54.5	6

	III A < 15 & R < 17		IV A < 15 & R ≥ 17		A < 15	
	%	f	%	f	%	f
1	30.9	13	9.6	4	40.5	17
2	21.5	11	2.0	1	23.5	12
3	29.2	7	16.6	4	45.8	11
4	22.2	4	22.2	4	44.4	8
5	35.3	6	17.6	3	52.9	9
6	46.7	7	0.0	0	46.7	7
7	15.4	6	5.0	2	20.4	8
8	27.9	12	9.3	4	37.2	16
9	45.5	5	0.0	0	45.5	5

	R < 17		R ≥ 17		Total	
	%	f	%	f	%	f
1	59.5	25	40.5	17	100.0	42
2	52.9	27	47.1	24	100.0	51
3	50.0	12	50.0	12	100.0	24
4	55.6	10	44.4	8	100.0	18
5	58.8	10	41.1	7	99.9	17
6	86.7	13	13.3	2	100.0	15
7	51.2	20	48.6	19	99.8	39
8	72.1	31	27.9	12	100.0	43
9	100.0	11	0.0	0	100.0	11
Total						260

Independent Confirmation

An independent study which indicates the relative orthogonality of A and R and their contribution to the factor structure of the MMPI has been reported by Williams and Lawrence [651]. They used a sample of 100 neuropsychiatric patients in an army hospital and correlated a series of Rorschach scorings, the Wechsler-Bellevue verbal IQ, and the clinical and validating scales of the MMPI plus Barron's Es scale [44 (see IV, 26)] as well as the A and R scales. The third factor showed the highest positive loadings for R and scale 3 (Hy) and significant negative loadings on scale 9 (Ma). Considering the loadings of both the Rorschach variables and the MMPI scales the authors state that the dimension "may best be labeled 'expressive-repressive'."

The fourth factor is a general MMPI dimension which they consider closely related to the first factor reported in many previous factor studies. (The first factor configuration was discussed earlier in this paper.) It shows the highest positive loadings on A and on scales 7 (Pt) and 8 (Sc) with a high negative loading on Es.

Therapy Study

The use of the A and the R scales to demonstrate therapeutic change has been reported by Welsh and Roseman [625]. Fifteen schizophrenic patients on an insulin coma regime had repeated the MMPI six times during the treatment proper and from one to five times after termination of treatment. Behavioral changes had been evaluated objectively by means of Lorr's Schedule D [r101]. A previous paper by Roseman [684] had reported the relationship between over-all profile changes as evaluated by competent MMPI judges and the behavioral changes.

Since A and R seem to be related to profile configuration it was likely that these scales would reflect the changing pattern which Roseman's judges had noted. Such proved to be the case when the seven or more MMPI records for each of the fifteen schizophrenics were scored for A and R. The changes in profile configuration that had accompanied clinical improvement were strikingly reflected in the factor scale scores. Patients who made the most improvement showed a marked drop in A scores with some tendency for R to be lower. Those who made the least improvement or got worse tended to show a rise in A with R falling either higher or lower. When these data are plotted in graphic form some of the shifts are quite dramatic.

Other Studies

Sherriffs and Boomer [547] utilized the A scale in a study of the effects of the rights minus wrongs formula which is frequently used by educators in an attempt to correct for guessing on examinations. They had given the group form of the MMPI to 450 students and used the A scale to identify "students who lacked self-confidence, especially confidence in their own judgment, who had difficulties in making decisions, and who were easily threatened by ambiguous situations." They explored systematically various relations between test scores and concluded "that students who score on the maladjusted end of the 'A scale' are handicapped by being scored on a 'R — W' basis. This holds true even when the students' knowledge of course material is held constant. The evidence suggests that these students are penalized by their tendency to omit more items, and to omit items the answers to which they know."

Autrey [31] used the A scale to select subjects for a study of communicative efficiency. She hypothesized that anxious subjects would be less effective in responding pertinently to a series of questions than nonanxious subjects. From a group of 307 college undergraduates she selected thirty-six subjects. Half of this group had scored from 24 to 35 on the A scale and were termed "anxious"; the "nonanxious" subjects had scored from 0 to 6 on the scale. The hypothesis was supported at the .025 level. Thus, in this experimental situation, subjects who had scored at the extremes of the distribution of the A scale showed marked differences in the appropriateness of their responses to a series of questions that were vague and personal in nature.

Diagnoses

No systematic studies of the relationship between A and R and psychiatric diagnoses have been reported. Some preliminary work has been carried out by the present writer and by John Pearson (reported in a personal communication), and tentative findings will be noted using the quadrant system described above. These are summarized below.

CLUSTERING OF PSYCHIATRIC DIAGNOSES IN A AND R QUADRANTS

I	II
High A, Low R	*High A, High R*
Paranoid schizophrenia	Reactive depression
Psychoneurosis, severe	Manic-depressive, depressed
Anxiety states	Anxiety states

III	IV
Low A, Low R	*Low A, High R*
Manic-depressive, manic	Psychoneurosis, mild
Alcoholics	Hysteria
Behavior and character disorders	Conversion reactions

It should be borne in mind that the cases in the various diagnostic groups distribute themselves quite generally over the area and only the most obvious clusterings of the largest groups can be reported here. The display is intended to be suggestive of general trends only, which may be investigated by those interested in this type of problem.

Normal Group

Some interesting findings have been related (in a personal communication) by Harrison Gough on the use of the A and the R scales with a group of normal subjects. The highest correlations with A for regular MMPI variables are K, —.71; L, —.37; Hy, —.32; Si, .45; F, .34; and Ma .30. Some of the variables on Gough's California Psychological Inventory, the CPI [257], show significant negative correlations: social responsibility (Re), —.41; tolerance (To), —.59; intellectual efficiency (Ie), —.46; academic achievement (Ac), —.50; psychological interests (Psy), —.60; a scale (Gi) designed to see whether or not the subject is trying to place himself in a favorable light, —.56. Positive correlations are found on a dissimulation scale (Ds), .59, and impulsivity (Im), .47. The Ds scale is described in an earlier article reprinted in the present volume [255 (see I, 4)]. The correlation of —.46 with Es is consistent with that found by Williams and Lawrence as noted above. The Strong Vocational Interest Blank [r156] key for specialist level was negatively related, —.31. Descriptive adjectives and phrases about subjects who scored high on A tended to reflect slowness of personal tempo, pessimism, vacillation, hesitancy, and inhibitedness.

In the same sample a number of positive correlations with the regular MMPI scales and R occurred: K, .53; L, .38; D, .44; and Hs, .41. A negative relation with Ma was found, —.44. On the CPI positive relations may be noted on some scales:

tolerance (To), .32; femininity (Fe), .33; and good impression (Gi), .43. Other CPI scales showed negative correlations: impulsivity (Im), −.64; self-acceptance (Sa), −.41; and social participation (Sp), −.35.

Table 7. Test-Retest Data Supplied by Stevens

Administration	Mean	SD	r_{tt}
First (N = 71)			
A	14.5	6.7	
R	17.1	3.9	
Second (N = 60)			
A	13.1	7.6	.70
R	17.6	4.2	.74

Consistency and Stability of Scales

Some data relating to the consistency of the A and R scales have been reported by Kooser [369] incidental to the main purpose of his investigation. For 108 college undergraduates a split half (odd-even) corrected correlation on A was .88; the comparable value for R was .48. These findings are in accord with the nature of the content of the two scales. It was noted earlier in the present paper that the A scale content was much more homogeneous than the R scale. But this does not mean that the R scale is less stable than the A scale. The 79 items comprising A and R had been given to a class of 71 college sophomores by Phyllis Stevens (reported in a personal communication). Sixty of these same subjects repeated the scales after a four-month interval. The product-moment correlations reported for the test-retest scores are A, .70; R, .74. It is important to note that these correlations were obtained despite the fact that the group showed much less variability than is usually found (see Table 8 below). These data are summarized in Table 7.

In Table 8 data for thirty different representative groups are listed. The means, standard deviations, and correlations where available for A and R are given. These data are arranged in order of the magnitude of the mean A score. It can be seen that the ten general psychiatric samples listed all fall above the normal groups. There is, however, a wide range of means for these normal groups from 14.5 in an eastern state teachers college all the way down to 6.0 for air force officers. Five of the ten psychiatric samples also average higher on R. The lowest scores on R occur with hospitalized chronic alcoholics, high school boys, and air force officers.

Twenty-five of the samples are separated for sex: 15 male samples and 10 female. If the cutting scores given in the quadrant arrangement previously suggested in this paper (A of 15, R of 17) are used, it is found that there is some tendency for the female groups to average higher than the comparable male groups on R. This is summarized in Table 9.

Summary and Conclusions

Two special MMPI scales, A and R, have been described. They were especially derived to measure dimensions of the MMPI which had been consistently noted in factor studies carried out by many investigators using diverse populations. An independent study has confirmed the relative orthogonality of these scales and their consistency in factor identification.

Table 8. Data on Scales A and R for 30 Representative Groups [a]

Group	N	Mean A	Mean R	SD A	SD R	r
1. Psychiatric intake I, female................	51	20.8	18.2	8.7	4.3	−.05
2. VA mental hygiene clinic I, male............	99	20.7	17.4	9.2	4.9	.09
3. VA mental hygiene clinic II, male...........	100	20.4	16.0	10.6	5.6	.34
4. Psychiatric intake II, female	140	20.1	18.5	9.5	4.3	−.10
5. VA mental hygiene clinic III, male..........	105	19.8	17.1	10.3	4.5	
6. Psychiatric intake III, female..............	136	19.0	18.9	9.1	4.2	−.25
7. Psychiatric intake I, male.................	73	17.9	16.2	9.3	4.5	−.06
8. Psychiatric intake II, male.................	30	17.1	18.1	10.1	4.6	−.46
9. Naval hospital (NP), male................	101	17.1	16.5	15.0	5.6	−.04
10. Psychiatric intake III, male...............	89	17.1	17.9	9.4	5.1	−.20
11. High school I, female.....................	131	16.3	16.2	8.9	4.1	
12. High school II, female....................	98	15.4	17.1	8.4	3.7	−.29
13. VA general medical and surgical hospital I, male	150	15.3	16.9	10.8	5.8	.00
14. College sophomores.......................	71	14.5	17.1	6.7	3.9	
15. Dermatoses, female.......................	54	14.3	17.2	9.3	3.8	−.32
16. College I, female.........................	36	14.3	16.1	8.4	4.0	
17. College undergraduates...................	307	14.2	15.9	7.4	4.4	.11
18. State prison, male........................	180	13.9	15.4	8.0	4.5	−.34
19. High school I, male.......................	151	13.7	14.1	8.0	4.5	
20. High school II, male......................	123	13.3	16.4	7.3	4.7	−.15
21. Dermatoses, male.........................	51	13.2	16.7	9.4	4.6	−.27
22. College I, male...........................	65	13.2	15.9	7.4	4.0	
23. Weight reduction, female.................	98	12.9	18.0	8.2	3.9	−.26
24. VA general medical and surgical hospital II, male	52	12.3	17.4	8.9	4.9	
25. Chronic alcoholics	64	12.0	12.0	8.8	5.2	
26. Graduate school, male	40	11.5	16.5	7.3	3.6	
27. College undergraduates	425	10.1	15.5 [b]	8.0	3.9 [b]	−.36
28. College II, female........................	96	9.7	17.4	6.9	3.5	
29. College II, male..........................	132	8.7	15.2	7.7	4.7	
30. Air force officers, male...................	153	6.0	14.6	7.1	4.1	−.29

[a] Data for this table were supplied as follows: O. R. Autry, group 17; D. S. Boomer, group 27; A. N. Button, group 25; H. G. Gough, groups 11, 12, 19, 20, 26, 28, 29, 30; E. deT. Kooser, groups 16, 22; R. LaForge, groups 1, 4, 6, 7, 8, 10, 15, 21, 23; F. B. Price, group 9; R. E. Smith, group 18; P. W. Stevens, group 14; and P. L. Sullivan, groups 2, 5.

[b] Statistics on R based on a smaller subsample.

Table 9. Frequency of Occurrence in A and R Quadrants of Means for 25 Samples Where Sexes Are Differentiated

	Low R	High R	Total
High A	(I)	(II)	
Male	3	3	6
Female	2	4	6
Low A	(III)	(IV)	
Male	8	1	9
Female	1	3	4
Total			
Male	11	4	15
Female	3	7	10

Table 10. T Scores for Scales A and R

Raw Score	Male		Female		Raw Score	Male		Female	
	A	R	A	R		A	R	A	R
40		101		102	19	59	57	55	53
39	84	99	78	100	18	57	55	54	51
38	82	97	77	98	17	56	53	53	48
37	81	95	76	95	16	55	51	51	46
36	80	93	75	93	15	54	49	50	44
35	79	91	74	91					
34	77	89	73	88	14	52	47	49	41
33	76	86	71	86	13	51	45	48	39
32	75	84	70	84	12	50	43	47	36
31	74	82	69	81	11	49	40	46	34
30	72	80	68	79	10	47	38	44	32
29	71	78	67	76	9	46	36	43	29
28	70	76	66	74	8	45	34	42	27
27	69	74	64	72	7	44	32	41	25
26	67	72	63	69	6	42	30	40	22
25	66	70	62	67	5	41	28	38	20
24	65	68	61	65	4	40	26	37	18
23	64	66	60	62	3	38	24	36	15
22	62	63	58	60	2	37	22	35	13
21	61	61	57	58	1	36	20	34	11
20	60	59	56	55	0	35	17	33	8

A description of the scales was given in terms of item content and by means of the overlap of items and the intercorrelations with regular MMPI scales. The item overlap with certain other scales was also indicated. Further clarification of the meaning of the scales was noted by listing covariation in a group of normal subjects of various test scores and behavioral correlates. Within psychiatric populations the relation of A and R to diagnosis was summarized.

Two studies have used the A scale independently. In one it was used to identify students who were handicapped in examinations by self-doubt. In another study subjects scoring high on A were shown to exhibit less efficient communication than low scorers.

The use of both scales together, however, may prove more effective. This was demonstrated in a study relating profile shifts to therapeutic changes: a plot of the A and the R scores together graphically illustrated the value of their simultaneous employment. Further evidence for the conjoined relation of the scales to profile configuration was examined by noting profile codes appearing frequently in psychiatric populations. Among diagnostic groups, for example, anxiety states fall high on A; but of those with high A scores who are also high on R, depression will be seen primarily, while those low on R will show schizoid features.

It is clear that high A scores are related to disability of a dysthymic and dysphoric nature in which anxiety is prominent. The disorders exhibited by high R scorers are characterized by repression and denial; low R accompanies externalized and "acting-out" behavior. Although it is not argued that A is a direct measure of anxiety and R of repression, the use of these two scales concurrently may lead to more adequate specification and definition of these concepts.

For the convenience of workers who may wish to utilize A and R in experimental or clinical studies, the item numbers for both the individual and the group forms of the MMPI are listed below. In Table 10 T scores are listed which will make it possible to compare the relative elevations of A and R directly with the clinical scales. These scores have been computed from data very kindly supplied by Dr. S. R. Hathaway. These data are based on a new and improved sample of Minnesota normals which is comparable to the original standardizing samples. The appropriate statistics are given below:

	Males (N = 226)		Females (N = 315)	
	A	R	A	R
M	12.20	15.57	14.78	17.74
SD	8.00	4.78	8.50	4.25

It is of interest to note that the sex differences previously pointed out are also found in this normal sample, that is, the mean scores for females are higher than those for males. In addition, the statistics for A follow the trend for normal subjects to score lower on this scale than psychiatric patients.

Item Lists

A Scale

Booklet (Group) Form					Box (Individual) Form				
True Items					*X Items*				
32	259	344	389	465	C-19	F-17	F-47	G-45	I-29
41	267	345	396	499	C-22	F-34	F-48	G-51	I-31
67	278	356	397	511	C-25	F-35	F-49	H-2	I-35
76	301	359	411	518	E-43	F-36	F-54	H-29	I-36
94	305	374	414	544	E-50	F-42	G-1	I -15	I-54
138	321	382	418	555	E-52	F-43	G-5	I -17	J-4
147	337	383	431		F-4	F-44	G-36	I -23	J-13
236	343	384	443		F-16	F-45	G-42	I -27	
	False Item: 379								

R Scale

Booklet (Group) Form					Box (Individual) Form				
False Items					*X Items*				
1	126	219	415	462	A-2	C-2	D-39	F-20	I-28
6	131	221	429	468	A-18	C-17	E-29	F-32	I-46
9	140	271	440	472	A-36	C-40	E-30	G-23	I-50
12	145	272	445	502	B-22	C-43	E-32	H-43	J-5
39	154	281	447	516	B-54	D-31	E-47	I -22	J-35
51	156	282	449	529					
81	191	327	450	550			*O Items*		
112	208	406	451	556	A-19	C-42	D-49	G-46	J-11
					B-4	C-48	G-31	I -49	J-14
					C-10	D-40	G-32	J -7	J-24

✦ ────────────────────────────────────

ARTICLE 30 *Configural Scoring*

ONE of the most important words in the vocabulary of clinicians is the word *pattern*. We speak of ourselves as thinking in terms of totalities, organizations, configurations; and we congratulate ourselves for being able to look upon case material in this patterned, nonatomistic way. The question as to how much we really do this, and how well it pays off in terms of predictive efficiency, is a very complicated one on which neither theoretical nor adequate empirical data as yet exist. But I am sure everyone, even the most hardheaded, who is at all acquainted with clinical work will at least agree that there are situations in which data are integrated in a "patterned" manner. The word *patterning* is ambiguous, and I have tried elsewhere to give a formal (mathematical) definition of patterning of variables for the continuous case [440]. One obvious, simple instance of patterning is the case in which a datum is taken as evidence *for* a certain hypothesis about the patient when seen in a certain context of other evidence; whereas the same datum would be taken as arguing *against* the very same hypothesis with the context different. For example, an objective history of extremely wide and vigorous athletic participation in high school would, statistically speaking, argue in favor of masculinity in the male. If we find such a history in a male aged 35, without heterosexual experience, living with his mother, and sponsoring boys' clubs, we begin to think of the latent homoerotic component as being strong; and the exaggerated athletic activity can be viewed as defense. So viewed, it is actually part of the evidential picture in favor of the hypothesis that the patient has a problem in the area of sexual role. We are all aware of the dangers involved in this kind of thinking, which has at times a certain "heads I win, tails you lose" flavor; but most of us would say that a person who cannot stand this kind of ambiguity in the evidence ought to get out of clinical psychology, because it is simply the case that such things as reaction formation *do* occur, and if you want to deal with human motivation as a subject matter you have to take the consequences.

A frequently voiced objection to structured personality tests is couched in terms of this configural character of clinical material. It is pointed out, quite justly, that the score on a test variable such as the MMPI Pd is obtained by simply adding the number of items to get a total, with no attention being paid to the meaning and pattern of the responses. While recent clinical use of instruments such as the MMPI has taken for granted the emphasis upon profile patterns rather than an atomistic

282

emphasis upon single scales [3, 90, 234 (see VI, 38), 235, 272 (VI, 41) 296 (III, 12), 341, 436 (V, 31), 449 (VII, 43), 528 (VI, 39), 532, 617 (III, 13)], this refers to patterning of the scored *variables* and does not meet the problem at the level of determining the single score itself, i.e., at the item level.

An interesting paradox which I developed recently during a preliminary oral examination seems to me relevant in this connection. I take the liberty of calling this a paradox because practically all the psychologists I have since asked about it give the same answer as the candidate, which is the wrong one. The question is this: Consider two dichotomously scored test items, which we wish to use in predicting a dicotomous criterion. Let us ignore sampling errors and confine the discussion entirely to parameters. Suppose that the dichotomous criterion is, say, "schizophrenic" versus "normal." For the present purpose the question as to whether some continuous variable or set of variables actually underlies such a clinical dichotomy is irrelevant.

Suppose now that (in the supply) *each* of the two items has exactly 50 per cent difficulty with *each* category, so that half of the schizophrenics and half of the normals answer each of the items True and half of each group answer each item False. Under these circumstances any of the usual methods of item analysis (phi coefficient, significance of difference of proportions, tetrachoric r, and so forth) will show both items to have zero validity for the criterion, and they will be eliminated. Under such conditions, is it possible to predict the criterion solely upon the basis of the response to these two items, and if so, how well could it theoretically be predicted? Almost everyone who is asked this question has the initial tendency to say that the criterion could not be predicted at all; and most people finally come out with this answer even after some paranoid ruminations. It is, therefore, interesting to consider an extreme case.

Table 1 shows the correlation between the two items in the first criterion category and tells us that all normal persons answer the two items in the "same way," although they do not have any tendency to answer them either True or False. Table 2 shows us that schizophrenics, while also having no tendency to answer either item True or False, are consistent in another way, since they always give "opposite" answers to the two items. However, each item, considered singly, has no discriminating power. Table 3 shows the predictive efficiency of scoring these items *configurally*. That is, we consider the response to the two items simultaneously on the scoring key rather than one at a time. Any person who answers the two items in the *same way* (either both true or both false), is predicted to be a normal; anyone who answers the items in the *opposite way*, whether in the true-false or false-true pattern, is considered to be a schizophrenic. In this hypothetical ideal case, we find a perfect predictability of the dichotomous criterion on the basis of the two items, even though each item has zero validity. It is obvious that this represents simply the extreme case of situations which can exist in lesser degrees.

The general condition for this kind of pair-wise scoring to create joint validity when each item singly has zero validity is that the *inter-item* correlation should be different in the two categories of the criterion. In the ideal case just treated, this disparity between the inter-item correlations in the two categories of the criterion is at a maximum, since the inter-item phi coefficient among the schizophrenics is −1.00, and the corresponding inter-item phi coefficient among the normals is

Table 1. Inter-Item Correlation
among Normals [a]

Item No. 1	Item No. 2		
	T	F	Total
T	50	0	50
F	0	50	50
Total	50	50	100

[a] $\phi_1 = +1.00$.

Table 2. Inter-Item Correlation
among Schizophrenics [a]

Item No. 1	Item No. 2		
	T	F	Total
T	0	50	50
F	50	0	50
Total	50	50	100

[a] $\phi_2 = -1.00$.

Table 3. Validity of Item-Pair
When Scored Configurally [a]

Response Pattern	Normal	Schizo-phrenics	Total
T-T or F-F	100	0	100
T-F or F-T	0	100	100
Total	100	100	200

[a] $\phi_j = +1.00$. Validity of each item = 0.00.

Table 4. Inter-Item Correlation
among Normals [a]

Item No. 1	Item No. 2		
	T	F	Total
T	35	15	50
F	15	35	50
Total	50	50	100

[a] $\phi_1 = +.40$.

Table 5. Inter-Item Correlation
among Schizophrenics [a]

Item No. 1	Item No. 2		
	T	F	Total
T	15	35	50
F	35	15	50
Total	50	50	100

[a] $\phi_2 = -.40$.

Table 6. Validity of Item-Pair
When Scored Configurally [a]

Response Pattern	Normal	Schizo-phrenics	Total
T-T or F-F	70	30	100
T-F or F-T	30	70	100
Total	100	100	200

[a] $\phi_j = +.40$. Validity of each item = 0.00.

Table 7. Inter-Item Correlation
among Normals [a]

Item No. 1	Item No. 2		
	T	F	Total
T	37	13	50
F	13	37	50
Total	50	50	100

[a] $\phi_1 = +.48$.

Table 8. Inter-Item Correlation
among Schizophrenics [a]

Item No. 1	Item No. 2		
	T	F	Total
T	22	28	50
F	28	22	50
Total	50	50	100

[a] $\phi_2 = -.12$.

$+1.00$. In a second artificial example, the discrepancy is considerably less although the inter-item phi coefficient does differ in sign for the two portions of the population which we wish to separate.

Table 4 shows that the inter-item correlation among normals is .40, whereas the inter-item correlation among schizophrenics (Table 5) is of the same absolute value but opposite in sign. Under these conditions, scoring the items configurally so that again a true-true or false-false pattern of response is considered normal and a true-false or false-true pattern is considered schizophrenic, we get the frequencies of Table 6, showing that the item-pair, scored configurally, has a validity coefficient of .40. The validity coefficient against the dichotomous criterion obtained from configural scoring of a pair of items when the inter-item phi coefficients are located symmetrically about zero is always the same as the absolute value of the phi coefficients. Thus, two items each of which has zero validity but which have a correlation of $-.60$ in one class and $+.60$ in the other, would yield when scored configurally a validity coefficient of .60 in separation of the criterion classes.

Consider next the case in which, although still opposite in sign, the inter-item phi coefficients are not symmetrical about zero. With the single item validities still held to zero, in Table 7 the inter-item correlation among normals is .48, while the corresponding inter-item correlation among schizophrenics is $-.12$ (Table 8). Calling the T-T or F-F configurations normal and the T-F or F-T configurations schizophrenic, we see the validity for configural scoring is at .31 (Table 9). The algebraic difference of the phi coefficients in the two categories of the population is .60, so that if such a difference $(\phi_1 - \phi_2)$ had been symmetrical about zero, i.e., an inter-item phi of .30 in the normals and $-.30$ in the schizophrenics, we would have a configural validity of exactly .30. So we see that a considerable asymmetry does not markedly affect the magnitude of validity obtained through configural scoring when the numbers are in this general range.

Table 9. Validity of Item-Pair When Scored Configurally [a]

Response Pattern	Normal	Schizo- phrenics	Total
T-T or F-F	74	44	118
T-F or F-T	26	56	82
Total	100	100	200

[a] $\phi_j = +.31$. Validity of each item $= 0.00$.

Table 10. Inter-Item Correlation among Normals [a]

Item No. 1	Item No. 2		
	T	F	Total
T	47	3	50
F	3	47	50
Total	50	50	100

[a] $\phi_1 = +.88$.

Table 11. Inter-Item Correlation among Schizophrenics [a]

Item No. 1	Item No. 2		
	T	F	Total
T	32	18	50
F	18	32	50
Total	50	50	100

[a] $\phi_2 = +.28$.

Table 12. Validity of Item-Pair When Scored Configurally [a]

Response Pattern	Normal	Schizo- phrenics	Total
T-T or F-F	94	64	158
T-F or F-T	6	36	42
Total	100	100	200

[a] $\phi_j = +.37$. Validity of each item $= 0.00$.

Next consider a case which is intuitively somewhat less satisfying but still shows how the configural scoring can generate validity. Tables 10 and 11 represent the situation of an item-pair which has a very high positive association among normals and a positive but considerably lower association among schizophrenics. In this instance, for both portions of the population the expected (modal) response pattern is one of agreement. That is, we expect the schizophrenics as well as the normals to answer both items in the same way, even though we have no expectations as to *which way* they will answer them. Under such circumstances if we score a T-F or F-T pattern as schizophrenic, it might seem somewhat unreasonable, as this is not what most of the schizophrenics do. But the alternative leaves us without any basis for making predictions. In Table 12 we see the results of scoring configurally by calling all T-T and F-F response patterns normal, and all T-F and F-T response patterns schizophrenic. This yields a configural validity of .37 which, it will be noted, is .07 higher than that obtained with a similar algebraic difference of the two phi coefficients when they are symmetrical about zero.

Since we are only now in the process of collecting some "real" material on MMPI test items, it has not seemed profitable to enter into the mathematical properties of such systems in any detail. I have, however, plotted the configural validity coefficient as a function of the algebraic difference of the inter-item correlations in the two criterion categories, plotting a separate such curve for various values of the point about which the phi coefficients are symmetrical. For points of symmetry as high as .60, the relationship between configural validity and the difference $(\phi_1 - \phi_2)$ is very close to linear; and as we saw for symmetry about zero is precisely so. The functions, however, become slightly positively accelerated for points of symmetry other than zero, so that the estimated configural validity obtained by taking the value

$$\frac{\phi_1 - \phi_2}{2}$$

is an underestimate. At the extremes this introduces a considerable error. For example, consider a pair of items for which the phi coefficients in the two categories to be discriminated are 1.00 and .80. The difference $(\phi_1 - \phi_2)$ is .20, which leads to an estimate of about .10 for the configural validity. However, when the point of symmetry is so far from zero as .90, the actual configural validity is approximately .23.

I have not been able to derive an exact formula for the configural validity expressed solely as a function of the two phi coefficients involved, although it is of course easy to get an expression for a joint (configural) validity in terms of the proportions in the eight cells of the two fourfold tables. If the technique should turn out to be of practical value, graphical methods would be adequate for purposes of selecting potentially valuable item-pairs. The sampling characteristics of the joint phi coefficients have not been investigated.

If items which behave in this way can be found in the field of personality and interest measurement, it seems to me that such a technique would have considerable practical importance. In the first place we have the straightforward argument that if validity can be achieved with items that have no validity considered singly, it may be possible to develop instruments of a structured type to perform functions which are not generally accessible to structured tests. A second important consideration is in the matter of subtlety. While advances have been made in recent years in the direction of an increase in subtlety of structured personality measuring instruments and in detection of distortions [134, 235, 329, r85, 424 (see II, 11), 441 (I, 2), 642 (IV, 22)], it must be admitted that very serious problems in this area still remain [53 (see VII, 44), 134, 339, 341, 529]. It is probable that these problems will be much more difficult to solve with respect to certain dimensions, e.g., paranoid components of personality, than with respect to others, e.g., somatization components. For example, the Pa scale of the MMPI is a relatively weak scale in the sense that a very sizable subgroup of clinically grossly paranoid individuals are able somehow to evade a high score without giving themselves away on the validity indicators. It would seem that the possibilities for subtlety when configural scoring is made use of are greatly enhanced since it would require much more sophistication to know in what way certain verbal responses would tend to hang together in variously defined groups of people than it would to know, in general, the kind of response which is "healthy" as opposed to "maladjusted."

If such items can be found in a pool like that of the MMPI, there might also be considerable theoretical significance in that it would leave us with a problem of interpretation from the factorial standpoint. For instance, at the present time, the theoretical conceptualization of the relation between so-called obvious and subtle items is very obscure. Wiener [641] has interpreted his findings on subtle-obvious relations in successful and unsuccessful salesmen by assuming that the subtle items of such scales as Pa reflect the paranoid tendency faithfully, but that those who show a very high subtle score contrasted with their score on the obvious component have learned to recognize their own abnormality and to avoid the more concrete overt expression of such tendencies. For this reason persons with subtle Pa higher than obvious seem by certain external criteria to be better adjusted. I am certainly not in a position to refute Wiener's hypothesis on any data available to me; but I should like to emphasize that there is an alternative interpretation which is as meaningful psychologically and would lead to the same psychometric consequences. Consider such an item as "Some people are so bossy that I feel like doing the opposite of what they request even though I know they are right" which is scored for Pa if answered False. This is an excellent example of Pa subtle, both in terms of its obvious content which is superficially *non*paranoid, and also in terms of its statistical property, namely, that the answer scored as paranoid is the answer given by the majority of the unselected normals of the standardization population. As has been pointed out in previous papers [441 (see I, 2), 628] this item appears also on the Guilford-Martin Personnel Inventory where the response False is scored as *non*paranoid (i.e., opposite to the MMPI scoring, derived empirically on paranoid psychotics).

Consider three groups of individuals who are not qualitatively distinct but who are clustered in three general loci on a paranoid dimension of some sort. Since this is a zero item, the "normal nonparanoid" individual in the general population will answer the item in the scored direction. That is, most normal, nonsuspicious people will *not* report that "Some people are so bossy that I feel like doing the opposite of what they request even though I know they are right." The preponderance of such nonsuspicious people in the general population sample accounts for the fact that this item is scored with "O" on the Pa scoring template. Consider now a second group of people, also well within the normal (nondiagnosable, nonpsychotic) population, but who are somewhat more suspicious, stubborn, and hostile toward mankind than the previous group. One would anticipate that such people would tend to give the obvious paranoid response to this item, i.e., they would tend to answer it True. Item derivations operating within the nonpsychotic range whether by an external criterion or by methods of internal consistency such as were used by Guilford, would assign the response True a scoring in the paranoid, suspicious, uncooperative direction — a scoring which, *operating within this range,* may very well be the valid one. Finally, let us consider a full-blown diagnosable paranoid psychotic who answers such obvious items as "Someone has it in for me" (True), "I am sure I am being talked about" (True), "I believe I am being plotted against" (True), and so on. This paranoid psychotic with reality distortions of delusional proportions has set up in addition the pseudo-objectivity which is a well-known facet of many of these patients as we see them clinically. They sometimes surprise us with the cautiousness and apparent intellectual honesty with which they consider alternatives to their formulations. As is true of many writers on controversial subjects, they raise the opponent's objections and proceed to deal with them — the only trouble being that they do not raise the right ones. Whether this almost pedantic pseudo-objectivity of fairly intact paranoid patients is a defense erected following earlier rebuff of their ideas by others, or a reaction against the suspiciousness which can afford to be spread widely over the area of mentation provided it does not encroach upon the specific delusional content, it is not important here to discuss. The main point is that such a clinically diagnosable paranoid patient begins to reverse the trend which was detectable as we moved toward the more suspicious and hostile end of the normal range. So that this patient (unlike the "normal paranoid" in the general population) gives the same response to the Pa subtle item as do well-adjusted, nonparanoid normals, although for very different reasons. This kind of thinking leads one to wonder whether the correlational properties of test items are not to be separately studied with the clinical picture and psychodynamics constantly in mind, at different positions on the continuum to be discriminated. It might turn out that people who give the response "Someone has it in for me" (False), and also the response "Some people are so bossy, etc." (False) are normal, well-adjusted, nonsuspicious people. Those who give the response "Someone has it in for me" (True) and "Some people are so bossy, etc." (True) are suspicious, hostile individuals in the nonclinical range, with also some tendencies to plus-getting on structured tests [441 (see I, 2)]. And finally those (very few) persons who give the response "Someone has it in for me" (True) but on the other hand *also* give the response "Some people are so bossy, etc." (False) are full-blown diagnosable paranoid psychotics who have moved in their illnesss to the point where they have developed the typical overmeticulous rigid pseudo-objectivity of the sick paranoid. It is obvious that the usual method of adding points of the Pa scale and similar instruments would not do justice to the complexity of these relationships if they exist. It remains to be seen whether this complexity, which everybody knows occurs in the interview situation and in the psychopathology of the patients, manifests itself sufficiently clearly to be useful in the verbal responses to the materials of a structural inventory.

The mechanics of searching for such configural-scored item-pairs present practical difficulties. With a relatively small pool of items to begin with it would be feasible to set up the material on punch cards and compute all possible inter-item phi coefficients separately for each of the two groups to be discriminated. Arranging the phi coefficients in parallel columns one could simply pick those item-pairs which showed a large discrepancy (algebraic difference) between ϕ_1 and ϕ_2. With any appreciable number of items, this procedure is too laborious, particularly when a priori considerations do not suffice to select likely pairs. Further, the aim of subtlety in configural scoring might be defeated by the selection of item-pairs on theoretical considerations. Short-cut methods of approaching the exact empirical procedure will be developed if the pilot studies in progress indicate sufficient advantages in the technique to warrant its development.

The pair-wise configural scoring is the simplest of a whole series of configural scoring procedures which could eventually amount to the scoring of fairly large numbers of items simultaneously. For example, it might be that we give the patient one point for hysteroid tendencies if he answers item No. 37 False, *on condition that* he has answered items No. 46 and No. 52 oppositely to each other. In other words, if we consider these three items in numerical order, the configurations F-T-F and F-F-T would be scored for the trait in question; whereas the configurations T-T-T, T-T-F, T-F-T, T-F-F, F-T-T, F-F-F would receive no credit. Here again there are practical limitations upon the cumbersomeness of scoring, although the obvious ease and objectivity of scoring in structured tests is such that if it is necessary to complicate it considerably in order to gain some of the advantages of projective techniques it would be clinically justified.

I have treated only the special case where the items considered singly have zero validity. The question as to how much it would pay to employ a configural scoring of item-pairs, triads, or *n*-ads when the component members already contain considerable validity is a complicated problem which I shall leave to mathematically abler workers. The aim of the present note is simply to bring this kind of scoring, for which I propose the designation *configural,* to the attention of clinicians and test-builders so that its possibilities may be explored in a diversity of testing areas.

SECTION V   Profile Analysis

WITH the completion of the full complement of clinical scales (described in Section II) the emphasis shifted from the study of the ability of each separate scale to make its appropriate psychiatric discrimination to the problems of total profile configuration. The mechanics of determining the degree of efficiency of a single scale applied to a single separation are relatively straightforward. This is not the case with nine scales interrelated and covarying in a complex manner. Thus, in the empirical MMPI tradition, the Minnesota group and other early workers utilized their clinical skill and experience to acquire familiarity with typical and atypical profile shapes. This experience led them to describe the observed configurations in terms of phase, slope, and peakedness, as well as over-all elevation. Such judgments were at first relatively crude and not easily communicated. It soon became apparent that some MMPI workers were extremely adept at this kind of thing while others, even with longer exposure to the test, were not very good. Thus it became important to objectify and, if possible, quantify profile relationships which the skilled clinician may have utilized in epitomizing configural properties of the profile.

One of the first attempts to set forth explicit and objective "rules" for making judgments based on the total configuration is seen in article 31. In this paper, Meehl unabashedly sets forth "cookbook" type rules which could be mechanically applied to make decisions in a sorting problem of differential diagnosis.

In article 32 an attempt is made to quantify certain aspects of the profile configuration seen in anxiety; an anxiety scale of items selected by clinicians' judgments is incidentally mentioned and related to the quantitative index.

An application of certain aspects of configuration which had been suggested by Meehl's article on configural scoring of items (see IV, 30) is considered by Sullivan and Welsh in article 33. Here there is clear evidence that it is possible to objectify aspects of configuration and that "signs" of the relation between two scales are useful where scales taken one at a time do not afford discriminations.

In article 34, Hovey takes up the practical description of normal personality phenomena by grouping the subjects first by profile. In this case the high and low scorers serve as the criterion groups against which the behavior ratings are checked. Here we find that elevation on the clinical scales — despite the implications in terms of their derivation (see II) — may be accompanied by favorable as well as unfavorable personality characteristics. In this paper, attention to the low scores appears in systematic form for the first time.

Gough attacks the problems of faking both as a clinical feature in malingering and as a methodological aspect of item distortion in article 35. Specifically the relation of two of the validating scales, F and K, is explored systematically and an index

290

described. The normative data given on the F minus K index has proved to be of value in both of these problems.

In article 36, a clinical-intuitive sorting of the profiles was used by Gough and Pemberton in an investigation of personality characteristics related to success in practice teaching. The cues used to sort the profiles are shown to be objectifiable and quantifiable, and to hold up in a cross-validation study. Once again we see that it is possible to reduce the profile experts' skill to an explicit set of rules of procedure.

The last and most recently published article, that of Little and Shneidman, uses one profile and eleven judges in an interesting application of Q sort and cluster analysis to establish the validity of profile interpretation. Although the mechanics of these methods may not seem so straightforward and obvious, a meaningful objectification of the complexities of the total pattern has been achieved.

In the sequence of the various methods developed in these articles there can be traced a growing sophistication in techniques which can be applied to problems of profile analysis. To be sure, we still need the profile expert but with his cooperation we can help him do even better.

The articles in this section came from the following sources: article 31 from P. E. Meehl, Profile analysis of the MMPI in differential diagnosis, *Journal of Applied Psychology*, 1946, 30, 517–524; article 32 from G. S. Welsh, An anxiety index and an internalization ratio for the MMPI, *Journal of Consulting Psychology*, 1952, 16, 65–72; article 33 from P. L. Sullivan and G. S. Welsh, A technique for objective configural analysis of MMPI profiles, *Journal of Consulting Psychology*, 1952, 16, 383–388; article 34 from H. B. Hovey, MMPI profiles and personality characteristics, *Journal of Consulting Psychology*, 1953, 17, 142–146; article 35 from H. G. Gough, The F minus K dissimulation index for the MMPI, *Journal of Consulting Psychology*, 1950, 14, 408–413; article 36 from H. G. Gough and W. H. Pemberton, Personality characteristics related to success in practice teaching, *Journal of Applied Psychology*, 1952, 36, 307–309; and article 37 from K. B. Little and E. S. Shneidman, The validity of MMPI interpretations, *Journal of Consulting Psychology*, 1954, 18, 425–428. We are indebted to the authors and to the publishers of the journals for permission to reproduce these articles in this form.

ARTICLE 31 *Profile Analysis of the MMPI in Differential Diagnosis*

A PERSONALITY test may be employed in several kinds of clinical situations. These include over-all differentiation of normals from abnormals or persons predisposed to abnormal developments as in "screening" in the military, industrial, educational, or general medical outpatient situation; differential diagnosis among abnormals; prognosis; evaluation of changes and results of therapy; and the assessment of certain components for other than strictly diagnostic purposes, such as the detection of important paranoid trends in a reactive depression even though diagnosis presents no problem.

This paper presents preliminary data on the use of the MMPI with respect to differential diagnosis, with secondary findings upon the subject of over-all identification of "abnormals" from people in general. Since the MMPI has been described elsewhere [303], it may merely be stated that the scale Mf (masculinity-femininity) has been excluded from consideration throughout, so that there are only eight personality components involved in this study.

The purpose of the present study was to evaluate the MMPI as used in the differential diagnosis of three main categories of hospitalized psychiatric patients: psychosis, psychoneurosis, and "conduct disorder." Gough [234 (see VI, 38)] and Schmidt [528 (VI, 39)] have stressed the importance of considering the "pattern" or configuration of the profile in addition to the elevation of single scores. An elevation on a single component, even if it is the highest or "peak" score of the profile, does not imply that the patient should be so diagnosed. For example, the most frequent peak score on abnormal profiles of all sorts is D (depression). It is clinically known that many different kinds of psychiatric difficulties involve degrees of depression, and the test reflects this fact. Again, a peak of 75 on Sc might suggest a schizophrenic picture, whereas if it occurs together with markedly elevated scores on the neurotic triad (Hs, D, Hy) and a Pt of, say, 85, it may better be taken to indicate a psychoneurosis with poor prognosis [292]. It must be emphasized that the patterning of a profile cannot be neglected in the case of structured tests any more than we would think of interpreting one determinant column of the Rorschach without considering anything else.

As yet, these configurational criteria on the MMPI have not been adequately treated in the literature. Locally, the Minnesota group have tended to form more or less crude clinical judgments and global impressions based upon accumulated experience. The articles by Schmidt and Gough have contributed materially to the objectification of procedure, although neither of these investigators published results in the form of percentage correct identifications for clinically diagnosed groups, a kind of treatment which is in many ways more meaningful than establishment of significant differences between central tendencies [r50, p. 19]. Furthermore, in both of these articles the similarity of "psychosis" to "severe psychoneurosis" in the MMPI profile is too close for comfort, a drawback of the MMPI which has been informally reported by a number of military clinical psychologists through personal communications.

In the present investigation, an attempt has been made to determine the approximate accuracy of a very rapid, inspectional diagnosis from the MMPI profile alone, using the more or less poorly defined criteria which have so far seemed valuable clinically. Naturally, it is not suggested that the profile be used in this way, but we want to know how much the test can contribute entirely on its own when so used. Because of the fact that recently hospitalized cases were not diagnosed independently of the MMPI, it was necessary to utilize old cases, before July 1941, on whose response sheets the present scales had been subsequently scored. At that time the MMPI had not been published and was still in the process of development. The only scales which appeared on the profiles then in use were H (a relatively less valid, uncorrected key for hypochondriasis) and D (depression). For all practical purposes, it may be assumed that the clinical diagnoses made on these cases at that time were almost wholly unaffected by the presence of these scores on the chart. Of course, none of the present "pattern" criteria could have been employed at that time; further, knowledge of and confidence in the test were negligible among the psychiatric staff.

The procedure of blind diagnosis was as follows: profiles of male abnormals were leafed through in the order of their appearance in the files (roughly chronological). Any profile showing a ? (Cannot Say) or L (Lie) score as great as 70 was recorded as "invalid," except that if any abnormal score reached a standard score of 80, an elevated L score was ignored, since defensive lying could hardly be the reason for such a positive elevation. F was allowed to reach a raw score of 16 (T = 80) before the profile was considered invalid. The terms *valid* and *invalid* are used hereafter to indicate the acceptability of the profile as an adequate measure in terms of ?, L, and F, and have no reference to the question of accuracy of identification. When it had been decided that a profile was valid by these criteria, it was classified as either *normal* or *abnormal*. Actually, of course, it was known that all of the cases were abnormal, so that the criteria of classification had to be made wholly objective and hence more rigid than would be the case in practice. Profiles were called abnormal under the following four conditions: (1) Any of the eight components showed T ≥ 90. (2) Any of the eight components showed T ≥ 80, *unless* K < 40. (3) Any of the eight components showed T ≥ 70, *unless* K < 50 and L < 60. (4) Any of the eight components showed T ≥ 65, *unless* K < 65 and L < 60.

It can be seen from the above criteria that the classification into normal or abnormal is a matter of spotting the highest T score, then reading to the right to see if the restrictions on K and L throw the profile into one group or the other. The profiles consist wholly of MMPI scores and a code number, so that there is no other source of information in making the diagnosis.

Application of these criteria to 294 profiles from our general population male sample yields 10 per cent invalid records on the basis of ?, L, and F scores set as above. Of the records which can be accepted as valid, there are 9 per cent indicative of abnormality by the criteria, which may be considered the upper limit of "false positives." Actually, of course, an unknown proportion of these false positives are profiles of persons who, although not under psychiatric care at the time of testing, were at least as psychiatrically deviant as some of the hospitalized abnormals. The figure 9 per cent is to be contrasted with the 3 per cent to 5 per cent found previously for single scales. It is to be kept in mind in what follows that the differentiations achieved among the hospitalized abnormals occur at the expense of almost 1 in 10 among the normal population. The remainder of this paper deals only with the differentiation among actual abnormals.

When a profile had been classified as abnormal by the above criteria, a quick inspectional classification was made using three categories: psychosis, psychoneurosis, and "conduct disorder." The last category is used to cover cases diagnosed constitutional psychopathic inferior, psychopathic personality, criminalism, alcoholism, except psychoses or deterioration, simple adult maladjustment, or "primary behavior disorder" such as the adolescent conduct problems not otherwise classified. The criteria employed in this subdivision of abnormal records were intentionally vague and subjective, since it was this sort of inspectional judgment which was to be evaluated. No "computations" of any sort were performed on the scores. In general, the criteria, insofar as they were explicit, were those described by Schmidt and Gough, and such personal impressions as the examiner had acquired from considerable clinical work with the MMPI. Psychosis was suggested by markedly elevated profiles, high F, Sc greater than Pt, Pa or Ma markedly elevated, the "psychotic" (right-hand) end of the curve reaching the level of the "neurotic" (left-hand) end, or a distinct spike on D, with the Hs and Hy scores on either side falling far below the D. Psychoneurosis was suggested by a less elevated profile, lower F, Pt greater than Sc, Pa and Ma not much elevated, the neurotic triad clearly elevated more than the rest of the curve, and the three scores of the triad closer to one another. Conduct disorder was suggested by elevations on Pd, Ma if not too high and especially with a secondary peak at Pd, neurotic triad low except for some Hy, psychotic end running about 60. The examiner restricted himself to ten seconds per profile in making his decision, and in most cases the judgment was made in less than five seconds. After the classifications were made, these were compared with the diagnoses of the psychiatric staff. All cases were eliminated in which the staff diagnosis was indicated as highly questionable or based upon insufficient study or cases of organic C.N.S. disease or feeble-mindedness. The actual composition of the abnormal group as subsequently determined was as follows: psychosis, 57 cases (schizophrenia 26, manic-depressive 21, paranoid condition 8, and involutional melancholia 2); psychoneurosis, 53 cases (hypochondriasis 14, hysteria 13, reactive depression 9, psychasthenia 7, anxiety state 5, mixed or unspecified 4, neurasthenia 1); and conduct disorder, 37 cases (psychopathic personality 21, psychopathic personality pathological sexuality 8, alcoholic 5, behavior disorder 2, adult maladjustment 1).

Of this entire group of 147 clinical abnormals, 25 (17 per cent) invalidated their records on the basis of the validity indicators. Seventy-eight (53 per cent) were correctly called abnormal, while the remaining 44 cases (30 per cent) were (erroneously) classified as normal. Tables 1, 2, and 3 present the data in various convenient breakdowns.

Table 1. Classification by Profile Inspection of 147 Records of
Hospitalized Abnormals (Male)

Group	Called Abnormal	Called Normal	Invalid Record
Total group (N = 147)...............	53%	30%	17%
Psychotics (N = 57)..................	60	21	19
Neurotics (N = 53)..................	47	36	17
Conduct disorders (N = 37)...........	51	35	14

Table 2. Classification by Profile Inspection of the 122 Valid Records
(Based on ?, L, and F Scores)

Group	Called Abnormal	Called Normal
Total group (N = 122)..................	64%	36%
Psychotics (N = 46)....................	74	26
Neurotics (N = 44)....................	57	43
Conduct disorders (N = 32).............	59	41

Table 3. Classification by Profile Inspection of the 78 Cases Called Abnormal

Group	Called Psychotic	Called Neurotic	Called Conduct Disorder
Psychotics (N = 34)..................	56%	29%	15%
Neurotics (N = 25)...................	24	68	8
Conduct disorders (N = 19)...........	16	16	68

From these tables, we see that in employing a criterion of abnormality which holds our false positives down to one in ten among general normals, we are able to detect only about half of the known abnormals (Table 1). This figure is not quite fair to the test, however, since those with invalid records would *not* under these conditions be erroneously classified as normal, but would either be requested to take the test over again with more precautions or have their profiles disregarded. If we confine our attention to records in which the validity indicators are satisfactory, we find that about two thirds of the abnormals can be identified (Table 2). It should be pointed out that the disappointingly large proportion of apparently invalid records among the abnormals (about one sixth of all the records) is in part due to the time at which these tests were administered. At that time patients were allowed to invalidate their testings by sorting large numbers of the cards into the Cannot Say category, sorting the cards at random, and so on. More systematic supervision now eliminates many of these uninterpretable profiles.

Setting up a contingency table for the 78 cases correctly classed as abnormal, we obtain a chi square of 34.016, which with 4 df is highly significant ($p < .001$). This corresponds to a contingency coefficient of .55, with the upper limit possible for a 3 x 3 table being .82.

In comparing the accuracy of identification for the three diagnostic groups, we shall consider only the valid testings, since the percentages of invalid records differ insignificantly among the three. While three fourths of the psychotics were identified as being abnormal as contrasted with between one half and three fifths of the neurotics, a test of significance in the proportion of false "normals" in the three diagnostic categories fails to show a significant difference (chi square 3.233, 2 df, $p > .14$). This being the case, most of the further subgroup differences in identification were not statistically analyzed. Mere inspection of Table 3, however, would suggest that the chief confusion occurs between neurotic and psychotic curves, rather than between either of these and the class of conduct disorders. Once a profile is correctly classed as abnormal, the probability of its being thrown into the appropriate one of the three categories is about two in three.

Detailed inspection of the table of actual-real classifications does not indicate much because of the small numbers of cases in various subcategories. In the case of the psychoneuroses, however, inspection suggests that some clinical subgroups are more likely to show apparently "normal" profiles than are others. The differences in the proportion called abnormal were tested by grouping the cases into four classes — hypochondriasis, hysteria, psychasthenia, and all others — and running a chi-square test on the resulting 4 x 2 table. This chi square was barely significant at the .05 level (chi square 8.303, 3 df, and $p < .046$). If we inspect the table for the source of the differences, we find that 11 of the 13 hypochondriacs were identified as abnormal, as compared with only half of the ten hysterias, and only one of the six compulsives. It has been recognized for some time that the Pt scale is relatively ineffective clinically, and the use of K as a suppressor for Pt in this crude way tends to increase the false negatives by leading to an under-interpretation of profiles because K is highly correlated (negatively) with Pt. More detailed treatment of the actual subcategory tables is not warranted by the numbers involved.

To summarize, the adequacy of the MMPI in differential diagnosis employing a rapid, inspectional method of pattern analysis of profiles was investigated by making "blind" diagnoses from records of 147 hospitalized psychiatric cases into three major categories of psychosis, psychoneurosis, and conduct disorder. The criterion was the clinical diagnosis of the psychiatric staff, made at a time when the present scales of the MMPI, with one exception, were not yet in existence. The findings were as follows:

1. Setting up arbitrary criteria for the over-all distinguishing of normal from abnormal persons, we find that about one in ten persons from the general population sample is called abnormal (false positive).

2. Approximately two thirds of actual abnormals are identified as such by these

criteria, if we exclude records obviously invalid on the basis of the validity indicators ?, L, and F.

3. Of the abnormal cases identified as abnormal, about two thirds are placed in the appropriate category of the three employed. The contingency coefficient for the agreement between blind diagnostic grouping and the actual diagnosis is .55.

4. There is a suggestion that some varieties of abnormality are more readily identified than others. Hypochondriasis is fairly easily identified, whereas hysteria and psychasthenia are less so.

In general, while the discriminations achieved are very much better than chance in the statistical sense, especially considering the fact that *no* skilled clinical time is involved in giving or scoring the test and less than 10 seconds was used here in "interpreting" it, it must be admitted that the proportion of false classifications is considerable. Two developments can be expected to reduce materially this margin of error: first, the more mathematically precise utilization of the suppressor K; second, the greater formalization of pattern interpretation.

ARTICLE 32 *An Anxiety Index and an Internalization Ratio for the MMPI*

ANXIETY is a basic psychological concept and its evaluation is important both in describing behavior and in understanding the psychodynamics involved in this behavior. The psychologist in the hospital or clinic is constantly called upon to make judgments of the amount or degree present in a patient.

A question that the therapist frequently asks is "Does this patient have enough anxiety to work with?" This expresses clearly the belief that success in treatment is somehow related to anxiety. A patient who refers himself for treatment because of "nervousness and tension" is generally considered to offer a more favorable prognosis than a patient sent by the court. The latter may have no complaints referable to anxiety but comes in because his attendance is a requirement for his probation.

In terms of diagnosis such statements as the following are often made: "He doesn't have enough anxiety to be a real psychoneurotic," or "He has too much free anxiety to be a good conversion hysteric." The reaching of agreement as to diagnosis may be in part, then, a function of agreement as to how much anxiety is present and how this anxiety is directed.

Unfortunately the measurement of anxiety is largely left to clinical judgment and to inference from psychometric data. Although dozens of tests are used by the psychologist, there have been very few attempts to objectify and quantify such measurement. By observing the subject's behavior in the clinic or test situation, or by a consideration of test scores obtained, the psychologist must make an estimate of the amount of anxiety shown. This estimate is for the most part dependent on the clinician's experience and his skill in extracting out of the patient's behavior some judgment of the degree of anxiety present.

Next, the estimate must be communicated. This is usually done with adjectival phrases such as "shows a marked degree of anxiety," or "there was little free anxiety." Thus, even though the assessment of the anxiety may be accurate enough, fineness of discrimination will be lost on such a gross and variable scale.

It would clearly be an advantage to have some objective measure of anxiety which could be reported in a single numerical value. This paper will offer a sugges-

298

tion as to how this aim may be accomplished with a widely used psychometric device, the MMPI.

On the MMPI no single scale has appeared to measure anxiety. The clinician must estimate the amount or degree present by an examination of the profile configuration; this inference is then reported by the use of some unprecise phrase such as noted above. Thus the objectivity inherent in the test's scores is lost.

There have been, however, some attempts to derive an objective score. Modlin [449 (see VII, 43)] has suggested the use of the combined scores of Hs, D, and Hy as an anxiety score (A score); this had previously been used by Ruesch [513] as a neurotic score (N score). Gough [234 (VI, 38)] had also used the mean of this combination of the neurotic triad (Nt score) as a measure of neuroticism, but reported that it proved less discriminating than D alone, in addition to obscuring important interrelationships among the scales.

It appears clear, then, on both empirical and theoretical grounds, that a simple additive statistic derived from the neurotic triad will not show the interrelationships of the three subscores, or their full implication as a reflection of anxiety. Consider three hypothetical cases and their MMPI T scores:

> a. Hs 80, D 70, Hy 60
> b. Hs 70, D 60, Hy 80
> c. Hs 70, D 80, Hs 60

In all three cases the mean will be 70, yet the clinician would probably rank them in terms of anxiety from most to least as "c," "a," and "b."

A failure to consider these relationships led Shoben [685] to accept as an indication of anxiety T scores of over 65 on the neurotic triad regardless of pattern. This may have been an important factor in his failure to confirm the results of Rashkis and Welsh [r136] in their study of anxiety on the Wechsler scale.

The Development of Profile Indexes

Anxiety as used in this paper is that condition attributed to patients complaining of subjective feelings such as tension, nervousness, apprehènsion, and fear, which is generally accompanied by somatic concomitants — vertigo, dyspnea, precordial pain, gastric distress, headache, and the like. Anxiety is not necessarily equated with neuroticism since it might be argued logically that the three cases above are equally neurotic. Thus the person with free-floating anxiety is conceived to have more anxiety in this sense than the hysteric who is expressing his illness in conversion symptoms. The latter case may be either more or less neurotic than the first.

In order to obtain a measure of anxiety from the MMPI we might consider the profile of the person showing the most anxiety, the anxiety neurotic. This profile is generally "neurotic" [234 (see VI, 38)], showing a bimodal curve with a peak score on D and a secondary elevation on Pt. A recent paper by Hovey [330 (VI, 40)] demonstrates the specific anxiety pattern very clearly; in it there is a generalized rise on the neurotic triad with D higher than Hs and Hy and a subpeak on Pt.

Hovey contrasted the average profiles of three diagnostic groups: dissociative-conversion, somatization, and anxiety reaction. In the first group 62 per cent of the cases had the pattern typical of the group average, in the second 41 per cent, while only 23 per cent of the anxiety cases conformed to the pattern. This suggests that the clinician will be less successful in inferring anxiety from an inspection of the profile configuration in the latter group. Yet the elevations on the neurotic triad and Pt may be highly diagnostic even though they may not always show the typical relationship. In Modlin's sample of 54 cases of free anxiety, 40 per cent had D as the highest score, 29 per cent Hs, 15 per cent Hy, and 6 per cent Pt. For 28 cases of combat anxiety the percentages were D 43 per cent, Hs 14 per cent, Hy 14 per cent, and Pt 7 per cent.

The index of anxiety which is here proposed includes the scores on these four scales and utilizes three basic features of the anxiety profile: a general rise on the neurotic triad, the anticlinal relation of D to Hs and Hy, and the secondary rise on Pt. It is defined so as to yield an expected value of 50 for a normal record and to give the highest values to profiles of the type described by Gough and Hovey. The formula is:

$$AI = \left[\frac{Hs + D + Hy}{3}\right] + \left[(D + Pt) - (Hs + Hy)\right]$$

It can be seen that profiles with D in a synclinal position, the so-called "D valley" [234 (see VI, 38)], will generally have a negative number on the second part of the formula. This will result in a lower value than that obtained for curves with D peaks even though the average of the neurotic triad is the same. By taking the relation of these scales into account the difficulties posed in the three hypothetical cases mentioned above are avoided. And yet cases which do not have the typical curve shape can still be assigned a quantitative measure of anxiety so that the problem noted in Hovey's discussion may be overcome.

In practical clinical use of the Anxiety Index (AI) it has been found helpful to consider another relationship which, although closely allied to this concept, emphasizes a somewhat different aspect of the profile. This is a ratio obtained by summing the three complaint, mood, or feeling scales: Hs, D, and Pt; and dividing by the sum of the three behavior or character disorder scales: Hy, Pd, and Ma. This may be called the internalization ratio (IR) and the formula is:

$$IR = \frac{Hs + D + Pt}{Hy + Pd + Ma}$$

This will obviously yield a theoretical value of 1.00 in normal cases. Subjects who tend to have many somatic symptoms and subjective feelings of stress — who "internalize" their difficulties — can be expected to obtain values above 1.00. Those who tend to act out and "externalize" their conflicts will obtain a ratio below 1.00.

These two statistics, AI and IR, have been computed from the group averages given in several different studies and are presented in Table 1 and Table 2. The profile codes [296 (see III, 12), 617 (III, 13), 619 (III, 14)] for the groups given in these tables are set forth in Table 3 for the benefit of those who wish to compare the curve configurations with AI and IR.

It is obvious that the average AI computed from group means will be exactly the same as that calculated by averaging the individual AI's. This is not necessarily so for IR since the above relation will be true for ratios only under certain conditions. The difference between average ratios computed collectively and those com-

Table 1. The Anxiety Index (AI) and the Internalization Ratio (IR) Computed from Mean Scores Given in Certain Studies of Psychiatric Groups and Including Controls Where Cited

Description of Group	N	AI	IR	Description of Group	N	AI	IR
Gough [234]				*Hovey [330]*			
Psychoneurosis, severe..	57	102	1.26	Anxiety reaction.......	60	87	1.21
Psychopathic personality	21	79	1.11	Somatization reaction...	105	53	1.10
Psychosis	22	77	1.13	Dissociative-conversion			
Psychoneurosis, moderate	24	66	1.08	reaction	34	42	1.00
Psychoneurosis, mild...	12	57	1.09	*Schmidt [528]*			
Normal	27	47	.98	Psychotic	13	85	1.13
Guthrie [272]				Psychoneurosis, severe..	64	74	1.14
Anxiety state..........	12	97	1.19	Constitutional psycho-			
Depression	7	93	1.25	pathic state, inade-			
Paranoid	15	68	.97	quate personality....	11	65	1.02
Psychopath, asocial type	25	67	.88	Constitutional psycho-			
Inadequate personality..	19	53	1.08	pathic state, sexual			
Manic condition.......	11	50	.78	psychopathy	7	65	1.00
				Psychoneurosis, mild....	26	50	1.12
				Normal	98	42	.99

Table 2. The Anxiety Index (AI) and the Internalization Ratio (IR) Computed from Mean Scores Given in Certain Studies of Nonpsychiatric Groups

Description of Group	N	AI	IR	Description of Group	N	AI	IR
Brown [89]				*Fry [209]*			
Male college students				College students			
Original	155	41	.96	Male veteran	86	57	.96
Industrial	66	46	.98	Male nonveteran	35	55	.93
Medical	82	48	.92	Male total	121	56	.95
General college	176	52	.94	Female	115	51	.92
Female college students				State prison inmates			
Original	155	42	.95	Male Negro	22	54	.84
Sophomores	110	48	.92	Male white	76	60	.89
Teachers' college ...	185	47	.92	Male total	98	58	.88
General college	366	49	.90	Female	109	59	.88
Capwell [112]							
Delinquent girls	99	61	.88				
Nondelinquent girls ...	89	48	.99				

puted individually will be slight if the individual ratios are relatively symmetrical about 1.00. If there is a preponderance of individual ratios above 1.00, the use of group means results in an average higher than that obtained when individual ratios are averaged. A lower average will result when most of the individual ratios fall below 1.00. The writer is indebted to Dr. Robert C. Tryon for his assistance in this regard and also for suggesting alternate forms for AI which may be more easily computed:

$$1.33D + 1.00Pt - .66Hs - .66Hy$$
$$\tfrac{1}{3}[4D + 3Pt - 2(Hs + Hy)]$$

In Table 1 the highest AI is shown by Gough's severe psychoneurotic group which consisted primarily of cases with an anxiety diagnosis. This is closely followed by Guthrie's [272 (see VI, 41)] anxiety state and depression groups. Hovey's anxiety reaction is next, with Schmidt's [528 (see VI, 39)] psychotic group showing a somewhat lower elevation. The lowest scores are obtained by Hovey's dissociative-conversion reactions and Schmidt's normals. We then find Gough's normals, Schmidt's mild psychoneurotics, and Guthrie's manic group.

In Table 2 the AI is highest for Capwell's [112] delinquent girls, but this value is lower than for all but the mild neurotics, inadequate personality, manic, somatization, and conversion groups of Table 1. Fry's [209] prisoners run slightly higher than his college groups but again the AI is lower than most of the psychiatric groups. The college groups cluster very closely about 50 like the previously noted normals.

Table 3. Profile Codes of the Groups Given in Table 1

Description of Group	Profile Code	Description of Group	Profile Code
Gough [234]		*Hovey [330]*	
Psychoneurosis, severe...	2°18<u>73</u>"46'<u>59</u>	Anxiety reaction........	21"<u>783</u>'46<u>95</u>
Psychopathic personality.	2183"4<u>6'7</u>–95	Somatization reaction...	1'<u>32</u>–7<u>49856</u>
Psychosis	21"<u>3867</u>'49–5	Dissociative-conversion	
Psychoneurosis,		reaction	31'2–<u>94</u> <u>785</u>/6
moderate	<u>231</u>'74–<u>8965</u>	*Schmidt [528]*	
Psychoneurosis, mild....	<u>312</u>'–<u>64</u> 78 <u>95</u>	Psychotic	2"86173'49–5
Normal	3<u>25</u>/19<u>4867</u>	Psychoneurosis, severe...	<u>21</u>"378'<u>46</u>–95
Guthrie [272]		C.P.I.	
Anxiety state..........	2"781'<u>394</u>–<u>56</u>	Inadequate	13286<u>4</u>'79–5
Depression	2" '761<u>38</u>–49(5)[a]	Sexual psychopathy...	85<u>6</u>'3<u>24719</u>
Paranoid	68'4792–13(5)[a]	Psychoneurosis, mild....	138<u>27</u>–649/5
Psychopath, asocial.....	4'98<u>27</u>–<u>36</u> 15	Normal	6/7<u>1894532</u>
Inadequate personality..	13'2<u>7894</u>–56		
Manic	9'48–67/132(5)[a]		

[a] Mf was not given in the original study because both sexes were included.

The IR values in Table 1 follow AI very closely but some interesting findings may be noted. Guthrie's anxiety-state group leads his depression group in AI but the latter has a higher IR; this seems consistent with the clinical impression of depressed patients who show "internalization" to a high degree. Guthrie's manics and Schmidt's mild neurotics both have the same "average" AI of 50; however, the former shows a very low IR — the most "externalized" of all the groups presented — while the latter has a slightly elevated IR.

The groups which have achieved a stability between internalization and externalization in the sense of an IR close to 1.00 are the two normals, Guthrie's paranoids, Hovey's dissociative-conversion, and Schmidt's two constitutional psychopathic groups. But at the same time these stabilized groups show distinguishing differences in AI. Hovey's group is characterized by a lack of anxiety, as are Schmidt's normals, while the paranoids and psychopathic states show a mild rise on AI.

From Table 2 it can be seen that the prisoners and delinquents externalize more than the college students although the former's anxiety is slightly higher.

These tables afford some evidence that the statistics proposed will in most cases follow the clinical expectations when the mean T scores for various groups are considered. High AI and IR values will be seen for cases of anxiety and depression and other groups with anxiety as a prominent clinical feature. A low AI may be expected in hysteria with IR at the average. And a low IR with low or only slightly elevated AI would fit the "acting out" behavior pattern of manics, psychopaths, prisoners, and delinquents.

The AI and IR in Relation to Therapy

In order to see how the proposed statistics will measure therapeutic effects a number of studies, of individual cases and of groups, utilizing different methods of treatment, will be considered.

A study by Hales and Simon [276] compared the MMPI profiles of twenty schizophrenic patients in a Veterans Administration hospital who were treated by insulin shock therapy. Ten patients showed improvement "ranging from moderate response to complete remission" and ten "failed to show any improvement whatsoever." The anxiety index has been computed from the mean T scores reported for the two groups on the tests administered before therapy. For the improved group AI is 75; for the unimproved, 63. Thus the improved group tended to show more anxiety before therapy, as measured by the index, than the unimproved. The values for IR are 1.05 and 1.08, suggesting that both groups were fairly well "settled down" in their illness.

Further confirmation of the predictive value of AI may be seen in a recent study by Carp [114]. He compared the MMPI profiles of schizophrenics in a Veterans Administration hospital before and after insulin shock therapy, and in general his results support the findings of Hales and Simon. There were 37 cases of which 15 were judged to be improved and 22 unimproved. The anxiety index and internalization ratio have been computed for each group from the mean T scores for the pretreatment tests. For the improved group the values are AI = 83, IR = 1.05; for the unimproved: AI = 58, IR = .94. In this study the improved patients showed both more anxiety and more internalization than the unimproved.

Rashkis and Shaskan [487] have reported on 22 psychiatric patients treated by group therapy in an army hospital. They were given the MMPI both before and after six weeks' treatment. Group mean T scores are not given in the article, but two cases are cited and scores reported. Both individuals were diagnosed as "anxiety state, severe, chronic." For the first case AI before therapy was 98 and this dropped to 61 after treatment; IR before was 1.12 and afterwards, .88. The second case showed the following values before and after: AI 107 to 62, IR 1.30 to .86. Although the authors had complained that the inventory had not measured "such clinical features as guilt, anxiety, or the expressions of the other emotions which group treatment is probably most successful in treating," it can be seen from the above values that the index and ratio do seem to be of value in quantifying such clinical change.

A severe psychoneurotic patient with anxiety as a primary symptom was seen by Andersen [20] for testing seven days before and five days after a prefrontal lobotomy. The MMPI was administered on these occasions and also four times subsequently at ten-day intervals. The AI values are as follows: preoperative 149, postoperative 103, 142, 119, 126, 114. For IR: preoperative 1.33, postoperative 1.21, 1.38, 1.32, 1.24, 1.08. There was an initial drop following the operative attack, but the anxiety rose to the previous level again. Toward the end of the testing periods there was some decline. These values seem to follow the clinical changes reported and reflect the high level of anxiety and internal stress noted in this patient.

A further study may be of interest although no treatment is reported. In a study by Wauck [612] the MMPI profiles of 80 diagnosed schizophrenics from a state hospital were used. The anxiety index for the total group is 73 and the internalization ratio 1.01. A subgroup of 31 paranoids shows AI to be 64 and IR to be .98; these are very close to Guthrie's paranoid group which obtained AI = 68 and IR = .97. The total group was also subdivided into three age groups: ages 15 to 29 (N = 33), 30 to 39 (N = 31), and 40 to 53 (N = 16). The AI values are 81, 69, and 60. For IR they are 1.05, 1.00, and 1.00. Although IR stays approximately the same, there is a clear tendency for AI to decrease in the older groups. This seems consistent with the clinical findings that younger schizophrenics generally respond better to treatment, and this may be reflected in the anxiety index.

Table 4. Distribution of AI for Three Psychiatric Populations

AI	Hospital A	Clinic B	Clinic C			
			Much imp.	Some imp.	No imp.	Not rated
160–179 ..	1	1				
140–159 ..	2	1	1			2
120–139 ..	6	6	0	6	2	8
100–119 ..	8	7	2	10	3	3
80–99 ...	12	14	3	4	3	18
60–79 ...	14	12		5	4	11
40–59 ...	13	11		3	2	13
20–39 ...	5	2			1	3
0–19 ...		1				
N	60	55	7	28	15	58
Mean	82	82	111	98	85	81
SD	28	31	27	27	27	31

Table 5. Distribution of IR for Three Psychiatric Populations

IR	Hospital A	Clinic B	Clinic C			
			Much imp.	Some imp.	No imp.	Not rated
1.60–1.69..			1	1		1
1.50–1.59..	1	1	0	1	1	1
1.40–1.49..	5	5	0	0	1	3
1.30–1.39..	8	8	3	5	0	4
1.20–1.29..	8	6	2	6	2	10
1.10–1.19..	6	13	0	9	3	10
1.00–1.09..	15	8	1	4	4	15
.90–.99...	8	9		1	3	11
.80–.89...	8	2		1	1	3
.70–.79...	1	2				
.60–.69...		1				
N	60	55	7	28	15	58
Mean	1.12	1.14	1.32	1.20	1.13	1.13
SD	.23	.20	.15	.19	.18	.18

The evidence is consistent in showing that a more favorable prognosis for treatment may be predicted for a high AI, other conditions being equal. It is also clear that clinical changes during treatment may be reflected by both the AI and IR values.

In order to ascertain the distribution of AI and IR for psychiatric populations, data were obtained from three sources: a midwestern Veterans Administration hospital (hospital A) and two West Coast VA mental hygiene clinics (clinic B and clinic C). In one of the latter (clinic C), information as to therapeutic outcome was available and will be discussed later. The records of white male patients only were utilized in this study. The actual distributions of AI are summarized in Table 4 and IR in Table 5.

In hospital A for 60 patients the range of AI was from 27 to 154 with a mean of 82 and a standard deviation of 28. The IR ranged from .78 to 1.54 with a mean of 1.12 and a standard deviation of .23. A product-moment coefficient of correlation calculated between AI and IR was +.58. The magnitude of the r shows that while the two are indeed related, they may be measuring aspects of the profile sufficiently different to make them both useful. It may be noted that the coefficient of alienation for the above r would be .81.

In clinic B with an N of 55 the range for AI was somewhat more extreme, 13 to 171. The mean is identical at 82 although the standard deviation of 31 is a few points greater. The lowest IR was .65 and the highest 1.58; this range is again slightly more extreme than the hospital group although the mean of 1.14 is practically identical. The standard deviation of .20, however, is not quite so large. The product-moment r for AI and IR in the clinic group is very similar to that obtained for the hospital: r = + .63.

Table 6. The Number and Percentage of Three Subgroups of Clinic C Exceeding Certain Cutting Scores on AI and IR

Subgroup	N	AI above 82		IR above 1.14		Both AI above 82 and IR above 1.14	
		N	%	N	%	N	%
Much improvement	7	7	100	6	86	6	86
Some improvement	28	19	68	21	75	16	57
No improvement	15	7	47	7	47	5	33
Total	50	33	66	34	68	27	54

In clinic C there were available 108 MMPI records on patients tested routinely on intake during a six-month period. Not quite half (50) had received treatment at the clinic for a long enough period so that judgment as to therapeutic gain was possible. This treated group was divided into three subgroups on the basis of the estimate of treatment progress given by the therapist in the closing summary. These subgroups are as follows: much improved, N = 7; made some improvement, N = 28; no improvement or got worse, N = 15.

The 58 unrated patients are listed separately and it may be seen that the range, mean, and standard deviation are very similar to those of hospital A and clinic B.

On the basis of the evidence advanced so far it might be anticipated that the subgroups making improvement in therapy would have higher AI and IR scores than those patients who did not improve. That such predictions are confirmed may be seen from Table 4 and Table 5. The much improved group exceeds the other two on both AI and IR, and the some improvement group had higher scores than the unimproved. All three of the treated subgroups exceed the unrated group.

An analysis of variance carried out on the three subgroups and the unrated group gives F ratios of 2.92 for AI and 2.66 for IR. The F ratios are both significant at the .05 level of confidence.

The amount of overlap among the different subgroups may be seen by referring to Table 4 and Table 5. In addition Table 6 has been compiled to show the number and percentage in each subgroup which exceed an AI of 82 and an IR of 1.14 (these are approximately the means of these two values for hospital A, clinic B, and the unrated cases of clinic C). In every case the much improved group has a greater percentage falling above these cutting scores than the other two groups, and the some improvement percentages exceed the unimproved.

We may combine the much improved and some improved groups and count the number over the cutting scores as hits while considering those in the no improvement group above these scores as misses. In the case of AI we will be successful 68 per cent of the time, for IR, 70 per cent, and for both considered together, 64 per cent. In terms of significance as computed by chi square the AI passes the .10 level and IR the .05, while the combination falls between .20 and .10.

This study confirms the findings noted in previously published accounts and suggests that AI and IR may be useful as predictors of success in therapy in addition to affording an objective measure of anxiety.

Evidence for the usefulness of the two measures in a normal population is afforded by an unpublished study of graduate students. For forty subjects the mean AI was 63 with a standard deviation of 16; the mean IR was 1.03 with a standard deviation of .14. The product-moment correlation between AI and IR was +.17. The students showed much lower scores than the psychiatric populations and the correlation between the two statistics is not of the same magnitude as that obtained in the former groups.

The students had been rated on a five-point scale by nine judges on a number of behavior traits and the following significant product-moment r's obtained: self-confidence and AI, −.44; poise and AI, −.29; poise and IR, +.33. An adjective check list had also been used and the number of times each adjective had been checked as present in the subject by the judges was correlated with the measures. Significant correlations are anxious and AI, + .25; spontaneous and AI, − .31; spontaneous and IR, −.45.

These findings seem to indicate that the proposed measures will be associated in a normal population with anxiety and related behavior in the same direction that would be predicted from the results of their use with psychiatric groups.

One final bit of evidence may be adduced to show that the Anxiety Index is measuring what clinicians consider to be anxiety. Prior to the development of the index ten judges had gone through the MMPI and checked the items they felt to be related to anxiety. There were eight items upon which all ten judges agreed, six items had nine agreements, and seventeen items eight agreements. These 31 items were made to constitute a scale called Ja for "judged anxiety." Fifty new records were obtained from clinic C and this scale scored and correlated with the proposed measures. The tetrachoric r's obtained are AI, +.91; IR, +.36.

Thus it is apparent that such an anxiety key might well be substituted for the Anxiety Index as a measure of anxiety. But AI has two important advantages: first, no additional scoring is necessary for its use; second, AI can be used when the answer sheet is not available since it can be calculated from the scale T scores alone.

Summary

From a consideration of profile configuration seen in MMPI records of psychiatric patients characterized by anxiety as a prominent clinical feature, a statistic — AI — has been proposed as an index of anxiety. Related to this is a concept of internalization for which another statistic is suggested, the internalization ratio or IR. Evidence is offered that these two measures may be of use in quantifying judgments of anxiety which up to now have been made largely from inspection of the profile. It is shown that they may be of help in diagnostic and descriptive considerations and that they may be related to therapeutic change.

P. L. SULLIVAN AND G. S. WELSH

ARTICLE 33 *A Technique for Objective Configural Analysis of MMPI Profiles*

THE one aspect of psychological testing about which clinicians have generally agreed is the necessity for taking a holistic attitude when evaluating protocols. The number of articles concerned with this and the number of references to it are legion. Such terms as "molarity," "configuration," "pattern," and "the total personality" are used to express this point of view. What is more, it has frequently been possible to demonstrate that the configural approach yields greater predictive accuracy than does the more atomistic.

For example, Gough's [235] four judges were able to detect MMPI dissemblers with greater precision than was achieved through the use of either the F or K scales alone. Aaronson and Welsh [1] showed that judges were able to assign the averaged profiles of psychiatric groups to the proper diagnostic categories even though Rubin [509] had not been able to accomplish this with the same data using analysis of variance of the individual scales. More recently, Guthrie [272 (see VI, 41)] has demonstrated that judges using the configural approach can accurately sort individual profiles into diagnostic categories. The judges in Hanvik's [287 (VIII, 55)] study of low-back pain were able to distinguish between "functional" and "organic" patients, as well as to classify the profiles into the standard psychiatric groups.

One problem in the use of judges is that they have been found to vary widely in their ability to sort protocols. This has been discussed briefly by Hanvik [287 (see VIII, 55)]. There have occurred, furthermore, instances [341] in which none of the judges participating was able to sort profiles at better than a chance level. From these observations it would appear that a method for objectifying some of the aspects of the configural analysis employed by judges would yield beneficial results in terms of consistency and accuracy.

The problem of configural analysis has been most cogently dealt with by Meehl [438 (see IV, 30)] and it was as an application of the argument presented by him that the present paper was conceived. Where Meehl, however, demonstrates the possibility of deriving differentiating measures from the patterning of items, the technique developed in this paper has for its basic unit the clinical scales of the MMPI. A further difference consists in the fact that here the ranks of the scales of two groups of persons are used, whereas Meehl used the direction of answers to

308

single items. There is an essential similarity in that each approach seeks to derive empirical signs or indices which differentiate identified groups from suitable control groups. A discussion of the implications and applications of the technique will perhaps be more meaningful if the method is first explained and illustrated.

The Technique

As was stated above, the essence of the method is the comparison of the ranks of the clinical scales of the MMPI's obtained from two groups of individuals. In order to facilitate this procedure, our first step was to convert the T scores of all the individual records to the coding system developed by Welsh [617 (see III, 13) and 619 (III, 14)]. In this system, each of the clinical scales is assigned a number from 1 to 9, the order of the numbering corresponding to the left–right order of the scales on the psychograms, i.e., Hs, 1, to Ma, 9. Appropriate symbols are employed to indicate the T-score deciles in which each of the scales falls. The scale code numbers are arranged in order of descending elevation, with the symbols placed to the right of the scales in a given decile. Inasmuch as our method requires only the rank order, these symbols need not be used.

Table 1. Rank Order Tabulation of Two Hypothetical MMPI Profiles [a]

Scale Pairs	Subjects A B C...n		Sums +	−	=	Scale Pairs	Subjects A B C...n		Sums +	−	=
1-2	+	−				2-5	+	+			
1-3	+	+				2-6	+	+			
1-4	+	=				2-7	+	+			
1-5	+	+				2-8	+	+			
1-6	+	+				2-9	+	+			
1-7	+	−				3-4	+	−			
1-8	+	=				3-5	+	+			
1-9	+	+				8-9	+	+			
2-3	−	+									
2-4	−	+									

[a] Subject A's profile code is 1'34–2876/95:. Subject B's profile code is 2°7"418'63–5/9:.

Looking forward to the future clinical application of the technique, we did not use the actual numerical ranks of the various scales. It appeared that the amount of time that would be necessary for numerical manipulation might outweigh the advantages gained by the use of the present procedure. Instead, rank comparisons were made with the use of plus, minus, and equal signs: the higher of two scales was assigned a plus, the lower a minus, while scales were considered to be equal if they were within one T-score point of each other. The actual comparisons of the ranks were made within each individual record (see Table 1). The group sums of the pluses, minuses, and equals were then obtained for each of the scale-comparison pairs, of which there are $n(n-1)/2$, or 36 for the MMPI. If a check on accuracy is desired, all 72 of the possible pairs can be made, but the second occurrence of each combination will show the signs reversed. Thus, if Hs is higher than D, the 1-2 comparison will be $+$, while the 2-1 comparison will be $−$.

Tests of significance of difference between the two groups were then applied to the totals of the pluses, minuses, and equals for each of the scale comparisons. Those differences which separated the two groups in both the plus-plus and minus-minus directions at the .05 level were tentatively accepted as "signs." Only plus and minus were considered because in this study the number of equals was usually negligible. They may, of course, be combined with either the pluses or minuses or used separately when analyzing data.

The next step was to ascertain the cross-validity of the signs, for which groups similar to the first two were independently selected. The MMPI profiles were assigned scores based on the number of signs they contained and the difference between the mean sign scores tested for significance. As a final step, derivation of signs from our cross-validation groups was also accomplished. Only those differences attaining the .05 level in *both* sets of data were accepted as the final signs. The final signs are suggested for general use, for they represent the significant findings in two sets of data after "shrinkage" has been allowed for.

An Illustrative Application

In order to determine the efficacy of the technique, the MMPI profiles of sixty male Veterans Administration Mental Hygiene Clinic patients were obtained. Thirty of these were known to have gastric ulcers, while the remaining thirty had neither an ulcer nor any other psychosomatic disorder. The results of the analysis of the sixty profiles, showing only the comparisons of the hypochondriasis scale with all others, will perhaps further clarify the procedure (see Table 2). These sixty individuals will henceforth be referred to as the criterion group.

Table 2. Results of Comparisons of Ranks of the Hs Scale with Other MMPI Scales Based on 30 Ulcer and 30 Nonpsychosomatic Neuropsychiatric Male Patients [a]

Scale Pairs	Ulcer			Control			Differences		
	+	−	=	+	−	=	+	−	=
1-2	15	13	2	4	24	2	11°	−11°	0
1-3	23	5	2	11	13	6	12°	− 8°	−4
1-4	19	7	4	13	16	1	6	− 9°°	3
1-5	23	6	1	13	15	2	10°	− 9°°	−1
1-6	25	4	1	19	9	2	6	− 5	−1
1-7	18	10	2	9	17	4	9°°	− 7°°	−2
1-8	21	8	1	9	19	2	12°	−11°	−1
1-9	23	4	3	19	9	2	4	− 5	1

[a] ° and °° signify phi coefficients significant at the .01 and .05 levels, respectively.

As may be seen from Table 2, the following scale pairs characterize the profiles of the ulcer group in both the plus-plus and minus-minus directions:

1. 1 (Hs) higher than 2 (D)
2. 1 (Hs) higher than 3 (Hy)
3. 1 (Hs) higher than 5 (Mf)
4. 1 (Hs) higher than 7 (Pt)
5. 1 (Hs) higher than 8 (Sc)

In addition, comparisons of the other scales with each other yielded three more tentative signs which identify ulcer patients' profiles:

6. 2 (D) higher than 3 (Hy)
7. 3 (Hy) higher than 4 (Pd)
8. 3 (Hy) higher than 5 (Mf)

Sixty more MMPI's were obtained from the male population of a Veterans Administration mental hygiene clinic. Thirty of these were ulcer patients and thirty were contributed by unselected patients; the latter group differed from the first control group in that they were randomly selected, i.e., psychosomatic cases were *not* eliminated. This appeared to be necessary because the working situation usually requires differentiations of particular kinds of patients from among the patient population at large. These records, which comprise the validation group, were scored for the eight signs shown above, the results for which are shown in Table 3. By use of a cutting score of 6, it is seen in Table 3 that 21 ulcer patients and 19 control patients, or 67 per cent of the total group, are accurately identified. The phi coefficient for this percentage of accuracy is 0.33 (p = .01).

These records were also subjected to the same analysis as the original sixty records, with the following significant differences resulting:

1. 1 (Hs) higher than 2 (D)
2. 1 (Hs) higher than 3 (Hy)
3. 1 (Hs) higher than 4 (Pd)
4. 1 (Hs) higher than 7 (Pt)
5. 1 (Hs) higher than 8 (Sc)
6. 1 (Hs) higher than 9 (Ma)
7. 2 (D) higher than 3 (Hy)

Table 3. Results of Scoring for Tentative Ulcer Signs in MMPI Records of the Validation Group (30 Ulcer and 30 Unselected Neuropsychiatric Male Patients)

Number of Signs	Ulcer Group	Control Group
8	4	3
7	13	5
6	4	3
Total	21	11
5	6	8
4	2	0
3	1	4
2	0	3
1	0	2
0	0	2
Total	9	19
N	30	30
Mean	6.27	4.57
SD	1.27	2.37
DM	1.70	
SEm	.49	
CR	3.47	
P	<.001	

Table 4. Results of Scoring for Final Ulcer Signs in MMPI Records of the Criterion (30 Ulcer and 30 Nonpsychosomatic Neuropsychiatric Male Patients) and the Validation (30 Ulcer and 30 Unselected Neuropsychiatric Male Patients) Groups

Number of Signs	Criterion Group Ulcer	Control	Validation Group Ulcer	Control
5	5	1	4	3
4	11	4	18	6
3	6	4	4	5
Total .	22	9	26	14
2	2	5	3	7
1	6	15	1	7
0	0	1	0	2
Total .	8	21	4	16
N	30	30	30	30
Mean ..	3.23	1.93	3.70	2.50
SD	1.34	1.26	.94	1.45
DM ...	1.30		1.20	
SEm ...	.34		.32	
CR	3.86		3.75	
P	<.001		<.001	

Thus there were five relationships which separated the ulcers from the controls in both instances:

1. 1 (Hs) higher than 2 (D)
2. 1 (Hs) higher than 3 (Hy)
3. 1 (Hs) higher than 7 (Pt)
4. 1 (Hs) higher than 8 (Sc)
5. 2 (D) higher than 3 (Hy)

Scoring all the records for the five ulcer signs yielded the distributions presented in Table 4. As will be noted, the mean differences in each of the ulcer-control pairings are significant beyond the .001 level. If a cutting score of 3 is used, 71.6 per cent and 70.0 per cent correct identification is achieved in the criterion and validation groups respectively. These percentages have respective phi coefficient values of 0.41 and 0.40, both of which are significant beyond the .01 level.

Table 5. T-Score Means, Standard Deviations, and Codes of Diagnostic Groups

Group	Hs	D	Hy	Pd	Mf	Pa	Pt	Sc	Ma
Criterion									
Ulcer (N = 30)									
Mean	77.3	79.4	74.0	65.0	63.7	59.0	73.3	69.0	60.3
SD	16.8	13.6	13.2	12.1	9.3	9.5	13.6	15.8	15.6
			MMPI Code: 21<u>37</u>'8459–6						
Neuropsychiatric (N = 30)									
Mean	66.0	79.0	66.3	68.7	71.0	60.3	72.0	72.7	59.3
SD	15.6	13.2	11.3	13.3	13.3	10.8	14.3	13.9	9.1
			MMPI Code: 2<u>875</u>'431 <u>6–9</u>						
Validation									
Ulcer (N = 30)									
Mean	75.3	72.7	71.7	61.3	62.0	54.7	64.0	60.0	54.7
SD	13.2	11.8	17.2	11.8	11.6	10.0	13.9	14.8	10.6
			MMPI Code: 1<u>23</u>'7<u>548</u>–<u>69</u>						
Neuropsychiatric (N = 30)									
Mean	75.0	79.7	73.3	64.3	58.0	57.7	71.7	70.0	61.0
SD	15.5	14.1	11.7	12.2	12.1	10.4	14.7	16.7	12.8
			MMPI Code: 21378'49–<u>56</u>						

As is also obvious from Table 4, the two ulcer and control groups were not combined and single means, critical ratios, etc., derived. The reason for not combining the control groups is apparent when it is recalled that they were not selected in the same manner. The ulcer groups were not combined because computation of the means and standard deviations of the individual scales revealed that the two groups contained significant dissimilarities. Table 5 presents these data, in which the depression, psychasthenia, and schizophrenia scales are significantly lower in the validation group than in the criterion group. These differences indicate that the criterion group was much more maladjusted in the sense of scale elevation than the validation group. Despite these fluctuations, it was possible to make accurate separations through the use of signs.

With the data contained in Table 5 in mind, we may address ourselves to another question, viz., is the assumption that inter-scale comparison is superior to intra-scale comparison justified? That is, might not the comparison of experimental and control individuals' Hs, D, etc., scores yield as good or better differentiation than the rank comparison method presented? This question lies at the heart of the "atomism" versus "configuration" argument with which we are concerned.

In order to determine the efficacy of the single-scale approach, distributions of the scores for each MMPI scale were made for each of our groups. Cutting scores which yielded the best possible separation between the ulcers and controls within the criterion and validation groups were determined. For the criterion group, three such cutting scores were derived which identified the ulcer patients: Hs greater than 70, Hy greater than 80, and Mf less than 70; for the validation group, two scores were obtained: D greater than 80 and Sc less than 60. Scoring the validation group for the signs obtained from the criterion group, and vice versa, yielded only chance differences between the ulcer and control patients within those groups. The fact that none of the indices is repeated is further evidence contraindicating the efficacy of this approach. It must be noted, however, that such complete failure might not be the case were the successive groups more homogeneous than ours.

Discussion

It is presumed to be apparent from the foregoing presentation that the technique elaborated is concerned with the assignment of individuals to classes of persons sharing some known commonality. Although we have presented data on patients with gastric ulcers — easily detectable by other devices — the method of analysis is as readily applicable to a host of variables, such as dissembling, aptitude for teaching, readiness for therapy, etc. That is, in any situation which allows for the separation of individuals on the basis of a given variable, it is possible to determine the existence of indices by the procedure outlined.

The application of such an analysis does not, of course, restrict the appraiser of an individual's protocol to this kind of consideration, nor does it detract from an elaboration of the nuances of the idiosyncratic make-up of the tested person. It does, however, lay stress on a nomothetic approach to the clinician's data. We would contend that such an attitude inheres in more of our clinical work than we might care to recognize. For example, it stands to reason that the judges in the study of Gough previously cited had some preconceived set of notions of what a dissembled record should look like, and that they consistently applied these expectations to the records judged. Similarly, in day-to-day work we look for patterned relationships which correspond to indices of classes, either derived through experience or conjured up rationally. We are proposing, then, that not only does the clinician employ class inferences, but also that what he does can be objectified and shown to be the most fruitful way of handling his data. The empirical technique presented offers a means of checking on the authenticity of patterns which are thought to identify some trend, trait, or diagnostic group.

To exemplify, it has become the custom to expect all psychosomatic patients to give MMPI profiles which contain the "psychosomatic V," i.e., Hs and Hy elevated over D in a synclinal relation. The analysis of the records of the particular psychosomatic group used in this study — ulcer — revealed that this patterning did not result. Instead, the D score was found to be higher than the Hy score in a significantly large number of cases.

Another advantage of configural analysis is that every possible relationship is appraised for its differentiating power. Scales of intermediate elevation may prove to be as predictive as those of maximum elevation when the relationships between them and the other scales are scrutinized.

It must be noted that rank comparisons do not give consideration to the absolute elevations of the scales but only to their relative magnitude. Ideally, a method of analysis would give consideration to both of these factors, and the failure of our method to achieve this must be regarded as a definite disadvantage. One of us (G. S. W.) is attempting to develop a technique which will handle the problem in its entirety. Even with this limitation, the method of configural analysis presented here does, as we have seen, permit us to make meaningful identifications of profiles.

Although the use of an objective pattern analysis with the MMPI is not new, it has not previously been systematically elaborated as a method which may be applied in a variety of clinical service and research settings. Pearson [473 (see IX, 60)], for example, writes of "tabulating a number of combinations of the MMPI scale values," from which he derived three indices of probable response to electric shock therapy. Again, Harris *et al.* [291] report the use of "prognostic criteria" which consisted of the relative elevations of certain MMPI scales in the records of a number of clinical groups. Rigorous scale comparisons utilizing all possible relative comparisons were not, however, reported. Hanvik [287 (see VIII, 55)] used pattern analysis of coded profiles but notes that "it could not be carried out in statistical terms."

Nor is the use of configural analysis limited to the MMPI. To cite one instance of possible application, the Wechsler-Bellevue lends itself readily to such treatment. Presenting the test characteristics of clinical groups, Wechsler [r167] couches the indices in terms of deviations from subtest means. If the presented indices actually allow differentiation of the various clinical groups, first coding the scales and then subjecting them to configural analysis would conclusively verify this fact.

Summary and Conclusions

A technique for objective analysis of psychological test profiles based on rank comparisons of the coded scales within individual records has been presented. Using the MMPI as the sample test with a group of patients known to have gastric ulcer, it has been demonstrated that the technique can be used to derive signs which differentiate them from nonpsychosomatic mental hygiene clinic patients. These signs were also shown to differentiate a validating population of ulcer patients from randomly selected psychiatric patients. The application to other tests which can be coded has been outlined.

ARTICLE 34 *MMPI Profiles and Personality Characteristics*

THIS study is concerned with comparing observed personality characteristics of nonclinical individuals with profiles they produced on the MMPI [305]. Contrary to the usual procedure of comparing test results with groups of individuals selected according to certain behavior criteria, this study started by grouping persons according to test results, and then ascertained what personality characteristics or traits appeared, a procedure similar to the one used in compiling *An Atlas for the Clinical Use of the MMPI* [307]. The population consisted of student nurses in practicum training, not because of a primary interest in nurses, but because data for the most part were already available and only waiting to be organized and analyzed. The population consisted of individuals who were making constructive social and vocational adjustments, who had been under discerning supervision of experienced psychiatric nurses and other staff personnel, and for each of whom anecdotal records with expressions of behavioral and personality characteristics had been made independently by eight of these personnel.

The program in the Veterans Administration Hospital at American Lake, Washington, carries on an intensive practicum for student nurses, admitting a class of from 16 to 24 students at a time, for a three-month period. Within the first day or two, the MMPI is administered with other tests and interviews. Then the students are separated into small groups and assigned to four supervisors in rotation. These supervisors record impromptu impressions of each student every few days, in addition to using a rating scale. Also, four additional staff members, by whom each student is observed in special assignments, record comments. These various notes are sent to central files.

Procedure

Copious notes and MMPI answer sheets were available for study on ninety-seven former students. The MMPI scores were computed, using K (and omitting Mf). There turned out to be ninety-two personality characteristics mentioned by at least two supervisors in describing students. One half represented assets, while the other half represented liabilities approximately opposite to the assets. Tetrachoric correlation coefficients (r_t) were computed between scores on MMPI scales and frequencies of characteristics or traits as mentioned by supervisors. For one scale at a time, the distribution of subjects in terms of scores was divided dichotomously at the 75th percentile. Whenever a dividing point could not be made close to this percentile because of a few subjects having the same score in that region, these few cases were separated according to the relationship of the subject's score on that scale to her own mean score for all the scales. (For instance, if three subjects had identical scores cutting the distribution to one side or the other of the 75th percentile on a scale under consideration, and one of the cases was needed in the high-scoring group to round it out closer to a quarter of the distribution, the subject with the lowest general profile level would be included since her score on that scale would be relatively higher than those of the other two subjects in terms of their over-all profiles.) In computing an r, the top 25 per cent, or high score, was compared with the remainder of the distribution for proportions in which a trait occurred. The same procedure was used for the low score, this time using the 25th percentile as the dividing point. Divisions were made near the ends of distributions rather than at the centers, because of interest in what the more extreme scores might represent, analogous to an interest in superior ranges of intelligence or in mental deficiency.

Comparisons were made for high and low scores on all eight of the clinical scales, with each of the ninety-two traits. High and low L, K, and mean score were also included. There were too few ? scores above zero, and the spread in F scores was too narrow to include these in the comparisons. For each scale and in both directions, the traits were listed which correlated with it at or above the .05 level of confidence. Coefficients which failed to reach this level were dropped from further consideration. In addition to traits, the MMPI scales were compared with elements evaluated by the supervisors on the formal rating scale.

These procedures were repeated on a new group of forty student nurses. Only correlations between MMPI scale scores and personality characteristics which reached the .05 level or better both times were considered as sufficiently significant for reporting here. The new group contained too few low K scores for use in computations.

Results

For the ninety-two traits considered in this study, there was a possibility of 1932 coefficients of relationship, of which 115 turned out to have r_t's at the .05 level of significance or higher, for both the original group of ninety-seven students and the new group of forty students. Below are listed deviations in the positive and negative directions for the various MMPI scales and the related traits. The traits are listed in descending order according to the size of r_t. The chi square test (χ^2) was applied, and those items which reached the .05 level or better for both the original and new samples are italicized. An asterisk (*) denotes that the relationship is supported by a significant one, at the .05 level, in the opposite direction for the group scoring opposite on the same scale. All remaining items in the list are similarly supported but not significantly so. When a trait in the list is followed by "— minus," a negative r is denoted. However, when significantly positive and negative relationships obtained for traits with the two extremes of scales respectively, only the positive ones are listed, the negative ones being implied by the asterisks.

High L: *Afraid of mental patients*, *Has difficulty expressing self orally, Persevering*, Passive, *Feels insecure about self

Low L: *Poised and at ease around others*, Not industrious, *Friendly*

High K: Reserved, *Mature*, Afraid of mental patients, Has difficulty expressing self orally, Friendly

Low K: (Too few cases in the new group for statistical treatment)

High Hs: *Adjusts slowly, *Alertness—minus, Ease of oral expression—minus*

Low Hs: (None other than opposite of first item for High Hs)

High D: *Shy, *Nonaggressive

Low D: *Initiative, *Poised and at ease around others, Participates actively in group discussions*, *Adjusts rapidly, *Good socializer, *Emotionally stable, Efficient*, *Ease of oral expression, Desires responsibilities

High Hy: *Immature, *Friendly, Enthusiastic*, Careless in personal appearance, *Cooperative, Cheerful

Low Hy: Industrious—minus, Self-confident

High Pd: *Participates actively in group discussions, *Initiative, *Aggressive, Desires responsibilities*, Not industrious, Adjusts rapidly, Self-confident, Shy—minus, *Unafraid of mental patients, Works persistently with assigned patients—minus, Enthusiastic

Low Pd: *Suggestions accepted willingly, *Persevering*, Stimulating personality—minus

High Pa: *Lacks self-confidence, *Dependent and submissive*, Outgoing—minus

Low Pa: *Adjusts rapidly*, Dependable—minus, *Poised and at ease around others

High Pt: *Participates little in group discussions*, Poor socializer, *Shy*, Ingenious—minus, Neat in personal appearance

Low Pt: (None other than opposite of first item for High Pt)

High Sc: *Participates actively in group discussions*, Ingenious, Initiative, Poor judgment, Not enthusiastic

Low Sc: Friendly, Alert

High Ma: *Ease of oral expression, *Initiative, *Ingenious, Self-confident, Efficient*, Conscientious—minus, *Reserved—minus*, Responsible, Effective with mental patients, Shy—minus, Immature, Poised and at ease around others, Leadership qualities

Low Ma: *Participates little in group discussions*, Adjusts slowly, Persevering

High ave: *Initiative, Ease of oral expression—minus

Low ave: Reserved

In view of the above results, the possibility of predicting final grades achieved in the course from MMPI scores was investigated. High and low deviation on each scale, high and low mean score, wide and narrow spread between scale scores were tried, but significant relationships were not found. The lack of significant relationships might be due to the students having already been screened for motivation and aptitudes connected with nursing and therefore not representing an unselected sample. It is also possible that some of these persons may have adequate counterbalancing assets that enable them to function effectively in spite of certain personality weaknesses, and such assets may or may not be reflected in the MMPI profiles. The lack of success for prediction of grades from profiles was about the same as Weisgerber's [614]. Also, in agreement with his study, there was little success in discovering the students who needed special counseling. A special scale for predicting grades was constructed, based on item analyses of A versus D students. But when the scale was applied to the new group of 40 students, prediction turned out to be little better than chance.

Discussion

The primary objective of the study was to ascertain what kinds of personality characteristics might be related to high and low scores on the various scales of the MMPI, for a group of normal individuals. The more significant relationships are listed above. Spontaneous notes made by the supervisor-observers were more discriminating than formal ratings made on a rating scale, the spontaneous characterizations correlating more significantly with MMPI scores. In fact, no significant r's emerged for relationships between the scales and the formal ratings. This may be due to the formal ratings' containing more comprehensive judgments, or possibly because they were not on-the-spot observations, or perhaps because they were used for purposes of motivation. Our findings here correspond also with Weisgerber's [614].

In most instances, as might be expected, a trait correlating with a scale did so in opposite directions for high and low scores for that scale. The list contains these instances. However, in some other instances, traits showed up as associated (according to r_t technique) with deviation scores in one direction only for a given scale. These are not in the list. For instance, high Pa correlated significantly with "persevering" but there was also a small positive correlation of this trait with low Pa. "Friendly" and "ingenious" were associated with low Hs, yet high Hs was not at all associated with a lack of these traits. High D was negatively correlated with "friendly" which means that supervisors noted relatively few of the individuals with elevated scores on this scale as being especially friendly, yet at the same time the high D groups did not contain any more than chance expectancy of subjects noted as being on the unfriendly side.

According to the r_t coefficients obtained, a scale elevation might either mean strength or else manifest weakness of the same characteristic. High Sc correlated positively with "participates actively in group discussions" and also with "participates *little* in group discussions." When high Sc was accompanied by high Pd and Ma, the individuals concerned tended to participate actively whereas if neither Pd nor Ma were high, they were prone not to participate. These relationships held for 13 profiles dominated by the three scales, versus nine profiles with both Pd and Ma being several points below Sc. The tally was 11 to 1, and 2 to 3, for "actively" to "little," for the two groups respectively. Again, when high Sc profiles for 18 individuals who participated actively were compared with 10 who did not, the medians for the latter group were nine points below the former on Pd and four points below it on Ma. Individuals with elevated Sc scores may be considered as having schizoid trends, and they may be inclined either to withdraw from group participation, or else be dominant in the group. One student who obtained a high Sc score accompanied by elevated Pd and Ma scores was characterized as "participating actively," and otherwise was noted to be very aggressively outspoken in class and to change the topic.

The list of characterizations not only reveals differences within one group of individuals but has also shown itself to have predictive value when applied to a new and similar group. So far, the list for predictions has not been used in individual cases, but such a study has been initiated. For groups at least, MMPI profiles can be used to predict personality characteristics which are not necessarily features of emotional illness. However, a word of caution may be in order should one try to predict those characteristics found in our study for other kinds of groups. For instance, although our coefficients reached significance in both our samples, they might apply only to student nurses who have achieved advanced training status in the Pacific Northwest, and who are observed by the particular supervisors who have been participating in our study.

The list reveals that some of the traits are correlated with more than one scale deviation. In such instances, the occurrence of two or more of the involved deviations in a sample should increase the proportion of the trait appearing in that sample. There were too few cases of the various kinds of profiles for comprehensive statistical analysis, but one sample tends to bear it out. There were 26 profiles with the two highest scores being on Pd and Ma, which was the largest number of profiles dominated by any two particular scales. These two scales are correlated with "participates actively in group discussions." The group of individuals producing those 26 profiles contained almost half again as high a proportion of persons with this characteristic as did two groups dominated by Pd and Ma separately. On the other hand, if a trait is correlated positively with one scale deviation and negatively with another, concurrence of the two deviations should tend to cancel so far as that trait is concerned. "Participates little in group discussions" happens to correlate with high Pt. There were 16 profiles dominated by elevations on this scale together with Pd or Ma but not both. The group producing these profiles contained no more of the trait within it than chance expectancy.

Deviations on every one of the individual scales were more loaded with significant relationships than in mean score or general level of profile. Only three traits correlated with high and low mean score, whereas the various scales excepting Hs carried from 5 to 16 trait relationships. Also, none of the items related to high and low mean score is supported by χ^2 while every one of the scales carries one or more such items. This may have something to do with the inability to select effectively by means of the total score students in need of counseling, or to predict grades better than chance. In this study, shape of profile was more fruitful than its general elevation.

Asset traits as well as liabilities may be associated with elevations on MMPI scales, and negatively valued traits may be associated with subaverage scores on the scales. From one to seven positive traits were associated with elevated scores on seven of the ten scales. One positive trait was even associated with a high over-all mean score. Conversely, from one to five negative traits were associated with low scores on all scales but Hs, Pt, and Sc, and also a negative trait was related to low mean score. When only those items supported by chi square are considered, the elevated scores are related to twelve "desirable" and eight "undesirable" traits. By the same criterion, the low scale scores are related to thirteen positive traits and six negative ones. Elevated scores in clinical practice tend to signify various kinds of maladjustment or potentials for it, and in view of this, it may be inferred from our results that there are some personality assets associated more with maladjustment potentials as measured by the MMPI than with relative freedom from such potentials.

Summary

A group of ninety-seven student nurses in practicum training had been given the MMPI, and during the training period the supervisors made notes relating to personality characteristics for each student. Tetrachoric r and also chi square were applied to ascertain any relations between high scores, and also low scores, on the various MMPI scales and observed personality characteristics. The procedure was then applied to a new group of forty student nurses. Traits are listed which correlated most significantly with one or more of the scales for both groups of students.

Impromptu notes made by supervisors showed more significant relationships with MMPI scale scores than did ratings made on the rating scales. Clinical observations to the effect that, for interpretation, deviations on individual scales must be considered along with deviations on other scales are supported by the data. Individual scores on most scales showed up as more meaningful than general elevation of profile. Some traits of positive value as well as ones of negative value were found to be associated with elevations of various scales, and some negative traits were related to low scale scores. In other words, potential for emotional maladjustment may carry along with it or enhance some positive personality characteristics.

ARTICLE 35 *The F Minus K Dissimulation Index for the MMPI*

A RECURRING problem in the use of any personality test is the question of dissembling. The MMPI is one of the tests which makes explicit recognition of this problem by the inclusion of an internal set of validity indicators. Three of these, the ?, L, and F scores, have been well described in the test *Manual* [303], and other articles [for example, 234 (see VI, 38) and 235]. A fourth scale, K [441 (I, 2)], may also be employed in the attempt to assess the dependability and trustworthiness of any obtained results.

All four of these indicators, considered singly, will identify unreliable or malingered profiles with reasonable accuracy, but their maximum efficiency, apparently, is realized in combination. One of these combinations, F minus K, which was proposed by the writer in an earlier paper [235], appears to be the most promising index to date, and the present discussion will be concerned with further applications of the F—K index, and with normative data.

It should be emphasized at the outset, however, that at least three of these scales (L, F, and K) have important personological attributes and implications in addition to their function as validity indicators; that is, scores on these scales have relevance for the personality structure of the test-taker as well as for the reliability and meaningfulness of his test protocol, per se. It is easy to make the mistake of overlooking the import of these scales in attempting to carry out a complete profile analysis. Accordingly, although the present paper will deal primarily with the validational aspects of these scales, the discussion should not be interpreted as a denial or underemphasis of their other potentialities.

Previous Studies

In the earlier paper on MMPI simulation [235] the efforts of a group of eleven clinical workers to feign two psychiatric syndromes were analyzed. The first syndrome was defined as "an acute, severe, anxiety neurosis which would lead to separation from the service, but not to commitment to a mental hospital," and the second as "a nondeteriorated, acute, paranoid schizophrenic psychosis." Skilled judges were able to identify eight of the eleven simulated psychoneurotic patterns when intermixed with sixty-eight authentic psychoneurotic records, and were able

321

to identify all the psychotic simulations when they were intercalated with twenty-four authentic profiles. At the same time, a simple combination of the F raw score minus the K raw score was able to pick out ten of the eleven simulated records in each of the two situations. The F—K cutting scores proposed at that time were plus 4 and over for neurotic profiles, and plus 16 and over for psychotic profiles. Either F, or K, utilized singly, was fairly successful in separating the feigned from the authentic profiles, but neither was as effective as the combination.

Several other studies have since employed this F—K index. Hunt [339] found that a cutting score of plus 11 and over would properly identify a substantial proportion of records given by subjects attempting to simulate psychiatric disorder, and would mistakenly identify about 12 per cent of the records of psychiatric patients in a veterans hospital. Hunt also extended the use of the F—K index in an attempt to detect records given by subjects trying to present an overly favorable test profile. A cutting score of minus 11 and below was fairly effective in picking up records of United States Navy prisoners who had been asked to conceal any abnormality or maladjustment, but this cutting score also sorted out 93 per cent of the supposedly honestly produced profiles of a group of 109 ASTP students. Hunt concluded that F—K scores of 11 and over were highly suggestive of "faking bad," but that more research would be needed before indices for the detection of "faking good" would be practically serviceable.

Sweetland [581] also used the F—K index in a study of MMPI test performance under hypnosis. Only a small proportion of the subjects instructed to simulate various psychiatric conditions under hypnosis were found to have F—K elevations above the critical levels previously recommended. The subjects who did score above the critical levels were, in every case, the most deeply hypnotized. Sweetland used evidence of this kind to argue that the hypnotically induced neuroses were close to the "real thing," and were not simulations in the conventional sense. Inspection of his profiles and tables suggests that the hypnotically induced depressions would be detected rather frequently by using a slightly lower F—K cutting score, but that the remaining dissemblings would elude this index. From this we might for the time being infer that hypnotic MMPI simulations are, indeed, undetectable for the most part; the consoling thought is that few of the subjects seen by clinical workers will be presenting themselves in trance states.

Another study of dissembling was carried out by Cofer *et al.* [134]. Three groups of college students were used in this study, one of which took the MMPI honestly and then attempted to present an unfavorable, emotionally disturbed, picture; the second took the test honestly and then tried to give the best possible impression; the third took the test twice under normal conditions. For the "fake bad" group the best discrimination of records reported in the paper was that given by F alone, in which a cutting point of 20 (raw score) and over identified all the dissembled protocols. A cutting point of 62 (T score) on K identified about 70 per cent of the falsified records. For the "fake good" records, a combination of K plus L gave the best results, correctly classifying about 74 per cent of the malingered profiles. An item analysis of these favorably dissimilated records against the same subjects' normal protocols resulted in a scale of thirty-four items which worked very well on the original samples, and which gives promise of being a very interesting addition to the pool of MMPI keys.

Cofer's study made no mention of the F—K index, but a personal communication reveals that an F—K cutting score of 16 and over would correctly classify 26 of the 28 "fake bad" profiles, and would not misidentify any of the 28 honest records. A cutting score of 5 and over would identify *all* the malingered cases, and would still not incorrectly classify any of the honest profiles. An F—K cutting score of minus 11 and below would detect 25 of the 27 "fake good" cases, but would at the same time pick up 19 of the 27 honest records. The general results in regard to F—K are quite similar to those of Hunt's study, in that profiles intended to simulate neurotic conditions are quite simply identified, but profiles attempting to give an overly favorable picture are not so easily detected.

A final bit of evidence on the efficacy of the F—K index is provided by an unpublished study by Charles Bird at the University of Minnesota. Bird had a class in abnormal psychology take the MMPI first under normal conditions, and then again in an attempt to simulate various specific diagnostic syndromes; following the completion of the course they were again requested to simulate these same syndromes. If we disregard the second attempt at simulation, and pool all the first attempts irrespective of specific diagnosis, it appears that a cutting score of plus 4 and over would detect approximately 81 per cent of the records turned in by students in the dissimulation situation, and would not misidentify a single record among the normal protocols obtained. Bird's students were noticeably better during their second simulation, as evidenced by a decrease in mean F—K from 17.19 to 9.86, giving a t ratio of 8.87. Interestingly, however, the correlation between first and second simulations (on F—K) was .44, SE .06, indicating that the better simulators on the first trial were also, for the most part, superior on the second.

Table 1. F—K Means and Standard Deviations

Group	N	M	SD
College students	269	−13.84	5.71
Adult normals	691	− 8.96	6.97
University psychiatric hospital patients, males	250	− 7.92	9.49
University psychiatric hospital patients, females	250	− 8.70	7.41
VA hospital psychiatric patients, males	100	− 7.08	8.12
Army hospital psychiatric patients, males	213	− 2.78	10.17
Experimental dissemblers, total sample	319	18.76	16.08
Army subjects	22	14.09	11.20
Cofer's subjects	28	41.75	13.18
Bird's subjects	269	17.19	14.25

All these studies certainly suggest that the F—K index is a useful indicator of the dependability and meaningfulness of an MMPI protocol. In order to colligate this material and make it more directly comparable, the writer has been able to procure the original data from the studies of Cofer and Bird, in addition to some new material, and in the following section various comparisons and normative facts are presented.

F—K Findings

Table 1 gives the means and standard deviations for the F—K distributions for the several samples included in this compilation. One clear-cut finding from this table alone is that all normal and clinical groups have F—K means of less than zero, whereas all dissembling groups have F—K means above zero. The differences between the dissemblers and all the other samples are all highly significant. For example, the t ratio of the difference between dissemblers and adult normals is 29.54.

One of the questions which arises from an inspection of Table 1 concerns the degree of susceptibility of the F—K index to factors of psychiatric normality or maladjustment as such. If the army sample is excluded, which is probably justifiable in light of the special conditions prevailing during wartime and the fact that many army patients were under great motivational stress to maximize their complaints, and if the college students, who are generally known to give somewhat compulsively favorable self-portraits and descriptions [see 441 (1, 2), or any of the papers describing the development of the MMPI clinical scales] are also excluded, it would appear that the clinical and normal groups are not differentiated on the basis of F—K.

Although this study does not give extended treatment to the problem of "faking good," the F—K statistics on Cofer's positively malingering group were calculated, giving a mean of —17.37, SD 5.39. The t ratio of this "fake good" group versus Bird's college students was 3.07, and of the college students versus the adult normals was 11.14. It thus appears that the college students tended toward the "fake good" end of the continuum, but were not altogether in the positive simulation range. It should also be mentioned that, although the mean of Cofer's positively dissembling group was significantly less than that of any other, there was still an almost complete overlap of cases. All of Cofer's subjects were in the low end of the F—K curve, but they were, nevertheless, blanketed by the distribution of adult normals.

Table 2. Analysis of Variance Table for University Hospital
Males, University Hospital Females, Veterans
Hospital Cases, and Adult Normals [a]

Source	Sum of Squares	df	Variance Estimate
Between	437.4418	3	145.814
Within	76,467.9076	1287	59.416
Total	76,905.3494	1290	

[a] $F = 2.454$; $P > 0.05$.

Table 3. Distribution of F—K Scores for the Adult Normal Sample ($N = 691$)

F—K Values	Frequency	Cumulative Frequency	F—K Values	Frequency	Cumulative Frequency
23–25	2	691	—4- —2	83	599
20–22	0	689	—7- —5	115	516
17–19	2	689	—10- —8	103	401
14–16	2	687	—13- —11	118	298
11–13	3	685	—16- —14	73	180
8–10	6	682	—19- —17	66	107
5–7	8	676	—22- —20	33	41
2–4	26	668	—25- —23	6	8
—1–1	43	642	—28- —26	2	2

Table 2 does, in fact, substantiate this impression since the F test of the significance of the mean differences among the four groups considered is not significant. This is a very helpful finding, for it suggests that F—K is not susceptible to distortion on the basis of psychiatric abnormality as such, certainly a most valuable property in any index which is to be used in screening dissemblers from normals and from actual psychiatric patients.

The sampling distribution of F—K for the original random sample of 691 adult normals is presented in Table 3. Although it is moderately positively skewed, inspection suggests that its departure from normality is not very great. In comparison with the rather pronounced skewness of both the F and K raw score distributions considered separately, this approximate normality of the combined distribution is all the more striking.

Another question which arises concerns the relative frequency of classification of profiles as malingered which would appear in the several samples as different F—K cutting scores are employed. These data are offered in Table 4. With F—K cutting scores of plus 7 and over most of the samples would show only a small proportion of cases called dissembled. The army psychopaths and psychotics would, however, show a sizable percentage of misclassified cases. One possible explanation of this would be that many army patients tended to exaggerate their complaints and exploit their difficulties in an attempt to facilitate medical discharge or to secure medical dispensation for a military offense. The proportion of dissembled cases actually detected drops gradually as the cutting score rises, but even at plus 16 and over, 58 per cent are identified.

The final step in the analysis was to consolidate all the authentic profiles, clinical and normal, into a total sample of 1773 cases, and to compare this sample with the dissemblers (319 cases) for the purpose of determining optimum cutting scores. For this analysis the proportion of hits and misses for each sample was calculated, and the fourfold point correlation (phi) was taken as an indication of the degree of success in classifying records which would be achieved by any particular cutting score. Table 5 contains this material.

From Table 5 it can be seen that the problem of setting an F—K cutting score is one of minimizing false positives and false negatives. The highest phi coefficient is given by a cutting score of plus 9. This score would correctly classify 97 per cent of the authentic records and 75 per cent of the simulated records. If a clinical worker would prefer to use a cutting score such that, say, he would call authentic records malingered no more than 5 per cent of the time, but would still maximize the number of simulated profiles he would call simulated, the best cutting score would be plus 7. An inspection of Table 5 will suggest other uses and other cutting scores for special situations.

Summary

Malingering and test dissimulation present problems in the clinical use of personality tests of all kinds. The validating scales of the MMPI were developed to assist in coping with such problems. Previous studies devoted explicitly to the problem of MMPI profile validity have shown that all the validating scales, but especially a combination of the F raw score minus the K raw score, have practical utility.

Table 4. Proportion of Cases in Each Sample Who Would Be Called Dissemblers with Various F − K Cutting Scores [a]

F−K Scores	Army Psychopaths (N = 29)	Army Neurotics (N = 153)	Army Psychotics (N = 21)	University Hospital Males (N = 250)	University Hospital Females (N = 250)	VA Hospital Males (N = 100)	Adult Normals (N = 691)	University Students (N = 269)	Experimental Dissemblers (N = 319)
0	59	27	61	20	14	21	11	2	88
1	52	23	55	17	11	17	8	1	88
2	48	19	55	16	10	14	7	1	86
3	48	17	52	13	8	12	5	1	85
4	48	13	52	12	7	11	4	b	84
5	48	11	48	10	5	11	3	b	83
6	45	10	39	8	4	8	2	b	81
7	38	8	39	7	3	8	2	b	79
8	28	8	32	7	2	6	2	b	76
9	28	6	29	5	2	3	1	0	75
10	28	5	26	4	1	3	1		72
11	24	5	23	4	1	1	b		70
12	24	5	16	3	b	0	b		68
13	24	4	16	3	b		b		64
14	14	3	16	2	b		b		63
15	10	3	16	2	b		b		61
16	10	2	16	2	b		b		58

[a] A cutting score of "2," for example, would mean that all subjects with F − K scores of 2 or more would be classified as dissemblers.
[b] Proportion is less than one, but not zero.

Table 5. Screening Efficiency of the F—K Index

F—K Scores	Authentic Profiles (N = 1,773)		Simulated Profiles (N = 319)		Phi Coefficients
	Proportion Called Authentic	Proportion Called Simulated	Proportion Called Authentic	Proportion Called Simulated	
0 and over	85.3	14.7	11.6	88.4	.597
1 " "	88.0	12.0	11.6	88.4	.637
2 " "	89.3	10.7	13.8	86.2	.644
3 " "	90.9	9.1	15.0	85.0	.674
4 " "	92.4	7.6	16.3	83.7	.694
5 " "	93.5	6.5	16.9	83.1	.713
6 " "	94.5	5.5	18.8	81.2	.724
7 " "	95.2	4.8	21.3	78.7	.723
8 " "	96.0	4.0	23.5	76.5	.728
9 " "	97.0	3.0	25.4	74.6	.742
10 " "	97.4	2.6	28.2	71.8	.736
11 " "	97.7	2.3	29.8	70.2	.736
12 " "	98.1	1.9	32.3	67.7	.729
13 " "	98.3	1.7	35.7	64.3	.710
14 " "	98.6	1.4	36.7	63.3	.718
15 " "	98.8	1.2	39.2	60.8	.706
16 " "	98.9	1.1	41.7	58.3	.690

The F—K index has been demonstrated to detect "fake bad" profiles quite readily, but has been less efficient in detecting cases of positive dissimulation.

A consideration of a large number of normal and clinical cases suggests that the sampling distribution of F—K is reasonably normal, and that this index is not distorted by psychiatric abnormality as such. Both of these properties strongly recommend it as a screening device for profile validity.

A table of phi coefficients for various cutting scores of F—K was provided which can be used by MMPI workers according to their own needs. The cutting score for the "faking bad" profiles which maximized the fourfold point correlation was plus nine.

H. G. GOUGH AND W. H. PEMBERTON

ARTICLE 36 *Personality Characteristics Related to*
Success in Practice Teaching

THE importance of personality characteristics for tasks involving personal interaction, leadership, and social understanding is incontestable. The difficulty in utilizing a principle such as this lies more in devising techniques and methods for its
adequate application than in proving the truth of the basic assumption. Advances
in the methodology of personality assessment and evaluation have yielded various
instruments which show promise of overcoming this technological barrier. This
study is concerned with the application of one of these devices, the MMPI [303],
to the problem of predicting success in student practice teaching.

This investigation is a revision and extension of an earlier one carried out by
Pemberton [682] as a doctoral dissertation in the School of Education at the University of California, Berkeley. In that project a sample of ninety-six males enrolled in a course in secondary school practice teaching was studied by means of
the MMPI and the group Rorschach. Neither scores on MMPI scales nor conventional scoring categories on the Rorschach yielded much in the way of significant
relationships to practice teaching ratings.

Students in practice teaching were rated twice during the semester on each
of four variables: (1) personal relations with students and teachers; (2) command
and use of subject matter; (3) teaching skill; (4) class management. The ratings
were expressed in qualitative terms: outstanding, excellent, good, fair, and poor.
In Pemberton's study only ratings on variables (1) and (4) were used, in an effort
to maximize the salience of personality characteristics. In the present investigation
the qualitative ratings were transformed into a scale of 5, 4, 3, 2, and 1, and the
entries were then summed over the eight (4×2) ratings. The total scores thus
derived served as criteria for the study.

At the same time, a clinical-intuitive sorting of the MMPI profiles (by H. G. G.)
did reveal a positive correlation with the ratings. The results of this sorting are presented in Table 1.

The favorable outcome for this procedure suggested that the MMPI profiles did,
in fact, depict significant facets of personality, but that the relationships were obscured by a conventional scale-by-scale analysis. This inference is in line with an
abundance of previous work with the MMPI which has underscored the necessity

328

Table 1. Evaluation of Clinical Sorting of MMPI Profiles
of Male Student Practice Teachers [a]

| | Practice Teaching Ratings | | | |
Sortings	Higher Ratings	Average Ratings	Lower Ratings	Total
Higher	9	14	3	26
Average	13	20	11	44
Lower	4	10	12	26
Total	26	44	26	96

[a] $\chi^2 = 8.51$; df $= 4$; and $p > .05$, $< .10$.

of considering patterns and configurations of scores in interpreting test profiles. The results of the present paper, it might be emphasized, lend further support to this admonition.

In the earlier study the test results of the female students were not considered. They were later scored, and the profiles given to another clinical psychologist for ratings on "potential success in practice teaching." The correlation of the clinical ratings with the criterion ratings for the 58 profiles involved was $+ .24$, SE .13. This prediction was achieved despite the fact that no single scale on the MMPI showed a significant relationship to the criterion ratings.

The decision was made, accordingly, to attempt to submit the intuitive cues used in test interpretation to analytical and quantitative investigation to determine whether any objective signs or indices on the MMPI could be isolated which would possess useful predictive power for the criterion of success in practice teaching.

The first step was to categorize both the male and female samples into those with higher, average, and lower ratings, and then to calculate mean scores for each of the MMPI scales available. Some of the original cases had not taken the complete form of the MMPI, and as we desired to use a number of nonpathological scales these records were eliminated. The total sample included 89 males and 58 females.

The additional scales used were Re (social responsibility), Do (dominance), St (status), Sp (social participativeness), Pr (prejudice), Ac (academic achievement, high school), Ds (dissimulation), Psy (psychological aptitude), Ie (intellectual efficiency), and Si (social introversion). These scales have been described in a series of publications too long to be enumerated here. As examples the reader is referred to those by Gough and Gough, McClosky, and Meehl [236 (see IV, 21) and 258 (IV, 24)].

For the female sample, none of the twenty-two MMPI scales considered yielded a significant F ratio when evaluated in this fashion. For the male sample, three of the scales show some promise in this analysis. The more successful male practice teachers tend to score lower on Hy (hysteria), lower on Pd (psychopathic deviate), and higher on Psy (psychological aptitude). Besides the scales listed in the two tables, two of the indices recently proposed by Welsh [620 (see V, 32)] were evaluated. Neither the anxiety index (AI) nor the internalization ratio (IR) revealed a significant relationship.

The results with individual scales confirmed the findings of the earlier analysis and indicated that any relevant factors on the MMPI would have to be identified by a more configural and intuitive approach. The steps involved in translating this deduction into a research design were first, a great deal of free association and ratiocination about the signs and clues involved in the intuitive sortings; and second, an attempt to write simple indices and functions summarizing them. Altogether some fifteen "signs" were devised and tested against the threefold criterion breakdown. Eight of these signs revealed some discriminatory potential. These signs are listed in Table 2.

Table 2. MMPI "Signs" Predictive of Success in Practice Teaching [a]

Sign	χ^2	df	p
1. Pa $\geq$ 50, $\leq$ 56	7.33	2	>.02, <.05
2. Ma $\geq$ 48, $\leq$ 60	6.74	2	>.02, <.05
3. Pa + L $\leq$ 56	3.27	1	>.05, <.10
4. Ma $\geq$ 48, $\leq$ 60, *and* Pd $\geq$ 46, $\leq$ 58	2.88	1	>.05, <.10
5. Hy $\geq$ Pd + 1[b]	1.69	1	>.10, <.20
6. K + Ie + 3 Do $\geq$ Pt + Sc + Pa + 15[b]	1.22	1	>.20, <.30
7. St + Re + Ie $\geq$ 102 [b]	2.84	1	>.05, <.10
8. Ma + K + D $\geq$ Pd + Hs + Pt	1.75	1	>.10, <.20

[a] All scales are expressed in T scores, except L, Ie (intellectual efficiency), St (status), Do (dominance), and Re (responsibility).
[b] These constants were selected so as to divide the sample of 147 as evenly as possible into those with sign present and those with sign absent.

Table 3. Predictive Efficiency of Eight MMPI Signs in the Original Sample [a]

Number of Signs	Practice Teaching Ratings			Total
	Higher Ratings	Average Ratings	Lower Ratings	
6–8	12	16	1	29
3–5	19	46	22	87
0–2	5	13	13	31
Total ..	36	75	36	147

[a] $\chi^2 = 14.29$; df = 4; and p < .01.

Table 4. Cross-Validational Predictive Efficiency of Five MMPI Signs [a]

Number of Signs	Practice Teaching Ratings		Total
	Higher Ratings	Lower Ratings	
4–5........	27	15	42
2–3........	39	54	93
0–1........	14	11	25
Total.....	80	80	160

[a] $\chi^2 = 6.21$; df = 2; and p > .02; < .05.

After these eight signs had been established each of the original records was scored for the presence or absence of each sign, with a total "sign-score" also being obtained. With eight signs, this score could range from zero to eight. As would be expected, these sign-scores were significantly related to success in practice teaching. The results are given in Table 3.

A separate analysis was made for each sex. For females the χ^2 was 7.3, df 4, p > .10, < .20. For males the χ^2 was 9.3, df 4, and p > .05, < .10. For the combined sample only 6 of the 147 cases are misclassified by two steps, and 71 cases are exactly classified on the diagonal. The over-all predictive efficiency would thus appear to be good for this sample.

A cross-validation of these signs was also attempted. MMPI profiles of students enrolled in courses in primary grades practice teaching were obtained. Eighty cases (forty of each sex) with quite high ratings were selected, and a second sample of eighty (forty of each sex) with rather low ratings was also chosen. These students had not taken the full form of the MMPI, so we were unable to compute the three signs involving K, Ie, Do, St, and Re. The results of this analysis are presented in Table 4.

The chi square here is significant between the .02 and .05 levels. From Table 4 it appears that the signs are more effective in identifying better practice teachers than in specifying poorer ones. In fact, there is actually a slight tendency for the sign-score to work backwards at the lower end. We would not anticipate this result if all eight signs were used, but at the moment there is no evidence for this disclaimer.

Judging from the cross-validational evidence, the method of profile interpretation advocated here does possess validity for predicting success in practice teaching. Its practical efficiency may not be high, but the empirical confirmation of the methodology indicates that a systematic and diligent search for signs and patterns might well yield predictors of practical utility. Certainly the results highlight the error involved in concluding that the MMPI does not "work" because single-scale analysis fails.

The predictive efficiency observed in this study is also, of course, attenuated by the unreliability of the criterion. It has not been possible to evaluate the ratings systematically, but the impression is gained that ratings vary considerably in accuracy and value. A further study such as the present one would want to ensure the obtaining of a valid and reliable set of criterion measures if a goal of practical forecasting efficiency is to be met. There is also the possibility that better results could be achieved by differentiating the criterion — performance in practice teaching — into its constituent phases, instead of treating it in an over-all way.

To summarize an attempt was made to predict success in practice teaching from personality test measures. Single scales on the MMPI showed little validity but various patterns and indices revealed considerable promise. Certain methodological implications of this study for projects devoted to goals of practical assessment and evaluation were discussed.

K. B. LITTLE AND E. S. SHNEIDMAN

◆ ─────────────────────────────────────

ARTICLE 37 *The Validity of MMPI Interpretations*

IN CLINICAL psychology, diagnostic tests are the most common source of personality descriptions. The descriptions range from short paragraphs, emphasizing a single salient characteristic of the subject, to elaborate many-paged analyses of several aspects of his psychological functioning. Very rarely are the conclusions drawn by the clinician restricted simply to a diagnosis. The protocol, whether in the form of the set of scores or a profile from a personality inventory or the verbatim responses to projective materials, leads the interpreter to make a large number of inferences, only one of which is a diagnosis qua diagnosis. These inferences seldom have a direct overt relationship to objective characteristics of the protocol; they are a function of the interpreter's experience, skill, personality, etc., as well as of the test itself.

This situation is taken somewhat for granted with projective tests but is frequently ignored in considering the more objective personality measures such as the MMPI. The pristine beauty of the quantitative scores on this inventory has generally led investigators into testing a single inference, i.e., diagnosis, when judging the test's validity. Yet in practice the MMPI is used quite differently. The clinician inspects the profile, occasionally scores additional scales, perhaps examines the actual responses to individual items, and somehow during the process arrives at a number of conclusions which he embodies in a formal or informal psychological report. The validity, in clinical practice, of the instrument would therefore seem best reflected by some measure of the number of correct inferences arrived at by the clinician. The present paper is the report of a study of the validity, as just defined, of the MMPI.

It is obvious that an index of validity as described above will vary with the clinician who does the interpreting and that no unique figure will be obtained. The authors have suggested in a previous paper [r100] that the central tendency of such indices among competent clinicians interpreting a variety of subject protocols might be considered the validity of the instrument itself. In this study, the results for a number of interpreters working with a single protocol are presented. They indicate only what *can* be achieved and not necessarily what might occur with other protocols. In addition, the results were examined to determine the types of inferences made on the basis of the MMPI and the relationship between the resultant types and their accuracy.

332

Procedure

The general procedure has been described in more detail elsewhere [r100] and is presented here in synoptic form.

Eleven psychologists, competent in the use and interpretation of the MMPI and accustomed to writing psychological reports from it, were presented with the MMPI profile of a subject identified to them as male, age 25, and single. The test materials and case history data of the subject are presented in *Thematic Test Analysis* [r148]. On the basis of the information conveyed to them by this profile, each made a Q sort [r154] of 150 items of personality description. The continuum was from "Most True" to "Most False" for the subject. The items were a stratified sample from a total item population of 1604 items abstracted from 17 psychological reports written about the subject on the basis of his TAT and MAPS test protocols. The 1600 items covered, so far as could be determined, the usual aspects of psychological functioning presented in psychological reports.

The intercorrelations of the distribution of items for the eleven MMPI judges are presented in Table 1.

Table 1. Correlations among the Q Sorts of Eleven MMPI Interpreters [a]

Inter-preter	2	3	4	5	6	7	8	9	10	11
1	63	62	50	65	73	56	68	64	56	67
2		68	56	62	66	51	68	72	61	55
3			62	56	50	55	64	68	51	49
4				48	45	52	60	66	47	49
5					68	42	72	51	67	62
6						54	63	61	61	67
7							50	64	43	48
8								60	66	56
9									52	55
10										58

[a] Decimal points are omitted.

The criterion consisted of the consensus of 29 experienced clinical psychologists and psychiatrists who Q-sorted the same 150 items, except that their sorting was made on the basis of a complete clinical folder about the subject. The folder contained medical examination reports, laboratory data, course of treatment notes, psychotherapy notes, social history, consultation reports, etc., but excluded the psychological test reports.

A factor analysis of the intercorrelations of the 29 criterion judges [r100] indicated that a single general factor would account for 90 per cent of the communality among them. Accordingly, a new Q sort was constructed for the criterion itself, as follows:

1. A multiple regression equation for estimating the criterion general factor was derived using the criterion judges' general factor loadings as correlations. It was found that with only three variables (judges) a correlation of .925 with the general factor was secured.

2. The Beta coefficients for these three criterion judges were used to weight

each of their Q-sort scores for the 150 items. The three weighted scores for each item were summed to form a new composite score for that item.

3. The 150 items were then ordered into the criterion Q sort on the basis of their rank position in the distribution of composite scores.

To determine the validity coefficients, the eleven MMPI judges were correlated with this composite criterion Q sort.

Results

A cluster analysis [r162] of the matrix of intercorrelations of the MMPI interpreters (Table 1) yielded three groups of judges. Table 2 gives the estimated correlations of each judge with each of the three cluster domains and also their communalities. (The correlation of a judge with the domain of which he is a member is analogous to a factor loading in a factor analysis.) Table 3 gives the correlations among the cluster domains themselves.

Table 2. Estimated Correlations of Each MMPI Interpreter with the Cluster Domains and the Validity Coefficient for Each Interpreter [a]

Cluster and Judge	Cluster Domain			h^2	Validity
	A	B	C		
A					
1	*.84*	.77	.73	.71	.72
6	*.84*	.77	.64	.71	.74
11	*.81*	.71	.63	.66	.70
B					
5	.78	*.84*	.64	.71	.71
8	.75	*.83*	.76	.69	.73
10	.70	*.81*	.62	.66	.58
C					
3	.65	.69	*.80*	.64	.70
4	.58	.62	*.79*	.62	.56
9	.72	.66	*.83*	.69	.66
2	.74	.77	*.81*	.66	.70
7	.63	.54	*.71*	.50	.52

[a] Italicized figures are the correlations of the judges with the domain of which they are a member.

To test the hypothesis that the three clusters were sufficient to account for all the common variance among the judges, a table of theoretical correlations was computed on the basis of each judge's correlation with the cluster of which he was a member and the correlations among the domains (Tables 2 and 3). A comparison with the 55 empirical correlations of Table 1 indicated that 44 (76 per cent) of the theoretical correlations were within one standard deviation of the corresponding empirical ones, 54 (98 per cent) were within two standard deviations, and only one theoretical correlation deviated from its empirical counterpart by more than two standard deviations. The mean absolute discrepancy between the two sets of correlations was .024. It appears, therefore, that the three clusters do adequately account for the common variance in the matrix.

To identify the groups of judges, an average Q sort was made for each of the

Table 3. Estimated Correlations among the
Cluster Domains

Cluster Domain	A	B	C
A.............	1.00	.90	.80
B.............	.90	1.00	.81
C.............	.80	.81	1.00

clusters. The 20 Most True items in each average Q sort were examined, and those items that appeared for one and only one cluster were isolated. The same process was also repeated for the 20 Most False items of the three clusters.

The Most True items for cluster A were:

He is in the early stages of paranoid schizophrenia.
He has strong latent homosexual feelings.
The psychological threat to him is really of a homosexual nature.
He has an enormous amount of hostility.
He would be threatened by interpretations given early in psychotherapy.
His principal conflict is in the sexual area.
He has at least bright normal intelligence.

The Most False items for cluster A were:

He does not have much anxiety.
He should be able to progress satisfactorily in psychotherapy without excessive support.
Masturbation creates no psychological problems for him.
He seems little concerned with his bodily well-being.
His ideation is not paranoid.

The Most True items for cluster B were:

He appears to be a solitary person.
An acute break with reality has probably occurred.
The total picture is consistent with a schizophrenic disorder with potential para-noid and hebephrenic coloring.
He avoids social disapproval by engaging in solitary activity.
He has never learned to solve his problems by other than avoidant means.
He has never adequately learned social skills.

The Most False items for cluster B were:

He appears to be an outgoing person.
For him, withdrawal is a relatively unimportant mode of reacting to frustration.
He has little guilt feelings concerning his aggressive impulses.
He has the well-preserved mind of a person who is not psychotic.
He is probably not disoriented.

The Most True items for cluster C were:

He perceives the world as consistently unloving.
He has marked guilt feelings.
His guilt feelings may overwhelm him.

He feels deprived of the oral gratifications of childhood.
He suffers from feelings of rejection.
In fantasy he longs for kind parents.

The Most False items for cluster C were:

He feels generally that he is master of his own fate.
He has little orality.
His superego is relatively mature.

This technique of identification emphasizes differences among the clusters; the actual high degree of agreement is apparent from the correlations among the cluster domains (see Table 3). However, inspection of the cluster-identifying items suggests that the judges of cluster A had a slight preference for emphasizing the nature of the conflicts (over sexual impulses) of the subject; the judges of cluster B had a preference for emphasizing the primary defenses (withdrawal) of the subject; and the judges of cluster C had a preference for emphasizing the affective reactions (feelings of rejection) of the subject. All are describing a person who is essentially schizophrenic.

The right-hand column of Table 2 gives the validity figure for each judge in the form of a correlation with the composite Q sort described previously. The mean value of this validity figure for cluster A was .72, for cluster B, .67, and for cluster C, .63, with an over-all value for the eleven judges of .67. An analysis of variance indicated that the differences among the three clusters were not significant.

Discussion

The data presented above indicated that substantial agreement may occur between descriptions of an individual based upon his MMPI profile and those based upon an elaborate clinical history. The degree of agreement can be emphasized by pointing out that the average general factor loading (or correlation with the criterion) of the criterion judges themselves was only .74 [r100] as compared with the average of .67 for the test judges with the composite criterion Q sort. Moreover, the former figure is a correlation with a criterion of unit reliability whereas the latter is with an estimate of that criterion only. Correction of the average validity figure of the MMPI judges for the unreliability of the "true" criterion estimate would further decrease the difference between the two figures cited.

Certain cautions need to be kept in mind in evaluating these data, however. The results indicate only what *can* be done by competent clinicians with a specific protocol and not what might occur with different interpreters or with the same interpreters and different protocols. The subject used in this study presented an ambiguous clinical picture at the time of testing but his MMPI profile appears to be anything but equivocal (see Table 4). A strong possibility exists, therefore, that the comparison of the MMPI Q sorts with the criterion Q sorts tested the agreement of two sets of statements about a certain nosological classification rather than inferences about a specific person. One critic was so unkind as to suggest that the data merely demonstrate the existence of a common delusional system among test and criterion judges. However, insofar as the statements made have a descriptive utility, agreement between test interpretations and those made on the basis of exhaustive

Table 4. MMPI Scores of the Subject

Item	?	L	F	K	Hs	D	Hy	Pd	Mf	Pa	Pt	Sc	Ma
Raw score	68	2	13	10	22	36	35	27	36	21	43	49	25
T score	60	43	73	46	90	95	85	79	80	88	111	120	75

MMPI Code: 8721°635″49 F′?−/KL

clinical material seems a desirable form of validity no matter how the statements are derived.

Three clusters of judges could be found among the eleven judges used in this study, but the differences among them do not seem to be related to their over-all validity. This would follow logically from the discussion set forth above. The variations in description represent different emphases upon certain aspects of the same disorder rather than disagreement as to diagnosis. Thus the average validity of the three clusters is about the same.

A final conclusion from the study is that the Q technique has considerable value in the study of the reliability and validity of clinical techniques. It permits the quantification of results without loss of the idiographic approach, a characteristic ideally suited to clinical research.

Summary

The validity of inferences made from the MMPI was tested using an interpreter population of eleven experts working with the MMPI profile of one subject. The criterion was the consensus, in the form of a general factor, of 29 clinicians who Q-sorted 150 items on the basis of a comprehensive clinical record of the same subject. A cluster analysis of the matrix of intercorrelations among the MMPI interpreters yielded three groups of judges. These groups were described in terms of the Most True and Most False Q-sort items peculiar to each cluster. Validity figures for each MMPI judge were computed as correlations with a weighted composite Q sort of the criterion judges. The general results indicated that MMPI interpreters can achieve a level of consensual validity on the basis of the MMPI profile approximating the average general factor loading of the criterion judges. Certain cautions in interpreting the results were presented, especially in the light of the rather unequivocal nature of the MMPI profile used in this case.

SECTION VI   Diagnostic Profiles

THE problems involved in working with configurations of several personality variables simultaneously are complex and many of them remain unresolved at this time. The various approaches made to configural analysis in MMPI work have been taken up in the previous section on profile analysis. Much of the initial work in this area involved gathering experience and empirical data from groups of known diagnostic composition. These findings are summarized in this section.

This material was gathered as the next logical step after the derivation work on the separate scales. If each of the scales performed its separate function moderately well, there still remained the problem of deciding what the composite set of scores indicated about a given patient. There was probably no time when the naive expectation of a simple one-to-one correspondence between a scale elevation and the diagnostic label was seriously entertained. Although it could have developed that the set of scales worked in such a way that only one scale would be high and all others at the mean for each case, it soon became apparent that multiple elevations were the rule and single peaks or spikes the statistical rarity. It was encouraging that the highest elevation among the scales proved to be consonant with the final psychiatric evaluation in over half of the cases [449 (see VII, 43)], but the conclusion that the diagnostic status was indeterminate in the remaining cases was quite fallacious [456]. The findings reported in the following articles are only part of the evidence against this belief. Using the external criteria of diagnostic subgroups, these workers have provided the core of knowledge about the common MMPI score configurations.

Work subsequent to this has now taken the independent direction of seeking for consistencies within the test findings, forming workable groups on this basis alone, and then seeking external evidence for the interpretive implications of these configurations. This work is reported in other places in this volume (see III, 15, 16, 17; IV, 25, 29; V, 34) and in such articles as those by Welsh [618], Brown [90], Gilberstadt [220], and Sutton [578].

Gough, in article 38, perhaps the most widely quoted paper on the MMPI outside of the construction articles, reports the mean profiles of several homogeneous psychiatric groups from an Army Service Force overseas replacement depot. Most of the groupings were formed on the basis of psychiatric nosology essentially similar to that used at Minnesota in the original derivation. The important exception was the group of psychopathic personality cases which Gough carefully distinguishes from the refined class of psychopathic deviates used to form the criterion group for scale 4 (Pd). The utilization of the army cases in Gough's study and in the groups upon which Schmidt reports in article 39, as well as the VA patients in Hovey's study in article 40, provides an opportunity to test the generality of the

MMPI for populations that differed in many important respects from the predominantly rural, low education, low socioeconomic status midwesterners of Nordic extraction used in the construction of the MMPI.

Even greater departure from the original normative groups was tried in the work which Guthrie reports in article 41 in this section. Here the MMPI is applied to groups of inpatients at two Canadian hospitals and the results are compared with staff diagnoses determined independently of the test findings. All these studies give evidence that there are no appreciable regional differences in verbal behavior which seriously affect the scales as developed on the Minnesota groups. This conclusion does not seem to be equally justified in the case of some of the validation scales, particularly the K scale (see Section II).

The articles in this section came from the following sources: article 38 from H. G. Gough, Diagnostic patterns on the MMPI, *Journal of Clinical Psychology*, 1946, 2, 23–37; article 39 from H. O. Schmidt, Test profiles as a diagnostic aid: the Minnesota Multiphasic Inventory, *Journal of Applied Psychology*, 1945, 29, 115–131; article 40 from H. B. Hovey, Somatization and other neurotic reactions and MMPI profiles, *Journal of Clinical Psychology*, 1949, 5, 153–156; and article 41 from G. M. Guthrie, Six MMPI diagnostic profile patterns, *Journal of Psychology*, 1950, 30, 317–323. We are indebted to the authors and to the publishers of the journals for permission to reproduce these articles in this form.

ARTICLE 38 *Diagnostic Patterns on the MMPI*

SEVERAL recent articles have discussed the usefulness of the MMPI in various clinical situations [3, 289, 386 (see VII, 42), 422, 525], and one has dealt with the problem of test profiles [528 (see VI, 39)]. These reports have yielded favorable conclusions, but others have criticized the inventory method [r83], and personal experience has revealed that many military psychiatrists and clinical psychologists are disinclined to accept the inventory as a useful and valid instrument. It is the author's opinion that much of the hesitance in utilizing the inventory is due to difficulty in its use and interpretation. There is, apparently, a tendency to consider subtest scores independently, and to neglect the interrelationships of subtests, or the *pattern* of test scores. It is the purpose of this paper to re-emphasize the importance of pattern analysis, and to describe certain patterns which were found to be diagnostically significant in a military environment.

Procedure

The MMPI was administered as prescribed in the *Manual* [304] to 136 consecutive admissions to the neuropsychiatric section of an army hospital. The cases were drawn primarily from an Army Service Force's overseas replacement depot, but included a small number from other installations on the post, such as a reception center and various headquarters companies. The sample included both white and Negro soldiers. The soldiers were admitted to the hospital on the recommendation of dispensary medical officers. After several days' orientation, and an interview with a psychiatrist, the subjects were referred for psychological examination, and took the inventory as part of a routine battery under standard conditions. As controls, a normal group of 27 was selected from soldiers on a duty status, in such a way as to match adequately the experimental group for age, race, education, length of service, and military rank. The deviate group was then broken down according to the dispositional diagnosis. These categories, and the number of cases in each, were as follows: (1) psychoneurosis, mild, 12; (2) psychoneurosis, moderate, 24; (3) psychopathic personality, 21; (4) psychoneurosis, severe, 57; (5) psychosis, 22. This last group was subdivided into two dichotomies: psychosis with paranoid features vs. psychosis with no paranoid features, 11 in each group; and psychosis with schizoid features, 12, vs. psychosis with no schizoid features, 10. ("No paranoid features" means, of course, no paranoid features of clinical significance; the same holds for the schizoid dichotomy.) Hereafter these groups will be referred to as PnM, PnMod, Pp, PnS, Psy, Psy with Pa, Psy with no Pa, Psy with Sc, and Psy with no Sc.

It should be pointed out that the grouping of psychoneurosis according to severity does not necessarily correspond to a strict clinical impression, but represents an accommodation of such impressions to military standards. For example, the diagnosis "psychoneurosis severe" was used when a medical discharge from the army was found necessary, the diagnosis "psychoneurosis moderate" when a soldier was considered unfit for overseas duty but fit for continental duty, and the diagnosis "psychoneurosis mild" when a soldier was found to be fit for overseas duty but unfit for combat duty. The psychopathic personality group included cases of inadequate personality, emotional instability, sexual psychopathy, drug addiction, chronic alcoholism, and the "amoral" or "asocial" type [r106]. The psychotic group compares with similar groups found in civilian hospitals and clinics. The diagnoses were made by competent psychiatrists, and in nearly all cases were made independently of the MMPI findings; where these findings were consulted, it was only as a check upon the psychiatric impression. The dispositional categories were then compared with the normal group, and with each other, in terms of mean differences, using the critical ratio as a measure of significance.

Findings

Table 1 shows the means and standard deviations for the normal and deviate groups on each of the inventory subtests. A brief inspection will reveal indications of pattern, and differences among the various curves.

The four deviate curves illustrate what can be called the basic psychoneurotic curve. It is a diphasic curve with unequal peaks. In this basic pattern the "neurotic triad" (Hs, D, and Hy), is higher than the psychotic phase of the curve (Pa, Pt, and Sc). It will also be noticed that this pattern is only slightly evident in PnM, but becomes increasingly pronounced in PnMod, Pp, and PnS. Also, as an increase occurs in the severity of the psychiatric condition, the curve changes its position on the vertical axis. Thus, the basic pattern of the curve suggests a psychoneurotic condition, and the elevation on the vertical axis, as well as the accentuation of typical elements, indicates the severity of the neurosis.

The psychopathic personality curve represents a special problem. Here the Pd subtest assumes a particular significance, being higher than on any other psychoneurotic curve; it is also on the same decile plane as its own neurotic triad. (The Pd *subtest* itself refers primarily to the amoral or asocial psychopath. The psychopathic personality *group* considered here is more heterogeneous, and for that reason it is noted as Pp. Nevertheless, the Pd subtest has discriminatory value for the broader grouping, as shown by the above data.) The discrepancy between Pt and Sc is also important for the Pp curve. For instance, on the PnS curve, which most nearly approximates the Pp curve, Pt and Sc are nearly equal. On the Pp curve, however, Sc is often found as much as one standard deviation above Pt. In distinguishing between a PnS and a Pp curve, this relationship between Pt and Sc is quite helpful. There is also a tendency for psychopaths to attain higher F scores than other clinical groups.

One other point deserves emphasis. Occasionally one finds a bizarre curve

Table 1. T-Score Means, Standard Deviations, and Codes of Various Diagnostic Groups

Group	?	L	F	Hs	D	Hy	Pd	Mf	Pa	Pt	Sc	Ma
Normals (N = 27)												
Mean	54.2	53.4	52.9	49.0	51.8	53.4	47.9	50.8	46.6	46.2	47.1	49.0
SD	3.3	2.4	1.9	7.6	9.9	7.9	10.8	10.5	7.2	8.8	8.5	10.5
MMPI Code: 325/19 4867 ?LF/												
Psychoneurosis, mild (N = 12)												
Mean	50.3	56.1	55.4	70.7	70.3	71.4	58.3	53.0	58.8	57.8	57.4	53.3
SD	0.8	5.4	6.3	11.0	8.7	9.6	8.9	5.4	11.2	10.6	9.9	10.4
MMPI Code: 312'–6478 95 LF?/												
Psychoneurosis, moderate (N = 24)												
Mean	50.7	54.0	58.4	71.9	76.0	75.2	60.8	54.8	57.0	62.7	59.8	59.4
SD	2.2	3.8	9.0	14.7	11.6	12.3	10.8	9.4	11.2	13.9	13.0	8.0
MMPI Code: 231'74–8965 FL?/												
Psychopathic personality (N = 21)												
Mean	52.5	55.0	71.9	85.1	89.9	81.0	79.2	58.4	70.6	69.9	83.9	59.9
SD	6.8	6.1	8.8	17.1	14.4	8.5	12.0	7.6	16.0	16.1	20.7	12.8
MMPI Code: 2183"46:7–95 F'–L?												
Psychoneurosis, severe (N = 57)												
Mean	53.7	53.6	67.4	88.6	100.0	82.3	72.4	60.8	71.9	82.9	86.8	60.8
SD	7.5	6.5	10.4	14.8	15.8	11.1	15.3	9.5	15.1	13.2	18.2	11.3
MMPI Code: 2°1873"46'59 F–?L												
Psychotics, total (N = 22)												
Mean	52.4	56.2	69.1	81.8	83.2	77.7	69.5	58.9	73.6	72.5	76.8	61.8
SD	6.4	8.3	11.0	16.0	15.3	7.8	8.7	10.4	12.6	13.8	16.6	13.2
MMPI Code: 21"3867'49–5 F–L?												
Psychosis with paranoid features (N = 11)												
Mean	50.6	57.1	71.5	77.7	84.7	74.8	69.6	55.4	80.5	72.8	76.9	58.6
SD	1.7	6.7	11.3	12.2	15.5	7.8	8.9	7.8	10.4	13.9	13.9	13.2
MMPI Code: 26"1837'4–95 F'–L?												
Psychosis with no paranoid features (N = 11)												
Mean	54.3	55.4	66.6	84.5	81.4	79.1	68.7	60.2	65.5	71.2	75.2	64.7
SD	8.8	9.7	10.7	15.7	15.7	6.5	7.2	11.4	9.0	12.9	18.5	12.1
MMPI Code: 12"387'4695 F–L?												
Psychosis with schizoid features (N = 12)												
Mean	50.0	55.2	67.8	79.4	83.8	75.3	70.7	54.4	75.5	75.0	78.7	62.6
SD	0.0	6.5	10.2	11.2	12.8	9.5	9.4	7.5	14.0	5.5	9.8	7.5
MMPI Code: 2"18 6374'9–5 F–L?												
Psychosis with no schizoid features (N = 10)												
Mean	55.4	57.1	70.2	82.6	82.4	78.3	67.9	61.4	70.9	69.5	73.8	60.9
SD	8.4	9.6	12.0	16.6	17.2	6.0	6.7	11.0	10.8	17.0	20.8	16.2
MMPI Code: 12"386'7459 F'–L?												

with marked elevations of many subtests, including the Pd subtest. It was quite often found that an atypical curve of this type referred to a case eventually diagnosed as a psychopathic personality. The high Pd score would appear to be the important sign in this type of curve.

The mean differences among the psychoneurotic groups, and between them and the psychopathic personality group, as well as the critical ratios, will be found in Tables 2, 3, 4, and 5.

Table 1 shows the normal, the basic psychotic, and two special psychotic curves. Here the pattern of the basic psychotic curve differs from both the normal

Table 2. Comparison of the Normals (No) with Psychoneurosis Mild (PnM), Psychoneurosis Moderate (PnMod), Psychopathic Personality (Pp), Psychoneurosis Severe (PnS), All Psychotics (Psy), Psychosis with Paranoid Features (Psy with Pa), and Psychosis with Schizoid Features (Psy with Sc), Showing Mean Differences and Critical Ratios of the T Scores [a]

Scale	No-PnM M_{diff}	CR	No-PnMod M_{diff}	CR	No-Pp M_{diff}	CR	No-PnS M_{diff}	CR	No-Psy M_{diff}	CR	No-Psy with Pa M_{diff}	CR	No-Psy with Sc M_{diff}	CR
?	−3.95	5.79	−3.50	4.28	−1.72	1.07	−.53	0.45	−1.79	1.20	−3.60	3.47	−4.20	6.58
L	2.68	1.65	0.62	0.69	1.58	1.12	0.14	0.14	2.80	1.54	3.68	1.77	1.78	0.84
F	2.55	1.38	5.51	2.94	18.98	9.75	14.55	10.20	16.23	6.85	18.63	5.44	14.93	4.61
Hs	21.69	6.23	22.91	6.88	36.14	9.04	39.57	17.40	32.84	8.86	28.74	7.25	30.42	7.95
D	19.49	6.20	24.28	8.00	38.12	10.40	49.38	17.47	31.42	8.44	32.97	6.54	32.04	7.16
Hy	17.99	5.67	21.77	7.33	27.57	11.53	28.82	14.32	24.30	10.69	21.39	7.61	21.87	6.48
Pd	10.38	3.14	12.96	4.29	31.29	9.38	24.54	8.48	21.67	7.78	21.76	6.41	22.83	6.39
Mf	2.17	0.86	3.97	1.43	7.60	2.92	10.00	4.22	8.03	2.68	4.53	1.46	3.57	1.15
Pa	12.18	3.45	10.39	3.88	24.03	6.40	25.34	10.64	27.07	9.03	33.93	9.86	28.93	6.22
Pt	11.63	3.34	16.31	4.95	23.68	5.88	36.65	15.05	26.30	7.76	26.61	5.90	28.80	11.87
Sc	10.29	3.14	12.66	4.07	36.80	7.68	39.68	13.65	29.69	7.62	29.78	6.61	31.57	9.04
Ma	4.27	1.18	10.40	4.02	10.90	3.15	11.77	4.67	12.84	3.71	9.66	2.17	13.62	4.38

[a] Difference is the second category less the first, with negative values given in certain cases.

Table 3. Comparison of Psychoneurosis Mild (PnM) with Psychoneurosis Moderate (PnMod), Psychopathic Personality (Pp), Psychoneurosis Severe (PnS), All Psychotics (Psy), Psychosis with Paranoid Features (Psy with Pa), and Psychosis with Schizoid Features (Psy with Sc), Showing Mean Differences and Critical Ratios of the T Scores [a]

Scale	PnM-PnMod M_{diff}	CR	PnM-Pp M_{diff}	CR	PnM-PnS M_{diff}	CR	PnM-Psy M_{diff}	CR	PnM-Psy with Pa M_{diff}	CR	PnM-Psy with Sc M_{diff}	CR
?	.45	.80	2.23	1.49	3.42	3.36	2.16	1.57	0.35	0.61	−.25	0.33
L	−2.06	1.18	−0.90	0.44	−2.54	1.42	0.12	0.05	1.10	0.43	−.90	0.35
F	2.96	1.15	16.43	6.25	12.00	5.28	13.68	3.67	16.08	4.17	12.38	3.35
Hs	1.22	0.28	14.45	2.96	18.08	5.01	11.05	2.38	7.05	1.46	8.73	1.84
D	5.79	1.68	19.63	4.89	29.79	9.13	12.93	3.15	14.48	2.73	13.55	2.85
Hy	3.78	1.00	9.58	2.87	10.83	3.52	6.31	1.94	3.40	0.93	3.88	0.95
Pd	2.58	0.76	20.91	5.70	14.16	4.32	11.29	3.54	11.38	3.05	12.45	3.18
Mf	1.80	0.73	5.43	2.40	7.83	3.98	5.86	2.17	2.36	0.84	1.40	0.50
Pa	−1.79	0.45	11.85	2.49	13.16	3.45	14.89	3.55	21.75	4.81	16.75	3.05
Pt	4.88	1.17	12.05	2.53	25.02	7.12	14.67	3.47	14.98	2.90	17.17	4.89
Sc	2.37	0.61	26.51	4.98	29.39	7.89	19.40	4.27	19.49	3.84	21.28	5.07
Ma	6.13	1.80	6.63	1.61	7.50	2.23	8.57	2.09	5.39	1.08	9.35	2.45

[a] Difference is the second category less the first, with negative values given in certain cases.

Table 4. Comparison of Psychoneurosis Moderate (PnMod) with Psychopathic Personality (Pp), Psychoneurosis Severe (PnS), All Psychotics (Psy), Psychosis with Paranoid Features (Psy with Pa), and Psychosis with Schizoid Features (Psy with Sc), Showing Mean Differences and Critical Ratios of the T Scores [a]

Scale	PnMod-Pp		PnMod-PnS		PnMod-Psy		PnMod–Psy with Pa		PnMod–Psy with Sc	
	M_{diff}	CR	M_{diff}	CR	M_{diff}	CR	M_{diff}	CR	M_{diff}	CR
?	1.78	1.14	2.97	2.66	1.71	1.18	−0.10	0.43	−0.70	1.40
L	0.96	0.62	−0.48	0.41	2.18	1.13	3.06	1.41	1.16	0.53
F	13.47	5.07	9.04	3.93	10.72	3.60	13.12	3.39	9.42	2.54
Hs	13.23	2.77	16.66	4.81	9.93	2.19	5.83	1.23	7.51	1.62
D	13.84	3.52	24.00	7.60	7.14	1.78	8.69	1.66	7.76	1.66
Hy	5.80	1.85	7.05	2.46	2.53	0.83	−0.38	0.11	0.10	0.03
Pd	18.33	5.37	11.58	3.88	8.71	3.02	8.80	2.56	9.87	2.68
Mf	3.63	1.44	6.03	2.64	4.06	1.39	0.56	0.18	−0.40	0.13
Pa	13.64	3.27	14.95	4.91	16.68	4.75	23.54	6.04	18.54	3.71
Pt	7.17	1.55	20.14	6.05	9.79	2.40	10.10	2.00	12.29	3.70
Sc	24.14	4.62	27.02	7.54	17.03	3.85	17.12	3.45	18.91	4.64
Ma	0.50	0.16	1.37	0.62	2.44	0.76	−0.74	0.17	3.22	1.13

[a] Difference is the second category less the first, with negative values given in certain cases.

Table 5. Comparison of Psychopathic Personality (Pp) with Psychoneurosis Severe (PnS), All Psychotics (Psy), Psychosis with Paranoid Features (Psy with Pa), and Psychosis with Schizoid Features (Psy with Sc), Showing the Mean Differences and Critical Ratios of the T Scores [a]

Scale	Pp-PnS		Pp-Psy		Pp–Psy with Pa		Pp–Psy with Sc	
	M_{diff}	CR	M_{diff}	CR	M_{diff}	CR	M_{diff}	CR
?	1.19	0.63	−0.07	0.03	−1.88	1.20	−2.48	1.68
L	−1.44	0.91	1.22	0.55	2.10	0.86	0.20	0.08
F	−4.43	1.88	−2.75	0.91	−0.35	0.09	−4.05	1.08
Hs	3.43	0.84	−3.30	0.65	−7.40	1.41	−5.72	1.11
D	10.16	3.10	−6.70	1.48	−5.15	0.92	−6.08	1.19
Hy	1.25	0.44	−3.27	1.31	−6.18	2.06	−5.70	1.61
Pd	−6.75	2.04	−9.61	2.99	−9.53	2.53	−8.46	2.14
Mf	2.10	1.00	0.43	0.16	−3.07	1.07	−4.03	1.40
Pa	1.31	0.32	3.04	0.69	9.90	2.11	4.90	0.87
Pt	12.97	2.54	2.62	0.56	2.93	0.53	5.12	1.26
Sc	2.88	0.56	−7.11	1.24	−7.02	1.14	−5.23	0.96
Ma	0.87	0.27	1.94	0.49	−1.24	0.26	2.72	0.74

[a] Difference is the second category less the first, with negative values given in certain cases.

and the psychoneurotic curve already described. It can be described as a diphasic curve with approximately coequal peaks. The neurotic triad is lower than in the PnS curve, slightly lower than in the Pp curve, and higher in PnM and PnMod. The psychotic phase is higher than in PnM and PnMod, lower than in PnS, and compared with Pp is higher on the Pa and Pt subtests, and lower on the Sc subtest. The basic psychotic curve does not show the same changes in accentuation from one category to the other, as does the basic psychoneurotic curve. In the Pn curve certain groups of subtests changed according to the diagnostic category, whereas on the psychotic curve the basic pattern remains the same, but changes occur on individual subtests. For example, on psychotics with paranoid features the Pa subtest is elevated, and on psychotics with schizoid features both the Pt and Sc subtests are slightly raised. There does not seem to be any gross elevation on the vertical axis corresponding to the severity of the psychosis. The essential diagnostic aids are the two approximately coequal peaks of moderate elevation (from 75 to 85 T-score points). Table 1 shows comparisons between two dichotomies of the psychotic group: psychotics with paranoid features vs. psychotics with no paranoid features; and psychotics with schizoid features vs. psychotics with no schizoid features. These curves emphasize the relationship of specific subtests within the framework of the basic pattern. The mean differences, and critical ratios, of the subtest scores are found in Tables 2, 3, 4, 5, 6, 7, and 8.

Special Considerations

In addition to the above patterns, the inventory was also found to be useful in furnishing diagnostic aids in less frequently encountered clinical groups. Unfortunately, there were not enough of these cases to justify statistical treatment. Patients complaining of cephalalgia and migrainous headaches gave a characteristic pattern on the inventory. The pattern was the basic psychoneurotic one, with closest similarity to PnMod, although with slightly greater over-all elevation. The distinguishing feature was the "depressive valley" in the neurotic triad. Both Hs and Hy were higher than D in most of the cases, an unusual and "out-of-pattern" relationship. The respective means were Hs, 81; D, 74; and Hy, 81. In a few of the cases either Hs or Hy was found above D, without the D valley. This appears to be a reliable modification of the pattern.

It may be debated whether the clinical entity of migraine can be compared, on the same level, to psychoneurosis proper. In the present material so much clinical evidence of psychosomatic mechanisms was found in the majority of cases that their validity, as superimposed on the organic pattern of migraine, can hardly be denied. It seems that because a ready-made pattern, such as migraine, is, in a given case, dispositionally available, the resulting psychoneurosis (or, as it may be called, "psychosomatoneurosis") turns out to be "successful." By this is meant that the neurosis is accepted without undue friction or resentment, and without the feelings of unpleasantness or depression found in other neuroses. These feelings of subjective distress are primarily reflected in the D score. On the other hand, psychoneuroses proper, as encountered in this study, were mostly of the depression-anxiety type, in a state of flux, tentatively devised in an acute emergency situation. These patients, even when they produce hysterical symptoms, rarely show the *belle indifférence* which sometimes characterizes well-established conversion hysterias, particularly in peacetime experience. The latter would probably show the D valley of these cases of cephalalgia and migraine, in contradistinction to the type characterized by a high D score, which might properly be termed anxiety hysteria, in the Freudian sense.

The inventory was not found to be useful in cases of sexual deviation. Quite often profiles revealed high Mf scores with no discoverable clinical evidence of deviation, and the known homosexuals rarely attained a significant Mf score on the inventory. This raises again the possibility of homosexuality as divorced from a feminization of personality, and a feminine interest pattern with normality of sex

Table 6. Comparison of Psychoneurosis Severe (PnS) with All Psychotics (Psy), Psychosis with Paranoid Features (Psy with Pa), and Psychosis with Schizoid Features (Psy with Sc), Showing the Mean Differences and Critical Ratios of the T Scores [a]

Scale	PnS-Psy		PnS–Psy with Pa		PnS–Psy with Sc	
	M_{diff}	CR	M_{diff}	CR	M_{diff}	CR
?	−1.26	0.75	−3.07	2.74	−3.67	3.70
L	2.66	1.35	3.54	1.60	1.64	0.73
F	1.68	0.78	4.08	1.11	0.38	0.11
Hs	−6.73	1.76	−10.83	2.66	−9.15	2.32
D	−16.86	4.36	−15.31	2.99	−16.24	3.58
Hy	−4.52	2.11	−7.43	2.75	−6.95	2.12
Pd	−2.87	1.04	−2.78	0.83	−1.71	0.48
Mf	−1.97	0.60	−5.47	2.05	−6.43	2.41
Pa	1.73	0.51	8.59	2.30	3.69	0.76
Pt	−10.35	3.03	−10.04	2.21	−7.85	3.18
Sc	−9.99	2.33	−9.90	2.04	−8.11	2.07
Ma	1.07	0.34	−2.11	0.50	1.85	0.66

[a] Difference is the second category less the first, with negative values given in certain cases.

Table 7. Comparison of Psychosis with Paranoid Features (Psy with Pa) with Psychosis with No Paranoid Features (Psy with No Pa), Showing Mean Difference and Critical Ratio of the T Scores [a]

Scale	Psy with Pa– Psy with No Pa	
	M_{diff}	CR
?	3.67	1.36
L	−1.74	0.49
F	−4.86	1.00
Hs	6.82	0.48
D	−3.37	0.51
Hy	4.28	1.32
Pd	−0.90	0.26
Mf	4.82	1.16
Pa	−14.96	3.61
Pt	−0.63	0.11
Sc	1.73	0.25
Ma	6.09	1.13

[a] Difference is the second category less the first, with negative values given in certain cases.

Table 8. Comparison of Psychosis with Schizoid Features (Psy with Sc) with Psychosis with No Schizoid Features (Psy with No Sc), Showing Mean Differences and Critical Ratios of the T Scores [a]

Scale	Psy with Sc– Psy with No Sc	
	M_{diff}	CR
?	5.42	2.22
L	1.90	0.55
F	2.37	0.51
Hs	3.18	0.53
D	−1.38	0.22
Hy	3.03	0.87
Pd	−2.79	0.81
Mf	7.02	1.77
Pa	−4.58	0.84
Pt	−5.50	1.05
Sc	−4.87	0.72
Ma	−1.68	0.32

[a] Difference is the second category less the first, with negative values given in certain cases.

behavior. (Harmon and Wiener have reported a similar finding with the Mf scale [289].)

It is not the purpose of this paper to discuss prognostic values of the inventory. However, R. E. Harris, at the Langley Porter Clinic in San Francisco, has accumulated data defining prognostic indices and patterns (unpublished studies). It is of course obvious that diagnostic patterns offer some evidence for immediate prognosis, according to what is known about the onset, development, and progress of the various diagnostic entities. Harris has also found the MMPI useful in predicting response to psychotherapy and shock treatment. There is a possibility that the greatest validity of the MMPI, when determined by external criteria, will be in terms of prognostic categories, rather than diagnostic ones. There is probably more unanimity among psychiatrists on the evaluation of recovery and improvement than there is on the differential diagnosis of particular cases, thus providing better defined and more uniform criteria against which to work out MMPI patterns.

Military psychiatrists and psychologists meet with cases of exaggeration and malingering to a much greater extent than in civilian practice, and the detection of this kind of behavior is of prime importance in the military situation. The MMPI is useful in providing clues for the discovery of this type of behavior. If there is a contradiction between the clinical pattern of complaints and behavior, and the MMPI pattern, the discrepancy should be investigated. Several cases of this type were found in which the unique dynamics involved accounted for the atypicality of the curve. In others evidence was obtained which led to a discounting of the patient's expressed symptoms. One certainly cannot prove malingering with the inventory, but it is useful in re-evaluating the declared symptoms of patients given to exaggeration and distortion. A similar situation is that in which the MMPI pattern indicates a condition more severe than the psychiatric picture. In these cases it is sometimes found that the patient has sought to impress the examiner with the severity of his symptoms, or to sort the cards as he thinks a person with his degree of disability should. The cards that are incorporated in such a sorting seem to show up in the scoring plates for Hs, D, Hy, Sc, and especially Pt, and as a result we obtain greatly elevated peaks, with perseverance of the basic psychoneurotic pattern. The existence of such a curve rarely delineates a condition of commensurate severity, but it does tell something of the attitude of the patient who finds it necessary to try to impress the examiner in this way. Such patients have usually been difficult to treat, and have resisted any improvement while in the military environment.

The inventory is often criticized when a delimited clinical symptom, such as conversion hysteria or paranoia, is not reflected on the appropriate scale. Those who criticize then proceed to "explain" this failure by pointing out that a minutely focused hysteria is not sufficiently diffused throughout the personality to affect a global Hy score, or that a tenaciously held, circumscribed delusion, with little psychic irradiation, would not be expected to be picked up by the Pa subtest, as would a multiple paranoid system. This is an erroneous approach to the inventory, which should be made clear to anyone who uses the instrument. It will be recalled that the procedure used in devising and validating the test was essentially an empirical one. The scoring plates were constructed on the basis of item analysis of the responses of known clinical groups. There was no preconceptions about the meanings of any particular cards or questions. In a sense, the scoring plates represent operational definitions of the clinical categories. By training and experience most clinicians are most interested in the pathological indices, both manifest and latent, of the major clinical syndromes. The MMPI, having no professional bias such as this, includes "normal" as well as pathological indices in its evaluation of a patient's behavior (considering the test as a sample of patient's behavior). For example, if a psychiatrist were to examine independently the various items comprising the Hy scale he would find many which are irrelevant to the typical conception of hysteria, and which would not, ordinarily, be thought of as having any relationship to a hysterical condition. Yet the MMPI shows that these items are an integral part of the total evaluation. These items can be considered as a subcluster of normal traits which are found in conjunction with the pathological traits utilized by clinicians in diagnosis. A useful analogy is that of an iceberg whose visible portion represents the entity as seen by the psychiatrist, but which beneath the surface is a unique cluster of normal traits providing the basis for the pathological emergence. This idea is current in psychosomatic medicine, where it has been found that certain personality types, within the normal range, usually develop certain psychosomatic disabilities (such as peptic ulcer, etc.) when they do become sick. In the MMPI we find that a certain clustering of "normal" personality traits is predisposing for the development of particular neuropsychiatric illnesses. For instance, the paranoia scoring key includes roughly 25 clinical items and 13 subclinical items; the Hy scoring key comprises 23 clinical items and 35 subclinical items. Following this, even in cases where the pathological symptomatology is restricted and delimited, the MMPI will detect it to the extent that it is based upon the typical subcluster of normal personality traits. The understanding of this phenomenon is of especial value in military practice, as in a case where a patient deliberately develops or describes a symptom or syndrome. In these cases the discrepancy between the verbal picture and the MMPI findings aids us in more adequately assessing the patient's problems and the dynamics leading to a disagreement between symptoms and personality. The 550 questions included in the inventory of course do not exhaust the traits that make up the different personality patterns predisposed to various psychiatric conditions, but they certainly provide a broader basis of understanding in this respect than is encountered in a delimited psychiatric conception of clinical entities — delimited, that is, to pathological traits. This is an area holding great promise for future research.

The validating scores (?, L, and F), also produce a differential effect on the clinical scores. The effect of a high ? score seems to be a general lowering of the entire curve, without much distortion of pattern. The high F score presents an interesting effect. Certain questions are included in the scoring keys of the clinical scales, as well as in the F scale. The extent of this overlap between the F scale, and the clinical scales, is as follows: Hs, 1; D, 2; Hy, 1; Pd, 5; Mf, 2; Pa, 9; Pt, 1; Sc, 13; Ma, 1. This gives an idea of the differential effect of a high F score. The main distortion will apear in the Sc score, next in the Pa score, and so on. In practice it has been feasible to devalue the Pa and Sc scores in profiles with a very high F score (over 16 raw score points); this should not be done on the Pd subtest, however, as it will be remembered that the high F score was one of the distinguishing signs for the Pp curve. The effect of the high L score was not investigated in this study.

Cautions

As in the case with all psychological tests, the MMPI must be used with the caution and prudence demanded of good clinical practice. Blind diagnoses, selection of subtest scores to meet preconceptions, and the inference of dynamics or trends on the basis of infinitesimal T-score variations are pitfalls which can be easily avoided. There are other points which should be stressed.

In the first place, the final interpretation of the findings should rest with the psychiatrist or psychologist who is most intimately acquainted with the patient, and who is actually in charge of the case. What appear to be discrepancies, or pathognomonic signs, within the frame of reference of the examiner unaware of the peculiar circumstances of the case, are often shown to be reconcilable within the personality structure of the patient when well understood. The test signs in these cases serve to emphasize and objectify the deviations. The final usefulness of the test is the extent to which its findings can be fitted into an integrated and meaningful picture of the patient and his maladjustment, and which can be utilized by the therapist in a positive and constructive manner.

As has been stressed above, subtest scores should not ordinarily be considered uniquely. It has not been possible, for example, to infer dynamics or trends from small variations on the separate scales, especially within the 40–60 range. No particular significance should be attached to a T score of 58, if other scores range from 48 to 53, etc. Some patients score high on Sc, but here again this should not necessarily be interpreted as a schizoid trend. The highest Sc scores in this study were drawn from the PnS group, and from a small group who seemed to be exaggerating their symptoms.

Super, in a recent discussion of Strong's Vocational Interest Scales, made the following statement: "Strong noticed that his scoring keys for group differences are generally based on a relatively small proportion of the total number of items in his inventory, which in turn led to the finding that the likes of persons in various categories are rather highly correlated" [r158].

The scoring keys for the MMPI are also generally based on a small number of the total items in the inventory. At the present time some 351 items are incorporated in one or more scoring keys, and 199 items do not affect scoring in any way. It is questionable whether or not these 199 cards should be deleted in order to save time in administering and scoring the test, as is sometimes done. All the questions contribute toward the context, or the "question environment," about which the test was standardized. The influence of these 199 questions on a subject's responses to the 351 scored items is an unknown, but important, factor, and until we know something of the effects of this interaction we have no accurate idea of the validity of the norms when the test is shortened in this way. Also, as new scoring keys are developed it is possible that some of these 199 items will be included in the new keys. Nevertheless, the fact that so many items were found to be nondiscriminatory for the clinical groups included in the test to date indicates again the similarity of attitudes and interests in even the neurotic and psychotic groups.

Although the MMPI is generally applicable to all adult groups, difficulty was experienced in using it with mental defectives, and persons of dull or borderline capacity. A subject who cannot read is not able to sort the cards alone; satisfactory results have been obtained in these cases by having an assistant read the questions to the patient. There are quite a few negative statements in the inventory, and the mentally retarded have had great difficulty in making positive sortings of these questions. One must be sure that such persons have understood a sufficient number of these negative statements to lend validity to the scoring. The presence of these somewhat confusing questions is a definite drawback to the use of the inventory with retarded groups.

Summary

An analysis of the MMPI records of 136 clinical cases was made. These cases included 12 psychoneurosis mild, 24 psychoneurosis moderate, 21 psychopathic personalities, 57 psychoneurosis severe, and 22 psychosis. These groups were then compared with each other, and with a normal group of 27 cases, in terms of mean differences, using the critical ratio as a measure of significance. A basic psychoneurotic curve was described, consisting of unequal peaks, with the neurotic triad (Hs, D, and Hy) being higher than the psychotic phase (Pa, Pt, and Sc). The modifications of this basic pattern in the psychoneurotic subgroups were pointed out, and the statistical significance of the differences embodied in these modifications was demonstrated.

The basic psychotic curve was found to have approximately coequal peaks of moderate elevation (75 to 85 T-score points). Two psychotic subgroups showed variations of specific subtest scores, but did not show gross differences of position on the vertical axis corresponding to the severity of the psychiatric condition, as did the psychoneurotic subgroups.

The MMPI was also found to reveal special aids for differential diagnosis, for the detection of exaggeration and malingering, and for the identification of lesser clinical entities, but was found to be of little value in detecting sexual deviates. Certain cautions pertaining to the use of the inventory were discussed.

✦————————————————————————————————

ARTICLE 39 *Test Profiles as a Diagnostic Aid*

THE purpose of this paper is to present some findings in the use of the MMPI in a clinical situation.

No attempt will be made here to describe the development of the test, or its applicability as a clinical instrument since these have been described elsewhere by its authors [300 (see II, 5), 420 (II, 6), 301 (II, 7), 421 (II, 8), 423 (II, 9), 303], by Leverenz [386 (VII, 42)], and by Schiele, Baker, and Hathaway [525].

The data have been gathered over a period of nine months from cases studied in the Consultation Service of an Army Air Force replacement pool.

Procedure

The MMPI was administered as prescribed in the manual of directions [303]. It was given insofar as practicable as part of the routine on the opening of a case. However, the pressure of time and the lack of sufficient test sets precluded the possibility of testing all cases coming to the Consultation Service.

All diagnoses were made by qualified neuropsychiatrists, employing classifications in common use in the army, which in the main follow civilian practice.

This was not a controlled experiment, in the sense that careful selection of normal cases was sought, or that pure-culture clinical groups were (or could be) employed. Yet, there is reasonable certainty that the test did not influence the clinical diagnosis. Three of the four neuropsychiatrists making diagnoses avoided the test, merely finding it interesting a posteriori that it seemed to agree with the clinical findings. The fourth neuropsychiatrist was quite interested in the test, but with a view to assisting in this validity study, he was careful not to see or to discuss the test on a particular individual until *after* he had made his clinical judgment.

The Subjects

The subjects were all white male enlisted members of the Army Air Forces. The clinical groups had been referred to the Consultation Service bcause of difficulty in adjusting to the army situation. The normal group was being re-evaluated, either because its records had been lost, were incomplete, or because there existed overages in particular occupational specialties, making reclassification necessary.

The deviate groups consisted of 121 subjects who fell into the following diagnostic categories: constitutional psychopathic state, inadequate personality; con-

351

stitutional psychopathic state, sexual psychopathy; psychoneurosis, mild; psycho-neurosis, severe; and psychosis. There were several other groups, such as organics, simple adult maladjustment, and alcoholics, but the cases were too few to have statistical significance and are not included here for that reason. Clinically, they were differentiable by profile. Table 1 gives descriptive data on the various groups as to number, age, intelligence, years of schooling, months of service, marital status, rank, number of states represented, population of the home town, and final disposition of the men who had been studied. This latter column consists of a percentage computation into 5 categories: discharge from the military service; limited military

Table 1. Descriptive Data for the Normal Group (No) and the Constitutional Psychopathic State, Inadequate Personality (CP), Constitutional Psychopathic State, Sexual Psychopathy (CH), Psychoneurosis, Mild (PnM), Psychoneurosis, Severe (PnS), and Psychotic (Psy) Groups

Item	No (N = 98)	CP (N = 11)	CH (N = 7)	PnM (N = 26)	PnS (N = 64)	Psy (N = 13)
Age (in years)						
Mean	24.9	24.4	27.3	24.6	24.7	24.9
SD	3.5	3.6	6.4	4.5	4.5	5.5
Range	18–36	20–31	20–40	19–37	19–36	19–34
Education (years completed)						
Mean	11.7	11.0	12.9	11.5	11.3	10.4
SD	1.6	2.7	3.4	2.3	1.8	1.9
Range	8–17	6–15	8–18	8–19	3–19	6–13
Service (in months)						
Mean	38.3	22.8	11.1	12.7	13.9	26.7
SD	27.8	27.9	8.3	10.6	10.5	38.7
Range	10–204	4–108	4–30	4–54	2–42	3–144
Intelligence (A.G.C.T.)						
Mean	114.3	105.7	105.2	117.6	108.4	108.2
SD	12.0	17.5	16.1	15.7	21.3	11.9
Range	78–139	75–128	74–121	76–142	74–145	86–129
Rank						
M/Sgt.	9					
T/Sgt.	24			1	2	2
S/Sgt.	16			1	3	
Sgt.	17	1	2	4	8	
Cpl.	11	2	1	5	8	
Pfc.	5		1	9	16	6
Pvt.	16	8	3	6	27	5
Marital status						
Married	50	3	1	13	30	4
Single	47	8	6	13	34	8
Divorced	1					1
Number of states represented	34	6	5	16	27	10
Population of home town						
0–1000	18	1	0	4	6	1
1000–10,000	22	1	0	3	8	2
10,000–100,000	33	2	1	6	11	5
Over 100,000	25	7	6	13	39	5
Final disposition						
Discharge		27.3%	85.7%	7.7%	50.0%	53.8%
Limited field duty		9.1		19.3	21.9	7.7
Full field duty	100%			3.8	9.4	15.4
Hospitalization		9.1			4.7	7.7
Duty (?)		54.5	12.3	69.2	14.0	15.4

duty; full field duty; hospitalization (in most cases general hospital is implied); and duty (?). The last-named category comprised those men on whom the follow-up data were incomplete, the only thing being known was that they were returned to duty, but whether on a full or limited duty status could not be ascertained.

The normal group (No) consisted of 98 subjects who upon inquiry manifested no evidence of overt or covert personality disorder. Their civilian and army histories were devoid of any indication of disturbance: some had been overseas, but in a quiet theater; some had "washed out" as aviation cadets, primarily for lack of psychomotor adaptability; but no trauma could be detected subjectively as attending either of these major sources of normal cases.

In all groups, by inspection, the descriptive data (Table 1) appeared to have a normal distribution generally and to be comparable. However, the intellectual distribution is skewed somewhat to the left, in that no Army General Classification Test group V's were given the test. This was because of the highly questionable ability of this low group to comprehend the various test items.

Results

Table 2 presents the means, sigmas, and ranges of all groups; and Tables 3, 4, 5, 6 and 7 give the differences, standard errors of difference, and critical ratios between the various groups (T-score values, uncorrected for small samples or beyond 1 decimal point).

It is at once apparent from inspection of Table 2 that the deviate groups present characteristic profiles different from those made by the normal group.

The profile for the No group is reasonably flat and approaches closely the T-score mean level of 50. It is somewhat lower generally than this mean range of 50 and lower than the normal curve found by Leverenz [386 (see VII, 42)]. Within its own configuration the low point is reached on the depression scale, while the high point is for paranoia.

The profiles for the deviate groups show obvious divergence from the normal profile. In all instances the curves are higher, being less so for the PnM group and maximum for Psy. The depression scale appears as an index to the seriousness of the difficulty. It is higher than either hypochondriasis or hysteria in the PnS and Psy groups, and lower for all the others. In the case of the CH group, the profile rises on the masculinity-femininity scale whereas in all the other groups the curve is depressed at this point. By way of indicating characterizing features of the various profiles, the following may be noted:

1. The No profile, although generally a straight line at T-score mean level, shows a low point at depression and a high point at paranoia.

2. The CP curve has high points about 2 sigmas above mean level through the psychopathic deviate scale, drops to nearly normal at masculinity-femininity, rises to paranoia, drops again slightly on psychasthenia, rises to schizophrenia, and falls off on hypomania.

3. The CH profile is approximately a straight line, between 1 and 2 sigmas above the mean level, with high points on the masculinity-femininity and schizophrenia scales.

4. The PnM profile, at about 1 sigma above normal, descriptively shows a high level at hypochondriasis-depression-hysteria (depression lowest), dropping sharp-

ly on masculinity-femininity, and rising sharply again to psychasthenia-schizophrenia.

5. The PnS curve shows a high plateau, 3 sigmas above normal at hypochondriasis-depression-hysteria (depression slightly higher), drops at masculinity-femininity, and rises again to schizophrenia.

Table 2. T-Score Means, Standard Deviations, and Codes of Various Diagnostic Groups

Group	?	L	F	Hs	D	Hy	Pd	Mf	Pa	Pt	Sc	Ma
Normals (N = 98)												
Mean	50.1	52.1	52.2	48.5	41.2	45.1	47.0	45.2	51.0	49.5	48.5	48.2
SD	0.5	3.5	4.1	8.2	12.7	10.0	13.1	9.7	8.9	8.4	7.7	9.4
MMPI Code: 6/<u>71</u>894<u>532</u> <u>FL</u>?/												
Constitutional psychopathic state (inadequate personality) (N = 11)												
Mean	51.7	52.8	61.0	77.1	73.7	75.1	71.0	54.4	71.5	68.0	72.6	66.6
SD	4.1	3.1	9.1	18.6	19.3	20.4	17.9	10.7	14.7	14.4	19.9	12.4
MMPI Code: 13286<u>4</u>'79–5 F–<u>L</u>?												
Constitutional psychopathic state (sexual psychopathy) (N = 7)												
Mean	50.0	50.0	61.7	65.7	66.6	69.0	66.4	71.4	71.4	66.3	74.7	61.0
SD	0.0	0.0	8.1	11.4	12.4	12.9	16.1	17.2	8.4	9.5	12.6	8.9
MMPI Code: 8<u>56</u>'3<u>24</u>719 F–<u>L</u>?												
Psychoneurosis, mild (N = 26)												
Mean	51.9	51.7	56.9	69.9	60.6	66.6	53.2	46.9	56.0	60.5	60.7	50.4
SD	5.9	4.1	8.1	16.0	21.4	19.7	14.9	11.5	14.4	14.9	15.1	12.1
MMPI Code: 13<u>827</u>–649/5 F?<u>L</u>/												
Psychoneurosis, severe (N = 64)												
Mean	51.1	51.9	60.9	80.3	80.7	79.3	66.3	56.5	66.2	72.9	73.6	59.5
SD	4.6	4.0	9.9	15.9	20.8	15.6	17.1	11.1	11.6	12.7	15.9	11.5
MMPI Code: 2<u>1</u>"3 87'<u>46</u>–95 F–<u>L</u>?												
Psychotic (N = 13)												
Mean	50.8	52.5	63.0	74.6	82.1	70.6	69.4	55.5	76.2	71.9	78.5	61.5
SD	2.7	6.9	10.8	16.2	27.5	20.0	23.2	13.9	25.1	15.7	18.6	13.5
MMPI Code: 2"86173'49–5 F–L?												

6. The Psy profile shows a high peak on depression at 3 sigmas above normal, a descending of masculinity-femininity to nearly normal, a sharp rise (2.5 sigmas) to parancia, a slight drop at psychasthenia, and a rise to nearly 3 sigmas at schizophrenia.

There is a decrease on all profiles on the hypomania scale.

For the validating indicators, ?, L, and F, the curve rises more sharply at F for the Psy group and has minimal accentuation for No.

From examination of Table 3, where the No group is compared with the clinical groups, CP, CH, PnM, PnS, and Psy, it will be noted that in all but six instances

Table 3. Comparison of the Normal Group (No) and the Clinical Groups of Constitutional Psychopathic State, Inadequate Personality (CP), Constitutional Psychopathic State, Sexual Psychopathy (CH), Psychoneurosis, Mild (PnM), Psychoneurosis, Severe (PnS), and Psychosis (Psy) on the Separate MMPI Scales Showing Difference, Standard Error of Difference, and Critical Ratio of T Scores [a]

Scale	No-CP			No-CH			No-PnM			No-PnS			No-Psy		
	Diff	SE_{diff}	$Diff/SE_{diff}$	Diff	SE_{diff}	$Diff/SE_{diff}$	Diff	SE_{diff}	$Diff/SE_{diff}$	Diff	SE_{diff}	$Diff/SE_{diff}$	Diff	SE_{diff}	$Diff/SE_{diff}$
?	1.6	1.2	1.3	—.1	.05	2.0	.8	1.1	.7	1.1	.6	.2	.7	.7	1.0
L	.7	1.0	.7	—2.1	.3	7.0	—.4	.9	.4	—.2	.6	.3	.4	1.6	.3
F	8.8	2.8	3.1	9.5	3.7	2.6	4.7	1.6	2.9	8.7	1.3	6.7	10.8	3.0	3.6
Hs	28.6	5.7	5.0	17.2	4.4	3.9	21.4	3.2	6.7	31.8	2.1	15.1	26.1	4.5	5.8
D	32.5	5.9	5.5	25.4	4.9	5.2	19.4	4.4	4.4	39.5	2.9	13.6	40.9	7.8	5.2
Hy	30.0	6.2	4.8	23.9	4.9	4.9	21.5	3.9	5.5	34.2	2.2	15.5	25.5	5.6	4.6
Pd	24.0	5.5	4.4	19.4	6.2	3.1	6.2	3.2	1.9	19.3	2.5	7.7	22.4	6.6	3.4
Mf	9.2	3.3	2.8	26.2	6.6	4.0	1.7	2.5	.7	11.3	1.7	6.6	10.3	3.9	2.6
Pa	20.5	4.5	4.6	20.4	3.3	6.2	5.0	2.9	1.7	15.3	1.7	9.0	25.2	7.0	3.6
Pt	18.5	4.4	4.2	17.8	3.7	4.8	11.0	3.0	3.7	23.4	1.8	13.0	22.4	4.4	5.1
Sc	24.1	6.1	3.9	26.2	4.8	5.5	12.2	3.1	3.9	25.1	2.1	12.0	30.0	5.2	5.8
Ma	18.4	3.8	4.8	12.8	3.5	3.7	2.2	2.5	.9	11.3	1.7	6.6	13.3	3.8	3.5

[a] Difference is the first of a pair from the second; hence, minus signs may occur. N's are as follows: No, 98; CP, 11; CH, 7; PnM, 26; PnS, 64; Psy, 13.

Table 4. Comparison of the Constitutional Psychopathic State, Inadequate Personality Group (CP), and the Clinical Groups of Constitutional Psychopathic State, Sexual Psychopathy (CH), Psychoneurosis, Mild (PnM), Psychoneurosis, Severe (PnS), and Psychosis (Psy), on the Separate MMPI Scales Showing Difference, Standard Error of Difference, and Critical Ratio of T Scores [a]

Scale	CP-CH			CP-PnM			CP-PnS			CP-Psy		
	Diff	SE_{diff}	$Diff/SE_{diff}$	Diff	SE_{diff}	$Diff/SE_{diff}$	Diff	SE_{diff}	$Diff/SE_{diff}$	Diff	SE_{diff}	$Diff/SE_{diff}$
?	−1.7	1.2	1.4	.2	1.7	.1	−.6	1.3	.5	−.9	1.5	.6
L	−2.8	.9	3.1	−1.1	1.2	.9	−.9	1.1	.8	−.3	2.1	.1
F	.7	4.1	.2	−4.1	3.2	1.3	.8	3.0	.3	2.0	4.1	.5
Hs	−11.4	7.1	1.6	−7.2	6.4	1.1	2.2	5.9	.4	−2.5	7.2	.3
D	−7.1	7.4	1.0	−13.1	7.2	1.8	7.0	6.3	1.1	8.4	9.6	.9
Hy	−6.1	7.7	.8	−8.5	7.2	1.2	4.2	6.4	.7	−4.5	8.2	.5
Pa	−4.6	8.1	.6	−17.8	6.1	2.9	−4.7	5.8	.8	−1.6	8.4	.2
Mf	17.0	7.2	2.4	−7.5	3.9	1.9	2.1	3.5	.6	1.1	5.0	.2
Pd	−.4	5.4	.1	−15.5	5.2	2.9	−5.2	4.6	1.1	4.7	8.2	.6
Pt	−1.7	5.6	.3	−7.5	5.2	1.4	4.9	4.6	1.1	3.9	5.9	.7
Sc	2.1	7.7	.3	−11.9	6.7	1.8	1.0	6.3	.2	5.9	7.9	.7
Ma	−5.6	5.0	1.1	−16.2	4.4	3.7	−7.1	4.0	1.8	−5.1	5.0	1.0

[a] Difference is the first of a pair from the second; hence, minus signs may occur. N's are as follows: CP, 11; CH, 7; PnM, 26; PnS, 64; Psy, 13.

Table 5. Comparison of Constitutional Psychopathic State, Sexual Psychopathy (CH), and the Clinical Groups of Psychoneurosis, Mild (PnM), Psychoneurosis, Severe (PnS), and Psychosis (Psy) on the Separate MMPI Scales Showing Difference, Standard Error of Difference, and Critical Ratio of T Scores [a]

Scale	CH-PnM			CH-PnS			CH-Psy		
	Diff	SE_{diff}	$Diff/SE_{diff}$	Diff	SE_{diff}	$Diff/SE_{diff}$	Diff	SE_{diff}	$Diff/SE_{diff}$
?	1.9	1.1	1.7	1.1	.5	2.2	.8	.8	1.0
L	1.7	.8	2.1	1.9	.5	3.8	2.5	1.6	1.6
F	-4.8	3.4	1.4	-.8	3.3	.2	1.3	4.2	.3
Hs	4.2	5.3	.8	14.6	4.7	3.1	8.9	6.2	1.4
D	-6.0	6.3	1.0	14.1	5.4	2.6	15.5	8.9	1.7
Hy	-2.4	6.2	.5	10.3	5.3	1.9	1.6	7.3	.2
Pd	-13.2	6.8	1.9	-.1	6.4	.2	3.0	8.9	.3
Mf	-24.5	6.9	3.6	-14.9	6.7	2.2	-15.9	7.6	2.1
Pa	-15.4	4.2	3.7	-5.1	3.5	1.5	4.8	7.6	.6
Pt	-5.8	4.6	1.3	6.6	3.9	1.7	4.6	5.6	.8
Sc	-14.0	5.6	2.5	-1.1	5.1	.2	3.8	7.0	.5
Ma	-10.6	4.1	2.6	-1.5	3.8	.4	.5	5.0	.1

[a] Difference is the first of a pair from the second; hence, minus signs may occur. N's are as follows: CH, 7; PnM, 26; PnS, 64; Psy, 13.

357

Table 6. Comparison of Psychoneurosis, Mild (PnM), and the Clinical Groups of Psychoneurosis, Severe (PnS), and Psychosis (Psy) on the Separate MMPI Scales, Showing Difference, Standard Error of Difference, and Critical Ratio of T Scores [a]

Scale	PnM-PnS			PnM-Psy		
	Diff	SE_{diff}	$Diff/SE_{diff}$	Diff	SE_{diff}	$Diff/SE_{diff}$
?	−.8	1.3	.6	−1.1	1.4	.8
L	.2	.9	.2	.8	2.1	.4
F	4.0	2.0	2.0	6.1	3.4	1.8
Hs	11.4	3.7	3.1	4.7	5.5	.9
D	20.1	4.9	4.1	21.5	8.7	2.5
Hy	12.7	4.3	3.0	4.0	6.8	.6
Pd	13.1	3.6	3.6	16.2	7.1	2.3
Mf	9.6	2.7	3.6	8.6	4.4	1.9
Pa	10.3	3.3	3.1	20.2	7.5	2.7
Pt	12.4	3.3	3.8	10.4	5.2	2.0
Sc	12.9	3.6	3.6	17.8	5.9	3.0
Ma	9.1	2.8	3.3	11.1	4.4	2.5

[a] Difference is the first of a pair from the second; hence minus signs may occur. N's are as follows: PnM, 26; PnS, 64; Psy, 13.

Table 7. Comparison of Psychoneurosis, Severe (PnS), and the Clinical Group of Psychosis (Psy) on the Separate MMPI Scales, Showing Difference, Standard Error of Difference, and Critical Ratio of T Scores [a]

Scale	PnS-Psy		
	Diff	SE_{diff}	$Diff/SE_{diff}$
?	−.3	.9	.3
L	.6	1.9	.3
F	2.1	3.2	.7
Hs	−5.7	4.9	1.2
D	1.4	8.1	.2
Hy	−8.7	5.9	1.5
Pd	3.1	6.8	.5
Mf	−1.0	4.4	.2
Pa	9.9	7.1	1.4
Pt	−1.0	4.6	.2
Sc	4.9	5.5	.9
Ma	2.0	4.0	.5

[a] Difference is the first of a pair from the second; hence minus signs may occur. N's are as follows: PnS, 64; Psy, 13.

a significant difference is apparent, the critical ratio being 3.1 or higher — ranging from 3.1 for No-CH on the Pd scale to 15.5 for No-PnS on the Hy scale. Of the six cases that diverge, four are in the No-PnM comparison on the psychopathic deviate, masculinity-femininity, paranoid, and psychasthenic scales, with critical ratios of 1.9, .7, 1.7, and .9 respectively. The remaining two are on the masculinity-femininity scale for No-CP and No-Psy, with critical ratios of 2.8 and 2.6 respectively.

In the matter of the validating items of ?, L, and F scales, no significant differences appear on the ? scale, although between No and CH the critical ratio is 2.0, the No group having the higher ? score. On the L scale, the only difference possessing significance is that between No and CH, where the critical ratio is 7.0, and where again the No group makes the higher score. The F scale shows significant differences in three of the comparisons, and borderline significance in the remaining two. In each instance the greater F score is made by the clinical group. The critical ratios in ascending order are respectively No-CH, 2.6; No-CP, 3.1; No-Psy, 3.6; and No-PnS, 6.7.

Table 4 compares the CP group with the other clinical groups. In only two instances here are there significant differences: the L scale has a critical ratio of 3.1 for CP-CH, the CP score being the higher; and the critical ratio for CP-PnM on hypomania is 3.7, the CP score being higher. Approaching significance is the critical ratio of 2.4 for CP-CH on the masculinity-femininity scale, the CH group being the higher; CP-PnM on the psychopathic deviate scale shows a critical ratio of 2.9, the CP group being higher; and on the paranoid scale, CP-PnM, the critical ratio is 2.9, CP being the higher.

Table 5 compares the CH group with the clinical groups PnM, PnS, and Psy. In the validating scales, only the L score for CH-PnS shows a difference that is significant — the critical ratio is 3.8, with CH being higher.

On the masculinity-femininity and paranoia scales for CH-PnM, and hypochondriasis on CH-PnS, the critical ratios are respectively 3.6, 3.7, and 3.1, with CH higher in the first two instances and the lower score in the latter. These are the only significant differences here; but noteworthy are critical ratios of 2.5 and 2.6 for CH-PnM on the schizophrenia and hypomania scales respectively, with CH in each case the higher score; in the CH-PnS comparison we find the respective critical ratios of 2.6 and 2.2 on the scales for depression and masculinity-femininity, with the PnS score higher on the depression scale and CH higher on the masculinity-femininity scale; while for CH-Psy on the masculinity-femininity scale the critical ratio is 2.1, CH being the higher score.

Table 6 compares the PnM group with the PnS and Psy groups. In every instance on the main scales the higher score is made by the more disturbed group. Significant differences are seen in the PnM-PnS comparison on all scales, the critical ratios being respectively 3.1, 4.1, 3.0, 3.6, 3.1, 3.8, 3.6, and 3.3 for hypochondriasis, depression, hysteria, psychopathic deviate, masculinity-femininity, paranoia, psychasthenia, schizophrenia, and hypomania.

In the comparison of PnM and Psy, only on the schizophrenia scale is a significant difference apparent, the critical ratio being 3.0, with Psy the higher score; but to be noted are the critical ratios of 2.5, 2.3, 2.7, 2.0, and 2.5 on the scales for depression, psychopathic deviate, paranoia, psychasthenia, and hypomania respectively — all scores being higher for Psy.

Table 7 compares the PnS and Psy clinical groups, where no significant differences can be observed. However, it is interesting to note that the trend is for the PnS group to score higher on the scales for hypochondriasis, hysteria, masculinity-femininity, and psychasthenia; while the Psy group is the higher on the scales for depression, psychopathic deviate, paranoia, schizophrenia, and hypomania.

Summary

As indicated earlier this is not an experiment in the usual laboratory sense; yet, every effort was made to maintain standard conditions for all groups and to prevent the intrusion of uncontrollable variables or artifact. The value of the MMPI as a predictive instrument and clinical tool depends upon its agreement with the clinical diagnoses. This is, of course, open to many pitfalls: the lack of a common psychiatric language; the lack of clear-cut clinical criteria for identifying personality abnormalities; the failure of an individual under study to present uncomplicated symptoms or to present crystallized behavior patterns; the lack of time for making a prolonged study of the individual. This explains to an extent the lack of greater definiteness in the diagnostic groups employed here. No attempt has been made to define the groups beyond the major classifications. Since a clinical evaluation had to be made with the minimum expenditure of time consistent with good procedure, and since verification of the clinical diagnoses was generally unpracticable, greater precision here would not necessarily mean substantiation in fact or in composite psychiatric or psychological opinion. Table 8 shows the recommendations made and the actual disposition on the 121 cases of this study. This is purely pragmatic. It must be borne in mind that final disposition of these cases rested with a board of medical or line officers, few of whom had any genuine training in psychology or psychiatry. Yet, this subjective system was in agreement with the clinical psychological–psychiatric findings minimally at 62.8 per cent: 41.3 per cent were discharged; 17.4 per cent were placed on a limited duty status, and 4.1 per cent were sent to a general hospital for further observation and disposition. The follow-up data are deficient in 29.8 per cent of the cases studied. These men were returned to duty, but the percentages could not be ascertained as to which were for full duty and which for limited status. All the psychiatrists making diagnoses were qualified neuropsychiatrists. Two of them were fellows in the American Psychiatric Association. Three of these showed little or no interest in the MMPI (or any psychometrics beyond intelligence examinations); the fourth neuropsychiatrist who had been on duty at the Consultation Service was definitely interested in the MMPI but purposely refrained from consulting it until after he had made a clinical evaluation.

Tables 3–7 indicate the agreement of the test with the clinical findings and point out its potentialities as an aid in differential diagnosis. Objective comparison of the diagnostic groups with a normal group has demonstrated statistically significant differentiations (Table 3). Even between the diagnostic groups, one finds distinctive and valid differences (Tables 4–6), typifying or peculiar to, a general class of disorder or diagnostic group. Thus, the depression scale appears as an indicator of the seriousness of the disintegration, being lower than both hypochondriasis and hysteria in the psychopathic group and mild neurotics, and higher in the severe neurotic and psychotic groups.

The lack of statistical significance between the PnS group and the Psy group (Table 7) may be due to the small number of cases in the Psy group and its large standard deviations. Qualitatively, however, the profiles are different. It is to be noted that the peaks for hypochondriasis, hysteria, and psychasthenia are more pronounced than for the other scales for the PnS groups, while in the Psy profile the peaks are for depression, paranoia, and schizophrenia.

The more probable explanation for the apparently close relationship between these groups (and also between CP, Psy, and CH-Psy) is the grossness or over-

Table 8. Recommended Action and Final Disposition of the CP, CH, PnM, PnS, and Psy Groups

Group	Discharge		Limited Duty		Full Duty		Admitted to General Hospital		Returned to Duty: Type Unknown		Total	
	N	% within Group	N	% within Group	N	% within Group	N	% within Group	N	% within Group	N	%
CP												
Recommendation ..	6	54.5	2	18.2	2	18.2	1	9.1	0		11	100
Actual ………	3	27.3	1	9.1	0	0	1	9.1	6	54.5	11	100
CH												
Recommendation ..	7	100	0	0	0	0	0	0	0		7	100
Actual ………	6	85.7	0	0	0	0	0	0	1	14.3	7	100
PnM												
Recommendation ..	2	7.7	13	50	10	38.5	1	3.8	0		26	100
Actual ………	2	7.7	5	19.3	1	3.8	0	0	18	69.2	26	100
PnS												
Recommendation ..	48	75.0	1	1.6	5	7.8	10	15.6	0		64	100
Actual ………	32	50	14	21.9	6	9.4	3	4.7	9	14.0	64	100
Psy												
Recommendation ..	10	76.9	1	7.7	0	0	2	15.4	0		13	100
Actual ………	7	53.8	1	7.7	2	15.4	1	7.7	2	15.4	13	100
Total (of all cases)												
Recommendation ..	73	60.3	17	14.1	17	14.1	14	11.5	0		121	100
Actual ………	50	41.3	21	17.4	9	7.4	5	4.1	36	29.8	121	100

allness of the classifications used here together with the generally noncrystallized reaction types.

That the test is sensitive is further suggested in the No group. The profile for this group is generally slightly below the T-score mean of 50, but has a peak on the paranoia scale. In terms of its own gestalt, this would indicate a slight reduction in affect and a slight fixation of ideas. When one considers (cf. Table 1) that this group has been in the Consultation Service somewhat longer than the clinical groups and that they have met with more success (attained higher ranks) than the other groups, one is intrigued by the No profile. It is essentially stable and essentially normal. Yet, it does differ from the expected T-score average and from the normal profile as found by Leverenz [386 (see VII, 42)]. Could this be the healthy, experienced soldier's profile — phlegmatic and purposeful — or has there developed in this group a subtle personality alteration?

Provocative, too, of further investigation in the No group are the slightly elevated L and F scores. Has this group learned to put its best foot forward, but within affectively controlled limits, and at the same time has it become possessed with an idea, has it a singleness of purpose?

Conclusion

The purpose of this paper has been to present some findings on the use of the MMPI in a clinical situation. The cases were all male white enlisted men of the Army Air Force who had been studied at the Consultation Service of a personnel replacement pool. Of the cases seen, 98 were problems solely of administration and became the normal group. The 121 cases seen because of maladjustment to the army situation were subsequently diagnosed through standard practices by qualified neuropsychiatrists as constitutional psychopathic state, inadequate personality; constitutional psychopathic state, sexual psychopathy; psychoneurosis, mild; psychoneurosis, severe; or psychosis. Diagnoses were made independently of the inventory. The data thus gathered indicate that the MMPI did in this empirical situation:

1. Distinguish graphically and with statistical significance between normal soldiers and those diagnosed as constitutional psychopaths, mild or severe neurosis, and psychosis.

2. Differentiate with significance between major clinical groups.

3. Present qualitative differentials, or hints for clinical query, in the more disintegrated or anomalous personality disorders.

The data are in agreement with Leverenz' [386] observation that although the clinical impression may not always be corroborated by the scores, the clinician is made aware of one or more personality abnormalities that require evaluation.

ARTICLE 40 *Somatization and other Neurotic Reactions and MMPI Profiles*

THE present study is concerned primarily with a comparison of composite MMPI profiles produced by patients grouped according to three types of psychiatric diagnoses: somatization, dissociative-conversion, and anxiety reactions; and with the extent of emotional distress within the three groups as reflected by the MMPI. These patients were a fraction of all patients hospitalized, usually for examination, observation, and treatment in connection with physical complaints.

Procedure

Between 10 and 15 per cent of all patients admitted to the Veterans Administra-tion Hospital (general medical and surgical) at Salt Lake City were referred for psychological evaluations during a period covering about seventeen months. The MMPI was administered to 446 of the patients so referred. For patients with less than a high school education the individual card-set form was usually administered. The group form was used as a rule with those patients having a high school educa-tion or better. The K factor for correction of test attitude was used in scoring the tests [424 (see II, 11)]. Cases which showed up as probably "faking bad" according to the F minus K raw score criteria as developed by Gough [245 (see V, 35)], to-gether with erratic profiles, were discarded. Also discarded were those cases suspected of "faking good" with a T score for K of over 75, and cases circumventing the test by using the cut corners of the cards for sorting [329]. About a dozen cases altogether were discarded as inadequate. The majority of all cases examined fel. into sundry diagnostic categories not studied for this report. These included latent schizophrenics, encephalopathies, pathological personalities, obsessive-compul-sives, hypochondriacs, and individuals with situational disturbances or no psychi-atric diagnosis.

The present study includes 199 cases classified into three groups with major psychiatric diagnoses as follows: 105 cases with somatization reactions, including psychogenic gastrointestinal, cardiovascular, and the like; 34 cases with dissocia-tive-conversion reactions; and 60 cases with anxiety reactions. These diagnoses were based on medical, psychiatric, psychiatric social, and psychological studies, and observations of behavior while the subjects were hospitalized. Final psychiatric

363

diagnoses were made by attending psychiatrists. The psychological studies included results from such instruments as the Rorschach, Wechsler-Bellevue Intelligence Scale, Self-Interview Inventory [r78], and the MMPI. The MMPI profiles may have had bearing on the diagnoses in some cases, but then only as supplementary data. At any rate, the profiles were not consulted in making final psychiatric diagnoses.

Results and Discussion

Table 1 presents for the three groups the mean T scores on each of the scales of the MMPI, the standard deviations, and codes. Table 2 presents the differences between means and significances of these differences. While studying relationships between MMPI patterns and clinical diagnoses, Gough [234 (see VI, 38)] found that over-all elevations of composite profiles increased with the severity of psychiatric conditions grouped as follows: psychoneurosis, mild; psychoneurosis, moderate; psychopathic personality, and psychoneurosis, severe. It may be noted from Table 1 that the composite profile for the anxiety reaction cases is in general higher than those for the two other groups. Modlin [449 (see VII, 49)] found that anxiety could be evaluated by averaging the scores of the Hs, D, and Hy scales to

Table 1. T-Score Means, Standard Deviations, and Codes of Various Diagnostic Groups

Group	N	?	L	F	K	Hs	D	Hy	Pd	Mf	Pa	Pt	Sc	Ma
Dissociative-conversion (N = 34)														
Mean	51.5	54.0	54.2	56.2	70.0	61.9	71.4	56.7	51.5	49.6	54.1	54.1	56.9
SD					9.6	13.1	10.1	10.5	8.6	9.8	9.0	8.9	9.1	12.2
MMPI Code: 31'2–94 785/6 KFL?/														
Somatization (N = 105)														
Mean	50.5	52.6	54.2	52.6	75.0	67.2	67.7	58.5	54.4	53.5	58.7	55.2	56.4
SD					8.2	13.4	12.8	9.5	9.6	8.9	9.6	10.6	11.0	12.9
MMPI Code: 1'32–749856 FLK?/														
Anxiety (N = 60)														
Mean	50.2	51.6	60.8	48.4	81.9	84.9	73.5	67.2	60.4	62.0	77.6	73.7	60.8
SD					11.1	12.3	12.3	10.9	12.8	10.0	10.0	13.6	15.7	12.6
MMPI Code: 21"783'4695 F–L?/K														

Table 2. Differences and t Values between Means of Each Group

Item	?	، L	F	K	Hs	D	Hy	Pd	Mf	Pa	Pt	Sc	Ma
D-C minus S													
Diff	−1.0	−1.4	0.0	−3.6	5.0	5.3	−3.7	1.8	2.9	3.9	4.6	1.1	−0.5
t						2.2				2.0	2.3		
D-C minus A													
Diff	−1.3	−2.4	6.6	−7.8	11.9	23.0	2.1	10.5	8.9	12.4	23.5	19.6	3.9
t				3.4	4.3	9.2		4.2	4.1	5.9	8.9	6.6	
S minus A													
Diff	−0.3	−1.0	6.6	−4.2	6.9	17.7	5.8	8.7	6.0	8.5	18.9	18.5	4.4
t				2.7	3.3	8.6	3.5	4.9	4.0	5.3	9.9	8.8	2.1

form an anxiety score. He presents a curve the left-hand side of which is similar to the "anxiety" pattern in Table 1, but the right-hand side of his curve approximates average. He submits another curve for cases with symptoms of longer standing and this curve contains a secondary elevation on the right-hand side. Our curve is comparable to this second curve and probably reflects those of our cases who had their anxiety conditions for some time prior to hospitalization. The composite profile for the somatization cases is lower in general than that for the anxiety cases, yet higher than that for the dissociative-conversion cases. This suggests that our group of anxiety cases was characterized by more emotional distress, as measured by the MMPI, than obtained for either of the other two groups. Second in extent of emotional distress according to the same criterion was the group with somatization reactions. The group of dissociative-conversion cases approximated normal profiles except for elevations on the hypochondriacal and hysterical scales. Findings by Gough [235] and others indicate that severity of emotional disturbance is most strongly reflected in the depression, hypochondriacal, schizophrenic, and psychasthenic scales of the MMPI, and roughly in that order. The differences between our groups were in general greatest on these four scales.

Clinical study indicated that patients given a major diagnosis of anxiety had, as a rule, considerable subjective distress. When examined they were likely to have such complaints as "internal nervousness," sensations of pressure inside the head, palpitation, excessive sweating, feelings of despair, etc. The usual patients with dissociative-conversion symptoms expressed little if any emotional stress. The patients with predominant somatization reactions frequently complained of nervousness and emotional problems in addition to the somatic features, but the emotional symptoms were usually not sufficiently severe to interfere seriously with their daily activities.

Although every individual in our three groups received a psychoneurotic designation, it would appear that emotional discomfort among the dissociative-conversion patients was not much more extreme than is found among so-called normal individuals, according to MMPI ratings. It is of course possible that such individuals have a ready means of disposing of emotional strains by developing hysteroid symptoms. These symptoms may serve as a form of adaptation to the distressing situation and as a special shield against increased stress. Apparently the somatization cases were less successful in relieving subjective distress through channeling into symptoms involving visceral systems. The anxiety cases apparently had little success in relieving tension although many of them were characterized by having hypochondriacal symptoms as one form of manifestation of the anxiety reactions. The above statistics are consistent with some findings made by Meehl [436 (see V, 31)] when using a "blind" diagnosis procedure from MMPI profiles. In his study only about half of 10 hysterias were identified as abnormal in contrast with the spotting as abnormal of 11 out of 13 hypochondriacs.

Aside from somatization and dissociative-conversion reactions being interpreted in terms of channeling and symbolic reactions, there are other possible interpretations. Some somatization cases might have a constitutionally low threshold for disturbance of autonomic balance involving innervation of one or more of the various visceral systems. The low threshold may render them especially susceptible to development of somatization reactions without emotional stress being severe. Also at time of examination some of the somatization cases may have been retaining residuals of earlier autonomic disruptions without having current emotional problems of a serious nature. Some anxiety cases seemed to have had symptoms attributable to generalized autonomic imbalance without a focus on any specific visceral system. Such cases as these might have constitutionally unstable autonomic mechanisms. Some dissociative-conversion cases might possess a physiology underlying cerebral integration which has a constitutionally low threshold for disruption or shunting. Then again, early conditioning or habit reactions may have disposed some of our somatization and dissociative-conversion cases to the particular clinical reactions, the conditioned responses being activated on occasion of only mild emotional stress. This could especially apply to the dissociative-conversion cases since processes primarily under voluntary control are usually more easily conditioned than those largely under involuntary control. There is a likelihood that several factors have been operative in the groups and a possibility that several factors like those mentioned above were operative in every case.

Our present study contains some data relating to the merits of MMPI profiles as diagnostic aids. The pattern obtained for the group of dissociative-conversion cases seems to be a distinctive one. A count was made of the number of individuals in each of the three groups who produced profiles with scores in the Hs and Hy scales higher than on any of the other scales of the neurotic and psychotic triads, and with a valley between these two scales. Approximately 62 per cent of the dissociative-conversion cases produced such patterns, 46 per cent of the somatization cases did so, and only about 8 per cent of the anxiety cases fell in this category. The composite profile for the somatization cases contains its highest peak on the Hs scale, the next two highest being on the D and Hy scales. About 41 per cent of the somatization cases had this kind of profile; 18 per cent of the dissociative-conversion cases and 7 per cent of the anxiety cases had it. The composite profile for the anxiety cases has its highest elevation on the D scale with the two next highest being on the Hs and Pt scales. This combination fitted 23 per cent of the anxiety cases, 4 per cent of the somatization cases, and none of the dissociative-conversion cases. According to these figures there was greatest consistency of MMPI response patterns within the group of dissociative-conversion cases, and least within the anxiety group, the somatization group falling in between.

Summary

Three groups of psychoneurotics were compared for their composite profiles produced on the MMPI. The groups were somatization, dissociative-conversion, and anxiety reactions. The group of anxiety cases had more anguish on the whole than had either of the other two groups, from the standpoint of MMPI patterns as well as from clinical observations. The somatization cases showed up as having less emotional distress than the anxiety group but more so than the dissociative-conversion group. Theoretical considerations are presented in an endeavor to account for some of the differences between the three groups. Possibly the dissociative-conversion cases tended to acquire their characteristic symptoms before emotional discomfort became more than mild. The somatization cases may have been especially vulnerable to autonomic disruptions involving circumscribed organ systems before emotional turbulations in themselves became incapacitating. The anxiety cases may have tended to develop physical complaints only after emotional distress became severe.

Representative MMPI profiles selected about 60 per cent of the group of dissociative-conversion cases, about 40 per cent of the somatization cases, and not quite 25 per cent of the anxiety cases. Overlap of the anxiety group with each of the other two groups amounted to less than 10 per cent in all comparisons. The dissociative-conversion and the somatization groups were much more nearly alike.

ARTICLE 41 *Six MMPI Diagnostic Profile Patterns*

The General Problem

SINCE the original publication of the MMPI there has arisen a general trend in techniques of interpretation toward an emphasis on the total pattern of the profile and away from a study of elevations of single scales considered by themselves. For that matter, the question of profile pattern is first presented in the original *Manual* [304], although the authors did not have sufficient information at that time to make definitive statements about the profile patterns which appear most frequently with certain more or less well defined clinical syndromes.

Emphasis on the pattern of the profile has arisen because experience with this instrument in a clinical setting has shown that any given scale is not specific to the disorder on which it was derived. Thus, for example, the depression scale, D, may be the most elevated on the profile of a patient whose symptom picture does not warrant the diagnosis of depression, and Pt (psychasthenia) may be markedly elevated when there is little evidence of obsessive-compulsive behavior. The misleading tendency to consider the scales separately is probably an outgrowth of the techniques used in the development of the inventory. The authors derived and assigned weights to each scale separately and identified the scales with symbols which are abbreviations of the disorders on which the scales were derived. In this way each scale was designed to differentiate a group of patients from a sample of nonpatients. The scales were not derived to separate one group of patients from another group of patients. For this reason each scale is loaded to varying degrees with characteristics which differentiate patients from nonpatients. By the same process any combination of scales may be loaded with common factors. The relatively high intercorrelation of Pd (psychopathic deviate) and Ma (hypomania) suggests that each scale is measuring the common characteristic of disregard for social controls and love of excitement as well as characteristics more specifically psychopathic or hypomanic.

In this light, then, there is no justification for attaching any significance to minor fluctuations within one standard deviation of the mean, as one might in saying that one person with a T score of 59 on Hs is somewhat more hypochondriacal than one who has a T score on the same scale of 49. There is further support for this contention in the results of a study by Stout [571]. With a population of more or less randomly selected college students, she found that three factors accounted for 93 per cent of the variance of the nine scales. There is some question whether similar results would be found with a population of persons in need of psychotherapy. Indeed, there is some reason to feel that factor analysis, using Pearson product-moment coefficients, may be an unsatisfactory method of studying the relationship of the scales. This is suggested when we consider the relationship of D and Ma in which an elevated D and an elevated Ma suggest an anxiety disorder, while an elevated D and a depressed Ma (below 60) are most frequently associated with a depressed condition. In this instance it is the deviation from linearity of relationship of the two scales that is of considerable diagnostic importance. The evidence available seems to indicate that just as the scales were derived empirically, the patterns must be derived empirically.

Problems of Validation of Profile Patterns

One of the most persistent problems in such validation studies as this, regardless of the instrument used, is that of finding some criterion with which to compare the results. With few exceptions, studies which have been done with the MMPI have used as criteria psychiatric diagnoses. The inadequacy of this criterion has been amply demonstrated by Ash [r12] and by many others. This criterion is particularly precarious when the investigator has little acquaintance, if any, with the subjects of his sample and when the final diagnosis is taken without question from the files. A further pitfall of this order is the possibility that the test was administered when the patient was unable or unwilling to cooperate, or after the patient had partially recovered from his illness. With respect to the last statement the author has noticed that a patient recovering from an acute schizophrenic episode is sometimes able to give a relatively normal MMPI profile a few days before his ward behavior is back to normal.

There are at least two avenues of escape from this problem of finding criteria to which we can relate test findings. We can reject diagnoses and set up different sorts of criteria such as length of stay in the hospital, ratings on the degree of recovery or tests of the degree of agreement between descriptions based on test findings and the findings of the case history. The alternative lies in recognizing the sources of error in diagnoses and in attempting to control them. In this study we adopted the latter method and set up three conditions to reduce the amount of error in the diagnoses and to facilitate the communication of our findings. Patients' profiles were included only when there was complete agreement among the psychiatric staff concerning their diagnosis. There was a strong indication in the patient's file that he was ill at the time of testing. Since there is intra-staff variation as well as inter-staff variation in definitions of diagnoses, a brief description of the outstanding characteristics of each group is included. This last condition should enable us to think in terms of the kinds of behavior associated with a certain profile pattern as well as a diagnosis — if we must think in terms of diagnoses at all.

Review of Relevant Studies

Of the reports that are available on MMPI profile patterns, five stand out as particularly pertinent to this investigation. In a study that did not take patterns into account, Benton and Probst [56] measured the relationship between psychiatric judgments of the characteristics measured by the scales and the scales themselves. Statistically significant relationships were found for Pd, Pa (paranoia), and Sc (schizophrenia). This study demonstrates the unsatisfactory nature of an approach which considers the scales separately. Morris [456] found that mean profiles of different diagnostic groups were not significantly different. He does not indicate that he worked with patterns. Rubin [509], using the analysis of variance technique, found significant differences for only Sc and Cannot Say on four groups of patients: chronic alcoholics without psychosis, psychopaths, psychoneurotics, and psychotics. He also reports that the patterns found by Gough [234 (see VI, 38)] did not stand up in his study, though he does not indicate that he actually had clinicians who were acquainted with the MMPI sort the profiles according to Gough's pattern criteria. The mean profiles presented by Rubin appear, on inspection, to be similar to those found by Gough. The characteristic profile patterns reported by Gough [234] and Schmidt [528 (see VI, 39)] will be compared with our own results in a following section.

Table 1. T-Score Means and Codes for Six Diagnostic Groups

Group	?	L	F	K	Hs	D	Hy	Pd	Mf	Pa	Pt	Sc	Ma
Anxiety state (N = 12).........	50	55	61	47	72	83	66	64	58	57	78	75	66
		2″781'394–56 F–L?/K											
Inadequate (N = 19)..........	51	56	55	55	79	69	73	60	55	52	62	62	62
		13'27894–56 LKF?/											
Psychopath (N = 25)..........	51	51	57	51	54	61	57	74	53	56	60	62	67
		4'9827–36 15 F?LK/											
Paranoid (N = 15).............	52	52	66	47	58	62	58	68	a	76	63	76	63
		68'4792–13 F–?L/K											
Depressed (N = 7).............	51	54	58	49	64	81	62	58	a	66	69	62	51
		2″ ″76138–49 FL?/K											
Manic (N = 11)................	50	53	63	52	48	47	48	62	a	59	51	62	78
		9″ '48–67/132 F–LK?											

a Mean Mf scores for these three groups were not computed since these groups included a number of women.

Procedure and Results

Source of Data. The data used in this study were collected during the author's internships at a mental hospital and at a veterans' hospital in Ontario. Safeguards of complete agreement of the diagnostic staff and illness of the subject at the time of testing were carefully observed. The influence of the psychometric findings on the diagnosis was minimal since the diagnosis of the psychiatrist was recorded before the psychometric findings were presented.

Profile Patterns. Six diagnostic groups, yielding a total of 89 cases, were large enough to warrant consideration. The mean profile of each group based on K-corrected T scores is presented in Table 1. In order to relate the profile to the characteristics of the syndrome rather than to the category name itself, there follows a brief description of some of the common features of each group and suggestions concerning the identifying features of each diagnostic profile.

Psychoneurosis, Anxiety State. These patients reported to the hospital with complaints of tenseness, worry, inability to sleep, and a variety of mild somatic complaints. Their final diagnosis, made at the time of their discharge from the hospital, indicated that all were in the recovered or improved category. This is in marked contrast to the following neurotic group who were frequently described in such terms as "at his own individual normal."

The distinguishing features of this profile are the prominent D elevation and a secondary elevation of Pt and Sc. In contrast to a psychotic's profile, F and Pa are usually close to 50, and in contrast to a depressed patient's profile, Ma is above 60.

Psychoneurosis, Inadequate Personality. The same term is used here as was used by the psychiatrist who had to do with the diagnosis of these neurotic patients. He placed in this category those neurotics who showed a long history of marginal adjustment, a low tolerance to anxiety, and a poor response to treatment. There is usually a strong component of somatic complaints which can best be described as neurasthenic. He did not include in this category those who had a history of delinquency.

The "D valley" and milder elevation of the psychotic end differentiate this group from the last one. From this evidence the author would suggest that it is frequently convenient to think of the D scale as measuring the discontent of the patient with his present condition and his motivation to improve.

Psychopathic Personality, Asocial Type. These patients were hospitalized for a variety of reasons including alcoholism, court referral, and anxiety complaints. Almost all of them gave a history of minor delinquency, unsteady work, and poor home relations. Summaries emphasized that few had profited from treatment.

This profile is characterized by a Pd spike and a secondary Ma elevation. In some instances a Pa rise reflected his reaction to the restriction of his freedom.

Paranoid Schizophrenia. Since the breadth of this category may vary from one diagnostician to another, only those showing strong evidence of hallucinations and/or delusions as well as other schizophrenic features were included in this group.

This profile is characterized by three high points: the Pa, Sc, and F scales. In this group Pt tended to be much lower than Sc though this last relationship may not be so marked in subsequent studies.

Depression. This category is included somewhat hesitantly since it is made up of four psychotic and three severe neurotic depressions.

With this small number these tentative profile characteristics are offered. There is a prominent D spike and an F elevation particularly with psychotic depressions. The Pt scale is elevated to near or above 70 and Ma is below 60.

Manic Conditions. Nine of these patients were diagnosed manic-depressive psychosis, manic phase, and the remaining two hypomanic.

Their profiles usually showed a gross elevation of the Ma scale with Sc and F approaching a T score of 70. The Pt scale of all of these patients is normal or below a T score of 50.

Results of an Analysis of Variance. An analysis of variance of the eight clinical scales, excluding Mf, using the method outlined by McNemar [r108], produced eight F ratios which were significant beyond the .01 level of confidence.

A Test of Patterns by Blind Sorting. It was felt that, while there are rather marked differences between the mean profiles of the various groups, the profiles found within one diagnostic group might be so heterogeneous that individual cases could not be sorted with a satisfactory degree of accuracy. The 89 profiles, identified only by a number, were given to seven members of the Department of Psychology at the University of Minnesota who were thoroughly familiar with this instrument. They were told the six diagnostic categories but were not given the number of cases which fell in each of them. They were asked to sort each profile into one of the six groups. After they had recorded their placements they were given the number which fell in each category and asked to change their sortings if they wished to with these N's in mind. The number of correct placements for each judge is shown in Table 2.

Table 2. Correct Placements for Each Judge

Judge	First Sorting	Second Sorting
A	54	51
B	42	52
C	51	55
D	a	55
E	43	47
F	38	42
G	36	32

a This judge was aware of the N of each group before he was asked to participate in this experiment.

These results are rather conclusive since even the poorest sorting is an improvement over chance significant beyond the .01 level. Frequencies were too small for individual judges to use a contingency coefficient. Combining all the judges' placements in a 6 x 6 table yielded a contingency coefficient of .71 for both sortings, but this value is somewhat inflated since the judges looked at the same profiles with the result that the events are not totally independent.

Discussion

The patterns of the mean profiles found in this study resemble rather closely those found by Gough [234 (see VI, 38)] and Schmidt [528 (VI, 39)], though there are considerable differences in terms of absolute elevations. The results of the blind sorting study indicate that there is considerable general agreement among those who have studied profile patterns. The marked discrepancy between the results of this analysis of variance and those found by Rubin [509], using the same technique, can be accounted for in part if we study Table 1. Combining the last three groups — paranoid, depressed, and manic — into a psychotic group would bring together a group with widely divergent means and would probably result in several nonsignificant F ratios. More nonsignificant F ratios would probably result from combining the groups called anxiety state and inadequate personality into one psychoneurotic category.

Summary and Conclusions

1. The mean MMPI profile patterns of six diagnostic groups totaling 89 patients are presented.

2. Blind sorting of these profiles by seven judges into the six diagnostic categories gave results which indicate that a high degree of accuracy of identification can be achieved by those who are thoroughly familiar with profile patterns.

3. Analysis of variance of eight clinical scales of the MMPI produced significant F ratios on each scale.

4. In using the MMPI as an aid in diagnosis one must take into account the profile pattern as well as the absolute elevation of any given scale.

IF THE MMPI was ultimately to fulfill the aims of its authors "to provide, in a single test, scores on all the more important phases of personality" [303, p. 2], it was imperative that the test should show useful associations with psychiatric criteria when applied in installations where there were variations in the clinical groups that were seen, in the psychiatric procedures employed, and in the populations treated. If the test failed entirely to show useful relationships in the face of these changes, it could not serve as the common language of communication so urgently needed throughout the field of psychiatry. However, it would be unlikely for the test to show identical functional relationships with psychiatric judgments in these new places if there were, as often contended, important semantic and procedural variations from installation to installation. The empirical research reported in this section provides a reassuring degree of evidence on the way the MMPI has stood up through these changes and the usefulness of the instrument in psychiatric problems other than diagnosis.

One of the earliest studies reported appears here as article 42. Leverenz reports on patients in medical and surgical wards as well as neuropsychiatric cases in an army hospital. Although the statistical treatment of the data is not as refined as in later studies, the confirmation of findings reported by the test authors is excellent. In his material Leverenz reports the test scores were useful in the prognostic work of differentiating those who could return to duty as opposed to those who had to be discharged from the service.

In article 43, Modlin also presents data obtained in a military setting. He reports in detail on the control group and various diagnostic groupings. By analyzing the use of the cutting score of 70 (or two standard deviations above the mean for Minnesota normals) on the various scales, he is able to show that, while for the majority of diagnoses the cutting scores are extremely effective, for specific subgroups of psychiatric cases they may lead to misses. He also proceeds to a form of profile treatment similar in many respects to the material reported in Section VI in this volume. His suggestion for an anxiety score based upon a composite of the neurotic triad did not meet general acceptance, probably because it did not properly weight the configurations among these three scales [620 (see V, 32)].

Benton in article 44 makes an explicit test of the diagnostic role of the various clinical scales on a small but carefully selected set of cases from a naval hospital. His findings are in general agreement with those reported previously in the literature and reaffirm the need for care in reaching definitive psychiatric diagnoses from the test data alone. In this paper he also reports one of the first of the test-faking studies which have proved so useful in subsequent MMPI research [235]. Unfortunately, the study is based upon the abbreviated form of the MMPI and some of the criteria now known to help identify dissimulation [245 (see V, 35)] cannot

374

be applied to his data. However, it is interesting to note several important features of these data not included in the original publication of the article but available through the courtesy of the author. Of the ten cases of homosexuality, four were not able to reduce their scale 5 (Mf) scores on the second administration sufficiently to change the original diagnostic significance (90 to 78, 69 to 65, 92 to 80, and 94 to 94). On the remaining cases the scale 5 scores shifted in such a way as to affect the clinical interpretation (82 to 49, 74 to 63, 69 to 43, 92 to 65, 78 to 63, and 80 to 41). On these successful fakings the clinical interpretation of the resulting protocols would have been guarded because of the simultaneous elevations on the L scale. By applying Meehl's [436 (see V, 31)] criterion of a raw score of seven or more on the L scale, four of the above six faked protocols would have been identified, although none of the original L scale values on the ten homosexual cases were as high as this value. Such studies should be repeated on the whole MMPI test.

In articles 45 and 46, Peterson takes up the important and closely related problems of identifying the need for hospitalization and the early diagnosis of schizophrenia in outpatient groups. Working with extremely carefully selected groups he has applied some of the most advanced pattern analysis procedures to MMPI data with gratifying results.

Hewitt's material in article 47 is one of the earliest applications of the MMPI to the problem of alcoholism. His finding of an elevated scale 4 (Pd) in all his cases selected from an Alcoholics Anonymous group has been subsequently confirmed in many studies, all of which indicate that this pattern is one of the most important of the several subgroups of alcoholic addiction [90, 429]. Hewitt also performed an item analysis on his group to determine if the separations he obtained were merely a direct description on the part of his subjects of their drinking activities.

In the last article in this section, Farberow has applied the MMPI to the extremely important but difficult problem of suicide. Obviously the very nature of the phenomenon itself makes the case material difficult to obtain and its statistical rarity also makes the criterion difficult to use [499]. However, in his analyses, Farberow uses the difference between mere verbalization of intent and some bona fide attempt as well as psychiatric judgments about the validity of the verbalizations and actions as a basis for scaling the subjects available for study. He was handicapped to some extent by the lack of test material acquired before the suicidal behavior, but he was able to set forth a number of excellent conclusions about the psychological significance for the subject's subsequent adjustment status of some demonstrable suicidal gesture.

The articles in this section came from the following sources: article 42 from C. W. Leverenz, MMPI: an evaluation of its usefulness in the psychiatric service of a station hospital, *War Medicine*, 1943, 4, 618–629; article 43 from H. C. Modlin, A study of the MMPI in clinical practice with notes on the Cornell Index, *American Journal of Psychiatry*, 1947, 103, 758–769; article 44 from A. L. Benton, The MMPI in clinical practice, *Journal of Nervous and Mental Disease*, 1945, 102, 416–420; article 45 from D. R. Peterson, Predicting hospitalization of psychiatric outpatients, *Journal of Abnormal and Social Psychology*, 1954, 49, 260–265; article 46 from D. R. Peterson, The diagnosis of subclinical schizophrenia, *Journal of Consulting Psychology*, 1954, 18, 198–200; article 47 from C. C. Hewitt, A personality study of alcohol addiction, *Quarterly Journal of Studies in Alcohol*, 1943, 4, 368–386; and article 48 from N. L. Farberow, Personality patterns of suicidal mental hospital patients, *Genetic Psychology Monographs*, 1950, 42, 3–80. We are indebted to the authors and to the publishers of the journals for permission to reproduce these articles in this form.

C. W. LEVERENZ

ARTICLE 42 *The MMPI: An Evaluation of Its Usefulness in the Psychiatric Service of a Station Hospital*

FROM the standpoint of the neuropsychiatric section of the Medical Corps of the United States Army, the answer to the question of whether a soldier is or is not fit for duty in the military service requires a major decision. The medical officers charged with the diagnosis, care, and disposition of neuropsychiatric patients admitted to the military hospital must make this decision. The patient's fitness or unfitness must be ascertained as quickly as possible, in order either to return him to duty or to secure his early separation from the military service.

The problem is slightly more complicated for the military neuropsychiatrist than for the civilian physician in the same category. Consideration must be given to the manifestations of subjection to the stress of performing military duties, the effects of change of environment, the excitement and the clash of the many personalities of a large group of persons hitherto unknown to each other, in addition to the usual factors involved in such cases. There are few medical settings where time-saving diagnostic devices would be more appreciated than in the clinical services of the medical department. Because of the shortage of trained psychiatrists in comparison with the number of troublesome psychoneurotic and psychotic problems which require evaluation, such an aid as the MMPI is particularly desirable in the fields of personality study.

In July 1942, after a consultation with Colonel W. G. Guthrie, commanding officer, Station Hospital, Fort Snelling, Minnesota, Dr. J. Charnley McKinley, professor of neuropsychiatry, University of Minnesota Medical School, and Dr. Starke R. Hathaway, associate professor of psychology, University of Minnesota Medical School, the author instituted this study to determine the applicability of the personality inventory to the military service. The test has more than proved itself to be sufficiently useful and therefore merits general attention as an additional instrument to assist in the clinical evaluation of psychiatric disorders. It has been in constant use at the Fort Snelling hospital for over one year, during which time more than 700 profiles have been completed. The inventory in its present form is

376

the result of five years' work by its authors at the University of Minnesota previous to this trial in the military service.

The patient will require from thirty minutes to several hours for completion of the test, depending on his intelligence and the presence of psychotic reactions, such as psychomotor retardation. In the presence of a psychosis with severe disintegration of thought processes (acute mania or delirium, for example) the test cannot be satisfactorily applied. No supervision is required other than routine caution and observation so that the patient receives no guidance from others in sorting the items.

The test was given in a room away from the patient group, the number present at any one time varying from one to four. The administration and scoring were carried out by an enlisted man who was trained in the work. He usually required twenty to twenty-five minutes for the recording and scoring of a test.

The final scores as they reach the clinician are in standard form and are plotted on a chart so as to provide a profile of the strength of the several traits. At present, the scores obtained are for hypochondriasis, depression, hysteria, psychopathic personality of the amoral type, masculinity-femininity of interests, paranoia, psychasthenia, and schizophrenia. Hypomania has been recently added to this group. Some of these scales are less dependable than others because more clinical material is needed for their satisfactory derivation and final validation, but all are acceptably useful for the clinician. In addition to these clinical scores, three others are included bearing on the validity of the subjects' responses.

Since the scores on the clinical traits are reduced to standard form, given numerical values have approximately the same meaning for all the scales. In terms of scores, 50 is average, 60 is rather high in the direction of psychiatric diagnosis, and 70 is borderline, but most abnormal persons attain scores higher than 70 at one or more points on the curve, or profile.

The test as applied to the clinical material in this hospital has made several important contributions. In the first place, it has aided greatly in giving direction to the inquiry in evaluating obviously psychiatric disorders. Routinely administered to subjects with such disorders, the test results have come to be of great assistance in catagorizing the disturbances of personality and in providing a measure of their severity. This has become increasingly true as experience with the test has demonstrated its validity in comparison with the usual clinical study. Secondly, the test has been of assistance in evaluating the borderline conditions and the mixtures of psychotic and psychoneurotic elements, on which definite decisions are difficult to make in a short period of observation and study. The test has also helped materially in the medical and surgical wards in disclosing the probable contribution of neurotic components in disturbances that have finally proved to be complex psychosomatic syndromes. At one time this may mean that surgical intervention and the more radical procedures are to be avoided, whereas at another time it may result in unusually early recognition of an organic disorder because of the presence of a normal profile and the consequent improbability of a neurotic basis for the complaint. Finally, the test has been valuable both diagnostically and prognostically for men who are under consideration for dismissal from the armed forces because of personality disorders.

Two checks of the validity of the results on military personnel were applied in this study. Fifty-four members from the medical detachment on duty at the hospital, picked at random, were given the test. This was done to determine whether the curves obtained for this group of presumably normal men would be within normal limits as given by the standard scores provided with the test sets. None of this group was a patient in the hospital at the time, and only one gave a history of persistent complaints. After appearing repeatedly on sick call, he had been observed, examined, and considered psychoneurotic before being given the test. His inventory verified the clinical impression to a high degree, in that his curve was clearly abnormal, and his scores were discarded. The median scores for these unselected and presumably normal men are shown in Table 1. Remembering that 50 is the average score expected and that 70 is a borderline abnormal score, the reader will see that the values for normal groups as given by the authors of the test are reasonably representative for these men.

Table 1. Median T Scores and Codes of Representative Groups

Group	N	H—C_H	D	Hy	Pd	Mf	Pa	Pt	Sc
Medical detachment	54	48	50	52	54	52	46	48	51
MMPI Code: 43582/176									
Surgical patients	105	53	52	53	55	54	50	49	53
MMPI Code: 451382 6/7									
Neuropsychiatric patients, hypochondriasis	48	83	72	78	54	53	51	57	55
MMPI Code: 1″32′–78456									
Neuropsychiatric patients, depression	28	67	81	66	57	57	57	65	57
MMPI Code: 2″ ′137–4568									
Neuropsychiatric patients, psychosis	29	56	77	65	62	53	66	74	79
MMPI Code: 827′634–15									

A second check on the stability of the normal points is provided by the median values shown in Table 1. These are the medians for 105 patients in the surgical wards, among whom one might expect a few neurotically inclined persons but for the most part persons who are normally equilibrated mentally. Of this number, 54 profiles gave values below 60 on all scales; 49 profiles had one or more points between 60 and 70. Two patients had profile values above 70. The somewhat higher values were obtained principally on the scores for hypochondriasis, depression, and hysteria, as one would predict, but the medians were clearly within the normal range. Again, the data indicate that the averages for normal subjects as given with the test are relatively stable.

The group of patients chosen at random in the psychiatric service was used for the basis of this report. A purpose of the study was to compare the validity of high scores obtained on the personality test with the clinical diagnosis. The group included men with diagnoses of psychoneurosis, psychosis, psychasthenia, hysteria, paranoid sensitivity, psychopathic deviate, or personality disorder, and men of abnormal sexual behavior. Clinical diagnoses were first made without the use of the inventory. A work-up of the case formulation included the use of all the means available to eliminate the presence of organic disease. These diagnoses and case formulations were then subsequently compared with the inventory scores for the same subjects. Even though the pressure of work at intervals and the amount of time available for each case made it difficult to study all with sufficient intensity to arrive at clinical diagnoses which were completely satisfactory, it was reasonable to assume that the majority of these were correct and that the test should confirm them. In the majority of the cases the scores on the inventory did confirm the clinical impression. This was especially true for the group with psychoneuroses, particularly those in which hypochodriasis was a prominent feature. As was to be expected, those subjects in whom there were complicated personality changes had similarly complex test scores. This group had the largest percentage of scores which did not verify the clinical impressions in their entirety; however, the clinician was still prompted to be cautious in his evaluation of these men relative to their fitness for duty.

Hypochondriasis [420 (see II, 6)] was prominent and was frequently present in the group of patients with disorders classified under psychoneurosis. Because of its frequency and because the authors of the inventory had completed the greatest amount of work on this scale along with those for depression and hysteria, particular emphasis was given to this part of the present study. It has been the impression here that persons subject to hypochondriacal trends in civilian life may in many cases be made more hypochondriacal under the stress of military service. It is felt that an increase in severity of the hypochondriacal aspect usually renders the soldier unfit for further military service. This was especially true for subjects whose high score for hypochondriasis was accompanied by elevated scores on the scales for depression and hysteria. It was not uncommon to obtain scores elevated above the borderline value of 70 for these three scales. In some cases elevation of the score on the scale for psychasthenia was additionally present. The inventory renders a definite aid to the clinician in such cases, because a score for hypochondriasis can be obtained quickly along with the other usual scores. He thus has at hand some measure of the severity of the personality defect or defects to assist him in his total evaluation of the case. Clinical impressions of a few cases were revised because of the unexpected elevation of certain test scores, which led the examiner to a more thorough examination, with the result that more positive findings were revealed.

Table 1 gives the median scores for patients with a diagnosis of psychoneurosis, hypochondriacal type. Further study of this group shows that 96 per cent obtained scores above the borderline value of 70 on the scale for hypochondriasis and that 100 per cent obtained scores above the high normal value of 60. Nine of the subjects (18.7 per cent) with pronounced hypochondriasis clinically had corresponding test scale values over 92. High scores on one or more of the other scales in addition to the hypochondriasis scale were made by 87.5 per cent of the subjects.

Depression [301 (see II, 7)] is a frequent component of many psychoneuroses and psychoses, and therefore it is to be expected that many of the profiles of the curves of patients selected for the depression aspect would show peaks on one or more scales other than depression. This is indeed true of this group. Table 1 shows the median results for subjects clinically judged as depressed; on the score for depression 93 per cent of the values were above 70 and 96 per cent were above 60.

The majority of these disorders were clinically recognized as having depression aspects, and usually this was verified by the test scale score; however, cases were encountered in which the depressive feature was not sufficiently considered. Here, again, the inventory proved of value in giving the clinician sufficient impetus to reconsider the depression aspect. Results for the other nonpsychotic disturbances, hysteria, psychasthenia, paranoid sensitivity, and psychopathic personality, were generally similar to those for the hypochondriacal and depressive groups as just presented. Subjects with abnormal homosexual behavior invariably revealed an elevated score on the masculinity-femininity scale.

As one would expect, psychotic subjects, when they were able to take the test, scored high on schizophrenia, paranoia, psychasthenia, and especially on combinations of several scores. Abnormal curves were obtained from 83 per cent of subjects with psychoses. The median values of the scales are shown in Table 1. The contrast is obvious in comparison with the third and fourth groups presented in the table, in which neurotic patients are shown to score high on hypochondriasis, depression, and hysteria.

Included in the series of patients from the psychiatric service subjected to the test was a small group for whom final diagnoses were not definitely established. Clinically, some members of the group seemed to have mixed types of psychoneuroses, while others exhibited both psychotic and neurotic personality changes. The inventory scores obtained for these patients were not in agreement with the tentative clinical impressions. In some cases the elevated scores resulted in bizarre profiles, while a few showed no significant elevated scores on any one of the scales. It is reasonable to assume that some of the patients in this group probably have complex personality disorders of one type or another which the inventory failed to reveal correctly. It is also the opinion of my colleagues and me that the clinical impression was not entirely correct in every case. Further work with the test may give more information on this phase.

An interesting group of patients for whom a positive diagnosis of peptic ulcer was made was also given the test. A high percentage of the group of forty-seven men revealed elevation of the scores for hypochondriasis, depression, and hysteria. In general, the results thus far seem to indicate that the most rapid improvement was obtained from patients having a relatively normal profile. On the other hand, patients with elevated scores on the scales indicated showed the least improvement clinically under treatment and were discharged from the military service. This group is at present being subjected to further study.

When the results of the inventory were studied from the opposite point of view, it was found that although persons who were neurotic or psychotic occasionally obtained normal profiles it was rare to observe an abnormal curve for a person when the abnormality could not be disclosed by conventional psychiatric observation. Those cases in which the personality deviations were of a mixed type usually offered the most difficult diagnostic problems. In many cases this difficulty was borne out by the values obtained on the inventory.

Report of Cases

Case 1. A soldier aged twenty-two was admitted to the Station Hospital, Fort Snelling, Minnesota, on February 12, 1943, because of an acute psychotic state. He was violent and suicidal, requiring personal restraint measures and a corpsman in constant attendance.

His record previous to admission to this hospital revealed that he had twenty-two months of service, of which the last twelve had been served on foreign duty in a cold climate. One week previous, the acute phase of his illness had been marked by a self-inflicted wound of the throat, made with a razor blade. Also he had been depressed, with probable delusions and hallucinations present.

Initial observations at this hospital were somewhat unsatisfactory because the patient was uncooperative. Two to three days later, it was revealed that pronounced depression complicated by some confusion was paramount to his persistent suicidal ideas. As the patient's attitude improved, it was further noted that the delusions were rather prominent and, in addition, there was occasional evidence of hallucinations. On one occasion soon after his admission, he attempted to tear away the sutures in the wound in his throat.

His care, in addition to the usual measures, included a special-duty corpsman in constant attendance for about ten days. At this point his acute phase had improved to the extent that it was deemed safe to remove the personal restraint. He was allowed the freedom of a single room in the closed ward under constant observation.

The period of improvement was characterized by less depression, but his delusions and hallucinations persisted. He became more talkative and cheerful. He took an interest in his surroundings and became less restless. At intervals he was preoccupied and the delusions were more pronounced. Smoking a cigarette was a source of great enjoyment. All through the early period of observation and improvement there was some evidence of impairment of insight. The laceration of his throat healed slowly because of the patient's previous attempt to remove the sutures.

Approximately three weeks after admission, the patient's improvement had progressed so that it was possible to obtain a complete and clear narration of the onset and progression of his symptoms previous to the attempt at suicide. The cardinal points are given in brief.

He stated that beginning in November 1942 he began to feel "nervous" and sleep became irregular. He worried concerning his continued and frequent masturbation's having an effect on his mind. Any kind of food eaten caused a "burning pain" in his "stomach," which he further described as "the burning pain of hell." Voices told him that he was "rotting away." With the persistence of his sensations and ideas over a period of at least two months and the thought that he was a failure in serving his country, he became increasingly depressed. The self-inflicted laceration of his throat climaxed his behavior.

At the end of the three weeks in this hospital, he was given the inventory, which yielded the profile code in Table 2. This type of code is representative for a relatively uncomplicated schizophrenia. The high scores are for schizophrenia, psychasthenia, and depression. These three points characterize the patient in a summary way. The prognosis for the condition portrayed by this type of score is poor.

At the time of the patient's transfer to a Veterans Administration facility for further care, his depression, delusions, and hallucinations were decidedly less but he still exhibited evidence of preoccupation and some lack of insight.

The clinical diagnosis was dementia praecox, type undetermined.

Case 2. A soldier aged thirty-four was admitted to the Station Hospital at Fort Snelling on April 18, 1943, with complaints of "asthma" and "nervousness" which had been present for the past ten to twelve years.

His record revealed that he was a member of the Quartermaster Corps with the grade of T/5 and that he had had a total of five and one-half years of service, four months of which had been on foreign duty in a cold climate. Two previous enlistments were dated 1925 to 1928 and 1928 to 1930. His present period of service began with his enlistment on October 14, 1942.

Table 2. T Scores and Codes of Representative Cases

Case	$H-C_H$	D	Hy	Pd	Mf	Pa	Pt	Sc
1. Dementia praecox 59		77	55	61	58	56	77	83
MMPI Code: 8″27′4–15 63								
2. Psychoneurosis, hypochondriasis 93		87	84	48	52	50	56	53
MMPI Code: 1°23″–7856/4								
3. Psychoneurosis, hysteria 88		80	87	50	53	56	43	51
MMPI Code: 132″–6584/7								
4. Dementia praecox, simple 40		46	40	52	63	62	66	70
MMPI Code: 8″756–4/213								
5. Psychoneurosis, reactive-depressive type 72		82	76	63	44	67	57	55
MMPI Code: 2″31′64–78/5								

The soldier's mother died of unknown causes when he was fifteen years old. He was cared for by a maternal uncle until the age of seventeen, at which time he falsified his age in order to enlist in the army. His previous personal history was otherwise noncontributory. His habits were considered to be normal. He was married in 1929 and had two daughters, whose ages were ten and twelve years respectively. The family relationship was considered normal.

The "asthma" was characterized by coughing and shortness of breath with no definite wheezing. He further emphasized that the "asthma" was almost continuous rather than occurring in definite attacks. He had consulted a physician in civilian life with variable frequency during the past five years for the same complaint. For three years he had worked only part of the time, for the same reason. Because of his poor health his wife had worked to assist in supporting the family.

He described his "nervousness" as contractions of the muscles in his legs, arms, and torso. Remaining quiet and inactive made the condition worse, but exercise gave a similar result. He had felt tired and weak most of the time for the past ten years, and exercise caused his heart to "pound fast," at which time he became restless. He was inclined to worry excessively regarding his health and in doing so became "anxious." He was unable to stand in one place long after any amount of exercise, because in being "warmed up" from the exertion his "nerves twitched" over his entire body. At these intervals he exhibited twitching and athetoid movements which he seemed to control while his attention was attracted to them but which recurred when he became occupied with something else.

A complete physical examination revealed nothing significant. His blood pressure was 110 systolic and 70 diastolic. A complete neurologic examination indicated normal conditions. Exhaustive laboratory investigation, including examination of the spinal fluid, disclosed no abnormalities. Psychiatric investigation revealed evidence of pronounced hypochondriasis. The patient was depressed over the long duration of his symptoms. He was not inclined to discuss his illness unless questioned at length. Clinically he was not suicidal. He was not a good "mixer" with the other patients in the ward. The clinical diagnosis was psychoneurosis, hypochondriacal type.

The code is shown in Table 2. This is a characteristic "neurotic" profile. Many such profiles change for the better with the improvement of the patient. Since such improvement usually leaves the patient with the susceptibility to further difficulty and since the facilities at this hospitial do not permit long treatment, he was considered unfit and was discharged from the service.

Case 3. A soldier aged twenty-two was admitted to the Station Hospital at Fort Snelling on February 17, 1943, complaining of dizziness, weakness, and pain in his right leg and foot. Mainly because of this, he was unable to walk without the aid of crutches, the right foot being carried in a "foot drop" position.

His previous history revealed that he had been inducted on July 21, 1942. He returned to his home on his postinduction furlough, and, he stated, about four days later, while on a field trip collecting zoology specimens, he accidentally shot himself in the right leg with his own .22 rifle. Previous to his induction, he had completed three and one-third years of college work in a premedical curriculum.

He was taken to the hospital near his home for care, and roentgenograms taken at that hospital revealed a fracture of the tibia of the right leg near the juncture of the distal and middle thirds. A cast was applied, and he remained in the hospital two weeks, after which time he was removed to his home and put under the care of his father, a physician. His activity was limited to movement about the home. In October 1942 the cast was removed. He stated that after a period of limited activity with the use of a cane his father encouraged him to try walking without a cane. He made such an attempt but returned to the use of the cane because, he claimed, the foot was too painful. Other activity included pushing a bicycle about with the use of one foot, but he was unable to ride normally. Regular hydrotherapy and massage of the right leg and foot had been instituted since removal of the cast, but improvement had been below normal.

On admission to this hospital, the patient was unable to walk without crutches. His weakness and dizziness kept him in bed. Roentgen examination of the right leg and foot revealed a well-healed fracture of the right tibia at the junction of the distal and middle thirds. There were talipes cavus and disuse atrophy of the bones of the foot and distal thirds of the tibia and fibula. There was a soft systolic murmur of the heart at the apex which was not transmitted and was considered to be functional. During the examination of the right leg, the patient flinched sharply whenever it was touched, no matter how lightly, any place from the knee down. Otherwise the physical examination was noncontributory. There were no areas of anesthesia or paresthesia and no other evidence of injury of the nerves of the right leg and foot. The laboratory investigation revealed nothing of significance other than the roentgen findings.

During the psychiatric interview the statement was elicited that the patient felt that he was "nervous," which he described as trembling accompanied by a "pounding of the heart" when excited or under stress. He would admit no depression or suicidal ideas. Dizziness whenever he sat up in bed or stood up on the floor was first noticed at the time the cast was removed, in October 1942.

His previous personal history brought out that at age eleven years his father had told him he had "leakage of the heart." As a result, his activities had been curtailed, and apparently he had experienced considerable anxiety about his heart. Then in 1939, while driving his father's car along a country road, he became weak and felt faint. He did not lose consciousness but became confused. The car ran into the ditch and was moderately damaged, but neither he nor his passengers were injured.

In 1940, while en route to a college class from his place of residence, he had a similar episode, in which he felt weak and "nervous." Although he trembled and felt like fainting, he did not lose consciousness. A physician was called, and the patient remained in bed, with weakness as the only remaining symptom. In 1941 he was subject to another episode in which he felt only weak. Again, he was kept in bed four days. Summing up all of his episodes, he admitted that excitement, noise, confusion, and some radio programs caused him to become extremely nervous, which was followed by weakness.

The clinical diagnosis was psychoneurosis, hysterical type. Although in this man there was evidence of hypochondriacal tendencies and of a cardiac neurosis, it was still felt that the hysteria was a prominent aspect coincident to the present episode. In spite of adequate physical therapy and psychotherapy in this hospital, he failed to show any great degree of improvement. He frequently protested that he had not tried to evade military service, when no mention of this question had been made.

The code is shown in Table 2. This is another example of the mixed type of psychoneurosis. Here the hysterical features clinically stand out more prominently. The underlying depression was expressed in the patient's anxiety. He was considered unfit for military service and was discharged.

Case 4. A soldier aged twenty-five was admitted to the Station Hospital at Fort Snelling on June 18, 1943, for mental observation. He had been absent without leave for three days following the expiration of his induction furlough. During the preliminary interview on admission, the patient was somewhat vague and preoccupied and easily suggestible. It was found that detailed questioning was necessary in order to ascertain the correct facts relative to his case.

Interrogation relative to his past history revealed that he had served twelve and one-half months in the navy before being discharged for a nervous disorder. It could not be definitely established through questioning the patient as to whether when inducted into the army he had volunteered the correct information about his discharge from the navy.

The patient's reason for being AWOL after induction into the army was that he was restless and desired to receive training as a member of the paratroops because he liked the excitement of such an assignment. He later refuted this statement when he admitted that it was impossible for him to learn his duties in the navy adequately because of the excitement and quick action necessary. It was also established that he had overstayed leave while on duty in the navy, previous to being hospitalized for observation. Immediately after his discharge from the navy, he sold all his uniforms and purchased civilian clothing before proceeding on the trip home. His explanation for doing this was that he was ashamed of having been discharged and that he did not want people to know he had ever been in the military service.

During the interval of seventeen months between his naval discharge and his induction into the army, he had changed his work four different times. He justified his acts by saying that he would become restless and nervous and that the work "preyed on his mind" whenever he remained in one place for any length of time. The patient stated that he felt he was "backward" and that the only way he could overcome this was to drink beer or whisky, which would result in his feeling much more "forceful" among people. He felt that frequent and continued masturbation had made him "backward" and had affected his mind and possibly would cause him to become insane. When people looked at him, he knew that they could tell that he was a masturbator. While in the naval service, he did not "pal around" with the other men of his ship while on shore leave for the same reason, preferring to go ashore alone and seek his own diversion and entertainment.

Detailed questioning revealed that he had an obsessive desire toward sexual relations with members of the opposite sex. The history seemed to indicate that this was first manifested during the period of his naval service. A short time previous to induction into the army, he had met a girl with whom he had had frequent sexual relations. He said that they were planning marriage soon. They were both of the same religious faith, but he stated that he had told her of his plans to change his religion so as to agree with that of his paternal grandmother. His fiancée did not agree with his views; however, this seemed to give the patient little concern.

Examination, which included physical, neurologic, and laboratory investigation, gave essentially normal results. Somatic complaints were absent. Psychologically there was definite evidence of preoccupation and vagueness, with obsessional trends. The presence of hallucinations was not established, but delusions were in evidence. His memory was extremely poor in some spheres and remarkably good in others, especially with reference to dates. Anxiety was conspicuously absent. While he was in the hospital, restlessness was much in evidence and emotional instability was noted at irregular intervals, especially during interviews. His lack of insight was not extreme but was rather variable in degree. His most frequent request while in the hospital was that he be given his release so that he could join a paratroop unit. He was not aware of the fact that he might be unfit for military service. The clinical diagnosis was given as dementia praecox, simple type. The code is shown in Table 2.

It was felt that this was a case of simple schizophrenia and that the patient was able to adjust to the demands of society in civilian life sufficiently to make institutionalization unnecessary. It was evident that he could not measure up to the exacting demands of the stress of military service. In general, the course of his inventory verified the clinical opinions while he was under observation in this hospital. He was discharged and returned to his home.

Case 5. A soldier aged twenty was admitted to the Station Hospital at Fort Snelling on June 14, 1943, complaining of weakness, loss of appetite, and weakness with dull aching pain of his legs. He also thought he had lost some weight. He had been a railroad carpenter in civilian life.

In a carefully taken history, it was noted that every morning for two weeks previous to the patient's admission to the hospital he had felt nauseated and had noticed a bad taste in his mouth. On several occasions he had vomited before breakfast, which had relieved the nausea. Usually little breakfast was eaten. Blood had never been noticed in the vomitus, nor had he ever had diarrhea or darkened stools. He had been irregularly subject to moderate constipation. During the day he had been free of any symptoms referable to his abdomen. In most instances his usual lunch and evening meals were eaten without incident in the company mess.

The patient stated that subsequent to exercise and especially after hikes his legs ached and felt weaker than formerly. He thought the weakness had ensued gradually over the two-week period previous to his admission. His sleep had been fair. During the first interview he would admit no cause for worry, anxiety, or depression. The existence of an abnormal situation in his unit which might give him concern could not be established. At the time of admission to the hospital, he had completed six and one-half months of military service, with a good record.

Routine laboratory investigation gave entirely normal results. The chest was normal on roentgen examination. A series of gastrointestinal tests revealed probable duodenitis but no other pathologic changes. The patient was given 10 minims (0.61 cc.) of tincture of belladonna and 1 fluidrachm (3.7 cc.) of elixir of three bromides three times a day. During the nine days that the patient was in the hospital, he was seen at several special interviews, in addition to the daily morning rounds.

During one of the special interviews, the patient finally admitted that he had several problems which were worrying him. A short time previously he had taken a loan from the Red Cross of $50 in order to pay for a trip home on an emergency furlough. The furlough was for the purpose of visiting his mother, who was said to have been ill with a "nervous breakdown." The patient stated that the loan was to be repaid at the rate of $15 per month until paid in full. His pay, less deductions for insurance, allotment to his mother, payment for a bond, and such incidentals as laundry, was insufficient to meet his obligations and leave a small balance for his own personal needs. Instead of attempting to make some readjustment of his financial obligations, he continued to keep his problem to himself and to worry about it. His anxiety continued, and with the passage of time he became depressed.

His second major worry concerned his own health. He was not able to understand the cause of his weakness, loss of appetite, and apparent loss of weight in such a short interval as two weeks. He thought of the aching pain and weakness of his legs after exercise as being due to the same cause as the symptoms referable to his abdomen. Careful interrogation revealed no concern that he might have a serious illness such as cancer or tuberculosis. He had harbored no suicidal tendencies.

Therapeutic measures included readjustment of his financial obligations, and he was given frequent reassurance that his illness was not serious and that he would recover. Later it was noted that his sleep improved and his appetite returned. His general attitude improved, and he presented a much more cheerful manner. Treatments with infrared rays and massage which had been instituted brought about pronounced improvement in the symptoms referable to his legs.

Inquiry into his family history revealed that his father had been found shot to death in the home five years previously. His own shotgun was lying beside him. The coroner's verdict had been suicide, but the family was convinced that the death was accidental. The family ties had been unusually close, and as a result of the sudden death of the father, the family was grief-stricken for some time. This was especially true of the patient's mother. The father had been retired as a railroad worker and had been in ill health for two years previous to his death. A paternal uncle, who was practically unknown to this soldier, had died as a patient in a hospital for persons with mental disease.

The clinical impression was psychoneurosis, reactive-depressive type.

Five days after admission to this hospital, the patient was given the MMPI. The code is shown in Table 2. Although the score on paranoia was relatively high borderline, no clinical manifestations could be elicited. It has been our experience that when such elevated scores appear without clinical justification, they are to be disregarded. Further experience with the inventory may reveal their true meaning in the future. Similar manifestations have occurred with all the scores except the first three, namely hypochondriasis, depression, and hysteria.

With reference to this case, it was felt that in all probability the abnormal personality manifestations were situational and therefore probably temporary in nature. This soldier was returned to duty in view of his striking improvement while in the hospital and because of his frank insistence that he usually did not react unfavorably to adversity. He also had a great desire to return to duty and be with his unit. He was later seen on the outpatient sick call and was found to be doing well. At the time of writing, it was felt that the decision was justified.

Summary

After an experience of over one year, the MMPI is considered to be of definite value in the neuropsychiatric service at Fort Snelling Station Hospital.

In some instances the psychiatric clinical investigation was redirected into new channels as a result of inventory scores which revealed hitherto unsuspected abnormal personality changes.

The clinical impression was not always corroborated by the scores obtained on the inventory; however, regardless of the final diagnosis, the clinician was made aware of the fact that one or more abnormal changes in personality existed which required evaluation.

The inventory, with a measure of the degree of abnormality, assisted the clinician in arriving at an earlier and more accurate impression than would otherwise have been possible. This contributed materially to the decision relative to the soldier's fitness or unfitness for military service.

ARTICLE 43 *A Study of the MMPI in Clinical Practice*

BECAUSE of its intricate subjectivity, psychiatry has until recently been able to lean only restrictedly on objective laboratory aids long essential to clinical medicine generally. For this reason, those conversant with the intangibilities of psyche and soma have eagerly explored potentialities in the psychometric testing of personality components.

Revolutionary psychiatric requirements of World War II stimulated and gave marked impetus to inquiry regarding this relatively new instrument, for the screening, evaluation, reassignment, and disposition of large masses of men within the military organization could not be accomplished through the individual handling traditional in clinical practice. Numerous valuable testing methods have been devised, and as Dr. Karl Menninger has stated [r116], "the practice of psychiatry without the assistance of modern psychological testing is as old fashioned and out of date as would be the practice of orthopedics without the x-ray."

Among the most ambitious attempts to objectify the data of clinical psychiatry is the MMPI developed by Hathaway and McKinley at the University of Minnesota. In a series of publications [300 (see II, 5), 301 (II, 7), 304, 420 (II, 6), 421 (II, 8), 423 (II, 9) 422], they have described in detail the compilation and validation of the test using manifold clinical media and types of controls. The test has been widely introduced to the armed forces, where it has been experimentally utilized in a wealth of case material, and it is receiving mention in neuropsychiatric literature with increasing frequency.

The purpose of the MMPI is to define the more important clinical phases of personality. This is accomplished by evaluation both of the symptoms and of the underlying personality structure. Some statements such as "My mouth feels dry almost all the time" and "Much of the time my head seems to hurt all over" are strictly symptomatic, while others inquire into attitudes toward parents, society, sex, etc. Such valuable features as are characterized by Murray's personality delineations [r127] and symptom catalogues of the Cornell Index [r168, r169] are combined in the test.

Indications for conducting the investigation reported here were several. First, a more extensive study of the individual application of the MMPI is necessary. Most of the statistical material of the authors and others is concerned with group comparisons rather than individual test results. That twenty-five hypochondriacs make

388

an average score of 74.2 on the hypochondriasis (Hs) scale [420] is interesting information; but it is desirable to enumerate those individuals making normal scores below the critical level of 70, those making significantly high scores on some of the remaining eight scales, and those patients in other diagnostic categories also making high scores on the Hs scale. The clinician does not see patients in pre-classified groups, and must be able to interpret individually the results on each MMPI record.

Second, the MMPI has not previously been applied to the largest single group of psychiatric disorders, the anxiety neuroses. There is no scale in the MMPI for anxiety, and none of the papers published by the authors or others have signified that research relative to this obvious defect has been undertaken. Clinical use of the test will be seriously limited if all patients with anxiety are to be ignored. The authors do state [304] that additional scales will be constructed from time to time from the original 550 questions, but it is doubtful that a satisfactory scale for measuring anxiety could be framed on the same basis as were the nine now in use. The peculiar affective drive termed anxiety permeates most psychiatric reactions, and is particularly prominent in all the subdivisions of neurosis. It is indeed possible that a scorable scale of characteristic statements discretely defining a pure anxiety type of personality could not be separated from the multiple symptomatological expressions of anxiety.

Third, it appears expedient to validate the authors' results. They state that several of their scales are only tentative because insufficient cases were used in forming them. It is advisable, if the test is to be of protean application, to evaluate it under conditions dissimilar to those under which the authors judged it [342].

Fourth, extension of the MMPI to all medical problems in which personality equations and functional factors figure is desirable. Ruesch and Bowman [515] have employed the test for evaluating post-traumatic headache; Abramson [3, 4] has applied it to minor deviations in "normal" officer personnel and to normal persons after ingestion of alcohol; Michael and Buhler [442] have tried it in ninety difficult diagnostic problems. The large numbers of enuretics, epileptics, alcoholics, somnambulists, migraine sufferers, etc., in the series reported here suggested excellent material for attempting to widen the scope of usefulness of the MMPI.

Fifth, the possibility of repeating the test at intervals to measure progress of a patient under treatment or to aid in prognosis should be investigated. Whether or not such a retest would be valid has not been studied to date.

Patient Material

The MMPI records in this report were obtained from 500 United States Army enlisted personnel. One hundred controls were chosen whose age and duty assignments were comparable to those of the 400 patients. The only specifications for inclusion of a man in the control series were that he be performing adequately in his military assignment and at the time be receiving no form of medical treatment. Of the 400 patients tested, results for 84 were discarded because of incompleteness, a doubtful diagnosis, or technical error; consequently, the findings are based on the scores of 316 testees.

Entirely normal records were obtained from 78 of the 100 control subjects, i.e., all nine diagnostic scores were below 70. Two sample normal profiles are shown in Table 1. Each of the remaining 22 records contained at least one score of 70. Twelve had only one score over 69, 6 had two scores over 69, 3 had three scores over 69, and 1 had four scores over 69. The abnormalities present were not marked since 13 were borderline (between 70 and 73), and only 4 of the 22 had a score over 76. The 10 patients making two or more high scores were interviewed, and definite evidence of anxiety was found in each. Since the intention was not to discover 100 normal MMPI records, but to differentiate between 100 noncomplaining soldiers and a group voicing symptoms, the 22 mildly abnormal records were retained in the control group. Separate studies of the 78 normal and of the 22 abnormal records revealed no significant qualitative differences. Hysteria (Hy) and hypomania (Ma) received the highest scores in each group, roughly in the same percentages.

Diagnosis

The authors state that the identifying diagnostic score may not be the highest of the nine made by the testee, but that it should rank among the highest three or four. The statistics presented here will illustrate complete agreement with that observation, particularly as applied to individual records rather than to group studies. Table 2 represents the potential value as a diagnostic aid of the four highest scores in an MMPI record. Only 20 per cent of the records of hypochondriacs scored highest in hypochondriasis (Hs), but 100 per cent had Hs as one of the four highest scores. Pd was the highest score on the record in only 14 per cent of the psychopathic deviations. Among the four highest scores, however, Pd occurred in 86 per cent of the records. Paranoia and hypomania are not represented in the 316 patients reported here. All figures are percentages. In the hysteria column, for example, 54 per cent of the 15 records showed hysteria (Hy) the highest of the nine scores, 18 per cent scored highest in depression (D), 18 per cent were highest in hypochondriasis (Hs), and 9 per cent were highest in psychasthenia (Pt). In comparison the lower half of the Hy column shows that 91 per cent of the records included Hy among the first four scores, and 91 per cent included D among the first four. The clinical diagnosis of the 117 patients detailed in Table 2 was discovered among the highest four scores in 92 per cent of the records.

Depression was most successfully verified by the MMPI, inasmuch as 88 per cent of 31 clinically classified depressives scored highest on the D scale. It is not surprising that a subjective tool such as the MMPI should accurately define an exquisitely subjective experience like depression. The success of the test in mirroring affective depression is exemplified by the high D scoring on test results for hypochondriasis, hysteria, and several other categories.

In this connection, the inadvisability of utilizing the MMPI as a substitute for clinical psychiatric knowledge in making diagnoses should be emphasized. Hathaway and McKinley do not state such an aim for their test, yet it has been criticized for failing to coincide with the clinical diagnosis [53 (see VII, 44), 442]. D was the highest score attained by 161 (51 per cent) of the total 316 cases; however, only 31 (10 per cent) of the patients were clinically diagnosed neurotic depressives. It follows that of every 100 patients scoring highest on the D scale only 20 will be primary depressives. Similar results were observed relative to hypochondriasis (Hs), hysteria (Hy), psychasthenia (Pt), and schizophrenia (Sc). Twenty-two

Table 1. MMPI T Scores and Codes of Various Curve Types

Curve Type	Hs	D	Hy	Pd	Mf	Pa	Pt	Sc	Ma
1, normal									
Example A	54	57	52	46	57	56	56	53	48
MMPI Code: 2567 183/94									
Example B	50	53	55	46	44	53	50	49	58
MMPI Code: 9326 17/845									
2, A score									
Example A	85	93	78	65	54	55	48	48	51
MMPI Code: 2°1"3'4–659/78									
Example B	93	81	84	58	59	52	52	56	52
MMPI Code: 1°32"–548679									
3	79	84	79	59	49	54	74	77	63
MMPI Code: 2"1387'9–46/5									
4, focal	58	56	82	60	55	57	49	53	52
MMPI Code: 3" '4–1625 89/7									
5, P score									
Example A	50	58	58	52	52	65	78	87	68
MMPI Code: 8"7'96–23 451									
Example B	48	54	52	53	54	63	72	78	84
MMPI Code: 9"87'6–2543/1									
6	84	92	88	88	78	83	89	86	89
MMPI Code: 2°7934816"5									

Table 2. Comparison in Each Clinical Diagnostic Category between the Highest and the Four Highest Scores on the MMPI (All MMPI Figures in Percentages)

Item	Controls	Clinical Diagnostic Categories						
		Hs	D	Hy	Pd	Mf	Pt	Sc
Number of cases	100	10	31	15	28	10	6	17
Highest MMPI score								
Hs		20		18	7		17	
D	11	60	88	18	50	30	33	28
Hy	27	20	6	54		20		21
Pd	9				14			14
Mf						40		
Pt					9	20	33	
Sc			6			14	17	28
Ma	25							
Among four highest MMPI scores								
Hs	43	100	71	82	50	50	50	57
D	59	80	97	91	72	80	84	79
Hy	73	80		91		50		
Pd					86			
Mf					45	90		
Pt		80	58				100	64
Sc			58		57		57	93
Ma	57							

records (8 per cent) were scored highest on the Sc scale; notwithstanding only 17 (5 per cent) were schizophrenic by clinical definition.

Hathaway and McKinley obtained an over-all correlation of 60 per cent between clinical diagnosis and MMPI diagnosis. The 76 per cent correlation in Table 1 can be explained by a lower incidence of normal records in this survey; that is to say, the proportion of the patients being studied that were subject to correlative scrutiny was increased.

Table 3 compares results reported by Hathaway and McKinley [301 (see II, 7), 420 (II, 6)], by Leverenz [386 (VII, 42)], and by this investigator. The first group of testees consisted of civilians, the two latter groups of military personnel. The appreciably higher percentage of abnormal records among the servicemen might be attributable to the acute stresses of military environment under which the tests were taken.

Table 3. Percentage of Patients Scoring 70 or Over on the Appropriate MMPI Scale, in Three Studies

Investigator	Hs	D
Hathaway and McKinley	76	68
Leverenz	96	93
Present study	100	97

Anxiety Neuroses

The application of the MMPI to the anxiety states proved to be the most stimulating aspect of this study. Although the MMPI does not record anxiety per se, it implies some anxiety by measuring several abnormal defenses against it, such as hysteria and psychasthenia. As shown in Table 4, 122 patients were classified

Table 4. Comparison in Each Diagnostic Subgroup of Anxiety Neuroses between the Highest and the Four Highest Scores on the MMPI (All MMPI Figures in Percentages)

		Diagnostic Subgroups					
Item	Controls	Free Anxiety	Combat Anxiety	Neurasthenia	Gastric Fixation	Headache	Total
Number of cases	100	54	28	6	9	9	122
Highest MMPI score							
Hs		29	14	17	45	22	21
D	11	40	43	33	45	45	49
Hy	27	15	14	33	10	11	15
Pd	9						
Pt		6	7				5
Sc						11	
Ma	25			17			
Among four highest MMPI scores							
Hs	43	90	67	83	68	56	86
D	59	90	81	83	79	79	86
Hy	73	70		83	44	56	63
Pt			70	33	33	44	51
Sc		60	53				
Ma	57						

anxiety neuroses and subdivided for statistical analysis under five headings. The 54 "free" anxiety patients exhibited predominantly autonomic symptoms such as palpitation, dyspnea, dizziness, hyperhydrosis, tension, and insomnia, and lacked more fixed somatization. The 28 post-combat anxiety states suffered anxiety, tension, irritability, and autonomic instability which began during combat and which persisted to a disabling degree for at least four months after the last combat experience. The neurasthenics were carefully chosen as conforming to the classical picture, with fatigue predominant. The groups with headache and with gastrointestinal fixation experienced sufficient anxiety and tension to exclude them from hysteria, early schizophrenia, or other clinically diagnosed categories. The remaining 16 of the 122 patients presented pictures, one or two patients to each, of neurocirculatory asthenia, arthritic pains, enuresis, alcoholism, etc.

This breakdown, as revealed in the test score percentages of Table 4, disclosed a remarkable similarity in most of the subgroups. D was most frequently the high score in all the columns, and Hs was second except in the neurasthenia column. Hy was usually third highest. Both quantitatively and qualitatively results for most of the subgroups closely corresponded to total results for the anxiety group, and the MMPI substantiated clinical judgment which grouped these several symptomatic variants under the single heading of anxiety neuroses.

N, P, A, and Av Scores

The fact that the MMPI record is composed of nine separate scores suggests manipulating and combining them in various ways. Of the possible combinations, two have been found eminently practicable. Hathaway and McKinley noted that high scores on the first three of the MMPI categories, Hs, D, and Hy, are often concurrent in the neuroses. Ruesch and Bowman, in their post-traumatic studies, totaled these three scores to make a neurotic (N) score. The latter also totaled the paranoid (Pa), psychasthenic (Pt), and schizophrenic (Sc) scores to obtain a psychotic (P) score, and found noteworthy clinical differentiations between groups of patients with high N and P scores.

Although it might be a splitting of nosologic hairs so to speak, the term "neurotic score" (N) for this total of Hs, D, and Hy would seem not completely applicable. Many neurotics (conversion hysterias, psychasthenics, and neurasthenics) do not produce high N scores while some schizophrenics and psychopaths do. This study of anxiety neurosis (Table 4) identifies the highest score as Hs, D, or Hy in 85 per cent of the records.

Although anxiety is generally accepted as common to all neuroses, it is an integrant of many other reactions, such as early schizophrenia, as well. It is hypothesized that compositely hypochondriasis, depression, and hysteria in the MMPI measure anxiety, and the combined score of these three categories will hereafter be called the anxiety score (A score).

The average score of the nine scales will be designated the Av score. Interpretation of the individual MMPI record is not measurably facilitated by utilizing this mean since it is less selective than assays already discussed; but if abnormal, i.e., 70 or above, it unexceptionally signifies major pathology spread among several scales. By computation of the Av score alone, the MMPI might be employed as a screening questionnaire or psychosomatic index. Numerous such interview procedures were applied in military neuropsychiatric examinations during the war with varying reports of satisfaction.

Cornell Index

Among the more successful of these psychosomatic inventories is the Cornell Index [r168, r169]. Composed of 92 questions, it can be administered in ten minutes and scored in one, and thus it is markedly time saving. The 92 inquiries concerning fears, inadequacy, moods, psychosomatic symptoms, sensitivity, and psychopathic traits are printed on one sheet with "Yes—No" opposite each. The testee simply circles the appropriate response. Each question has a value of one. Scores of 0–12 are normal, 13–22 mildly abnormal, 23 or above moderately severe or severe. The aim of the test is to detect individuals with serious personality problems, not to attempt a diagnosis.

In a comparative study, 126 miscellaneous cases were tested by the MMPI and the Cornell Service Index (CSI). The number of patients to each clinical diagnosis was as follows: 4 hypochondriasis, 6 psychasthenia, 20 depression, 8 hysteria, 54 anxiety, 6 schizophrenia, 2 hypomania, 2 migraine, 2 alcoholism, 6 psychopathic deviate, 6 enuresis, and 10 epilepsy.

The Av score, the A score, and the number of MMPI scores over 70 (70 score) were selected as results adaptable to a comparison with the score of the CSI. For collation with the CSI divisions of normal, mild, and severe, the Av and A scores were evaluated to make below 60 normal, 60–69 mild, and 70 or over severe. For parallelism in interpreting the 70 score, 0 was considered normal, 1–2 mild, and 3 or more severe.

Table 5 gives the percentages of agreement and disagreement between the patients' records from the two tests. The degree of pathology, when it differed, was greater or lesser by one division in all but 3 of the 126 cases; e.g., an evaluation of mild according to the MMPI record might be according to the CSI either normal or severe, and vice versa. The three exceptions were neurotics who were adjudged severe by the CSI but normal by the Av scoring of the MMPI. Misleadingly normal scores from both tests occurred in the same types of patients (hysteria, enuresis, migraine). These data indicate that the two psychometric techniques probe similar personality factors; it should therefore be unnecessary to subject the patient to both.

The 92 questions of the CSI, desirably frugal of time, and the 550 of the MMPI appear to be similarly accurate in discovering psychopathological material. In the evaluation of a single patient, however, when no need exists for screening methods, the Cornell score contributes negligibly to the clinical history; whereas the personality profile of the MMPI supplements it constructively.

Curve Patterns

The nine diagnostic categories have been so organized that the transference neuroses come first, psychoses, including rigid psychasthenia, last, and the psychopathic, homosexual, and paranoid reaction types in the middle group. Under this arrangement certain characteristic patterns are formed when the scores of the nine scales are charted and joined by a continuous line. Some curve patterns thus produced did not yield noteworthy correlations with any clinical picture, and some were too few in number to allow of conclusions, but those illustrated in Table 1 have proved useful. In analyzing the *individual* MMPI score sheet these curves supplant the N and P scores which are laborious to compute, and which are of chief value in statistical estimation of *groups* of patients.

The type 2 curve is representative of anxiety neurosis, neurotic depression, and hypochondriasis. It rarely appears otherwise, and is associated with a high A score. Curve 3 also chiefly typifies neuroses, but this pattern characterized 6 of the 17 early schizophrenics too. An anxiety component in incipient schizophrenic reactions is not uncommon. Because it sensitively depicts anxiety, the MMPI's functioning to distinguish early psychoses from neuroses is limited.

Table 5. Comparison of Degree of Severity in Personality Impairment Shown by CSI and MMPI Test Results on the Same Patients (126 Cases)

Degree of Severity	Percentage of Cases
Av score and CSI	
Same	64.6
Av greater	10.7
Av lesser	24.7
70 score and CSI	
Same	74.0
70 greater	16.9
70 lesser	9.1
A score and CSI	
Same	71.4
A greater	15.9
A lesser	12.7

In the neuroses a type 3 curve usually denotes a longer standing, more incapacitating reaction than a 2 curve. The secondary elevation on the schizophrenic scale was puzzling until the questions which make up the score on this scale were analyzed. It was ascertained that neurotics answer in a scorable direction statements related to confusion, concentration, memory defect, worry, and depression. The schizophrenic rise in these cases does not spring from questions on seclusiveness, withdrawal, hallucinations, or delusions.

The type 4 curve, which is of superior diagnostic value, unfortunately prevails in only a small number of cases. It is identified mainly in conversion hysteria, psychopathic deviation, homosexuality, and some simple depressions. It does not appear in the records of patients suffering primarily from anxiety. Curve 5, compatible with an elevated P score, is undoubtedly valuable, when it occurs, in indicating a psychotic reaction; but in early psychotic patients who are sufficiently in contact with reality to produce a valid test, anxiety or depression is so general that curve 3 usually results. The type 6 curve is found most often in mixed cases in which diagnosis is difficult and controversial. Therefore it offers little aid in arriving at a definitive conclusion, but it does reflect the clinical problem.

Normal Responses

In evaluating MMPI results, certain quantitative measurements must be considered along with the qualitative comparison of relative scores of the nine diagnostic categories and category groups. Table 6 shows the percentage of normal records for the groups thus far discussed. In a normal record all scores are under 70. Abnormal records, therefore, may have from only one to all nine scores of 70 or over. For the 316 patients, the average number of abnormal scores per record (70 score) was 5.66.

Table 6. Comparative Percentages of Normal Responses on the MMPI in
Eight Clinical Diagnostic Groups

		Clinical Diagnostic Groups							
Item	Controls	Anxiety Neurosis	Hs	D	Hy	Pd	Mf	Pt	Sc
Number of cases	100	122	10	31	15	28	10	6	17
Percentage of normal records	78	6	0	0	27	0	30	0	0

A close correlation with clinical expectations is seen in most of the categories. As evidence of the efficiency with which the MMPI detects depression and anxiety, no normal records were found in hypochondriasis, depression, psychasthenia, psychopathic deviation, or schizophrenia cases. Those illnesses in which anxiety is most successfully converted, hysteria and neurasthenia, showed a substantial number of normal records, 27 per cent and 33 per cent respectively. In the anxiety subgroups, in addition to neurasthenia, the post-combat anxieties showed fewer abnormal records, probably due to the fact that these were not true character neuroses but, rather, affective prolongations of situational difficulties. In assessing a single MMPI record, a normal result in patients with Hs, D, Pt, Pd, or Sc would cast doubt on the diagnosis. An abnormal record in cases of hysteria or neurasthenia would strongly verify the clinical impression, while a normal test result would neither affirm nor deny the diagnosis.

Patients who present a clinical picture of a definite neurosis, but who attain a normal MMPI record, may be assumed to have adjusted their neurosis to their environment with a minimal degree of residual anxiety or depression. Their normal scores, far from being misleading, are an important segment of the clinical whole.

Retests: Progress and Prognosis

An exceedingly worth-while instrument for objectively measuring the progress of a patient's illness has been realized in the MMPI. It correlates almost exactly with clinical calculations in this respect. In Table 7 are shown two descriptive cases with the first MMPI results, and the retest results three weeks later. The amazing parallelism of original and retest curve patterns, although at different quantitative levels, increases confidence in the validity of the results.

In the first case in Table 7 the clinical course was downhill with deepening depression and restlessness; and prolonged hospitalization resulted. The other portion of Table 7 represents partial resolution of anxiety under psychotherapy. On

17 cases thus retested, improvement or increased illness as shown by the MMPI corresponded in every instance with the clinical appraisal.

The MMPI has also proved a useful tool in estimating prognoses of acute psy-chotic patients. Of six acute psychotic reaction cases, too ill on admission to take the test, two were destructive, one was a retarded depression, and three had re-gressed to a mute, negativistic state. All were notably improved within two weeks, and, due to the manpower shortage occasioned by the breakthrough at Aachen, their prompt return to duty was expedient. They were tested by the MMPI, five making normal records and the sixth scoring 76 for Hy and 71 for D but insisting that he felt very well. All returned to military duty under psychiatric observation for about three months while they completed basic training and other assignments. The five whose test results were normal experienced no further trouble and maintained acceptable duty performance; but the sixth became tense after a month at duty, was rehospitalized in a mildly confused state, and was ultimately returned to civilian life.

Table 7. MMPI Scores and Codes of Two Cases Retested after Three Weeks

Case	Hs	D	Hy	Pd	Mf	Pa	Pt	Sc	Ma
Case 1, regression									
Original	79	80	78	56	52	56	62	72	68
MMPI Code: 2"138'97–465									
Retest	84	98	83	65	58	59	66	77	72
MMPI Code: 2°13"8974–65									
Case 2, improvement									
Original	88	90	81	52	50	43	58	54	55
MMPI Code: 2°13"–79845/6									
Retest	72	71	71	48	50	39	42	47	50
MMPI Code: 123'–59/487:6									

Borderlands

The application of the MMPI to various illnesses with functional components (alcoholism, migraine, post-traumatic headache, epilepsy, enuresis, somnambulism) is shown in Table 8. This tabulation fails to demonstrate a few pertinent details. In chronic alcoholics, for example, there were two competely normal records, three frankly neurotic records (curve 2), one homosexual record (curve 4), three with a high Pd score, two with a high Ma score, and one with a mixed score. Forty-one per cent of the migraine patients had nonneurotic, normal records, and 57 per cent had a high anxiety score, illustrating the diverse features of this syndrome.

In the cases of post-traumatic headache, clinical and psychometric results of other investigators of this type of patient were supported [r2, r141, 515]. Six cases with a history of severe injury produced two normal records and two with a high P score (type 5 curve). Nine minor head injury cases, with no normal records, had uniformly high A scores suggesting functional disorder. Among the epileptics only 13 per cent had normal records; a majority (66 per cent) evidenced anxiety or de-pression by a type 2 curve; and 42 per cent also had a P score over 70, due chiefly to high scoring on the schizophrenic questions concerning confusion, concentration, and withdrawal. Of the habit reactions, enuresis and somnambulism, 63 per cent and 60 per cent respectively showed normal records. A few cases within this psychosomatic grouping were symptomatic of neuroses, and the MMPI indicated this etiology by type 2 and 3 curves.

With respect to epilepsy particularly, MMPI records emphasized the presence of emotional reaction. All 22 cases had abnormal EEG's and a convincing clinical history of organic illness; yet MMPI results revealed 87 per cent emotionally maladjusted, and the desirability of psychotherapy was unmistakably suggested.

Table 8. MMPI Results for Various Psychosomatic Problems (All MMPI Figures in Percentages)

Item	Controls	Migraine	Post-Traumatic Headache	Alcoholism	Epilepsy	Enuresis	Somnambulism
			Clinical Diagnostic Groups				
Number of cases ...	100	12	17	12	22	22	5
Highest MMPI score							
Hs		58	38				
D	11	26	44	17	67	37	20
Hy	27	16			7	27	
Pd	9		6	17	7		20
Mf							20
Pa						9	
Pt						27	
Sc			12	17	13		
Ma	24			17			20
Among four highest MMPI scores							
Hs	43	100	87		67	72	
D	59	86	87	58	93	91	
Hy	73	100	50			72	60
Pd				58			40
Pt			56	75	67		60
Sc		43		83	46	45	
Ma	57						80
Percentage of normal records	78	41	6	17	13	63	60

Discussion

Utilitarian aspects of psychometry became forcefully apparent during the war as adequate handling of masses of men was immeasurably expedited by testing devices. The salvage value for civilian psychiatry of these tests, however, is not proportionate. It is hardly to be anticipated that screening methods which sifted out a high number of psychopathological service problems will, without alteration, suit the needs of the clinical psychiatrist confronted with a single nervous patient.

Under some existing situations, relatively large groups of potential or actual psychiatric cases may be advantageously surveyed *in toto* (in large, understaffed clinics, veterans' hospitals, industrial plants); but personal and individual relationships are inherent in the practice of psychiatry, and psychometric procedures profitable to the clinician must be adaptable to individual application and interpretation.

In this connection the MMPI excels most measuring tools of its type. As stated before, if the test is not erroneously employed as an exact diagnostic delineator, but is interpreted as only one part of the psychiatric investigation, it can be a practical adjunct to clinical decisions. With the chief features of the clinical mosaic in mind, the psychiatrist can utilize in the MMPI the several highest scores, the curve patterns, the quantitative scores including normal responses, and retest comparisons to obtain additional relevant data, thus broadening his view of the personality problem.

The MMPI is a personality schedule by definition of Hathaway and McKinley, not a substitute for clinical diagnosis. In fact, the more successful the MMPI is in its avowed purpose of defining personality structure, the less utilizable it becomes as an absolute diagnostic tool. Its inability to accomplish single, accurate diagnoses in a high percentage of cases has evoked a certain degree of criticism which is not surprising, since the results are scored entirely in diagnostic terms, and since the authors themselves in time became concerned with the diagnostic acumen of the test [304].

But why dwell upon one clear-cut diagnosis? No one should be more preoccupied than the psychiatrist with total personality organization and reaction. No one should decry more vigorously than the psychiatrist unimaginative attempts to catalogue sick personalities conveniently in an arbitrary nosology. How much more important that the psychiatrist recognize the anxiety element in early schizophrenia, the depressive affect in a psychopathic personality, the hypochondriacal trends in psychasthenia!

It is precisely the MMPI's faculty for displaying multiplex surfaces of the disturbed personality which fosters confidence in its validity and increases its effectiveness beyond that of a testing tool yielding a single result only. The MMPI requires interpretation, as do most separate laboratory procedures, in the light of the clinical picture. It is not a substitute for the psychiatrist; it is, rather, implicit in his total clinical fact findings; for "in the evaluation of any case we must go beyond the limited objective judgment of the test and obtain an evaluation of the total situation involved. For such purposes there is no substitute for the human mind. A test cannot think but a clinical psychologist can." [r82]

Internists and surgeons have been encouraged to employ the MMPI for determining psychoneurotic and psychosomatic symptomatology in their patients [422]. For the practitioner inexperienced in mental pathology to expect the MMPI to serve as an alternate for psychiatric consultation would constitute over-estimation of the test's capacity and misunderstanding of its aim. Without the auxiliary knowledge of a qualified psychometrist or psychiatrist in interpreting the results, the uninitiated physician would indeed be disconcerted upon discovering (Table 2) that 51 per cent of psychiatric patients score highest on the D scale; that 21 per cent of schizophrenics score highest on the Hy scale; or that only 14 per cent of psychopathic personalities score highest on the Pd scale.

The MMPI, provided that it is properly interpreted by an expert, might be considered a candidate to fulfill the urgent need for a reliable psychiatric evaluative procedure in routine use on medical and surgical wards. A large percentage of current diagnostic errors with resultant ineffectual therapeusis can be ascribed to the organically oriented doctor's incomprehension of neurotic, psychotic, and psychosomatic diseases. The magnitude and ubiquity of this intraprofessional insularity has been exposed recently by Bennett [r15] who found that his 150 frankly neurotic or psychotic patients had, prior to recognition of the true nature of their illness, been subjected to a total of 811 nonpsychiatric therapeutic measures (496 medical, 244 surgical, 71 cultist).

He concluded that "Mistakes in diagnosis and treatment of patients with functional, psychosomatic, psychoneurotic or actual psychotic disorders are so common as gravely to discredit the acumen of the medical profession. The most important problem before our profession is the need for greater interest and more accurate knowledge about psychiatry." One approach to this problem, one step toward establishing a beneficial liaison between psychological and organic medicine might well be the adoption in general hospitals of routine psychometric screening methods.

It can conservatively be stated that a laboratory test of the MMPI type would reveal a greater amount of significant and unsuspected pathology than do standard tests such as the blood Kahn, which are universal requisites of clinicians. In the likelihood that intricacies in its interpretation would controvert the feasibility of the MMPI's widespread use in extra-psychiatric medicine, it should be recognized that the gains which could be realized would heavily outweigh a considerable bulk of minor deterrents.

Tests such as the MMPI have the strong recommendation of objectivity, and advantages are gained by eliminating the inevitable influence of the psychiatric interviewer's personality. All questions are introduced with equal force and emphasis; most functions of the psychobiological organism are examined; possible bias in selection of material by the interviewer is avoided; the patient is not tempted to give answers aimed to please or to antagonize the psychiatrist; a true scale of subjective responses is obtained.

Unfortunately, the test lacks the constructive attributes of the patient-interviewer contact. All biographical data are not in the same ratio of significance, and evaluation of the patient's story is necessitated. Question and answer techniques of this type depend solely upon the subject's own concept of his anamnesis and beliefs, without regard to his behavior performance. Only a single expression of the testee's behavior is recorded, his subjective reaction to a long series of objective statements.

Use of the MMPI encourages the patient to trust that his case is being thoroughly investigated. The new patient tends to approach the psychiatrist, as he does his family physician, with an organic outlook, and is often assailed with doubt and uncertainty when first acquainted with the intangible nature of his illness. A mathematically scored test, comparably with a thermometer, a blood count, or a B.M.R., creates an impression of concreteness in the clinical procedure, and is consequently of therapeutic value in allaying some anxiety and reinforcing the psychiatrist's authority.

The MMPI has been disparaged as lengthy and unwieldy. Admittedly it does exact an hour's attention from the testee and 15–20 minutes from the tester for scoring. It is, on the other hand, most helpfully economical of the doctor's time. In the length of the test certain advantages are innate. The very weight of 550 statements, with the time required to study them, discourages dissembling, evasion, understatement, neurotic exaggeration. To maintain an assumed attitude through such labyrinthine interrogation is difficult.

The liability of tests such as the MMPI to conscious and deliberate distortion prompted the inclusion of "lie" and "validity" statements in an effort to circumvent such misuse of the test. The 15 lie questions indicate whether the subject is attempting to place himself in an improbably acceptable light. Sample statements are "I do not read every editorial in the newspaper every day" and "I gossip a little at times." Sixteen of the 400 patients made lie (L) scores over 70, and their records were discarded. Clinical evaluation of these patients substantiated for the most part the possibility of their malingering. All of the 100 control records contained normal L scores.

The validity (F) score is obtained from responses to 64 statements not used in forming any of the nine diagnostic scales and only very rarely answered scorably by normal control testees. Hathaway and McKinley believe a high F score usually invalidates the record, but Kazan and Scheinberg [357] have recently taken exception to this view. This writer's results agree completely with the conclusion of the latter authors. Thirty per cent (93) of the 316 patients had an F score above the critical level of 70. Manifestly, declaring 30 per cent of the records invalid would nullify the whole test.

Kazan and Scheinberg found also that a high F score is generally associated with multiple high scores on the diagnostic scales, and, rather than a negation of the MMPI, is a reliable indicator of major pathology. Out of a possible 9 in the diagnostic categories, the 93 patients mentioned above averaged 7.9 abnormal (over 70) scores; while the total group of 316 patients averaged only 5.66 abnormal scores.

The MMPI type of criterion, designed to disclose abnormalities of personality structure, fills a potentially vital niche in the rack of psychiatric armament. It is based on the sound psychobiological principle that immediate symptoms of psychic maladjustment stem from long-term developmental aberrations in the personality. The ultimate in objective questionnaire techniques of this character is yet to be evolved; but the MMPI, which has been painstakingly validated over a period of years and complies with psychological statistical standards of accuracy and deviation, seems the best approach to date.

Conclusions

1. The MMPI was evaluated by application to 416 United States Army enlisted personnel. Results in this study present convincing evidence that the test is a valuable psychometric adjunct to clinical psychiatric practice.

2. It does not establish definitive diagnoses; it sometimes overemphasizes certain personality distortions and minimizes others; it requires interpretation in the light of the total clinical picture; it is not a substitute for the psychiatrist.

3. Anxiety may be satisfactorily measured by averaging the scores of the first three MMPI scales, hypochondriasis (Hs), depression (D), and hysteria (Hy), to form an A (anxiety) score.

4. The MMPI elicits significant data in several psychosomatic illnesses. In migraine, post-traumatic headache, epilepsy, somnambulism, and enuresis it meets clinical expectations to a high degree.

5. MMPI retests at intervals prove dependable in following the clinical course and helpful in determining the prognosis.

6. The MMPI makes its most constructive contribution to clinical medicine in illuminating the study of individual cases through combinations of its multiple scores which reveal many facets of the disturbed personality.

ARTICLE 44 *The MMPI in Clinical Practice*

THE purpose of this study was to make a critical evaluation of the applicability of the MMPI to some of the diagnostic problems encountered in naval psychiatric practice. The inventory is currently enjoying wide use and it was believed desirable to assess its diagnostic accuracy before using it as a practical clinical instrument. Accordingly, the test was given to 85 patients with known disorders and concerning whom there was no doubt in respect to the diagnosis. Patients in the following five diagnostic categories were given the test:

Schizophrenia. These 10 patients exhibited unmistakable schizophrenic disorders and after a period of observation all were transferred to a veterans' hospital for psychotic patients.

Hysteria. These 9 patients showed classical conversion symptoms such as anesthesia, paralysis, and aphonia. Painstaking neurologic examination had been done and the possibility of an organic basis for the sensory or motor defect excluded. The possibility of conscious simulation had been carefully considered and dismissed as quite unlikely.

Delinquency (psychopathic deviate scale of the MMPI). These 16 men had clear histories of delinquency prior to entry in the naval service. All had been in trouble with the law in civilian life and most of them had spent some time in reform school.

Homosexuality. Ten men were confessed homosexuals who were awaiting discharge from the naval service.

Organic disease. These 40 men, patients on the medical wards of a naval hospital, had established diagnoses of diabetes mellitus or cardiovascular disease (valvular heart disease, arterial hypertension, angina pectoris). Seventeen had diabetes mellitus and 23 had cardiovascular disease. They were not considered to be psychiatric problems.

The range of ages in the total group was wide (17 years to 60 years) but the group as a whole was a young one (median age, 21 years).

In evaluating the test scores of patients in the first four groups, the results were considered to be "positive" if either one of the following two criteria was met: (1) if the trend in question (e.g., hysteria, femininity) showed a T score [see 422] of 70 or more, without regard to the relative strengths of the other trends elicited in the test; (2) if the trend in question showed a T score of 65–69 and was the highest score on the test. In evaluating the test scores of patients in the organic disease groups, a patient was considered to have shown psychoneurotic trends on the test if either one of the following two criteria was met: (1) if either the hypochondriasis or the hysteria T score was 70 or more, without regard to the relative strengths of the other trends elicited in the test; (2) if either the hypochondriasis or the hysteria T score was 65–69 and was the highest score on the test.

Test papers with ? or L scores above 66 were rejected as being of questionable validity. When an F score of 64 or more was made, the questions contributing to the high F score were personally reviewed with the patient to determine whether he fully understood the statements on the cards. If it appeared that the high score was due to faulty comprehension of the statements, the test was rejected but if the high score apparently represented a genuine individuality in attitude the test results were considered to be valid.

Results

The results thus obtained with the patients in the various diagnostic categories were as follows:

Schizophrenia. Five of the 10 schizophrenic patients gave positive results on the schizophrenia scale of the test.

Hysteria. Five of the 9 hysterical patients gave positive results on the hysteria scale of the test.

Delinquency. Thirteen of the 16 delinquents gave positive results on the psychopathic deviate scale of the test.

Homosexuality. Nine of the 10 confessed homosexuals gave positive results on the femininity scale of the test. These men had been assured that their performance on the test would not affect the outcome of their cases in any way and they were encouraged to be frank and honest in taking the test. The 9 men for whom the test results were positive were given the test again, this time with directions to conceal, if they could, the fact of their homosexuality. On this retest, 6 of the 9 men gave negative results on the femininity scale of the test.

Organic disease. Of the 17 patients with diabetes mellitus only 2 made positive scores on the hysteria or hypochondriasis scales of the test. In contrast, 13 of the 23 patients with cardiovascular disease made positive scores on the hysteria or hypochondriasis scales.

Discussion

This investigation is concerned with the validation of five of the scales of the MMPI. Strict criteria were observed in the selection of cases so that there would be no doubt as to the correctness of the diagnosis. For example, in the selection of cases of hysteria only cases with the classical conversion symptoms of anesthesia, paralysis or aphonia were accepted. The numerous cases in which the presenting symptom was headache or gastrointestinal disorder thought to be a hysterical conversion symptom were rejected because of the possibility of diagnostic error in these cases. This caution in the selection of patients accounts for the small number of cases in the hysteria group.

The findings in the group of schizophrenic patients, i.e., 50 per cent positive results, are in accord with the findings of Hathaway and McKinley. The schizophrenia scale is designated by the authors as "preliminary" and must be considered as such.

Certainly in its present form it cannot be considered a reliable diagnostic instrument for practical use.

The group of carefully selected hysterical patients is small and from the quantitative point of view it is a rather inadequate sample. As far as the data go, they show the inventory to be relatively ineffective in identifying these cases of conversion hysteria.

The inventory is definitely more successful in identifying psychopathic deviates (delinquents), correctly classifying over four fifths of the cases tested.

Nine of the 10 confessed homosexuals scored positively on the femininity scale of the MMPI. These men had been encouraged to be frank in their responses and had no motivation to be otherwise. When, however, the 9 positive scorers were instructed to attempt to conceal the fact of their homosexuality in taking the test again, 6 of the 9 were able to bring their "feminine" scores down to normal limits. In other words, two thirds of the positive-scoring homosexuals had sufficient insight to be successful in concealing their psychosexual trends. It seems that we should be justified in concluding that the inventory will elicit the "feminine" response in certain male homosexuals only if these men are frank and honest in their responses, or, assuming that they are not willing to be frank and honest, if they lack sufficient insight to hide the fact of their homosexuality. With respect to the second possibility, the findings indicate that a significant proportion of homosexuals do not lack this degree of insight.

The purpose in giving the test to patients with established organic disease and noting the strengths of the hypochondriacal and hysterical trends was, aside from the intrinsic interest of such findings, to evaluate in an indirect manner these scales of the MMPI. The Minnesota *Manual* is rather contradictory on the subject of the relationship between organic disease and strength of hypochondriacal and hysterical trends. In the discussion of the hypochondriacal scale, it is stated that "common organic sickness does not raise a person's score appreciably, for the scale detects a difference between the organically sick person and the hypochondriac" [303]. However, in the discussion of the "hysteria" scale, it is stated: "As in the case of hypochondriasis, the subject with a high Hy[steria] score may have real physical pathology, either as a primary result of concurrent disease, such as diabetes or cancer, or as a secondary result of the long-time presence of the psychological symptoms."

The findings in the groups of organic cases indicate that probably no statement can be made concerning the influence of the presence of physical disease in general on neurotic trends as elicited by the MMPI. Apparently different disease groups will be associated with different strengths of hypochondriacal or hysterical trends. Certainly, until further evidence concerning the relationship between various organic disorders and these trends is available, the presence of these trends in excessive strength in a patient should not of itself be considered to militate against a judgment of physical pathology in the case. The contrast with respect to the strengths of neurotic trends in the two groups with organic disease investigated in this study is striking. In the group of young diabetics the incidence of stronger-than-average hypochondriacal and hysterical trends was probably no greater than in an unselected healthy population, while the group of patients suffering from cardiovascular disease showed a significantly higher incidence of stronger-than-average hypochondriacal and hysterical trends. The application of the inventory as an investigative tool in various disease groups should furnish valuable information concerning psychosomatic relationships.

Summary and Conclusions

A study of the application of the MMPI to a group of 85 male patients suffering from known disorders yielded the following results:

1. The MMPI identified psychopathic deviates (delinquents) and confessed homosexuals with reasonable accuracy. In the case of the homosexuals, however, the inventory showed itself susceptible to "score-faking," in that a majority of the homosexuals were able to conceal the fact of their homosexuality on the test when requested to attempt to do so.

2. The MMPI was less successful in identifying schizophrenics and hysterics.

3. Investigation of a group of diabetics and a group of patients with cardiovascular disease showed an average incidence of neurotic scores in the former group and a significantly higher incidence of neurotic scores in the latter group, indicating that no general statement can be made concerning the influence of physical disease on MMPI scores, but that the various disease groups merit separate consideration.

It is concluded that in its present stage of development the MMPI should not be regarded as a practical clinical test, the results of which can be accepted at face value by the practicing psychiatrist and the internist. By this is meant not that the MMPI is completely valueless as a diagnostic tool but that it must be employed with considerable caution. At this time it is best considered to be a promising diagnostic instrument which warrants further critical analysis and development in order that its positive values and its limitations may be defined and its diagnostic value thus enhanced.

ARTICLE 45 *Predicting Hospitalization of Psychiatric Outpatients*

THERE is a definite clinical need for an instrument which can aid in isolating from the heterogeneous population "psychiatric outpatients," those cases who not only fail to profit from therapy but who become even more seriously disturbed as treatment continues. One of the patients in the present study had killed his wife. Two had attempted murder. Six had attempted suicide. Treating such cases on an outpatient basis seems rather imprudent, and means for predicting their behavior should permit wiser disposition. More generally, increased accuracy in predicting such an event as hospitalization should lead to improvement in the efficiency of outpatient treatment from the point of view of the patient, his therapist, and society as a whole.

This study constitutes an attempt to meet the need for greater predictive accuracy, but it was also designed to provide a partial definition of the concept "latent psychiatric illness." It is ordinarily assumed that any patient who develops a personality disorder severe enough to require institutionalization has, before the manifest outbreak of symptoms, certain predispositions to illness. Meaningful definition of these predispositional tendencies is dependent upon measurement of behavior during the period of "latency," and it is this measurement which constitutes the second aim of the investigation.

A survey of research on prognosis reveals only one empirical study [r51] where hospitalization was employed as a criterion of psychiatric outcome, and for it the sample was drawn from a population not already in the hospital. While the results of that study suggest the possibility of predicting hospitalization through use of a psychometric test (the Cornell Selectee Index), general inference is limited by the size of the sample ($N = 10$) and the fact that the procedures used are not commonly employed in present clinical practice. The literature on prognosis from psychometric data has recently been surveyed by Windle [655]. The studies examined in that review have offered hypotheses for test in this investigation; they have served as a fund of possible psychometric predictors. A list of possible nonpsychometric factors was compiled by examining the studies of Wittman [r172], Dunham and Meltzer [r46], Clark [r36], Jenkins [346], Kant [r87], Fisher and Hayes [r57], Chase and Silverman [r35], Mayer-Gross and Moore [r114], and Lewis [r96].

Method

Plan of Investigation. In most respects, the procedure employed in this study follows that outlined by Horst [r76] for general prediction problems. The following steps have been carried out:

1. A criterion was defined as admission to a psychiatric hospital following psychological testing and two or more interviews by staff members at a VA mental hygiene clinic.

2. Every case in the clinic file was examined, and all those who met the criterion were placed in the "hospitalized" category. Certain nonpsychometric data and the results of the Wechsler-Bellevue, MMPI, and Rorschach were recorded for each member of the sample. Hereinafter, these hospitalized patients will be referred to as Group I (N = 108).

3. A sample of nonhospitalized patients at the same clinic was gathered by going through the psychological test file and selecting every tenth card which showed that the patient had had all three of the tests considered in the study. All subjects who had been hospitalized were left in Group I. Again, those cases who were interviewed only once were excluded, but no further restrictions were made. Results of the tests and nonpsychometric data were recorded for the remaining cases, hereinafter referred to as Group II (N = 114).

4. In accordance with a double cross-validation design [r125], each group was split into two subsamples by alphabetizing the data sheets and sorting them alternately into two piles. Four groups were consequently formed, specified as follows: Group I-A, hospitalized (N = 54); Group II-A, not hospitalized (N = 57); Group I-B, hospitalized (N = 54); Group II-B, not hospitalized (N = 57).

5. Next, a sort of gross item analysis was performed. One set of significantly differentiating signs was isolated by comparing Group I-A with Group II-A (the combination of these two groups will be referred to as Sample A). Similarly, a set of discriminating signs was derived by comparing Group I-B with Group II-B (this combination will be referred to as Sample B).

6. For each sample, the following indices were made up: (a) a device consisting only of nonpsychometric signs; (b) a device consisting only of signs from the MMPI; (c) a device comprising both nonpsychometric and MMPI signs; (d) a comprehensive device, including all signs which discriminated between groups.

7. Each index derived from Sample A was cross-validated on Sample B; conversely, those derived from Sample B were cross-validated on Sample A. This procedure resulted in an estimate of the efficiency which the lists of signs would probably have if employed with new samples.

8. Groups of false positives and false negatives were selected and case histories carefully studied in an effort to find ways of improving prediction.

9. Finally, indices combining data from both samples were constructed by including only signs which differentiated at the .05 level of significance for both samples.

Subjects and Procedure. All subjects had been patients at the Veterans Administration Mental Hygiene Clinic, St. Paul, Minnesota, at some time during the period from 1947 through 1951. The clinic is available only to veterans with a "service-connected" psychiatric disability. "Service connection," in this sense, is a rather broad concept which includes origin of a neuropsychiatric disorder, aggravation of such a disorder, or "emotional" contribution to some nonpsychiatric disability. Nearly all the patients are male, white, and live in the vicinity of Minneapolis and St. Paul. Veterans of both world wars are included in the sample, although by far the majority served only in the second one. Almost without exception they had had psychotherapy, mainly with psychiatric residents, less often with clinical psychology trainees and social workers. All therapy was supervised by psychiatric and psychological consultants.

Most of the psychometric tests had been administered, scored, and interpreted by trainees in clinical psychology, but scoring of the Wechsler-Bellevue and Rorschach was checked in an unusually careful way by the chief psychologist. For the Rorschach, the scoring system employed most nearly approximates that of Hertz [r75] for location, form, and specification of popular responses. Determinants were scored more like the Klopfer system [r91] than any other.

The Item Analysis. The statistical procedure most extensively used was chi square. Calculation was done in accordance with the method suggested by McNemar [r108, formula 87, p. 207] for $2 \times k$ tables. Wherever any expected frequency in a 2×2 table fell below 10, a formula incorporating Yates's correction was applied. Cutting points were established as rationally as available literature and common sense would permit before the tests were calculated. For certain unimodal continous distributions, the t test was employed [r84, formula 5.03, p. 74]. Where heterogeneity of population variance seemed likely, the Cochran-Cox approximation method was used. Generally speaking, if no population difference was suggested by t, the variable was henceforth ignored. If, however, the t test did suggest a reliable difference between means, chi square was also used, with a cutting point approximately midway between the two sample means. Only if the latter test indicated significant discrepancy was the sign included as a member of a predictor set.

Statistical tests were performed with respect to the following nonpsychometric variables: age, present job status (employed or unemployed), education, job stability (number of jobs held since discharge from the service), occupational level, marital status, number of children (if married), place of residence (if single, widowed, or divorced), parents (living or dead), siblings (present or absent), birth order, evidence of broken home (arbitrarily defined as dissolution of the home by separation of the parents, or death or institutionalization of one or both parents before the patient was fifteen), number of previous hospitalizations, mention of drinking as a problem in the intake interview, impressions of patient behavior during testing (psychologist's description), and diagnosis (service-connected disability, beginning diagnosis at the clinic, and closing diagnosis).

For the Wechsler-Bellevue, no type of complex pattern analysis was attempted. Reviews by Rabin [r134], Rabin and Guertin [r135], and Schofield [r145] suggested that such analyses were likely to be unprofitable. In consequence, only the full-scale IQ and the relationship between verbal and performance IQ's were examined.

For the MMPI, the literature on pattern analysis [234 (see VI, 38), 436 (V, 31), 528 (VI, 39)] suggested several possible discriminators. The relationship between the "neurotic" end of the profile (Hs, D, and Hy) and the "psychotic" end (here defined as including Pa, Sc, and Ma), the relative elevation of Sc and Pt, the height of D in relation to Hs and Hy, the difference score calculated by subtracting F from

K (T scores), the total number of scores over 70, and gross elevations on F and Pd were all tested by chi-square methods.

Tests were made for each of the following Rorschach signs and scores: R, emphasis on W, D, Dr, and S, F%, F + %, A%, W:M, (H + A):(Hd + Ad), M:ΣC, ΣC, FC, CF— and C, FC:(CF + C), M, M+:M—, M:FM, Fm, (VIII–X)%, Fc, Fk, FK, FC', cloud, fire, blood, or smoke content, sex, food, positional responses, and abstractions. Both original and additional responses were counted for the last two signs. For all others only the original responses were considered.

Results

Formation of Indices. In all, 56 variables were examined by chi-square techniques. Of these, nine appeared to discriminate between hospitalized and nonhospitalized patients in Sample A; eleven appeared effective in Sample B. Overlap occurred for seven variables. All signs were weighted in accordance with observed frequency trends, and the indices shown in Table 1 were made up.

Estimates of Predictive and Discriminatory Efficiency. On the basis of the signs listed in Table 1, every patient was given four scores, one based solely on nonpsychometric data, one based only on the MMPI, one obtained by adding these two scores, and one based on all signs which seemed to show differentiating power. Cutting scores were established by equalizing false positives with false negatives in each derivation sample, and cross-validation was carried out by examining the percentage of correctly classified cases in the samples from which the indices had *not* been derived. Thus, indices derived from Sample A were cross-validated on Sample B; those derived from Sample B were tested with Sample A. Final indices were formed by considering only those signs which discriminated between hospitalized and nonhospitalized patients in both samples. For these indices, percentages of accurate classification over the entire sample were computed. The results are presented in Table 2.

Investigation of False Negatives and False Positives. In an effort to isolate additional variables which might aid prediction and to account for the predictive failures that occurred, an intensive case study was undertaken for certain patients who were incorrectly classified by all devices. A set of false negatives was selected by searching Group I (i.e., the total hospitalized sample, consisting of Groups I-A and I-B) for cases in which scores on all four predictive devices were below the critical level for predicting hospitalization. Eleven individuals who fit that description were found. The nonhospitalized group was similarly examined for patients who were inaccurately categorized by all statistical methods. Twelve such cases were isolated.

Telephone conversations with ward secretaries revealed that four of the apparent "misses" were spurious. Prediction for them would actually have been correct, but did not appear so because of clerical errors. Two of the false negatives had never been under neuropsychiatric treatment. They had gone to the hospital, but not to the psychiatric wards even though the records indicated that they had. Conversely, two of the apparent false positives were found to have received treatment in the psychiatric section of the hospital after examination and therapy at the clinic, but notation of this was not found in the case history (in one instance because the author missed it.)

Table 1. Predictive Indices Derived from Chi-Square Analysis

Variable	Sample in Which Discrimination Occurred	Class	Weight
Nonpsychometric			
Diagnosis	A and B	Psychosis	2
		Psychoneurosis, mixed or unclassified, depressive reaction, or obsessive-compulsive reaction	1
		Any other diagnosis	0
Previous hospitalization	A and B	Two or more	2
		One	1
		None	0
Marital status	A and B	Single	2
		Divorced or widowed	1
		Married	0
Drinking as a problem	A only	Mentioned in intake interview	1
		Not mentioned	0
Employment status	B only	Unemployed	1
		Employed	0
MMPI			
"Neurotic" scores	A and B	Pa or Sc or Ma $>$ Hs or D or Hy	1
"Psychotic" scores	A and B	Pa and Sc and Ma $\leq$ Hs and D and Hy	0
Sc:Pt	A and B	Sc $>$ Pt	1
		Sc $\leq$ Pt	0
F	A and B	>60	1
		≤ 60	0
Pd	A and B	>65	1
		≤ 65	0
D:Hs and Hy	B only	D $>$ Hs or Hy	1
		D $\leq$ Hs and Hy	0
Number of scores over 70	B only	Four or more	1
		Less than four	0
Wechsler-Bellevue			
full-scale IQ	A only	<105	1
		≥ 105	0
Rorschach A%	B only	<30	1
		≥ 30	0

Table 2. Percentage of Cases Correctly Classified by the Various Indices

	Accuracy Percentage	
Index	Derivation Sample	Cross-Validation
Nonpsychometric index derived from Sample A	70.37	63.21
Nonpsychometric index derived from Sample B	66.04	69.52
Final nonpsychometric index	64.95	
MMPI index derived from Sample A	67.62	66.67
MMPI index derived from Sample B	71.00	68.57
Final MMPI index	67.32	
Combined index (nonpsychometric plus MMPI) derived from Sample A	71.57	73.20
Combined index derived from Sample B	73.20	73.74
Final combined index	71.36	
Comprehensive index (all signs) derived from Sample A	73.68	75.00
Comprehensive index derived from Sample B	73.68	73.40

Prediction for the remaining group was genuinely wrong. Careful rereading of the material in the clinical file and examination of all available collateral data suggested that incorrect prediction resulted variously from patently faulty diagnosis, the operation of contingency factors, and omission of individually important variables. Inspection of all the records yielded only one quantifiable factor, out of several examined, which might profitably have been included as a general predictor. Five of the ten married patients in the hospitalized group were expectant fathers. Only one of the five married veterans in the set of false positives was in that situation. One cannot expect that addition of a "pregnant wife" sign will increase predictive accuracy to any great extent, but it may offer enough promise to warrant further examination.

Analysis of the factors which led to incorrect prediction, however, clearly indicates the need for more careful diagnosis and inclusion of such nebulous but important factors as the relationship between patient and therapist if prediction is to be materially improved.

Use and Interpretation of Final Indices. By considering those signs in Table 1 which were found to be effective discriminators in both half-samples, three scores can be assigned to any case: one can be derived from his standing with respect to the three nonpsychometric variables, one can be obtained through examination of his MMPI profile, and one can be obtained by adding those two numbers. Scores above two for the nonpsychometric index, above one for the MMPI index, and above three for the combined index suggest the likelihood of future hospitalization. Use of these cutting scores should result in approximately equal *percentages* of accurate prediction in the positive and negative directions. For a large sample of new cases, however, the absolute number of false positives will probably be considerably larger than the number of false negatives, and cutting scores can be altered in terms of the demands of the particular situation where prediction is required.

Cautious interpretation is recommended. The indices are "final" only in the context of this study. The devices, as they stand, have not actually been used to predict, although the items which make them up have been cross-validated with more than usual rigor. Validity needs to be checked on other groups, but considering the almost infinitesimal shrinkage which occurred for each half-sample instrument on cross-validation, it seems reasonable to assume that they will hold up quite well with other cases drawn from the same population.

On the "average," the person who not only fails to profit from outpatient psychotherapy, but who actually becomes worse, is single, has been previously hospitalized, is likely to have a psychotic diagnosis, and has a seriously disturbed MMPI profile (see Table 3). From these behavior patterns, we ordinarily infer strong tension and anxiety, without a healthy, or even a neurotic, complement of defenses. The mechanisms employed can more accurately be described as psychotic; they include withdrawal from the world of objective affairs, various distortions in perception of the environment, and emotional frigidity.

In all important respects, the pre-illness MMPI profile conforms to the characteristic pattern found in manifest psychosis [436 (see V, 31)]. We can probably assume that, at the time these patients were tested, psychotic behaviors were not clinically apparent in full form; that, if they had been, the patients who showed them would have been sent to the hospital immediately. If this is a safe assumption, predispositional tendencies to severe psychiatric illness can be defined in terms of the following test conditions: (1) clinical observation reveals no obvious symptoms severe enough to warrant institutionalization, but tendencies in that direction may still be present, as evidenced by increased likelihood of a psychotic diagnosis; (2) examination of biographical data shows a history of adaptive failure, as evidenced by prior hospitalization and single marital status; (3) scrutiny of the MMPI record reveals a profile that is different in no essential respect from that found in manifest psychosis.

The heterogeneity of the sample, however, reduces the meaning of interpretations of this sort, and studies of more specifically defined groups are badly needed. To this end, an investigation of a group of latent schizophrenics is now under way (see VII, 46).

Table 3. MMPI Means and Codes of Both Patient Groups

Group	N	?	L	F	K	Hs	D	Hy	Pd	Mf	Pa	Pt	Sc	Ma
Hospitalized	108	53	53	63	51	73	77	70	68	60	64	76	80	61
	MMPI Code: 8″2713′4695 F–?LK													
Nonhospitalized	114	51	52	58	51	74	72	70	60	55	56	68	66	57
	MMPI Code: 123′784–956 FL?K/													

Summary

This study constitutes an attempt to devise simple, widely applicable, and maximally precise indices to aid in predicting hospitalization of psychiatric outpatients, as well as to formulate a partial operational definition of the concept "latent psychiatric illness."

Data were gathered at a VA mental hygiene clinic for all patients who underwent psychological examination, were seen for at least two interviews by clinic staff members, and later were admitted to psychiatric hospitals. In all, 108 such patients were found. They were compared with 114 nonhospitalized patients at the same clinic in terms of certain nonpsychometric data and the results of three psychological tests, the Wechsler-Bellevue, the MMPI, and the Rorschach. To minimize chance effects, samples were split in accordance with a double cross-validation design. Indices were derived separately for each half-sample and cross-validated on the other. Percentages of accurate classification ranged from 63 for one of the nonpsychometric devices to 75 for an index composed of four nonpsychometric signs, four MMPI signs, and one sign from the Wechsler-Bellevue. Generally, prediction made on the basis of nontest data alone or from the MMPI alone would have been correct about two thirds of the time; predictions based on indices comprising both nonpsychometric and MMPI signs would have been correct for a little less than three fourths of the cases.

Individual false positives and false negatives were then selected from the hospitalized and nonhospitalized groups. Such patients, for whom prediction was wrong in terms of all devices, were submitted to intensive case study. Clerical errors regarding hospitalization had been made in some of the individual records; accurate prediction would in fact have been made for 4 of the 23 apparent misses. For the remaining 19, contingency factors, inaccurate diagnosis, and omission of uniquely important variables seemed to account for most of the predictive failures.

Predictors derived from the subsamples were combined into single indices by including only those signs which discriminated at the .05 level of significance between hospitalized and nonhospitalized patients in both half-samples. Three forms of index were derived, one consisting only of nonpsychometric variables, one consisting only of MMPI signs, and one comprising both nontest and MMPI factors. The choice will depend on the amount of data available.

The findings contain a partial basis for definition of predisposition to severe psychiatric illness. The mean MMPI profile of the subsequently hospitalized patients is that of manifest, not latent, psychosis, even though such deviations could not have been flagrantly obvious in other clinical behavior at the time of testing. Inference of this nature, however, is limited by the heterogeneity of the group, and a study of the prepsychotic behavior of a group of latent schizophrenics is now in progress.

D. R. PETERSON

✦━━

ARTICLE 46 *The Diagnosis of Subclinical Schizophrenia*

ONE way to refine a scheme of psychiatric classification is to examine patients who, when certain developments in the course of their illness have been considered, turn out to have been incorrectly diagnosed. Careful study of behavior recorded at the time of their diagnoses should permit more definite limitation of class boundaries and more accurate placement of other patients for whom a diagnosis is required.

This study is concerned with the behavior of a group of veterans who should have been diagnosed as "latent," "incipient," or "subclinical" schizophrenics, but who in fact received some other designation. The importance of making the classification correctly for the protection of other members of society, for promoting maximal economy in treatment, and generally for facilitating wise patient disposition should be obvious.

Subjects and Procedures

Group 1. A set of false negatives was obtained by searching the complete file of case records at a VA mental hygiene clinic for all male, white patients who met the following criteria: (a) They were examined by a psychologist and were seen for at least two interviews by staff members at the clinic. (b) They received some diagnosis which contained no derivative of the word "schizophrenia." (c) They were later sent to a psychiatric hospital and there were said to be schizophrenic.

Group 2. A sample of true negatives was selected by examining data previously recorded [479 (see VII, 45)] for a sample of nonhospitalized patients at the same clinic. Each false negative in Group 1 was considered in turn, and was compared consecutively with each patient listed in the data for the nonhospitalized sample until one was found who had received a primary diagnosis identical with that given his counterpart in Group 1. For these cases, neither diagnosis nor outpatient status was subsequently changed. The sample was again limited to male, white veterans.

Group 3. An exhaustive sample of true positives was found by searching the clinic files and selecting those patients who, as in the other groups, had received psychological and psychiatric examination at the clinic, whose diagnoses were "latent," "incipient," or "subclinical" schizophrenia, or "schizophrenia in remission," and who later were sent to the hospital and received some variety of the diagnosis "schizophrenia" there. Once more, all cases were male and all were white.

Groups 1 and 2 each contained 33 cases. For Group 3, N = 27. Data were gath-

415

ered with regard to age, education, Wechsler-Bellevue IQ, and MMPI profile, and the false negatives compared with each of the two control samples by means, chiefly, of a chi-square analysis, as specified by McNemar [r108, formula 87] for 2 by k tables. This method was employed for testing differences in education and for investigating the discriminatory effectiveness of six signs said by Meehl [436 (see V, 31)] to be commonly employed in differentiating MMPI psychotic profiles from neurotic ones. The signs, modified only to make objective counting possible, are as follows:

1. T scores on four or more of the clinical scales over 70.
2. $F > 65$.
3. Sc > Pt.
4. Pa or Ma > 70.
5. Pa or Sc or Ma > Hs and D and Hy.
6. D > Hs and Hy.

In addition, the t test was applied for all continuous variables [r84, formula 5.03]. Where an F ratio suggested dissimilarity in population variance, a method for approximating t was used which involved no assumption of homogeneous variance [r84, pp. 74–75].

Results and Discussion

The diagnoses actually received by the false negative group are presented in Table 1. They seem to have been most often confused with cases of anxiety reaction or mixed psychoneurosis.

Differences in age, education, and intelligence were not significant either in the comparison between Groups 1 and 2 or that between Groups 1 and 3. Examination of T-score means for the various MMPI scale suggested that the false negatives differ from the members of Group 2 on six of the scales, while they differ from the

Table 1. Primary Diagnoses of Patients in the
False Negative Group

Diagnosis	Number
Psychoneurosis, mixed or unclassified..............	9
Anxiety reaction.................................	9
Conversion reaction, hysteria, or somatization reaction..	4
Obsessive-compulsive reaction.....................	3
Inadequate personality	1
Nonpsychiatric diagnoses.........................	7

Table 2. MMPI Means and Codes of Three Criterion Groups

Group	N	?	L	F	K	Hs	D	Hy	Pd	Mf	Pa	Pt	Sc	Ma
True positive	27	51	53	65	55	67	72	68	66	57	64	68	76	60
	MMPI Code: 82'371469–5 F–KL?													
False negative	33	53	55	65	51	75	81	70	69	56	66	82	85	64
	MMPI Code: 872"13469–5 F–L?K													
True negative	33	51	53	57	51	71	70	70	58	56	56	66	63	57
	MMPI Code: 123"78–4956 FL?K													

members of Group 3 with regard to three scales. Results of this type are not revealing enough to warrant interpretation.

Pattern analysis, even of the simplest kind, seems to yield far more meaningful information. A striking aspect of the profiles presented in Table 2 is the essential similarity between test patterns of the latent schizophrenics who were not correctly diagnosed and those who were. When Meehl's psychotic signs were tested, not one produced a significant chi square. In terms of the test pattern, however, the patients in Group 1 are obviously very much *unlike* the sample of true negatives, even though, as a group, they had been given identical diagnoses. Every one of the six signs yielded a chi square significant at or beyond the .05 level. In view of the informal way in which the criteria were established, the results are surprisingly good.

After-the-fact examination of the profiles leads me cautiously to suggest utility for one sign not included in this list or any other I know. It is the relationship between Hy and Pd — in inferential statement, a relationship between the repressive, inhibitory tendencies of the patient, and his propensity for "acting out" whatever impulses he may have. The "significance" which it yields here has little meaning, but the sign does not appear to be mentioned in other studies [479 (see VII, 45), 644] and might be worth including in future investigations of this type.

The implications furnished by the data are clear. Adequate information was there for the diagnosticians to use; it just was not employed as effectively as it might have been. By assigning to all cases one point for the presence of each sign, it is possible to derive a total psychotic score for any patient. When this was done, and a cutting score for class designation placed between one and two, it was found that 88 per cent of the incorrectly diagnosed patients in Group 1 would have been accurately placed. This increase, however, would have been gained at the expense of incorrect diagnosis for 39 per cent of the cases in Group 2. A cutting score between two and three would have led to correct designation for 67 per cent of the members of Group 1, and incorrect diagnosis for 18 per cent of the Group 2 cases. The overall percentage of accurate classification would have been 74 for both cutting points.

These figures are far short of ideal, but they offer some hope for nosologic differentiation that is considerably better than that which has been made before. Groups 1 and 3 are exhaustive samples of their respective patient classes, and consideration of their relative sizes suggests that the diagnosis of subclinical schizophrenia is missed more often than it is correctly made.

That the problem with which we deal is one of inaccurate diagnosis, and not one of essential change in the patients themselves, is suggested by the results of a follow-up scrutiny of nineteen members of Group 1 who were retested at the hospital. Neither configural analysis of the type described above nor a trend analysis of the direction of sign movement produced statistically reliable results. Either the patients did not change much or the MMPI is too insensitive an instrument to measure any changes that did occur.

Summary

Refinement in psychiatric classification can be effected through specification of the behavioral characteristics of groups of false positives and false negatives. By isolating cases who are found, in the light of later developments, to have been incorrectly diagnosed, and by measurement of the behavior they exhibited before these facts were known, it is possible to improve diagnostic precision.

The present study is concerned with the diagnosis of subclinical schizophrenia, an important but difficult diagnosis for the clinician to make. Thirty-three patients had been examined at an outpatient clinic, and had received there some diagnosis containing no form of the word "schizophrenia." They were later hospitalized and were designated schizophrenic by staff members at the institution.

Comparisons were made between this group and another group of clinic patients, matched for initial diagnosis with regard to age, education, Wechsler-Bellevue IQ, and performance on the MMPI. Similar comparisons were made between the criterion group and an exhaustive sample of twenty-seven outpatients who, like the first group, were later hospitalized and diagnosed schizophrenic, but for whom the diagnosis had been correctly made at the clinic.

No differences in age, education, or intelligence were found. Neither did any clearly interpretable results emerge from analysis of the MMPI by means of the t test. Configural analysis through application of a group of psychotic signs, however, indicated that the MMPI patterns of the false negatives were essentially like those of the patients for whom the diagnosis subclinical schizophrenia had been accurately applied, and were substantially different from those produced by the group of patients with whom they had originally been classed. Diagnosis made in terms of these signs would have led to a considerable increase in classificatory precision.

ARTICLE 47 *A Personality Study of Alcohol Addiction*

THIS study was originally undertaken with the object of investigating personality trends in a group of alcohol addicts who, because they were active members of the fellowship of Alcoholics Anonymous (AA), were readily accessible and unusually cooperative. Later, when it appeared that somewhat unexpected conclusions might be drawn from the survey, it seemed worth while to add a number of other alcoholic subjects drawn at random from the city workhouse and the probation office, as well as some nonaddicted drinkers. The significance of the results obtained from the testing of the presumably highly selected fellowship cases might be thus increased by comparison.

The AA fellowship is composed of men and women whose excessive drinking, usually over a long period of years, has brought about collapse or near collapse of their life organization. Some had deteriorated to a life of vagrancy and destitution. A large number had served series of workhouse sentences, had been hospitalized in every kind of institution purporting to treat chronic alcoholism, or had been under treatment by psychiatrists. The publicity given to the success of the movement by several national publications, and the interest of the medical profession, have assured the organization of a steady stream of "prospects."

The work is carried on solely by alcohol addicts who have successfully arrested their own and one another's disorder. Treatment is based on a set of simple spiritual formulations built around the central theme that the alcohol addict must look to some "higher power" for help to do those things for him that he admits he can no longer hope to do for himself. With recovery, it is said, comes an emotional rebirth and a deep change in personality. They believe that only a confirmed alcoholic, one who has passed through the same devastating experiences and has the same devious thought processes, can understand and establish rapport with another alcoholic. By making themselves responsible for the rescue of other unfortunates and giving their time and efforts unselfishly, they are able to maintain their own precarious balance. Absolute acceptance of the principle that an alcoholic can never learn to drink moderately, and a sincere desire to quit drinking, are fundamental to their creed.

The purpose of the present study has been only to expose a few selected groups to analysis by a new psychometric instrument, the MMPI. All that can be claimed, according to the method employed and within its limitations, as yet unknown, is that certain traits have been found to predominate to a marked degree.

The writer stationed himself at the organization's Minneapolis center and secured thirty-seven members of AA as subjects for testing as the opportunity afforded. No individual was excluded, although two of the subjects were still suffering from the effects of a recent spree, and there was no selection of "interesting subjects" for examination. Membership in AA was presumed to be prima-facie evidence of alcohol addiction.

A group of nine alcoholic women was tested including two members of AA. The other seven subjects were provided for examination by the Minneapolis probation officer. The number is small, but the profiles secured were sufficiently consistent to point to the possibility of a significant sex difference.

Six male alcoholics serving sentences at the Minneapolis workhouse were tested and graphed separately, but as the profile obtained did not vary significantly from the AA graph, it is not shown. The fact that it was very similar, however, is worth noting. Twelve other subjects (five men and seven women) who enjoy the effects of alcohol but rarely drink to excess were also tested. It was thought that their profiles might deviate in the same directions but to a lesser degree than that of the alcohol addicts. This was not the case; their composite profile did not resemble the curve of the addicts in any way and showed only normal deviation.

Table 1. Means and Standard Deviations of the MMPI Clinical Scales for Two Groups of Alcoholic Addicts

Group	$H-C_H$	D	Hy	Pd	Mf	Pa	Pt	Sc
AA males (N = 37)								
M	52.2	59.8	57.2	67.3	55.6	59.3	57.4	57.4
SD	10.9	15.8	10.0	10.9	5.9	11.8	13.3	14.0
		MMPI Code [a]: 4–26 78351						
Female alcoholics (N = 9)								
M	38.4	57.2	50.1	70.0	38.0	68.0	59.0	63.0
SD	...	...	...	...	...	...	...	...
		MMPI Code [a]: 4'68–723/:15						

[a] Editors' Note: These codes are not comparable to other codes in this volume since the Ma scale values were not reported, the $H-C_H$ scores are not equivalent to the revised Hs scale values, and the K corrections have not been applied. No validity scores were reported.

In Table 1 are reported the scores from the two main groups. As stated previously, predominating personality phases typical of a group, if indicated on the composite MMPI profile, may be considered more significant than if found on an individual profile. Moreover, the authors of the schedule state that even on an individual score "the high points on even the normal profile are likely to represent the salient personality characteristics." One may therefore suppose that, on a composite profile, the validity of high scores would be proportionately greater. It is important to note that the composite profile shows significant deviations on most of the traits measured.

Hypochondriasis Scale. The average score obtained for this trait was 52.2. One might expect a greater preoccupation with bodily ills from those who have drunk to excess for many years. According to most investigators, 15 years of excessive drinking is the average length of time required for organic damage to become manifest. These subjects averaged 13.3 years of excessive drinking.

Depression Scale. A comparatively high depression score of 59.8 does not seem particularly significant in view of the disorganized life situation confronting the majority of the members of AA. Also, the average age of 44 years might be expected to contribute to a higher than normal score.

Hysteria Scale. The mean score of the group was 57.2. Together with depression and hypochondriasis, this trait clearly demonstrates the presence of neurotic elements. In view of this it is puzzling that hypochondriasis yielded a relatively low average score. The profiles, however, are by no means consistent, there being very few in which high depression scores were accompanied by high scores on either hypochondriasis or hysteria.

Psychopathic Deviate Scale. This phase is not only the most predominant but also the most consistent trend. The average standard score is 67.3 Sixteen subjects scored higher on this scale than on any other, and it tended to be high among neurotic as well as paranoid and schizoid profiles. Only six subjects scored below 60 (1 SD above normal). It is not surprising that many psychopathic personalities are found among excessive drinkers, but it was not expected that this phase would predominate to such an extent among so many varying personality types, and especially in a group which appears to have gained some insight and which is responding with considerable success to an emotional appeal. One would expect more frequent high scores in the direction of hysteria, psychasthenia, hypochondriasis, and depression.

Masculinity-Femininity Scale. Many writers, especially of the psychoanalytic school, have emphasized the homosexual component in alcohol addicts. It is therefore particularly interesting that the average score on this scale is only 55.6. The highest score, 65, was made by a 67-year-old man, none of whose other personality trends was scored above 52. Older subjects usually score higher than average in the direction of feminine interests because of gradual withdrawal from activities common to younger men. Although AA has been aware that homosexuals might be attracted to the group, and has discouraged those whose appearance was suggestive of abnormality from becoming members, one might expect that a test which was devised to reveal latent as well as overt inversions would have produced several such subjects among so many addicts.

Paranoia Scale. The mean score of the group on this scale was 59.3. High scores on this scale were usually associated with high scores on psychasthenia and schizophrenia and not with the neurotic end of the profile. It is interesting to note that one of the highest standard scores, 94, was made by a man who had been previously diagnosed by a competent psychiatrist as a psychopath but whose psychopathic deviate score was 65. This subject volunteered the information that AA had totally freed his mind from suspicious attitudes and distrust of others. All those with high paranoid scores had manifested suspiciousness and quarrelsome behavior toward their fellow members but showed no insight when questioned about this specifically.

Psychasthenia Scale. During the course of the very brief interviewing of the subjects, none whose scores were high on this scale confessed to compulsive acts, although a number admitted obsessive thinking. Doubtless, further examination would have produced examples. The mean score was 57.4.

Schizophrenia Scale. The mean score was 57.4. Data on this scale showed a number of high individual scores which, for the most part, were closely associated with paranoia. One subject who scored 88 on paranoia and 87 on schizophrenia revealed, on questioning, a history of definite paranoid episodes and schizoid behavior. Another, however, who scored 70 on both paranoia and schizophrenia, was a particularly successful person whose business depended on interpersonal relationships. Only his drinking habits and lonely childhood seemed to confirm, partially, the schizoid trend shown by his profile. When drinking, he tended to be seclusive and untidy in dress, and to seek very inferior companionship—prostitutes, "bar flies," and other gentry of a like caliber.

The authors of the schedule are aware that this scale is not as clearly delimited as the others and that it must be interpreted with great caution.

Intelligence Scale. The standard mean score on the Pressey Senior Classification Test was 59.1, SD 8.5. The tests were valuable in weighing the validity of those profiles in which there were very unusual responses. They also supported the common assertion that abnormal drinkers are often above average intelligence.

Some popular writers on inebriety have characterized the "typical alcoholic" as having an extroverted, expansive personality; and members of AA seem to have this idea about themselves. Actually their responses show a strong feeling of social inadequacy. A tabulation of the frequency of certain answers bears this out. The following responses were made in the infrequent direction 18 times or more by the 37 members of AA.

F-36. I wish I could be as happy as others seem to be. (True) F-9. I frequently have to fight against showing that I am bashful. (True) F-8. It makes me uncomfortable to put on a stunt at a party even when others are doing the same sort of things. (True) E-46. I do not mind being made fun of. (False) F-5. I wish I were not so shy. (True) E-44. I find it hard to make talk when I meet new people. (True) H-32. I have been afraid of things or people that I knew could not hurt me. (True) I-26. I am easily downed in an argument. (True) F-2. In a group of people, I would not be embarrassed to be called upon to start a discussion or give an opinion about something I know well. (False) F-11. I strongly defend my opinions as a rule. (False) E-18. I do not mind meeting strangers. (False)

Since there are few, if any, pure extroverts or introverts, these responses should not be given too much weight, especially as the wording of the statements is fixed. But this does suggest that many alcoholics suffer from feelings of inadequate social adjustment and inferiority which are relieved by alcohol.

Some of the profiles deviate so widely from the norm that one wonders how such persons have managed to avoid a frank breakdown. Haggard and Jellinek [r69] distinguish between true addicts and symptomatic drinkers, both of whose drinking is endogenously determined, by postulating that the addict is able to resolve his psychic problems, however disastrously, by alcohol but that the drinking of the symptomatic drinker is often superficial and that sooner or later the underlying psychosis breaks through. In only one of the subjects of this study was the behavior sufficiently bizarre to have forced its attention upon the other members of the group. A diagnosis in this case has not been made, but the symptoms point to paranoid schizophrenia. One might describe this person as a symptomatic drinker, and all the others with high scores but without overt symptoms of psychosis as true addicts whose drinking is, nevertheless, endogenously determined by serious maladjustment. One wonders what will be the ultimate effects of abstinence on such persons and whether the personality disorders will eventually become manifest in a more pathologic form than excessive drinking.

The nine women who were tested showed consistently greater deviation on all traits except depression, hypochondriasis, and hysteria (see Table 1). The mean depression score of 57.2 was only slightly below that for the AA members, but on the hysteria scale their score was 50.1 as compared with 57.2 for the male group; on the hypochondriasis scale they scored 38.4, a difference of 13.8. This is probably due to the presence of an obscure selective factor.

That alcohol addiction among women is indicative of greater personality disorganization than among men seems borne out by the scores. This may be reasonably explained on the ground that excessive drinking meets with stronger social disapproval for women than for men, and that consequently a woman who drinks to excess might be expected to be less well adjusted to her environment.

It is noteworthy, also, that the psychopathic deviate score of 70 is the highest of all the traits measured and that, aside from the exceptions noted above, the profile resembles that of the larger group.

Cleckley [r37] has written an exceedingly arresting analysis of the psychopath. He believes that the psychopath is a sharply defined psychiatric entity and that the term "constitutional psychopathic inferior" is a rather meaningless term because it has been applied to too many abnormal types and because it stresses the constitutional factor which, although it may be present, has never been demonstrated. He suggests the term "semantic dementia" and states his belief that it is a true psychosis although unlike any other described in psychiatric textbooks.

Cleckley compares this condition with schizophrenia, in which there is fragmentation of the personality. In the psychopath there is also a splitting process which, however, does not destroy the structure of the personality but follows its contour. Affect is cut away as an apple might be pared by separating the skin from the fruit, leaving both intact. Thus, a psychopath presents to the world an imitation. He is a man, complete in every detail, but no more capable of experiencing life than a Tussaud wax figure. He is an emotional robot, like Sherrington's dog able to simulate emotions but incapable of feeling them. He believes that the psychopath's outrageously asocial behavior stems from an unconscious will-to-fail, a consistent tendency not so much toward death as non-life. Drinking is resorted to by the psychopath as a means of fulfilling this unconscious drive and because of the unbearable aridity of his emotional life.

Cleckley's definition of psychopathic personality seems to fit the type of person who scores high on the psychopathic deviate scale, although the case histories he uses as illustrations do seem more bizarre and extreme than those of the personalities considered in the present study. Unlike many writers, he does not ascribe to the addict strong sex drives, either normal or abnormal. In fact, he is convinced that the psychopath is less strongly sexed than other types and that he indulges in all manner of sex activity from lack of inhibition and because it affords him momentary and casual gratification.

If the MMPI is a valid diagnostic tool, then psychopathic personality is the major trend in the groups observed in this study and probably in a large proportion of inebriates. Perhaps the neurotic drinker so well described by Strecker and Chambers [r155] is merely a neurotic with a strong psychopathic component whose real personality structure has been obscured by his alcoholic behavior.

In determining the validity of the psychopathic scores it is necessary to examine some of the questions which have weight on this scale.

It is important to remember that it was not, presumably, constructed on the principle that inebriates are, per se, psychopaths, as has been claimed by some. In administering this test, however, subjects again and again remarked that many of the questions seemed to pertain particularly to the state of drunkenness and its inevitable sequelae. The following questions are taken from the schedule and the answers are those given most frequently by the inebriates:

A-21. I have had blank spells in which my activities were interrupted and I did not know what was going on around me. (True) B-42. I have used alcohol excessively. (True) B-48. I believe that my home life is as pleasant as that of most people I know. (False) B-49. There is very little love and companionship in my family as compared to other homes. (True) B-50. My people treat me more like a child than a grown up. (True) B-52. My parents have often objected to the kind of people I went around with. (True) B-53. My parents and my family find more fault with me than they should. (True) B-55. I have very few quarrels with my family. (False) E-12. I have never been in trouble with the law. (False) E-17. I have never been in trouble because of my sex behavior. (False) E-50. I do many things which I regret afterwards. (True) G-4. I have not lived the right kind of life. (True) H-3. I am sure I am being talked about. (True) H-12. I have had very peculiar and strange experiences. (True) H-26. I know who is responsible for most of my troubles. (True) I-13. My hardest battles are with myself [34 of the 37 AA subjects answered this as true].

Each of the above questions has significance on the psychopathic deviate scale and it is probable that any alcoholic answering truthfully would respond in the normally infrequent direction. With these responses added to the expected number of deviant responses that any normal subject might make on this scale, the resulting standard score would then be greater than a standard deviation above the mean. It is therefore pertinent to consider whether the high psychopathic deviate score achieved by the majority of inebriate subjects is explainable as a function of alcoholic behavior or as the manifestation of a deep underlying personality disorder characteristic of psychopathic personality.

It is probable that in some subjects a high score can be explained quite simply as the reaction of the personality to disorganizing situations consequent upon uncontrolled drinking, the etiology of which might be sought in other disabling traits. On the other hand, there can be little doubt that psychopathy, in the sense in which it is used here, is the outstanding character deficiency in many of these subjects. It is unfortunate that alcohol addiction often masks the subject's personality to such an extent that it is seldom possible to dissect away behavior due to alcohol alone so that the essential structure can be examined.

One cannot predict how successful AA will be over a long period, or whether the fellowship will be able to maintain its present vitality and freshness. Its success thus far, however, augurs well for the future. The average member is 44 years old, began drinking occasionally to excess when he was 19 years old, and has been drinking to excess continually for a period of about 13 years. The average length of time that the members reported in this study have remained entirely abstinent is 10 months. If some of these had not had one or two lapses since joining, the average time would be much longer. Ten months of abstinence is not proof of cure; but the Minneapolis group is only two years old, and for an alcoholic who has enjoyed few sober periods in a large part of his adult life, this represents a change for the better that has seldom been equaled by more scientific procedures.

There are, of course, other factors operating favorably on behalf of this group. Considering their histories, remarkably few of them are divorced or single, and many have children. Their intelligence, as noted above, is considerably above the average. Many of them have demonstrated unusual ability and seem to have no great difficulty in finding work once they have convinced their associates that they can remain sober. Finally, their social and economic backgrounds are relatively superior to the average, thereby affording protecting elements that should not be minimized.

Members of AA probably do not differ essentially in personality structure from those who are more often in conflict with the law, but they are superior in intelligence, education, occupational skills, and social status. The similarity of the various composite alcoholic profiles is misleading in that the individual variability is very great, and because only a high proportion of certain types of deviation seems to prevail. There is no evidence to support a belief that an "alcoholic personality" exists. In view of the low score on the masculinity-femininity interest scale, it seems probable that neither latent nor overt homosexuality is typical of alcohol addicts in general. Abnormal sex behavior in the group studied appeared to be a symptom of psychopathy rather than of abnormal sex drive.

The use of alcohol as a social solvent and euphoric drug is extremely dangerous to the maladjusted personality, and in direct proportion to the degree of maladjustment. To the well-integrated personality, able to achieve satisfaction through legitimate and normal channels, it is doubtful that alcohol presents any permanent hazard.

Alcohol addiction is a psychiatric problem, the solution of which will be found in the treatment of the total personality and the total environment. Alcohol addiction is a symptom, not a disease entity, and as such it is associated with all types of disabling personality abnormalities. Progress in treatment will be achieved when treatment is directed away from the symptom toward the underlying psychic structure.

The statement made by some psychiatrists that AA can help only certain types of personality does not seem to be borne out. Schizoid and paranoid subjects as well as neurotics and normal excessive drinkers all benefited from associating with a group; they appeared to change their social attitudes because of it and to establish more nearly normal relationships with their environment for the first time in years. In the one case of frank psychosis, AA was of no value. The subject attended meetings only because she was brought by her husband. It seems probable that only prepsychotic personalities can benefit from association with others who are experiencing similar personality disorders. Meetings held by the fellowship provide a kind of group psychotherapy and opportunity for self-expression and catharsis.

The fellowship deserves the support and recognition of psychiatrists, physicians, social agencies, and the courts. It should not, however, be interfered with in any way by misguided enthusiasts or sentimentalists, or be used by them to foist individuals upon the organization for treatment. Only those who come to it under no other compulsion than their own sense of defeat and need for help can have any hope of remission. For the cheerful psychopath who has no desire to mend his ways, the moronic addict whose feeble mental powers cannot grasp the relation between cause and effect, or the frankly psychotic, there is no hope of recovery through this organization.

To summarize, alcohol addiction in the groups studied in this survey seems to be associated, with but few exceptions, with deep personality disorders. Even those exceptions are doubtless more apparent than real. There were very few whose drinking was exogenously determined and whose habituation was brought about chiefly by long exposure to alcohol.

Nearly all the alcohol addicts in this study showed marked psychopathic deviation which was often associated with neurotic, paranoid, or schizoid trends.

N. L. FARBEROW

ARTICLE 48 *Personality Patterns of Suicidal Mental Hospital Patients*

THE population of this study consists of 96 male patients of a Veterans Administration mental hospital. The design of the experiment is such that the population is of two major types, experimental (suicidal) and control (non-suicidal).

Experimental (Suicidal) Group

This hospital maintains an observation ward where patients suspected of suicidal tendencies are placed for continual twenty-four-hour observation. On this ward they are under observation until, in the opinion of the psychiatrist in charge and a consultant who reviews the case in a staff meeting, the immediate danger from suicide is passed. The experimental group, consisting of 64 patients, was gathered from this ward while they were still on observation status and so still considered suicidal. This group was then broken down for purposes of comparison in two different ways:

A. Suicidal action	B. Psychiatric judgment
1. Attempts (A)	1. Serious (S)
2. Threats (T)	2. Non-serious (N)

Under the suicidal action classification, cases were divided into those who had made an abortive attempt at suicide (A), and those who had only threatened suicide but who had not yet attempted it (T). Since the reason for their placement on this ward was a matter of record, it was a simple process to gather cases until 32 of each had been collected. The classification of the experimental group was in terms of expert opinion. It is a well-known fact that many suicidal attempts are mere gestures, attention-getting devices and the like, and that no serious intent is ever present to carry the act through to its ultimate end. However, it was decided not to rate the seriousness of the attempt, for this is frequently very misleading, but rather the seriousness of the suicidal tendency. Therefore, the psychiatrist in charge was asked to rate his patients in terms of seriousness and non-seriousness, with the criterion being his opinion as to whether or not the patient, if left to his own devices and not given adequate care and surveillance, would probably successfully carry out his intention to destroy himself. This rating by the psychiatrist was made on all

427

the suicidal patients included as subjects for this study. Thus, the second differentiation was made regardless of type of attempt or kind of threat, and was based entirely on an expert's opinion as to whether or not the suicidal tendency was a serious one. Cases were collected until there were 32 in each of the serious (S) and non-serious (N) groups. This actually makes for four subgroups in the experimental group with 16 patients in each: attempt-serious (AS), attempt non-serious (AN), threat serious (TS), and threat non-serious (TN). In general, however, our analysis will be concerned with the comparison of the attempts group and threats group with the control group and with each other, and with comparison of the serious and non-serious groups with the control group and with each other. All experimental patients were tested by the examiner upon their entrance on the observation ward. Most of them were given the group tests used in the study in groups averaging about four, and then were given the projective test individually. The one essential criterion, besides suicidal tendencies, was testability, that is, whether the patient was in good enough contact and amenable enough to respond to the tests.

Control (Nonsuicidal) Group

The control group (C) is made up of patients from the same hospital. Every effort was made to have them as much like the experimental group as possible, except for the one essential distinguishing feature of being nonsuicidal, i.e., they had never attempted suicide, never threatened it, or even admitted to ever contemplating it. The methods used to check these tendencies were as follows: Each patient, as he is admitted to the hospital, is interviewed briefly by a psychiatrist, who then fills out an admission sheet. This sheet contains a space where the presence or absence of suicidal tendencies is checked. No patient was included among the control group unless this space was checked in the negative. A second check was effected by having the patient answer Yes or No to two questions: Have you ever attempted suicide? Have you ever seriously threatened or considered suicide? These questions were substituted for two others in the middle of the Cornell Selectee Index (one of the tests used in routine testing of all new patients), so that they received no special emphasis for answer in either direction. Only those who answered negatively to these two questions were included among the control group. A third check was the close perusal of the case histories written by the psychiatrist to whom the case was assigned. Where any mention of any suicidal tendencies of any kind occurred, the case was discarded. Thus, the patients in the control group, insofar as these three methods of checking could ascertain, were not suicidal and never had been. Testing of these patients was carried out in the same way as for the experimental group, the objective tests being administered in groups and the projective test being administered individually.

Biographical Data

Summarizing the biographical data gathered on the patients, we see that the suicidal and the control groups show a remarkable similarity in almost all major aspects. They had spent approximately the same length of time in the hospital before being tested, and they were approximately the same in age and religious distribution. Diagnostically, they closely approximated each other in neurotic, psychotic, and organic classifications, except for a tendency of the suicidals to have more reactive-depressives than the controls. Military histories and number of previous hospitalizations were very similar. They showed the same kinds of family histories and early environments, but the threats group revealed a slightly greater tendency to come from families which were more unstable. The suicidal group also tended to come from slightly larger families than the controls. In education, approximately 50 per cent of each of the groups had a high school education. They showed approximately the same occupational status and indicated that a poor work history was common to all groups, 75 per cent reporting this fact. The marital status was also very similar in number unmarried, married, divorced, separated, or widowed, but there seemed to be a tendency toward less marital stability among the suicidals than the controls. Reasons for attempting or threatening suicide were compared for the suicidal groups only, with the feeling of having been rejected by a loved one appearing most frequently for the attempts group and economic difficulties most frequently for the threats. The attempts were found to use sedation and slashing of the wrists in their suicidal efforts most frequently. It was also reported that both the threats and the attempts reveal histories of attempts at self-destruction both prior to and subsequent to the time of testing, lending weight to the possibility that the threats are, in reality, pre-attempts.

Results

The group form of the MMPI was used to study the personality characteristics of these groups. Instead of the 550 items contained in the individual form of the test, only 373 items were given. This was accomplished by presenting the first 365 statements (the only ones used in scoring any of the clinical categories in the MMPI) and presenting the seven items for the K factor, which are included among those numbered 367–550, on a sheet inserted in the test booklet and renumbered as items 367–373. Twelve of the scales were scored in this study, the ? score being eliminated because it is a score gained from the number of questions left blank, and there were relatively few instances of this in the study.

Table 1 presents the mean T score on each of the twelve scales of the MMPI for the various groups and subgroups. As can be seen, all groups present a very similar picture, with many scores above the critical one of 70. The least disturbed profile of the A, T, and C groups appears to belong to the A's, who are below the scores for the C's in every diagnostic scale except depression. The T's show the most deviant profile with their scores falling below 70 on only two of the diagnostic scales, Mf and Ma. When S, N, and C are compared, it is obvious that the S group obtains the most deviant profile, while the N's, in general, seem little distinguished from the C's. The factor of threatening suicide added to either serious or non-serious seems to emphasize the abnormality of the profile.

Before one can speak about specific scale differences, however, it is necessary to determine whether the differences are statistically significant. After the analysis of variance was computed for each scale, the F ratios were obtained for each analysis. These results are tabulated in Table 2.

The results from Table 2 indicate that eight scales, the L, F, D, Pd, Pa, Pt, Sc, and Ma scales, differentiate in some manner, yet to be determined, among A, T, and C; and that two scales, the L and Pa scales, differentiate among S, N, and C. It is also apparent that the possibility of differentiation among the subgroups, AS, AN, TS, and TN, could exist only in those scales where significant ratios were found in both A, T, and C and S, N, and C. These were the L and Pa scales. The test was made to determine whether any significant differences might exist between these subgroups but no significant F ratio was found, the results yielding a minus ratio for the L scale, and 3.081 for the Pa scale.

Table 1. Mean T Scores and Codes on the MMPI for Controls and Suicidals
Grouped in Various Categories

Group	N	L	F	K	Hs	D	Hy	Pd	Mf	Pa	Pt	Sc	Ma
Controls	32	55	62	56	72	75	73	73	62	62	72	74	60
				MMPI Code: 283417'569 F–KL									
Attempts	32	52	61	54	71	78	67	70	61	61	68	68	56
				MMPI Code: 214'783 56–9 F–KL									
Threats	32	51	68	51	77	86	75	80	66	73	85	88	68
				MMPI Code: 8274"136'95 F–LK									
Serious	32	52	66	50	75	84	71	74	65	71	79	81	60
				MMPI Code: 28"714 36'59 F–LK									
Non-serious	32	51	64	54	73	80	71	76	62	63	74	75	65
				MMPI Code: 2"48713'965 F–KL									
Attempts													
Serious	16	53	61	51	72	81	67	68	62	62	71	73	54
				MMPI Code: 2"817'43 56–9 F–LK									
Non-serious	16	52	61	51	70	75	67	73	59	60	65	64	59
				MMPI Code: 241'378 6–59 F–LK									
Threats													
Serious	16	51	70	49	77	88	75	80	67	80	87	89	66
				MMPI Code: 827 46"13'59 F'–L/K									
Non-serious	16	55	67	52	76	85	75	80	65	66	83	87	71
				MMPI Code: 8274"139'65 F–LK									

The t ratios were then computed in those instances where the F ratios were significant. The results are tabulated in Table 3.

As can be seen from Table 3, in all the scales except the L scale the threats were differentiated significantly from the attempts and controls, with the T's receiving the highest or the more deviant score. In the L scale, they scored lowest and were differentiated significantly from the C's but not from the A's. If we compare the serious, non-serious, and control groups, the L scale yields a significant difference between the C's and the N's, but not between the other groups, with the C's again receiving the highest score. On the Pa scale, the S's were differentiated significantly from both the C's and the N's with the S's receiving the highest or more deviant scores.

Conclusion

Some of the conclusions which seem warranted by the MMPI results may be stated as follows:

1. One of the most important findings is the apparently sharp cleavage within the suicidal group, with the threats showing marked differences from the attempts.

Table 2. F Ratios on the MMPI for Controls and Suicidals Grouped in Various Categories [a]

Groups	L	K	F	Hs	D	Hy	Pd	Mf	Pa	Pt	Sc	Ma
A, T, C......	4.010*	2.152	5.017**		4.323*	2.866	5.510**	2.367	8.219**	8.186**	8.351**	8.343**
S, N, C......	3.545*	2.772			2.673				5.040**	1.292	1.012	1.712

[a] Necessary for significance at the .05 level of confidence (*), 3.10; at the .01 level (**), 4.85.

Table 3. The t Ratios between Suicidals and Control Mean Scores on Eight Scales of the MMPI When Significant F Ratios Were Found

Group Comparisons	L [a]	F	D	Pd	Pa	Pt	Sc	Ma
T > A		2.943**	2.101*	3.191**	3.525**	3.855**	4.027**	3.955**
T > C		2.487*	2.833**	2.388*	3.496**	2.951**	2.765**	2.862**
C > T	2.756**							
A > T	1.517							
A > C			0.732					
C > A	1.480	0.456		0.803	0.003	0.904	1.262	1.094
S > N	0.604							
S > C					2.465*			
C > S	1.853				2.965**			
N > S								
N > C					0.501			
C > N	2.266*							

[a] Df = 31, requiring 2.04 and 2.75 for .05 (*) and .01 (**) levels of confidence. Df for all other columns = 90 with 1.99 and 2.63 required for .05 (*) and .01 (**) levels of confidence.

It becomes clear that one cannot speak of suicidals as a group unless sharp definition of the types included is made.

2. The threats are the most seriously disturbed. They present a picture of a person with much anxiety, high obsessive tendencies, and considerable psychopathy. One of the main points differentiating them from the other groups is their tendency toward acting out of their impulses (higher Ma).

3. The attempts reveal what seems to be a firmer grasp on reality than the threats (the psychotic end of the scale, Pa, Pt, Sc, and Ma, is lower). They apparently still feel depressed and guilty but not nearly so much as the T's. The A's may also be said to be the least agitated of the three groups, lowest Ma). This may be the result of having already acted out their impulses, dispelling much of their hostility (lower Pa and Pd), and so no longer feeling the need to express such tendencies.

4. The suicidal act seems to diminish considerably the hostility feelings expressed (lower Pa, Pd in the A's). If it may be assumed that the A's are the same as the T's who have carried out their threat, apparently the suicidal deed itself acts as some sort of abreactive mechanism which greatly diminishes the seriousness of the overt personality disturbance.

5. The threats and the non-serious may both be said to feel that it is not necessary to present a favorable picture of themselves (low L). Possibly, by lying less they will appear more deserving of attention and help.

6. The serious, like the threats, are very hostile people, while the non-serious resemble the controls in that they show less hostility.

Medical Problems

ONE of the original purposes of the MMPI was the detection of psychoneuroses in medical practice [422]. It is variously estimated that from one third to three fourths of all patients who present themselves to the general practitioner will be found either neurotic or suffering from neurotic complication of their symptoms. The advantage of a practical measuring instrument for the harassed physician is obvious [635].

The articles in this section are all related to medical problems of one kind or another. The range of groups studied and the kinds of problems attacked vary tremendously. In all of them, however, it is possible to see how the investigator was able to objectify various concepts and findings about different diseases by means of the MMPI.

In article 49 Wiener uses the MMPI profile as objective evidence of the degree of psychological involvement in the following disorders: arthritis, asthma, flat feet, gunshot wounds, heart, malaria, skin, and ulcers. The personality descriptions gained from the profile configuration are compared with each other as well as with a control group. It is interesting to note these findings with flat feet, gunshot wounds, and malaria, groups which are not ordinarily compared with such diseases as arthritis and ulcers.

Some very exciting findings are reported in article 50 where the MMPI is used to point out personality differences between patients with fast-growing cancers and patients with slow-growing cancers. In a preliminary study it was clear that the MMPI showed marked differences beween the two groups which were not disclosed by the Thematic Apperception Test, the Rorschach, or the Wechsler-Bellevue scales. A follow-up study strikingly confirms the original findings. This report will undoubtedly instigate a number of investigations in this area.

The next two articles, 51 and 52, are based on the findings in the University of Minnesota starvation project. In the first article Schiele and Brozek select from the thirty-six subjects in the study nine case histories to illustrate by means of psychiatric studies and MMPI profiles certain psychological changes in personality which appeared during the starvation period and which for the most part were reversed during the period of rehabilitation. The next article presents further material arguing for the interpretation of these phenomena as reflecting an actual psychoneurosis controlled by the experimental procedures. Brozek and Kjenaas studied the items on the neurotic triad, scales 1, 2, and 3, to show that the kinds of items elevated during the semistarvation period are for the most part those very items which are found to be operative in psychoneurotic patients. The verbal behavior of this group does not appear to be merely a direct reflection of their organic symptoms.

433

In article 53 the MMPI profiles of patients with frontal lobe injury are contrasted by Andersen and Hanvik with those of a series of patients who sustained parietal involvement. The reader might compare this group profile approach with the work on the scale for caudality (see IV, 25). The value of the MMPI profile in describing the personality structure of patients with multiple sclerosis is seen in article 54. Canter provides a striking illustration of the remarkable consistency of the profile under test-retest conditions with this particular group.

In the last paper, article 55, Hanvik shows the difference between two groups of patients with low-back pain, one of which showed organic pathology to account for the pain while the other had no demonstrable pathology. Not only the group mean profiles but also the individual profiles of the patients can be distinguished through his procedures. An incidental finding in this last study is some material on the relative ability of judges in carrying out sorting procedures. This has already been referred to in Section V on profile analysis.

It seems to us that the articles in this section point up the adaptability of the MMPI and its value in diverse medical problems. Considerable variety in the treatment of the data shows that it is not necessary to limit the research design but that it can be varied to suit the situation.

The articles in this section came from the following sources: article 49 from D. N. Wiener, Personality characteristics of selected disability groups, *Genetic Psychology Monographs*, 1952, 45, 175–255; article 50 from E. M. Blumberg, P. M. West, and F. W. Ellis, A possible relationship between psychological factors and human cancer, *Psychosomatic Medicine*, 1954, 16, 277–286; article 51 from B. C. Schiele and J. Brozek, "Experimental neurosis" resulting from semistarvation in man, *Psychosomatic Medicine*, 1948, 10, 31–50; article 52 from J. Brozek and Nancy K. Erickson, Item analysis of the psychoneurotic scales on the MMPI in experimental semistarvation, *Journal of Consulting Psychology*, 1948, 12, 403–411; article 53 from A. L. Andersen and L. J. Hanvik, The psychometric localization of brain lesions: the differential effect of frontal and parietal lesions on MMPI profiles, *Journal of Clinical Psychology*, 1950, 6, 177–180; article 54 from A. H. Canter, MMPI profiles in multiple sclerosis, *Journal of Consulting Psychology*, 1951, 15, 253–256; and article 55 from L. J. Hanvik, MMPI profiles in patients with low back pain, *Journal of Consulting Psychology*, 1951, 15, 350–353. We are indebted to the authors and to the publishers of the journals for permission to reproduce these articles in this form.

D. N. WIENER

◆

ARTICLE 49 *Personality Characteristics of Selected*
Disability Groups

PSYCHOLOGISTS, working with unselected cross sections of any large population, often face disabled persons whose physical disabilities, with their emotional
concomitants, must be as carefully considered as are their abilities, interests, background, and environment, if counseling is to be successful. Certain relationships are
assumed in counseling the disabled. One is the relationship between the limitations
imposed by an individual's disability and those imposed by the requirements of
the job. A second relationship, that between personality and job requirements, is
recognized as essential for the accurate prediction of occupational success of both
disabled and able-bodied. A third relationship, that between personality and physical disability, is the focus of this study. This area appears to be the least systematically studied, although the literature suggests that its roots are perhaps the oldest.
It is an essential side of the triangle of the three relationships which must be understood before there can be fully effective large-scale counseling, therapy, social adjustment, and vocational placement of the disabled.

While the influence of physical disability upon personality is generally accepted, the effect of personality upon disability is much less often recognized.
There are fewer references to this relationship than to the reverse one which is
documented by objective data.

While the studies reviewed, and conclusions reached, by Barker *et al.* are chiefly
in terms of emotional disturbance following incurrence of the physical handicap,
they recognize the mutual interaction of the two factors in these words:

Usually the state of health which the individual seems to be leaving is highly
attractive to him while the immediate symptom forcing him to seek medical attention is unattractive because it is likely to be painful, expensive and time consuming.
. . . On the other hand, medical attention may lead to almost immediate remission
of symptoms and a return to the state of good health. Thus the persons is inevitably
in a state of confusion the magnitude of which will depend on his concept of the
degree of attractiveness of these symptoms. Inevitably he will vacillate and exhibit
behavior which may affect his physiological functioning, and cause, during the
interview, "conflict, caution, emotionality, exploration, vacillation." [r14]

Specifically, however, the possibility that the occurrence of the disabilities may
actually be determined by personality structure has only recently begun to be

435

explored. Menninger's discussion of the term "sickness prone" [r117] and Dunbar's work with the "accident habit" [r47] suggest that a physical illness or disability may meet a person's psychological needs.

Menninger writes:

It is quite certain that many physical disabilities are based on a definite, although unconscious wish. . . . Such individuals certainly differ in a practical way from those whose unconscious trends lead them in the direction of a depression or neurosis. For this reason a definite personality tieup would seem to be indicated, which might be called a *sickness prone* type. For just as accident prone persons find slippery steps and speeding cars to coöperate with their inner wishes, so the sickness prone type finds noxious agents in the external world with which to coöperate. [r117]

The suggestion also has been made that the nature of disabilities may be determined by the predispositions of personality. There is a "gathering body of evidence against the old pathological concept that specific agents give rise to pathognomonic tissue disturbances. . . . The organism is capable of reacting to noxious events with a limited number of efforts involving one or more organs." [r173]

The possibility of the active psychological development of specific physical symptoms is imaginatively described by Dunbar in these words:

They have asked for it, and in the hidden recesses of their minds have even made a blueprint of the disease they want. They select symptoms in much the same way that healthy people select clothes, choosing carefully for style, fit, and the effect upon others. Yet many do not know they have done it. [r48]

The present study was designed primarily to test whether personality characteristics are differentially associated with various disabilities. The MMPI was the measure of personality. Chiefly from the field of psychosomatic medicine, selected literature was reviewed which described personality concomitants of the physical disabilities to be studied, with emphasis upon objective studies.

The attempt was made to determine whether relationships cited in the literature were confirmed by the personality test results. When these or other relationships were found, the attempt was made to describe a meaningful personality pattern for each group. The comparisons stressed for each disabled group were with a nondisabled control group, but they were also made for each disabled group with every other disabled group studied.

The disabled groups thus were compared with a nondisabled group drawn from the same veteran population rather than with a representative group of men in general. Only by using both disabled and control groups drawn from the same World War II veteran population did there seem to be reasonable likelihood of holding relatively constant such selective factors as military service, social background, and motivation for counseling, and of obtaining tested samplings for disabled and control groups over a similar period of time. It was not possible to obtain test data for a representative sample of disabled men in general, or for nondisabled men in general. Further effort might permit the use of student groups in the elementary school grades as a relatively general population, although representing only a limited range of age and disabilities.

An estimated 30,000 World War II veterans had received counseling through the Minnesota Advisement and Guidance Section by June 30, 1948. There were approximately 300,000 World War II veterans in Minnesota at the time. Of the approximately 30,000 state veterans who had military service-connected disabilities, about 15,000 had received counseling. Roughly 10 per cent of Minnesota's total World War II population had received counseling, compared with about 50 per cent of the disabled veteran population. Since the disabled men probably needed more help than the nondisabled in readjusting to civilian life, it seemed logical that they used the counseling service in relatively greater numbers.

Over 90 per cent of the disabled veterans were given the MMPI as part of the psychometric procedure. It was omitted only when time or the person's disability did not permit administration. Among the background facts routinely obtained were age, education, color, sex, and intellectual level.

Counseling was provided by guidance centers strategically located throughout the state to serve the veteran population as equally as possible. While it was likely that veterans from the immediate vicinity of the guidance center used the counseling services more frequently than those living farther away, the fact that there were centers throughout the state ensured a broad geographical coverage of the World War II veteran population of Minnesota.

Before beginning training under the vocational rehabilitation program, the disabled veteran had to apply for and go through the counseling process at one of these centers. All procedures were essentially the same at all guidance centers for disabled and nondisabled counselees alike.

The records of all disabled veterans who had completed counseling in the Minnesota Veterans Administration program from June 1946 through May 1948 were reviewed for the present study. Data were recorded for the first 50 cases of generalized arthritis, the first 50 cases of asthma, the first 50 cases of duodenal and stomach ulcers, the first 50 cases of flat feet, the first 100 cases of gunshot wounds, the first 100 cases of malaria, the first 50 cases of skin disease, and the first 50 cases of valvular heart disease.

One of the major problems in studying disabled groups is that the terminology of medical diagnoses is not standardized. Diagnoses by different physicians are often based upon different approaches, or reflect varying purposes. Physical examinations of the same man for the army and for insurance might well produce different results.

It was possible partially to overcome this problem in the present study by using only diagnoses which had been made by Veterans Administration medical officers all for the same purpose—to determine compensation for a military service-connected or aggravated disability. Diagnoses and ratings were made according to the highly standardized and detailed procedure outlined in a manual used nationally for this purpose [r179].

All degrees of severity were included among the disabled cases of the study except for the most extreme cases for whom vocational rehabilitation seemed to be definitely and permanently impossible. A few veterans from among all disabled groups were counseled in hospitals or in their homes. The majority of those so counseled were veterans with pathological heart conditions.

The control group of 100 cases was composed of nondisabled veterans who completed counseling under the GI Bill from June 1946 through June 1947 at

Veterans Administration guidance centers in Minnesota. These cases were selected from central files containing summaries of all cases counseled at Minnesota centers. The first veteran's records were taken from each folder which divided the case records equally in filing cabinets until 100 were accumulated. Since filing was alphabetical, the cases fell throughout the alphabet except that it was necessary to go through about one third of the folders a second time to obtain 100 cases. In this way a slight bias may have been introduced. The selection of cases was thus not entirely random, as the use of random number tables and a controlled time period would have ensured.

Several inadequacies in the actual selection process of the samples from the veteran population used may be noted. First of all, war veterans are not completely representative of the general population even within the limitation of age, sex, color, and geography already cited. Generalizations from their results to the general population are therefore hazardous.

Many Minnesota men who were mentally or physically sick, who had family responsibilities, or whose work as civilians was considered essential were not drafted. A smaller number successfully hid mental or physical deficiences in order to get into military service. Generally, however, so many men were taken, and so few rejected, that the veteran population may well have been basically representative of the state's young male nonhospitalized population.

Perhaps a more serious source of bias lay in the fact that generally only veterans who sought vocational or educational benefits from the Veterans Administration went through counseling and were included in the study. There is evidence, however, that persons seeking counseling do not differ appreciably from the population from which they come [r144].

A further possible source of bias lay in the method of choosing the individual cases. Since all disabled cases were taken as they completed counseling until the desired numbers had been accumulated, this problem mainly concerns the possible unrepresentativeness of the time period covered. Perhaps veterans studied earlier in the war would have had fewer combat-connected disabilities. Perhaps more volunteers would have been found earlier. Perhaps older men developed disabilities first.

There were subtler aspects of selection within the disability groups which should be recognized as possibilities even though they cannot be evaluated. They will be mentioned now, and also later in the text. They will surely be supplemented by the reader who understands the military environment.

The gunshot wound group probably included a greater than chance number of men who were willing to accept dangerous assignment. Youthfulness or lack of family reponsibilities might be factors, as well as more basic personality characteristics. Factors that determined whether a man was sent to the relatively undesirable Pacific Island assignments might be related to the incurrence of malaria and skin disease.

There was a continual jockeying in the military service, as in civilian life, for positions matching personality structures and needs. Many variables including safety, prestige, and geography were taken into account by soldiers and often affected their military assignments. There was less freedom of action, however, in military service than in civilian life. We may therefore conclude that selection of environment, with the resulting effect upon exposure to disease and disability, was less likely to exist in military than in civilian life although it exists in both contexts in many ways.

All these possible sources of bias must be recognized. In view of the evidence cited, and that which follows comparing the samples to populations, it is difficult to isolate particular biases that may have been operating during the time period covered. Biases of an unknown nature may have operated which canceled each other, or they may have been persistent and cumulative. Neither the literature nor the evidence available provides an answer to the possibilities raised.

Data recorded for each case included all MMPI scores except for Cannot Say and Lie, and were corrected for K [441 (see I, 2)]. Cannot Say and Lie scores were not analyzed since practically all T scores were at the mean for these two scales. Age, education completed, and an estimate of intelligence were also recorded. While MMPI results were available for all cases, "age" was missing for 13 of the 600 cases. "Education completed" was omitted for two cases, and intelligence was not available for 13 cases.

The MMPI was administered in either the individual or group form. The two forms yield closely similar results for groups [638]. Age was taken to the nearest birth date at the time of counseling, while education was recorded as the number of school grades completed.

Intelligence was estimated by equating results of the different intelligence tests given in individual cases. Results for the Otis Self-Administering Scales, the vocabulary and analogies sections of the Unit Scales of Aptitude, or the Ohio Psychological Examination, Form 21, were available in all but 13 cases. General population norms were used for the Otis and Unit Scales tests, while for the Ohio Examination, the University of Minnesota "UTB, SLA-GC" norms were used. According to published [r178] and unpublished data for Minnesota veterans who had taken all three of the tests, a rough equation of their results is obtained by using T scores based upon general population norms for the Otis, averaging the T scores for the vocabulary and analogies sections of the Unit Scales, and subtracting 10 T-score points from the general university population norms for the Ohio.

It was not possible to obtain marital status, residence, or occupation for all cases; these very important areas were therefore not studied. Sex and color were controlled in the sense that only male white veterans were included in the study.

After tabulations were made of MMPI scores, education, age, and intelligence estimates, analysis of variance was done to determine if the disabled groups could be considered to have been drawn from the same population. Critical ratios were computed to determine the significance of the differences between the means of each group and the control group on each MMPI scale and background factor. In addition, they were computed between the means of the disabled groups compared with each other by pairs on those factors where the analysis of variance indicated that they were probably drawn from different populations.

It is recognized that certain statistical extensions and refinements would have been desirable. Chief among these would have been analyses of covariance to hold age, education, and intelligence constant, and more precise tests of significance based upon homogeneity of variance where it existed. Besides the enormously extended amount of analysis and interpretation which would have been necessary, the additions would also have resulted in different methods of analysis for the different groups according to the characteristics of the particular group and factors. An alternative would have been to work with only one or two disabled groups as intensively as possible. The choice was made, however, to use as many disabled groups as possible in the attempt to obtain differential data, then to use statistics providing underestimates of the relationships.

While the opinions of physicians and psychologists concerning the importance of psychosomatic relationships are frequently expressed in the literature, there is little uniformity of context among them. No published studies could be found which were based upon an analysis of the relative significance of the psychosomatic component among a group of disabilities.

Barker *et al.* [r14] have suggested several ways of distinguishing between symptoms which are primarily "psychosomatic" (psychological cause, somatic consequence), and those which are primarily "somatopsychological" (somatic cause, psychological consequence). In the psychosomatic case, symptoms are magnified and the effects of therapy depreciated. In the somatopsychological case, symptoms are minimized, and the effects of therapy are exaggerated. In the psychosomatic, the mood is depressive and pessimistic; in the somatopsychological, optimism and hope are likely despite discomfort and ineffectual therapy. Finally, in the psychosomatic case, symptoms are variable and when one is curbed, another will appear. In the somatopsychological case, symptoms are more constant and related to the real physical condition.

To make the above determinations, clinical records would be needed which were not available for the cases of this study. The attempt was made, however, to determine the relative degree of importance of the psychological factor in each of the disabilities studied.

Since an important aspect of this study is the attempt to describe personality differences among a variety of disability groups it seemed important to attempt to obtain systematically the opinions of psychiatrists and psychologists regarding them. These opinions would be significant as a reflection of current clinical thinking on the subject. It would then be possible to compare the MMPI scores of each group with relative rankings by experts as well as with findings from the literature.

The rank-order correlation method was used to analyze the data. Seven psychiatric staff members of the University of Minnesota were asked to rank the eight disabilities studied according to several possible psychosomatic relationships.

They ranked the disabilities in three areas according to their estimations of the severity of emotional reaction in the patient; the uniqueness of personality concomitants; and the likelihood that the disability was caused by emotional factors. Mean ranks for three of the raters were correlated with those of the other four. Rank-order correlation coefficients were +.74 for reaction; +.81 for uniqueness; and +.80 for causation.

Mean rankings by the psychiatrists of each of the three factors are shown in Table 1. The results of the rankings in the three areas were so close that the results were grouped together under the general heading of "psychosomatic component." Rank-order correlations between the parts were +.79 (reaction-causation), +.82 (reaction-uniqueness), and +.88 (causation-uniqueness).

For only two of the diagnostic groups were there differences of more than one step in the rank orders among the three factors. One exception was for the flat feet group where emotional reaction was considered less likely than uniqueness of personality. The other exception was the malaria group where uniqueness of personality was considered less likely than emotional reaction.

From the results of the psychiatric rankings, the disability groups can be classified according to amount of psychosomatic component as follows: Asthma and duodenal ulcers are considered the most likely to have psychosomatic relationships. Skin disease and arthritis are also considered likely to have such relationships. The heart group is intermediate among those ranked, while the other three groups—flat feet, gunshot wounds, and malaria—are ranked relatively low.

The MMPI profiles for the eight disability groups, unidentified as to diagnosis, were shown to two psychologists, experienced interpreters of the MMPI, who were asked to rank the profiles according to the three psychosomatic relationships. Their mean rankings are shown in Table 2. Rank-order correlations with each other were +.98 on reaction, +.98 on uniqueness, and +.79 on causation. Although presum-

Table 1. Rankings by Psychiatrists of Disability Diagnoses According to Psychosomatic Component

Diagnosis	Rank Order of Mean Rank [a] (a)	Emotional Reaction [b] (b)	Uniqueness of Personality [b] (c)	Psychological Causation [b] (d)	Mean Rank of Three Components [c] (e)
Arthritis	3.5	3.8	3.3	4.2	3.8
Asthma	1	2.7	2.6	1.7	2.3
Feet	8	8.0	5.1	6.7	6.6
Gunshot	6	4.8	6.1	6.7	5.9
Heart	5	4.1	4.7	6.2	5.0
Malaria	7	4.8	7.1	6.2	6.0
Skin	3.5	4.4	4.1	2.8	3.8
Ulcers	2	3.1	2.8	1.7	2.5

[a] Column a gives the rank order of the groups according to column e.
[b] These columns are the averages of the rankings by the seven psychiatrists.
[c] Column e is the average of columns b, c, and d.

Table 2. Rankings by Psychologists of Disability Group Profiles According to Psychosomatic Component

Diagnosis	Rank Order of Mean Rank [a] (a)	Emotional Reaction [b] (b)	Uniqueness of Personality [b] (c)	Psychological Causation [b] (d)	Mean Rank of Three Components [c] (e)
Arthritis	4	3.5	3.5	4.0	3.5
Asthma	3	3.5	3.5	3.0	3.3
Feet	6	6.0	6.0	6.5	6.2
Gunshot	7	7.0	7.0	6.5	6.8
Heart	1	1.0	1.0	1.0	1.0
Malaria	8	8.0	8.0	8.0	8.0
Skin	5	5.0	5.0	4.0	4.7
Ulcers	2	2.0	2.0	3.0	2.3

[a] Column a gives the rank order of the groups according to column e.
[b] These columns are the averages of the rankings by the psychologists.
[c] Column e is the average of columns b, c, and d.

ably three fairly separate aspects of psychosomatic relationships were being considered—emotional reaction, uniqueness of personality, and psychological causation —the mean rankings were practically identical for them. Rank-order correlations were +.96 (reaction-causation), +1.00 (reaction-uniqueness), and +.96 (causation-uniqueness).

With the conspicuous exception of the heart groups, the rankings of the profiles by the psychologists were very similar to the rankings of the diagnoses by the psychiatrists. Chiefly because of this exception rank-order correlations between the psychiatrists and the psychologists were as low as +.63 for reaction, +.78 for uniqueness, and +.43 for causation. For the three factors combined, the rank-order correlation between the two groups was +.73.

Generalized Arthritis

The arthritis group consisted of 50 disabled veterans with arthritis whose diagnoses were not limited to a single area such as a digit or limb; the single location would often result from accidents or wounds, which were studied separately. Arthritis had to exist in more than one location for these men and was not usually the result of a specific injury.

Background. The average age of the arthritis group was 29.6, the average education was 10 grades completed, and the average intelligence was at a T score of 50. While closest of all groups to the national average in age and intelligence, it is significantly different in all three background factors from the control group. It is older, lower in intelligence, and has completed less education. It is second highest among the groups in age. (See Tables 3 and 4 for background data.)

Personality. Hypochondriasis and hysteria are the high points in the MMPI profile, with secondary elevations on the depression, psychopathic deviate, psychasthenia, and hypomania scales. Hypochondriasis and hysteria are significantly higher for this group than for the control group, while femininity is significantly lower.

The pre-eminence of hypochondriasis in the profile suggests that obvious symptoms of emotional disturbance predominate in contrast, for example, to the more subtle symptoms suggested by the elevation on hysteria of the heart group. In this respect the arthritis profile is closest to those of the asthma and flat feet groups.

While the predominance of hypochondriasis is the most unique characteristic of the arthritis group, there is also some elevation on most of the other scales.

Discussion. The fact that stress and emotional shock are emphasized in the literature as precipitating factors in arthritic attacks suggests the likelihood of psychosomatic relationships. On the other hand, psychiatrists ranked arthritis about midway among the eight groups in such likelihood (Table 1).

The MMPI profile for the arthritis group was ranked at about the middle among the eight groups for psychosomatic component by the psychologists. The indication of neurotic tendencies in the literature is found in the MMPI profile, while the unusually large number of coded elevations on the profile suggests extensive though not necessarily strong psychological concomitants.

Low educational level and intelligence, older age, and pre-eminence of hypochondriasis characterize this group. The obvious symptoms of hypochondriasis are in contrast to the symptoms of the other groups, where there is apparently less obvious expression of symptoms. The fact that both psychiatric staff and psycholo-

Table 3. Background Data for Control and Disability Groups

Group	Age			Education			Intelligence		
	N	Mean	SD	N	Mean	SD	N	Mean	SD
Control	90	24.5	4.2	98	11.7	1.6	98	56.4	8.8
Arthritis	50	29.6	5.6	50	10.1	1.8	50	50.2	6.9
Asthma	50	26.2	6.5	50	10.5	2.4	45	53.1	8.3
Flat feet	50	27.0	4.8	50	11.0	2.0	50	54.6	8.2
Gunshot wounds	100	24.8	3.7	100	11.1	2.0	100	51.9	9.0
Heart	49	27.4	7.0	50	10.5	2.4	47	51.4	9.0
Malaria	100	25.9	4.8	100	10.4	3.9	100	53.2	8.1
Skin	49	26.1	5.0	50	11.0	2.0	47	51.7	8.9
Ulcers	49	29.9	6.7	50	10.6	2.2	50	51.0	8.0

Table 4. Means, Standard Deviations, and Codes for Control and Disability Groups

Group	F	K	Hs	D	Hy	Pd	Mf	Pa	Pt	Sc	Ma
Control (N = 100)											
Mean	51.0	55.2	53.5	52.4	55.4	55.5	56.9	50.8	54.4	56.1	56.8
SD	5.8	9.6	9.6	11.4	8.6	11.8	9.4	8.6	10.1	9.5	11.5
MMPI Code: 598437126/											
Arthritis (N = 50)											
Mean	51.5	56.6	61.3	55.1	59.3	54.7	52.1	50.7	56.0	55.5	56.5
SD	7.6	9.7	12.2	10.4	11.8	10.7	9.7	9.5	8.3	10.4	10.5
MMPI Code: 1–39782456											
Asthma (N = 50)											
Mean	53.1	55.1	60.5	54.2	60.3	56.2	52.3	53.2	55.1	55.2	56.5
SD	7.3	9.3	9.3	13.2	9.0	10.3	9.7	12.3	9.6	11.1	8.5
MMPI Code: 13–9487265											
Flat feet (N = 50)											
Mean	50.5	56.5	58.5	57.4	58.0	54.5	54.2	52.7	55.5	56.5	55.5
SD	7.0	9.4	10.4	9.5	9.9	8.6	10.2	8.4	8.2	8.8	10.0
MMPI Code: 132879456/											
Gunshot wounds (N = 100)											
Mean	52.7	53.1	58.0	56.3	56.5	57.5	51.6	51.6	54.0	57.3	59.3
SD	6.9	8.7	11.3	11.4	11.1	10.4	9.0	7.5	10.0	9.1	9.4
MMPI Code: 914832756/											
Heart (N = 50)											
Mean	52.1	56.2	62.7	58.2	64.0	54.6	52.2	51.4	53.9	53.3	51.9
SD	7.6	9.0	11.8	9.2	11.0	10.7	8.2	9.2	10.3	9.3	8.1
MMPI Code: 31–2478 596											
Malaria (N = 100)											
Mean	53.2	53.4	55.1	52.7	55.8	53.2	53.4	50.8	55.5	55.6	58.8
SD	7.5	8.1	13.3	12.3	9.6	11.1	8.6	8.0	9.9	10.4	10.0
MMPI Code: 93871 5426/											
Skin (N = 50)											
Mean	52.1	51.4	56.4	56.1	58.5	54.4	53.6	49.3	56.6	56.0	57.5
SD	7.7	8.6	11.4	8.9	10.1	9.4	9.7	8.2	11.2	9.0	10.2
MMPI Code: 397128 45/6											
Ulcers (N = 50)											
Mean	51.4	53.6	62.8	57.3	55.4	53.9	51.0	47.9	53.5	52.8	54.5
SD	5.1	10.3	11.8	10.7	10.0	8.7	8.7	6.8	10.7	8.7	9.7
MMPI Code: 1–2394785/6											

gists rank this disability midway among the groups suggests that obvious somatic complaints may be considered less symptomatic of psychosomatic component than are more subtle complaints which may be related to the hysteria scale.

Asthma

The asthma group was composed of 50 veterans with diagnosed bronchial asthma.

Background. For the asthma group, the mean age was 26, the mean education was 10.5 grades completed, and the mean intelligence was at a T score of 53. Both intelligence and education were significantly lower than for the control group. This group is one of three which were not significantly different from the control group in age. Neither was it unique among the eight disability groups in age.

Personality. Hypochondriasis and hysteria are high points in the MMPI profile of the asthma group, with secondary elevations on psychopathic deviate, psychasthenia, schizophrenia, and hypomania scales. The scores for this group are significantly higher than for the control group in hypochondriasis and hysteria, and significantly lower in femininity; in these respects the asthma group resembles the arthritis group. The score on the psychopathic deviate scale is next to the highest among all groups. The coded profile (Table 4) is most like those for the arthritis and flat feet groups.

Discussion. The emphasis in the literature upon hysteria and anxiety is found in the test results which indicate elevations in hypochondriasis and hysteria. The overactivity suggested in the literature is not found on the hypomania scale. The considerable concern in the asthma literature with psychosomatic relationships is matched by the judgments of the psychiatric staff which placed asthma first among the groups in likelihood of emotional reaction, uniqueness of personality, and psychological causation (Table 1).

The background of the asthma group is not unique among the groups studied. The MMPI profile was ranked third in likelihood of psychosomatic component by the psychologists, second in suggesting psychological causation (Table 2). Significant and approximately equal elevations in hypochondriasis and hysteria characterize the profile.

The individual MMPI scores of the asthma group do not appear sufficiently deviant to account for the strong psychosomatic relationships indicated in the literature and by the psychiatric ranking. This interpretation, combined with the relative lack of depression on the MMPI in the face of so aggravating a disability, suggests that the asthma may be a relatively adequate substitute for overt emotional symptomatology rather than a disability devoid of psychological significance.

Flat Feet

The flat feet group consisted of 50 veterans who, like those in the other groups, had to prove acquisition or aggravation of their disability in the service. Congenital conditions are presumably not included, since such defects supposedly prevent acceptance into the service originally.

Background. The group with flat feet has an average age of 27, an average education of 11 grades, and an average intelligence T score of 54.5. Only in its higher age does it differ significantly from the control group. It is the only group that does not differ significantly from the nondisabled in intelligence, while it is one of only two groups not differing significantly in education. In education and intelligence the flat feet group is closer than any other to the control group.

Personality. For the flat feet group, hypochondriasis is slightly higher than hysteria, although both are primary in the profile along with depression. There are secondary elevations in psychasthenia, schizophrenia, and hypomania. The only significant differences from the control group are in hypochondriasis and depression. The over-all profile does not show as high elevations as for the other groups studied: there are no elevations above 58.5. Only the skin group showed a similar lack of elevation.

The high elevation in depression relative to the other groups as well as to the nondisabled is the most unique characteristic of the flat feet group. Overconcern with physical symptoms is also unusually prominent in the profile. This group is most comparable in its primary elevations to the asthma and arthritis groups (Table 4).

Discussion. Psychiatrists rank the flat feet diagnosis last in probability of psychosomatic component (Table 1). The original hypothesis of possible aggressiveness and emotional insensitivity finds no support in the test profile. However, overconcern with health is indicated, which, rather than an originally suspected psychopathic tendency, may be the basis for pension-seeking.

This group is very similar to the control group in background. Along with the malaria group, it has the fewest significant deviations from the control group on the MMPI. It has relatively few profile elevations, and is outstanding among the disability groups only on the depression and hypochondriasis scales.

Since this group has established military service connection for the disability, the hypochondriasis and depression scores probably represent either direct reactions to the disability, reactions to severe emotional stress in the military service which led to an overconcern with physical condition, or a personality pattern predating military service. It seems unlikely that the disability itself could cause any severe emotional reaction. Furthermore, since the disability was seldom the reason for discharge but rather was the subject of a pension application afterwards, it also seems unlikely that it resulted from severe emotional stress in military service. It seems most reasonable to assume that, perhaps because of basic personality tendencies, these men were overconcerned about a common physical condition, and capitalized upon it.

Gunshot Wounds

The gunshot wound group consists of 100 veterans who had been wounded in any part of the body except the head. Head wounds were exempted because neuropsychiatric complications were likely.

Background. In background the gunshot wound group has an average age of 25, an average education of 11 grades, and an average intelligence T score of 52. In age it is the closest of all groups to the control group, and younger than any other disability category. It has completed more schooling than any other group but is still significantly lower than the nondisabled. It is also significantly lower than the nondisabled in intelligence.

Personality. Descriptively the most prominent elevations in the MMPI profile were in hypochondriasis and hypomania. Depression, hysteria, psychopathic deviate, and schizophrenia scales also were elevated. Statistically there were significant differences from the control group in F, hypochondriasis, and depression, in an elevated direction, while femininity was significantly lower. The hypochondriasis and depression scores of this group may have been reactions to the wounds. The coded profile for this group is unlike that of any other group (Table 4).

Discussion. The descriptions in the literature of restless tension, extroversion, impulsiveness, and desire for action in accident-prone groups find little confirmation in the test profile compared with the control group although the hypomania and psychopathic deviate scores are the highest for any disabled group. On the other hand, the elevations in hypochondriasis and depression on the test find no apparent correlates in the literature. The psychiatric rankings suggest that these elevations may represent reactions to serious physical impairment. While the gunshot wound group was ranked third from the bottom by the psychiatric staff in probable existence of a psychosomatic component (Table 1), emotional reaction was considered more likely than was uniqueness of personality or psychological causation.

It is particularly difficult to evaluate the elevations on the hypomania and psychopathic deviate scales. They are pre-eminent in the MMPI profile, confirm what appeared to be a logical original hypothesis based upon the literature and extensive clinical observation, and are higher than for any other disabled groups; however, they are not significantly different from the nondisabled at the .05 level apparently because the nondisabled are also especially elevated on these two scales. Since the latter criterion is the primary one of the study, the null hypothesis on lack of relationship in this study must be maintained despite some secondary evidence to the contrary.

The psychologists ranked the profile as a whole near the bottom in likelihood of psychosomatic component despite the fact that the test profile pattern was one of the most unusual among the groups. This result may stem from the fact that tendencies which may be antithetical to those of hysteria are most prominent in the test pattern, namely elevations on the scales of psychopathic deviate and hypomania.

Malaria

One hundred veterans with ratings for malaria were studied. Veterans were given ratings for malaria originally on the basis of past history, but had to show evidence of recurrence after discharge to maintain the rating. Practically all cases studied have therefore had recurring attacks.

Background. In all background factors the malaria group is significantly different from the control group. It is older, and of lower education and intelligence. Its mean age is 26, the mean education is 10.5 grades completed, and the mean intelligence is at a T score of 53. It is closer to the control group in age than any other except the gunshot wound group, while in intelligence it is slightly closer to the control group than any other except the flat feet group.

Personality. Descriptively, the high point in the MMPI profile for the malaria group was hypomania. There was somewhat less elevation in hypochondriasis, hysteria, psychasthenia, and schizophrenia.

This group had fewer significant differences from the control group than did any other disability category. It was equal to or lower than the nondisabled on four out of the nine personality scales. In paucity of significant deviations as well as in the results of the profile code the malaria group was more similar to the controls than was any other disabled group (Table 4).

Discussion. If malaria does have a debilitating effect upon its victims as has been suggested [r117], it is apparently a temporary phenomenon which is not found in the present test results for those who have recovered. Nor did the psychiatric rankings of the diagnosis indicate that psychosomatic relationships were likely, although emotional reaction was considered more possible than psychological causation or uniqueness in personality.

While in background this group is significantly different from the nondisabled, in personality test profile it is more like the controls than is any other category. In addition, the psychologists considered the MMPI profile the least likely of any to indicate emotional reaction, uniqueness of personality, or psychological causation.

Valvular Heart Disease

Fifty cases were included in the group with diagnoses indicating valvular heart damage. This condition is often a result of rheumatic fever, particularly when congenital defects can be ruled out. Congenital conditions are not likely here since these men were presumably free of heart pathology at the time of induction into military service. Data for this group cannot be generalized beyond this one subdivision of the heart-diseased; an extensive previous study indicated that the personalities of heart-disease victims varied according to the specific nature of the diagnosis [r47].

Background. The mean age of the heart group was 27, the mean education was 10.5 grades completed, and the mean intelligence was at a T score of 51.5. In all three categories this group was significantly different from the control group, lower in education and intelligence, and older in age. It was third oldest among the eight groups in age.

Personality. Pre-eminent in the profile of the heart group is hysteria, with hypochondriasis and depression scores also relatively high. Conspicuous too is the relatively low hypomania score. Statistically there are significant differences from the control group in elevated hysteria, hypochondriasis, and depression scores, and depressed femininity and hypomania scores.

This group is higher than any other in hysteria and depression, and is higher than any other but the ulcer group in hypochondriasis. At least partly because many items on the hysteria scale are the same as symptoms of heart disease, the prominence could be anticipated. The test indications of depression, and obvious worry about health, might also be anticipated, as reactions to a serious physical ailment. Coded, it is more similar to the ulcer group than to any other (Table 4) in kind and paucity of elevations. There are, however, more significant deviations from the control group on MMPI scales than there are for any other group.

Discussion. Descriptions in the literature of hysterical tendencies are supported by the pre-eminent elevation of hysteria in the MMPI profile. The depression score on the test finds a correlate in the brooding and guilt feelings mentioned in the literature, while the timidity and submissiveness suggested in the literature are indicated by the lowest of all hypomania scores (17, 19).

The psychiatric rankings placed the heart group approximately midway among the eight groups in likelihood of a psychosomatic component (Table 1). The group was ranked higher for emotional reaction than for psychological causation. The relationship between cause and effect appears especially difficult to evaluate for this group, perhaps because considerable anxiety often attaches to the diagnosis, and because certain physical symptoms of the disability are similar to items on the hysteria scale of the MMPI.

The psychologists ranked the test profile first among the eight groups in likelihood of a psychosomatic component (Table 2). This considerable deviation from the psychiatric rankings of the diagnosis apparently stems from emphasis upon a high hysteria test score, and makes an evaluation of this scale crucial in the discussion of the heart group.

There are at least three possible explanations of the elevation in hysteria: One is that the symptoms of true organic heart disease are so much like those of hysteria that a personality test used with this group should attempt to eliminate those items most similar to the symptoms of organic disease. A second is that many of the heart cases studied are hysterical in nature. Third, hysteria and valvular heart disease are inextricably interrelated and so interact with each other that a meaningful separation of their symptoms is not possible at this time. The third possibility is preferred here if only because it is the most general, and the data are too inadequate for more specific interpretation.

It seems apparent that many symptoms of emotional disturbance exist for these heart cases, more than for any other group studied, and that these symptoms are especially of a neurotic nature. Longitudinal studies, such as that of the Laboratory of Physiological Hygiene at the University of Minnesota, must be completed before the basic problem of etiology can be fully explored.

Skin Disease

The skin group consisted of 50 veterans with varying degress and locations of skin outbreaks ranging from conditions covering the whole body to those limited to hands or feet.

Background. In background, the skin group was significantly different from the control group only in its lower average intelligence, at a T score of 52. For age, its mean was 26, and for grades completed, 11.

Personality. Descriptively, the high point in the profile for the skin group was hysteria. Hypomania, psychasthenia, hypochondriasis, depression, and schizophrenia also were elevated, in that order. The only statistically significant differences from the control group, however, were in the elevation on depression, and the low points on the femininity and K scales. There was little obvious concern with health; the hypochondriasis score was next to the lowest among the groups.

The profile differs little among the groups or with the control group. The coded pattern is not very similar to any other, although it is perhaps closest to that for malaria (Table 4). The K score suggests an unusual degree of freedom from suppressive tendencies for a disabled group, while the depression score is perhaps most likely to represent a reaction to a serious annoyance.

Discussion. The psychiatric rankings place the skin group at approximately the middle of the eight categories in likelihood of psychosomatic relationships (Table 1). The literature generally also seems neither unusually strong nor weak on the same subject. Both the judgment of the MMPI profile and an evaluation of the individual scale scores, however, provide less meaningful data than the psychiatric rankings and the literature suggest should exist.

The question arises here again as to whether the lack of significant test results stems from a true lack of psychosomatic relationship or whether it reflects a relatively complete substitution of a physical ailment for emotional symptoms. The former alternative must be preferred in view of the null hypothesis and the lack of more specific data; the latter alternative must be considered in future research in light of the literature and what is in a sense a surprisingly good adjustment and lack of suppressive tendency in the face of an exceedingly irritating and often handicapping disease.

Duodenal and Stomach Ulcers

Fifty cases composed the group with diagnoses of peptic, gastric, duodenal, and stomach ulcer or ulcers.

Background. The average age for the ulcer group was 30, the average education completed was 10.5 grades, and the average intelligence was at a T score of 51. In all three respects the means of this group differed significantly from those of the nondisabled. It was the oldest of the groups in age, and next lowest in intelligence. Along with the arthritis group, it deviates most in background both from the nondisabled and from the other disabled groups themselves.

Personality. High point in the MMPI profile of the ulcer group is hypochondriasis, with secondary elevations in depression and hysteria. It is significantly different from the control group in its elevations on hypochondriasis and depression and in its depressions on femininity, paranoia, and schizophrenia.

Overconcern with physical symptoms and depression appear to be the most positive personality test data for the ulcer group. Projection of guilt and withdrawal tendencies are conspicuously low as indicated by paranoia and schizophrenia scores. On the code results the profile is closest to that of the heart group (Table 4). Hysteria is highest for the heart cases, however, while hypochondriasis takes its place for the ulcer group.

Discussion. The diagnosis of duodenal or stomach ulcers is second highest among the disabled groups in the psychiatric rankings of psychosomatic component (Table 1); it was high on all three factors—reaction, causation, and uniqueness. While no specific correlates were found on the MMPI for this general ranking, certain specific correlates were found for specific characteristics described in the literature. Depression as an emotional disturbance frequently associated with ulcers finds a correlate in the depression score on the MMPI. Suggestions in the literature of early concern with health, centering in gastric complaints, can be related to the elevated hypochondriasis score.

Considerable conflict is ascribed to the ulcer patient in the literature. While the MMPI profile as a whole is ranked high in indication of psychosomatic component, conflict in terms of competing scale elevations or hysterical or withdrawal tendencies is not indicated. Here again there are not enough data to go firmly beyond the statement that no evidence of conflict was found. Nevertheless the need is apparent for further investigation of the possibility that the physical ailment has become an adequate substitute for gross emotional symptoms of conflict.

The disability itself does not seem severe enough among the groups studied to account for the highest hypochondriasis score among them. Further study might indicate whether overconcern with health predates development of this ailment particularly.

Conclusion

The attempt has been made to describe personality characteristics associated with various disabilities. Most of the disabilities studied are becoming increasingly prominent in health surveys in the United States. As contagious and childhood diseases are brought under control, as the civilian population grows older, and more specifically as the number of disabled veterans, who already receive the greatest part of the medical services being rendered by the federal government, increases, the problem of chronic disability becomes more pressing.

The findings of this study have direct implications for future medical and psychological service to both veteran and civilian populations. While the veteran group was younger, had fewer important ties in the community, was initially a healthier group, and was exposed to more severe stresses than the general adult male civilian population, it seems desirable in this section to seek out possible implications of the differences found between disease and control groups for the civilian and veteran populations.

Concerning the background of disabled persons generally, the only suggestions found in the literature indicated above-average intelligence and socioeconomic level. The common deficiency of these observations was that those persons who recognized their own pathological symptoms and who could afford to go to physicians probably tended to be above average in education, intelligence, and socioeconomic level. No comprehensive differential data comparing a number of disability groups with each other or with a control group was found except for Dunbar's work. Her observations also placed disabled groups above the average in background generally, but her data, too, probably suffered from the same sampling bias cited above.

The present data suggest that the disabled groups were below the nondisabled drawn from the same population in education completed and in intelligence, and were also older than the controls. Two of the groups considered least likely to have psychosomatic components were most like the control group in their backgrounds, while two of the groups considered most likely to have psychosomatic involvements were least like the controls in their backgrounds. If older age can be considered an unfavorable factor (in a physiological sense) along with relatively low education completed and low intelligence, then there appears to be some relationship between unfavorable background and psychosomatic phenomena.

The literature on relationships between disabilities and personality factors was replete with clinical observations and case histories. Several emotional factors were particularly stressed as frequent concomitants of physical disabilities. One was the frequency of emotional disturbance in the family and individual histories of disabled persons. Usually, however, the control group was available for comparison with the disabled, and the reports of the interviewer and patient may have been biased in seeking out symptoms of emotional behavior in the history for the disabled. The observation of past nervous behavior was usually made too casually and indiscriminately to make it useful in this study.

The data of the present study threw little light on the question of previous emotional behavior. Elevations were frequent on the neurotic scales, but projection of such factors back into the individual's life history could not be done objectively from the available data. Given the commonness of neurotic traits in the test results of the disabled, however, it may be that a readiness was thus indicated for becoming disabled, with the form of the disability being determined by other factors. Or it may be that overconcern with health and depression are natural consequences of being disabled. While the possibilities were explored more specifically for the individual groups, the general conclusion must be that both possibilities exist and that the assignment of which is more important must await the completion of comprehensive longitudinal studies.

The attempt to give meaning to the various characteristics and differences found has been extremely difficult. Several general kinds of interpretations which were made seem to stand out. The most common concerned the obvious symptoms of emotional disturbance, indicated most frequently by elevations in hypochondriasis and depression relative to hysteria, and prominent for the arthritis, flat feet, gunshot wound, and ulcer groups. The problem of distinguishing between predisposition and reaction has been particularly obvious here but insoluble. On the one hand, overconcern with health and depression should provide a fertile breeding ground for a disability like ulcers, and, on the other hand, would seem to be a natural reaction to disablement from severe gunshot wounds.

A second kind of interpretation concerned the prominence of the hysteria score, especially for the asthma, heart, and skin groups. High scores on hysteria have commonly been interpreted as indicating a tendency to develop physical symptoms under emotional stress as the result of a tendency to repress normal emotional reactions. In terms of possible predisposition, the disabilities of these groups may result from a tendency to repress emotional behavior, rather than from an inclination to be overconcerned with physical symptoms as hypochondriacal tendencies suggest for the other groups.

A third general kind of interpretation was made regarding the relative lack of emotional involvement of certain disabilities. For the asthma group in terms of depression, and the skin group in terms of the hypochondriasis score, there seemed to be less emotional concomitant than was expected in comparison, for example, with the arthritis, heart, and ulcer groups. The question was raised as to whether, for the asthma and skin groups especially, the disability might not be a relatively adequate substitute for any extensive emotional involvement.

Once the existence of psychosomatic relationships is appreciated, understanding of and working with the more complex aspects of human behavior can occur, going beyond the matching of physical capacities and tested interests and abilities with job requirements. Furthermore, the rehabilitation counselor will be better prepared to help the client modify the emotional effects of the disability, through psychotherapy.

E. M. BLUMBERG, P. M. WEST, AND F. W. ELLIS

ARTICLE 50 *MMPI Findings in Human Cancer*

WITHIN the past year, three independent research teams have reported similar, potentially significant observations relating personality characteristics of cancer patients to the clinical course of their disease [r13, r137, r161, 631]. Bacon, Renneker, and Cutler describe the average breast cancer patient as one incapable of adequate outward expression of such basic drives as anger, aggressiveness, or sex, in whom a resultant inner turmoil is "covered over by a façade of pleasantness." In contrast to this, Cutler describes his cases with disseminated metastases who have survived for long periods with little or no therapy as rather unusual individuals who seem to have acquired, in devious ways, a peculiar aloofness or inner confidence in spite of the disease which threatens their existence. An example is given of a ten-year survivor who had always violently refused treatment of her breast carcinoma because of fanatical religious beliefs. A challenging question is then proposed: "What role could this character structure have played in her miraculous span of life with cancer?" [r13]

Trunnell's group, in the course of their studies of prostatic cancer, have made similar observations. Their average patient appeared to be of a fairly uniform personality type described as "unusually tractable," "nice," "eager to please," and in general "of a remarkably unaggressive nature." These investigators have therefore set up a program to study the influence of emotional patterns with respect to the incidence of the disease and its course, once established.

Our own psychological research likewise had its origin in daily clinical observation of large numbers of cancer patients. For the most part, these were male veterans who received palliative treatment with radiation or antimitotic drugs for inoperable cancer. The principal diseases involved were the lymphoblastomas, the leukemias, and carcinoma of the lung, prostate, and testicle. We also were impressed by the polite, apologetic, almost painful acquiescence of the patients with rapidly progressing disease, as contrasted with the more expressive and sometimes bizarre personalities of those who responded brilliantly to therapy with long remissions and long survival. In fact, our impression is that the very development of cancer in man might conceivably result from the physiological effects of long-continued inner stress which has remained unresolved by either outward action or successful adaptation. In other words, it seems that human cancer could represent, at least in many instances, a nonadaptation syndrome. Quantitative and qualitative abnormalities

452

in adrenal corticosteroid output have been demonstrated in the cancer patient by Dobriner. Olmer and Gascard have presented interesting evidence in support of the concept that the acute leukemias may represent a disorder of adaptation. However, to attempt to present data with respect to causative factors is far beyond the scope of this paper. This report is limited entirely to a study of the personality characteristics of individuals with established malignant disease and the relationship of such findings to the actual rate of growth of the neoplasm.

Method

The preliminary investigation upon which subsequent work was based utilized a complete battery of psychological tests, including the MMPI, the Rorschach, the Thematic Apperception Test, and the Wechsler-Bellevue Intelligence Test, on fifteen of our most contrasting cancer patients with respect to disease activity, survival period, and ease of control with irradiation or chemotherapy. There was no preconceived idea of what tests or factors, if any, might differentiate these two groups psychologically.

Early in the investigation it became apparent that the simplest, most objective test of the group, the standard MMPI, which is commonly considered as relatively superficial, indicated striking differences between the two groups of cancer patients. This finding was encouraging, providing it could be validated, since the MMPI is self-administered and machine scored. Thus it appeared that the difficulty of interpreting and rating the more subjective tests, to say nothing of the formidable task of quantifying psychiatric opinions of psychodynamics, might be temporarily by-passed. In extending the study to include fifty cases, the original observations were substantiated and the results form the subject of the present paper.

While the above approach to the problem might well be considered by many experts as very elementary, nevertheless it has objectivity and reproducibility in its favor. If the MMPI can serve the important function of being the first psychological test to relate, in a quantitative way, personality structure and neoplastic activity, it will have served a useful and historic purpose by opening the way to more intensive study in this field.

The most striking features of the MMPI profile which differentiated the original two groups of cancer patients may be considered under three headings. Full details of scoring methods and interpretation of the various scales have been described elsewhere [307, 439, 635]. The profiles of patients with rapidly progressing cancers usually showed two or more of the following characteristics:

1. Highly negative $F - K$ values (-12 or more negative), considered indicative of high defensiveness or a strong tendency to present the appearance of serenity in the presence of deep inner distress.

2. D values of 55 and over without accompanying increase of the neurotic factors Hs and Hy, considered indicative of anxiety or depression unrelieved through neurotic or normal channels of discharge.

3. Low Ma scores (under 60) suggesting an abnormal lack of ability to decrease anxiety through usual outward corrective action.

The exact criteria used in the present study for the classification of cancer patients from MMPI profile data are summarized in Table 1.

Table 1. Criteria for Classification of Cancer Patients by Use of the MMPI

	"Defensiveness" (Raw Score)	Rating	"Anxiety" (T Score)	Rating	"Acting out" (T Score)	Rating
"Fast"	$F - K < -11$ ($-12, -13$, etc.)	+	D: level with or above Hs and Hy	+	Ma: below 60	+
"Slow"	$F - K > -12$ ($-11, -10,$ -9, etc.)	−	D: 54 or below or D: below Hs and Hy (about 5 T-score units)	−	Ma: 60 or above	−
"Slow"	"Normal" record: no T score above 54, except Ma and Pd					−

Control of Variables

Patient's Knowledge and Awareness of His Disease. Since the great majority of the cases studied were accepted for treatment with the physicians' hope of successful and prolonged palliation, every patient was informed of the nature of his illness and given an optimistic view on the possibility of indefinite control of the malignancy by chemotherapy, irradiation, or both. We insist upon honesty between this type of patient and his physician in order to reduce or abolish imaginary fears and to avoid identification of the patient with a relative or friend who had, for example, gastric carcinoma and for whom it was considered that "nothing could be done."

Great care was taken to avoid psychological or physiological testing on the patient when the disease was active. In fact, it may be said that we leaned in the opposite direction. Our studies were done when the patient was in remission, usually on an outpatient basis, gaining weight, without pain, free from the influence of narcotics or therapeutic agents, and in a relatively hopeful state of mind. In the rapidly progressing cases, such a remission may be of short duration and possibly the only one obtainable. Since there is no way of forecasting this, the various tests were done as soon as possible after improvement had taken place. The very "fastest" cases were thereby automatically eliminated from the study since even temporary response to treatment did not occur. Some of these were tested, out of pure curiosity, but it is realized that, due to the possible interference from physical awareness of active disease, they could not form a part of the final data.

Variables Such as Age, Socioeconomic Status, Nationality, Religion, and Intelligence. In the cases reported in this paper, almost identical age ranges and intelligence levels were present in both of the contrasting clinical groups. The randomization of the other variables tended to cancel them out. No particular nationality or religion was found to be concentrated in any one category. Socioeconomic status is a rough variable, but was equated as far as could be done.

Criteria for Clinical Grouping of Patients

Each neoplastic disease which is not cured by surgery or irradiation has a characteristic average duration which is familiar to clinicians with experience in this specialty. From the great volume of statistics accumulated on this subject some of the more comprehensive reviews were used as a guide [r27, r49, r121, r122, r128, r129, r146, r147].

For example, the average patient with chronic lymphatic leukemia lives about four years from the time of diagnosis. Terminally, almost all of them swing over into a more acute phase. But why are there such striking exceptions to the average time at which this happens? Many of these patients succumb in less than a year although recently we examined a patient with the same diagnosis not treated for eighteen years. She had adenopathy, white blood count 102,000, with 90 per cent mature lymphocytes, normal hemoglobin, and minimal symptoms. The former group we term "fast progression" in relation to average expectation, and the latter, "slow." Any surviving plus or minus 50 per cent of the mean expected period (in this example two to six years) are classified as average. Duration of response to a specific chemotherapeutic agent is often a valuable pronostic index since it is almost invariably found that the period of remission is far greater in the long survivors than in the short ones.

In acute myeloblastic leukemia (average duration 4 to 6 months) 1 month is "rapid progression," 12 to 18 months is "slow," and 2 to 8 months is "average." Thus each neoplastic disease is considered only in relation to itself, and the thousands who have died before of that particular neoplasm provide the statistics.

Results of Psychological Testing

The psychological classification of the patients according to the three criteria previously defined is summarized in Tables 2 and 3. Table 2 presents the results of tests on those patients with rapidly progressing, uncontrollable disease, together with their diagnoses. The contrasting group of patients, those with stationary, slowly progressing, or readily controllable disease, is shown in Table 3.

From these data it is noted that the medical and psychological classification of patients coincided in 22 out of 25 cases (or 88 per cent) in the group with rapidly progressing disease (Table 2), and in 17 out of 25 cases (or 68 per cent) in the group with slowly progressing or stationary tumors (Table 3). In predicting a total of 39 out of 50 cases in their proper categories, on the basis of psychological data, the over-all accuracy of prediction was 78 per cent, or 28 per cent better than could be expected on the basis of pure chance. The special correlation method used was that of the phi coefficient, with conversion to chi square in order to determine the level of statistical significance. The obtained phi was 0.57, which was converted to a chi square of 16.245. Since a chi square of 16.245 is significant beyond the .01 level, the obtained phi is likewise significant. This means that there is less than 1 chance out of 100 that such a correlation could have occurred by chance alone.

Clinical Examples

Rapid Progression of Neoplastic Disease. Most of the patients showing rapid growth of cancer had MMPI profiles similar to that of the following patient.

R. B. (Hodgkin's disease). This 59-year-old white male was admitted to the hospital on May 27, 1951, because of chills, fever, heavy sweats, and a 30-pound weight loss of two months' duration. Fever to 103° F. had been occurring in cycles of approximately one week, accompanied by chills and severe malaise and alternating with approximately one week of relative well being.

Table 2. Scores on MMPI Criterion Scales Made by Group I Cancer Patients with Rapidly Progressing, Uncontrollable Disease, Rating of Each Scale, and Total Evaluation

Patient	Diagnosis	F − K	"Defensiveness" Rating	Hs	D	Hy	"Anxiety" Rating	Ma	"Acting out" Rating	Total Evaluation [a]
1	Ca of lung	−14	+	72	63	62	+	48	+	+ + + F
2	Hodgkin's disease	3	−	59	68	53	+	86	−	− + − S
3	Ca of breast	1	−	46	73	49	+	40	+	− + + F
4	Hodgkin's disease	−16	+	67	72	67	+	52	+	+ + + F
5	Hodgkin's disease	−21	+	85	80	78	+	48	+	+ + + F
6	Osteogenic sarcoma	7	−	62	70	58	+	53	+	− + + F
7	Ca of lung	−7	−	67	63	56	+	48	+	− + + F
8	Ca of breast	−13	+	62	71	66	+	28	+	+ + + F
9	Hodgkin's disease	−22	+	72	58	71	−	50	+	+ − + F
10	Melanoma	−17	+	52	29	56	−	58	+	+ − + F
11	Hodgkin's disease	−14	+	72	63	76	−	55	+	+ − + F
12	Ca of testicle	−8	−	80	70	64	+	58	+	− + + F
13	Hodgkin's disease	7	−	41	65	38	+	50	+	− + + F
14	Ca of colon	−18	+	85	80	73	+	38	+	+ + + F
15	Acute leukemia	−13	+	52	56	53	+	45	+	+ + + F
16	Ca of prostate	−18	+	75	56	69	−	63	−	+ − − S
17	Ca of testicle	−9	−	72	65	65	+	75	−	− + − S
18	Melanoma	−22	+	59	58	58	+	55	+	+ + + F
19	Ca of lung	−25	+	93	80	89	−	45	+	+ − + F
20	Hodgkin's disease	−24	+	57	51	62	−	40	+	+ − + F
21	Ca of testicle	−18	+	62	58	58	+	55	+	+ + + F
22	Ca of breast	−13	+	66	47	63	−	45	+	+ − + F
23	Acute leukemia	−13	+	75	92	73	+	48	+	+ + + F
24	Melanoma	−18	+	72	65	67	+	43	+	+ + + F
25	Lymphosarcoma	−5	−	54	58	55	+	55	+	− + + F

[a] A final evaluation of + + or + + + is rated "F" (fast growing neoplasm); otherwise the case is rated "S" (slowly growing neoplasm).

There was a history of myocardial infarction 13 years before, with residual exertional angina. Since that time the patient had been retired.

Abnormal physical findings on entry included prominent lymphadenopathy in the anterior and posterior cervical, supraclavicular, axillary, and inguinal areas, and chest film showed marked lobulated hilar adenopathy. Liver and spleen were moderately enlarged. His temperature rose to 104° F. daily, with a spiking chill. Cervical node biopsy on June 4 showed typical Hodgkin's lymphogranuloma.

Nitrogen mustard 15 mg. was given intravenously on June 15, following which there was dramatic improvement. The patient stated he felt better than he had "in years." His fever disappeared, there was remarkable regression of the external adenopathy, and he gained 14 pounds in 19 days.

On the nineteenth day following the mustard therapy the patient returned from convalescence at home with a fever of 103° F. and recrudescence of all symptoms. He received 20 mg. of nitrogen mustard on July 9, and again felt very well, and was quite euphoric. He was free of fever and symptoms for only 10 days when he again manifested chills, fever to 104° F., and drenching sweats. The peripheral nodes remained small, but the liver and spleen remained enlarged. Triethylene melamine 10 mg. orally was given for three days. This produced partial remission of symptoms for 9 days. The patient was becoming exhausted from continual high

Table 3. Scores on MMPI Criterion Scales Made by Group II Cancer Patients with Slowly Progressing or Easily Controllable Disease, Rating of Each Scale, and Total Evaluation

Patient	Diagnosis	F − K	"Defensiveness" Rating	Hs	D	Hy	"Anxiety" Rating	Ma	"Acting out" Rating	Total Evaluation
26....	Hodgkin's disease	−18	+	59	51	65	−	58	+	+ − + F
27....	Multiple myeloma	−16	+	52	68	58	+	30	+	+ + + F
28....	Ca of lung	−9	−	65	60	62	+	63	−	− + − S
29....	Ca of lung	−14	+	72	80	75	+	58	+	+ + + F
30....	Ca of colon	3	−	41	51	36	−	65	−	− − − S
31....	Myeloid leukemia	No diagnostic scale above 54: "normal"								− − − S
32....	Myosarcoma	−9	−	98	75	75	+	73	−	− + − S
33....	Ca of prostate	−16	+	80	70	78	−	55	+	+ − + F
34....	Hodgkin's disease	10	−	108	106	89	+	70	−	− + − S
35....	Lymphatic leukemia	−11	−	59	53	53	−	60	−	− − − S
36....	Acute leukemia	−3	−	57	53	44	−	73	−	− − − S
37....	Hodgkin's disease	−13	+	49	53	53	−	68	−	+ − − S
38....	Lymphatic leukemia	−21	+	65	48	65	−	48	+	+ − + F
39....	Ca of prostate	−2	−	75	82	62	+	73	−	− + − S
40....	Hepatoma	−11	−	67	72	64	+	48	+	− + + F
41....	Hodgkin's disease	−16	+	80	63	75	−	63	−	+ − − S
42....	Ca of prostate	−12	+	82	75	71	+	45	+	+ + + F
43....	Ca of breast	−13	+	66	65	59	+	48	+	+ + + F
44....	Hepatoma	−6	−	88	75	91	−	53	+	− − + S
45....	Lymphosarcoma	No diagnostic scale above 54: "normal"								− − − S
46....	Lymphatic leukemia	−9	−	93	80	84	−	60	−	− − − S
47....	Hodgkin's disease	No diagnostic scale above 54: "normal"								− − − S
48....	Ca of breast	−7	−	62	59	66	−	58	+	− − + S
49....	Melanoma	−11	−	44	44	51	−	53	+	− − + S
50....	Ca of breast	−9	−	58	53	61	−	50	+	− − + S

fever and chills and his angina was markedly aggravated. A total of 17 pints of whole blood was given to maintain adequate hemoglobin. As a last resort, he received another 10 mg. of nitrogen mustard on August 27, 1951, without apparent effect. He continued highly febrile and toxic, became lethargic and comatose, and died on September 7, 1951. Autopsy confirmed the diagnosis of extensive Hodgkin's disease.

Duration of the illness was 5 months from onset of symptoms, slightly less than 3 months from first treatment.

During the initial period of remission, in which both patient and doctors were encouraged by the exceptional response, psychological testing was done with the results shown in Table 4. It will be noted that all three of the psychological criteria associated with rapid growth were present at this time. The fact that the patient appeared so well and was in the earliest stages of his illness suggested, on clinical grounds, that he might approach the average duration of life for this disease. This was in marked contrast to the results of the MMPI which suggested the subsequent rapid downhill course.

It is of interest that in the preceding few years this patient admitted having made several passive attempts at suicide by refusing to take medication prescribed for relief of angina, with the hope that the "heart attack" would thereby prove fatal. During his Hodgkin's illness he took obvious satisfaction in proving that his physicians could not obtain the prolonged type of palliation for which they had hoped.

Although his last month was miserable, the rapid course of his disease seemed to give him much comfort, as if it were fulfilling a deep desire to escape from life, its unbearable problems and stresses.

This case is by no means unique in this respect. One of the most frustrating things met by the physician working in this field is the frequently almost willing acceptance of the disease by those who prove to have a highly active malignant neoplasm resistant to all available types of treatment.

Table 4. Codes and Signs of Three Representative Cases

Case	Rate	Code	Signs		Total Signs
R. B......Rapid		12"34'68–57/9 K'–L?F	F − K = −21	+	+3
			D = 80	+	
			Ma = 48	+	
G. H......Slow		79–518 6234 K?/FL	F − K = −11	−	−3
			D = 52	−	
			Ma = 60	−	
F. D......Slow		1°4"2398'7–56 LF–K?	F − K = − 9	−	−2
			D = 75	+	+1
			Ma = 73	−	

Slow Progression of Neoplastic Disease. Although most of the patients in whom rapid growth of cancer occurred gave the MMPI profile typified by that in the preceding example, considerable variety was found in the profiles of the slow growers. A few gave normal records, suggesting that these individuals had the happy faculty of handling, without undue stress, the fact of their disease together with other problems of living. The remainder of the profiles in this group gave evidence of escape from stress through one of several familiar mechanisms, including neurosis, psychosis, psychopathy, and regression. Space does not permit a detailed clinical account of more than two of the variations encountered.

G. H. (Lymphatic Leukemia). This 42-year-old white male truckdriver developed pulmonary coccidioidomycosis in April 1947. Diagnosis was established by sputum culture following a small hemoptysis. The patient never had other symptoms and the lesion became quiescent.

Incidental findings during this first hospitalization were generalized lymphadenopathy, liver enlarged two finger-breadths below the costal margin, and firm splenic enlargement to the level of the umbilicus. Entrance blood counts showed a red blood count of 4.1 million and a white blood count of 78,000 cells with 83 per cent mature lymphocytes. Because of this, a bone marrow examination was done which showed the typical picture of chronic lymphatic leukemia. Army records obtained after establishment of the diagnosis showed the presence in 1945 of "generalized adenopathy and splenomegaly."

At no time has the patient ever received treatment for his leukemia. He has continued to be asymptomatic and, as of March 1953 is working full time. He still evidences adenopathy, splenomegaly, and hepatomegaly. A recent blood count showed RBC 4.65 million and WBC 163,000 with 94 per cent lymphocytes.

The duration is 6 years since diagnosis, probably at least 8 years since the first manifestations.

Since only 15 per cent of the cases with chronic lymphatic leukemia survive a period of 7 years, and the patient has remained asymptomatic during this time without receiving any therapy, this may be considered as an example of a relatively inactive neoplastic process. Results of the MMPI (Table 4) are in agreement with the known clinical facts, all three criteria associated with rapid neoplastic proliferation being absent. Defensiveness and anxiety scales are both below critical values. No unusual emotional tension or imbalance is indicated from the psychological tests in this case.

F. D. (Myosarcoma). This 32-year-old white male first noted a mass in his right upper thigh and groin in May 1945 while on active duty with the armed forces. When it grew rapidly he sought medical attention. Biopsy followed by surgical excision in August 1945 showed a highly cellular myosarcoma. There was rapid recurrence, and by November 1945 the patient had lost 40 pounds. However, the tumor apparently became stationary, and the patient had gained back most of his lost weight by January 1946. Because of the obvious tumor, he was given deep X-ray therapy (3200 r.) to the right groin in March and April 1946.

A repeat biopsy in July, 1946, still showed the residual myosarcoma, and 3600 r. additional was given to the right groin in August and September 1946.

From September 1946 to September 1947, a total of four more biopsies each showed myosarcoma. The patient by this time had lost much weight, had considerable pain and a draining ulcer at the site of previous surgery and irradiation, and was bedridden. He was discharged from the service and transferred to the Veterans Administration hospital nearest his home for terminal care. He developed increasingly severe back and right leg pain, and in May 1948 had a cervical cordotomy for pain relief. He improved following this procedure and regained weight and strength. In January 1949 the residual tumor was again removed from the right groin, the pathologic diagnosis again being myosarcoma, showing many mitotic figures. He had deep X-ray therapy in May 1949, and has had no further treatment since then.

As of March 1953, the patient is completely free of any evidence of disease, is married, employed full time, and leading an apparently normal life.

The total duration since onset is 8 years.

This patient has had a highly anaplastic tumor for an unusually long period of time. While much therapy was given, on two occasions the patient was considered preterminal. In view of this history, the present outcome is most unexpected, and a lesion which was once considered hopeless is, after 5 years, completely under control. The results of the MMPI are consistent with the remarkable controllability of this neoplasm. Through fortunate circumstances, a MMPI profile on the patient which had been taken in the army prior to the onset of his disease was available. It is significant that it showed a similar pattern to that obtained 6 years later (Table 4). Thus the MMPI personality pattern of slow growth could not be considered to be a result of the controllability of the tumor. Psychiatric study has confirmed the impression gained from the MMPI that this patient is schizophrenic.

Discussion

The occurence of wide variations in the behavior of the same type of cancer in different individuals is a little understood and commonly overlooked phenomenon. In a recent paper by Shimkin [r146] this important fact receives re-emphasis. While the influence of inherent factors of host resistance in the course of many diseases, including tuberculosis [r44], is becoming more widely recognized, there has been an unexplained reticence on the part of most physicians to apply the same concept to the unusual cancer case. The trend in the past has been to consider the host as a nonparticipating bystander, and the tumor as the only variable. This trend continues in spite of our growing knowledge of the far-reaching physiological changes which result from nonspecific stressful stimuli and of the effects of hormonal changes in the patient on the rate of growth of certain tumors.

If the validity of the findings reported in this paper is supported by the results of our own further work and by independent investigators, one might begin to think of explaining host resistance in the cancer patient in terms of ability to reduce or adapt effectively to stresses induced by environmental and emotional conflicts. Such a concept does not in any way detract from the brilliant work already done on the problem of carcinogenesis, but merely seeks to explain why, for example, of two radiologists who develop the same type of leukemia following similar exposure to X-rays, one lives out his normal life span with little inconvenience from his disease and the other dies of leukemia in a matter of months.

The ability to worry and build up internal emotional stress to an overwhelming intensity is apparently almost exclusive to man. It is not surprising that cancer research based on observations of lower animals has failed to reveal the importance of cerebral cortical functions in the human disease. Most of the cancer patients that we have observed who seemed to possess exceptional resistance to growth of their neoplasms were successful in either avoiding or reducing excessive emotional stress by one or more of the following means: normal outward activity; psychopathic activity; "successful" anxiety-reducing neurotic activity, such as conversion hysteria; psychotic activity.

Ideally, the first method is obviously preferable, but the ability to utilize effectively any of these well-known mechanisms appears to be singularly lacking in the average cancer patient and particularly in those with rapid growth. They were noted to be consistently serious, over-cooperative, over-nice, over-anxious, painfully sensitive, passive, apologetic personalities, and, as far as could be ascertained from family, friends, and previous records, they had suffered from this pitiful lack of self-expression and self-realization all their lives.

Summary

1. A comparison has been made of the personality characteristics of cancer patients with rapidly advancing disease and similar cases in which the period of survival was far longer than the average expectancy.

2. The psychological differences between patients in these two extreme clinical groups were of such magnitude that in a significantly high percentage of cases they were readily detectable from the results of a single, relatively simple, objective test, the MMPI.

3. The data obtained suggest that long-standing, intense emotional stress may exert a profoundly stimulating effect on the growth rate of an established cancer in man.

4. The major differentiating features of the psychological data are defined, and the possible significance of the findings in relation to host resistance is discussed.

B. C. SCHIELE AND J. BROZEK

ARTICLE 51 *"Experimental Neurosis" Resulting from Semistarvation in Man*

IN SPEAKING of "experimental neurosis" one has in mind, as a rule, the type of behavior change studied in animals by the method of conditioned responses, developed by Pavlov [r132] and utilized in this country by Gantt, Liddell, Maier, Masserman, and others [see, for example, r105, pp. 122ff]. In such experiments the "stress" consists classically in the inability of the animal to discriminate between two conditioned stimuli, such as auditory tones of decreasing difference in frequency, making it impossible to anticipate the "correct" response and resulting in a conflict between the excitatory and inhibitory processes. The behavior manifested by the animal is similar to human behavior under conditions of severe frustration and anxiety.

Behavior disturbances may be produced also by alterations in the internal environment of the organism [r113]. The changes in behavior resulting from toxic factors have long been of interest to psychiatrists, but it is rare that one has the opportunity to study this type of stress under controlled conditions in human beings. We have earlier reported the profound effects of severe vitamin B complex restriction on personality in normal young men [94]. More recently we had an opportunity to study changes resulting from a prolonged, severe semistarvation. The resultant personality alterations in the majority of instances could be classified as "psychoneurotic." They were induced by the starvation regimen and reversed by diet therapy, and can be considered, therefore, as a type of "experimental neurosis."

The current psychiatric terminology does not contain terms which would *precisely* denote the changes observed in experimental semistarvation. We had a choice of either attempting to coin new categories or of using the available terms and specifying their meanings. We propose to use the term "semistarvation neurosis" to refer to those changes produced by the experimental regimen and reduced during the course of the nutritional rehabilitation which were *common to all the subjects* and have a parallel in natural starvation [r25, r97, r150]. These changes were described in detail elsewhere [r59]. In addition to the commonly occurring reactions some of the subjects developed *unusual or severe personality and neurologic disturbances.* In this paper we shall present case studies of these individuals.

461

Purpose of the Experiment and Experimental Design

The starvation-rehabilitation experiment was carried out at the Laboratory of Physiological Hygiene, University of Minnesota, in 1944 and 1945, with follow-up studies extending through 1946 [r90]. The primary purpose of the experiment was to investigate, under controlled conditions, the relative effectiveness of different types of diet in bringing about recovery from prolonged inanition. The experimental subjects were 36 healthy young male volunteers who represented, within normal limits, a wide range of individual differences in body build, physical fitness, and personality. The men were recruited among conscientious objectors who prior to the experiment had participated in various projects of national importance under the program of the Civilian Public Service (C.P.S.) [r177].

The experiment proper lasted for approximately a year. Control observations were made during three months (November 1944–February 1945), in which the subjects were maintained on a "good" diet which provided an average of 3492 calories per day. Six months of semistarvation followed (February–July 1945) when the average daily intake was reduced to 1570 calories. The diet was planned to simulate food available in western and central Europe under the conditions of food shortage during World War II. The semistarvation period was followed by three months of controlled nutritional rehabilitation; this ended in October 1945. During this period the caloric intake was increased for all subjects. The men were divided into four groups, receiving an additional supplement of 0, 400, 800, and 1200 Cal.

Methods

In the control period and the semistarvation and rehabilitation phases of the experiment a great many methods were used to study personality and behavior. In addition to standardized tests and inventories [r23, r24] these included autobiographies, diaries kept by the subjects, formal interviews, and a variety of informal contacts. The case studies to follow are based, for technical reasons, on only a fraction of the quantitative information available. The MMPI is the only psychometric instrument utilized in this paper.

Semistarvation Changes Common to the Group

The striking anatomic and physiologic changes resulting from semistarvation such as weight loss, weakness, low pulse, and reduced BMR are well known and easily understood. The psychologic changes, although more complicated and more difficult to measure, are just as characteristic as are the physical changes. The chief psychologic manifestations which were found characteristically in all subjects are intense preoccupation with thoughts of food, emotional change tending toward irritability and depression, decrease in self-initiated activity, loss of sexual drive, and social introversion.

The composite MMPI profile (see Table 1) for the 32 men who completed the entire experiment will serve as a general frame of reference for the individual case studies. Scores on the validating scales (?, L, and F) were normal throughout, varying between 50 and 55. The profile obtained during the control period is also completely normal, except for the elevated femininity-masculinity (Mf) score, a fact which was discussed above. The elevation of the neurotic end of the profile (Hs, D, and Hy) during semistarvation gives a quantitative indication of the personality changes observed clinically. In rehabilitation these changes were reversed, although the profile obtained at the end of controlled rehabilitation is still above the normal. In this connection it may be pointed out that the first twelve weeks of rehabilitation were in reality a continuation of the stress. This was especially true of the first six weeks and of the men in the lower caloric groups. It was only some time after release from the controlled diet that complete rehabilitation was effected. Profiles on 20 subjects obtained after thirty-three weeks of refeeding had returned to the "normal," prestarvation level.

Table 1. T-Score Means and Codes of Successive MMPI Testings on the Experimental Group

Test	Hs	D	Hy	Pd	Mf	Pa	Pt	Sc	Ma
Control (N = 32) 46	46	54	59	52	70	54	46	48	51
MMPI Code: 5'–326 49/817									
Starvation (24 weeks) (N = 32) 63	63	74	70	53	68	54	52	56	51
MMPI Code: 23'51–86479									
Rehabilitation (12 weeks) (N = 32) 54	54	66	65	53	68	53	49	49	50
MMPI Code: 523–146 9/78									
Rehabilitation (33 weeks) (N = 20) 44	44	51	60	50	67	52	42	44	49
MMPI Code: 53–624/9 187									

The average score on the Pd scale was initially low and there was little change during semistarvation. This indicates an absence of a tendency to develop aggressive, antisocial reactions, or "character neuroses." It is of interest that 3 of the 4 subjects who failed to complete the experiment (and were not included in the group profile) did show significant elevation in Pd score. The moderate elevation of the scores on the Pa, Pt, Sc, and Ma scales was entirely within "normal" limits and is further evidence of the absence of "psychotic" types of reaction in the average subject. This was not true of a few individuals who showed more severe or unusual symptomatology. The mean score on the femininity-masculinity interest scale (Mf) changes but little; the slight drop is consistent with a clinical impression that the Mf tends to go down as neurotic reactions develop.

Case Studies

In any severe and prolonged stress situation involving as many as 36 subjects, one would expect a certain percentage of frankly psychopathologic responses. Although many of the subjects had periods during which their distress was quite severe, there were only 9 whose symptoms went beyond the usual range of the semistarvation deterioration. There were 4 cases (Nos. 234, 235, 232, 233) whose reaction took the form of a character neurosis; they were unable to stay on the semistarvation diet. In one of these cases (No. 234) the reponse to the stress was particularly violent and bordered on a psychosis. The case history of one subject (No. 130) is of interest in view of the fact that he successfully completed the experiment in spite of a history of cyclothymic personality difficulties. Two men (Nos. 29, 101) had neurologic disturbances (paresthesias). One (No. 5) exhibited neurologic symptoms of probable hysterical origin. One (No. 20) developed a hysteroid neurotic reaction which led to self-mutilation. The case of subject No. 2 who made an optimal adjustment to the semistarvation stress is included to provide a contrast to those who developed more severe symptoms.

Case No. 2. This subject is an example of the men who showed the least psychologic deterioration.

The subject was a 24-year-old law student who had had a happy childhood. In college and law school he became a social and professional leader. He was given a number of honors and repeatedly demonstrated his ability in many areas. This successful pattern continued in various Civilian Public Service assignments.

Neurotic traits in this individual were minimal. In his youth he had been shy and self-conscious with girls, was slow to learn to dance, and worried for some time over severe facial acne. The subject's sex drive was moderate. He had been interested in a number of girls but usually kept these relationships secondary to his work and professional ambition. Observations during standardization confirmed the impression that the subject was capable, successful, and well integrated. He was adaptable, had a workable philosophy of life and definite goals, both immediate and future. He was well poised and accepted by both the staff and the members of the group.

He suffered a full share of the consequences of semistarvation. His physical symptoms were of average severity except for a relatively large amount of edema in the last weeks of the semistarvation period. His weight at the beginning of semistarvation was 73.5 Kg., at the end of semistarvation 55.9 Kg. with a low of 54.6 Kg. five weeks earlier; the gain was due to accumulated edema. His psychologic symptoms were likewise typical of semistarvation. He was lethargic, mildly depressed, and somewhat irritable. The latter two symptoms were less marked in this subject than in many. He suffered from hunger pains and was preoccupied with thoughts of food as were all the other subjects, although he seldom talked about it. Sexual interests dropped off severely in the early part of semistarvation. At the beginning of the experiment he became interested in a girl and was greatly surprised to note the degree to which his depression and loss of sexual feeling reduced his interest in their friendship.

On the positive side it may be said that he had little or no temptation to break the diet, and that he complained less than the average subject in spite of showing the same amount of physical deterioration. When he entered the experiment, he set about completing the last semester of his law school studies. On obtaining an L.B. degree he began taking courses in political science, completing most of the requirement toward an M.A. in that field. He was able to do this in spite of the distressing symptoms. He showed his maturity of judgment by anticipating that the early part of rehabilitation would be a continuation of the stress.

During rehabilitation he was in the experimental group receiving a supplement of 800 calories. In spite of this he felt little or no progress for the first three and a half weeks of the rehabilitation period; actually his body weight decreased from the average of 56.9 Kg. for the first week to an average of 55.5 Kg. for the third week of rehabilitation because of loss of edema fluid. However, the satisfactory completion of the starvation period did offer him some mental relief and tangible evidences of recovery gradually became manifest.

The MMPI profiles for standardization and after thirty-three weeks of refeeding (Table 2) were normal. At the end of semistarvation the profile shows a moderate elevation of the neurotic triad (Hs, D, and Hy), the rise of the scores on all three scales being of about the same magnitude. The profile fits in with the clinical picture of a mild neurosis.

In summary, the neurosis in this case was minimal yet was definitely present. Its experimental character is demonstrated by the fact that it developed as a result of the semistarvation stress and disappeared on rehabilitation. This case will serve as a contrast to those who had more severe and complex symptomatology.

Table 2. T Scores and Codes of Successive Tests on Case No. 2

Test Period [a]	Hs	D	Hy	Pd	Mf	Pa	Pt	Sc	Ma
C	47	51	62	60	80	53	44	46	54
	MMPI Code: 5″ '34–962/187								
S24	60	62	74	50	70	52	43	44	57
	MMPI Code: 35'21–964/87								
R12	49	57	68	48	67	53	39	40	53
	MMPI Code: 35–269/14 8:7								
R33	42	48	62	45	67	53	39	43	53
	MMPI Code: 53–69/2481:7								

[a] C refers to the control (prestarvation) values, S24 to the 24th week of starvation, R12 and R33 to the respective weeks of rehabilitation.

Case No. 234. This subject found himself unable to stay on the semistarvation diet in spite of his strong desire to do so, and the ensuing conflict precipitated a borderline psychotic episode which necessitated his removal from the experiment.

The subject was charming, handsome, and artistic, and his standing in the group was high. He held a salaried position as a church organist while serving in the experiment. His obvious assets gave the false impression that the subject was more mature than was actually the case.

He came from a comfortable urban home in which servants carried the major burden of raising the six children. It appears that the subject was never very close to his parents and that, particularly in his youth, he was not well accepted by those of his own age. Being talented musically, he planned to follow music as a vocation. Throughout life he had more interest in boys than in girls and for several years he carried on a "beautiful friendship" which gave evidence of a personality inversion.

The development of the unusual response to the experimental stress may be outlined as follows: In the first few weeks, while suffering the usual symptoms resulting from reduced food intake, he was troubled by strange dreams of "eating senile and insane people." During the eighth week he impulsively broke the diet, eating several sundaes and malted milks, and stealing penny candies. He promptly confessed this episode, became self-depreciatory, and felt he was not good enough to be retained in the experiment.

To judge from the content of his diary, he was clearly aware of the conflict between his desire to save face and his desire to leave. In an apparent attempt to strengthen himself, he listed his reasons for sticking to the experiment. This may have been partially effective, for his next diet violation was halfhearted; he stole and ate a few raw rutabagas (cooked ones being one of the main articles of the diet).

Early in the ninth week, as the conflict became more intense, he spoke of being unable to stop the whirling ideas going through his mind about "food, food, food." In the next few weeks he began to display serious personality disturbances. He became overwrought and began to write voluminously in his diary. A minor spree of shoplifting, stealing trinkets which had little or no instrinsic value for him, may have served as substitute behavior. Next he began a series of frank dietary violations which he concealed for a time by falsely recording his weight.

Since it now was plain that he was unable to control himself, he attempted to save face with a number of rationalizations. There were threads of self-depreciation and guilt, but these became less evident as time went on.

After discussions with the Laboratory staff he once more attempted to get back in line; he volunteered to give up his money and checkbook, and he even asked for a "buddy" to constantly supervise him. When this failed utterly, and it became necessary to place further restriction upon him, he developed a violent emotional outburst with flight of ideas, weeping, talk of suicide, and threats of violence. Because of the alarming nature of his symptoms he was released from the experiment and admitted to the psychiatric ward of the University Hospitals.

At this time he presented the picture of a hypomaniac; he was overly talkative, emotionally unstable, and somewhat elated. Within a few days' time, however, his symptoms subsided. Though he ate large amounts of food, he did not stuff himself to the point of becoming sick, and at the time of his release from the hospital he showed little gross evidence of personality disturbance.

The MMPI (Table 3) taken during standardization is normal; the profile secured in the tenth week of semistarvation (just before his release from the experiment) is clearly pathologic. The elevation of the Pd scale and of the entire right of the profile is indicative of a serious type of personality disorganization; these changes are in a marked contrast with those obtained in subject No. 2. There was also a rise in the score on the F scale, from 50 in the control period to 73 in the tenth week of semistarvation. In this case the elevation cannot be interpreted in the sense of F being a "validation" scale but as an indication of severe personality disturbance. Responses yielding a high F score were previously found to reflect a clinically established presence of psychiatric disturbances [357].

Table 3. T Scores and Codes of Successive Tests on Case No. 234

Test Period	Hs	D	Hy	Pd	Mf	Pa	Pt	Sc	Ma
C	46	47	52	50	72	47	49	49	52
			MMPI Code: 5'–39 4/78 261						
S10	62	78	77	68	77	62	74	80	70
			MMPI Code: 8"23579'416						

In summary, the subject is a bisexual individual with poor personality integration and weak self-control, although he appears to have sufficient assets to adjust to ordinary circumstances of life without much difficulty. He first slipped on impulse; this resulted in remorse and guilt, though he received some relief on confession.

The mechanism of substitution, expressed in such acts as stealing trinkets, was ineffective. When threatened with forceful restrictions he "blew up." This is the only instance in which the experimental stress precipitated a reaction pattern which could be considered psychotic. In spite of the short duration of the psychotic symptoms it had many features of a manic psychosis. Many clinicians, on the other hand, would prefer to classify this disorder as a borderline psychotic episode in a psychopathic personality.

Case No. 235. This subject, age 25, is another man who failed to adhere to the diet. He exhibited a mild clinical neurosis and, in addition, developed hematuria.

He and his seven siblings were raised on a farm, and had a happy home life. After completing high school the subject worked for a time in an automobile factory and later attended college. This man appeared to be a perfectly satisfactory member of the group: He was well met, friendly, and enthusiastic. He had definite plans for the future, intending to make rural cooperative farming his life work. He had a healthy interest in the opposite sex and during the experiment he corresponded regularly with the girl he hoped to marry.

However, it became evident that the subject had many hysteroid mechanisms and other signs of a neurotic temperament. In interviews, he was good-natured and easygoing but showed an immature "Pollyanna" attitude. He wrote copiously in his diary and ended every other sentence with an exclamation point.

This subject's particular pattern of response began to show itself in the first few weeks of semistarvation. Though he had no outward difficulty, he talked excessively about how *well* he was taking the stress: he suffered little or no food craving; he had no temptations even when handling food at his job in a grocery store; his adjustment to the routine was complete.

During the seventh week of the semistarvation period he became unsettled and restless. One evening while working in the grocery store he suffered a sudden "complete loss of will power" and ate several cookies, a sack of popcorn, and two overripe bananas before he could "regain control" of himself. He immediately suffered a severe emotional upset, with nausea, and upon returning to the Laboratory he vomited. He promptly made a complete confession to the staff, making at first an attempt to save face by referring to his loss of control as a "mental blackout."

In the next few days his pattern of defense began to reassert itself: he was sure that he had learned his lesson, that he would be alert to the possibility of temptation. A few days later he stated that he was "serene and secure" with a feeling of "complete control." The only evidence of his underlying uncertainty was found in his pressure to talk and write about his "little difficulty." On the surface all went well for the next few weeks. However, his weight failed to go down in spite of drastic cuts in the diet—a strong indication that he was again taking food. As this became evident, signs of a definite though mild clinical neurosis began to appear. The subject became increasingly restless and uneasy. He was self-depreciatory, expressed disgust and self-criticism. He made vague and ambiguous remarks about additional dietary irregularities, but was unable to face the issue squarely.

In midstarvation he began to experience hematuria, a disorder which he had had some years previously; the urologist reported inflammatory changes of obscure etiology in the posterior urethra. Because of the discrepancies in the weight curve and because of the urologic complications the patient was released from the starvation diet during the eighteenth week.

On the neurotic end of the MMPI the peak is on Hy (Table 4). This elevation is moderate and, taken by itself, would hardly be considered as having clinical significance. However, in view of the very high scores on one of the validating scales (L scale), ranging from 68 to 78, the elevation on Hy assumes added significance and indicates a hysteroid temperament. In terms of the items which constitute the L scale of the MMPI, the subject appeared to himself as a "perfect" person who always tells the truth (item J42), likes everyone he knows (J47), never feels like swearing (J51), and has table manners just as good at home as when he is out in company (J54). Such an individual must be singularly resistant to self-revelation.

Table 4. T Scores and Codes of Successive Tests on Case No. 235

Test Period	Hs	D	Hy	Pd	Mf	Pa	Pt	Sc	Ma
C	43	58	61	48	60	58	41	39	40
	MMPI Code: 35–26/4179:8								
S12	53	60	68	47	58	52	41	45	49
	MMPI Code: 32–516/9487								

In summary, the restlessness, the self-depreciation, and the eating off diet followed by an emotional reaction and vomiting may be considered as evidence of a clinical neurosis. That the neurosis was mild is accounted for by the fact that the stress was terminated early, that it was mitigated by taking the extra food, and that the hematuria provided a ready-made face-saving device and source of rationalization. Since the neurosis developed out of the conflict between his hunger drive and his personal standards and ideals, and since it disappeared when he was released, it may be considered as an "experimental neurosis." His ability to dissociate himself from reality (e.g., eating when in a "mental blackout") and to rationalize served as a psychologic protection and allowed him to reduce his suffering by breaking the diet without very severe feelings of guilt.

Case No. 232. This case is presented because of the subject's incapacity to adhere to the diet and the development of a frank personality disorder, psychoneurotic in type.

The subject, age 25, was a husky athletic individual. He attended college for two years. There were many evidences of latent neurotic characteristics in his personality make-up. He was a friendly, boyish type of individual, with a strong tendency to try to appear as he thought one should. His past history is full of episodes during which he was indecisive and unable to formulate his goals clearly. His struggle with the problem of pacifism is typical. He was imbued with pacifistic principles from childhood and finally became a conscientious objector although he was never completely sure of his stand.

In the first few weeks of starvation the subject showed the usual reactions of hunger and loss of energy. However, by the ninth week it became apparent that he was tense and worrying considerably. After the story of subject No. 234 became known, he confessed minor irregularities of diet such as eating a crust of bread; these appeared to trouble him greatly. At this time, along with two or three others, he began to chew gum in enormous quantities (up to 40 to 60 packages per day). By the middle of the starvation period (S12) the patient was in a sorry state. His finances would not stand his heavy expenditures for chewing gum, his mouth became sore, and though he made valiant efforts to control the gum chewing, it only became worse; on one occasion he was known to have stolen a package of gum.

During the last six weeks of the starvation period his restlessness, sense of guilt, and general nervousness increased decidedly. In spite of having very little money he bought an old suit for $10.00 which was evidently of little use to him. He was disgusted because of his inability to control his gum chewing. Many ambiguous references were made to his previous minor dietary irregularities, and he talked a great deal about how awful it would be to break the diet.

Since his weight failed to go down in spite of drastic cuts in his diet, he was dropped from the experiment at the end of the starvation period. This meant that the subject left the Laboratory and was completely relieved of all restrictions. However, his neurotic manifestations continued in full force and even increased for a while. He repeatedly went through the cycle of eating tremendous quantities of food, becoming sick, and then starting all over again. He sought interviews, complaining that he needed psychologic rehabilitation. He was emotionally disturbed enough to voluntarily seek admission to the psychiatric ward of the University Hospitals. He ran away within twenty-four hours, giving as his reason that he must find a job. After a few days he again returned asking for further psychiatric help. During the subsequent interviews he was self-depreciatory, and felt confused and defeated. He appeared to derive little benefit from the psychiatric contacts, and was unable to make plans or decisions, still attempting to cling to impossible solutions and face-saving devices. Follow-up information indicates that the problem gradually subsided over a period of weeks and that the subject eventually made a satisfactory adjustment.

In the MMPI the profile (Table 5) indicates a definite neurotic pattern at the twelfth week of starvation, which was accentuated still further toward the end of the semistarvation period. In addition to the elevation on the "neurotic" end of the profile there was also a significant rise in the scores on the "psychotic" scales, even though without control values the semistarvation scores would not be considered as definitely abnormal. The score on the F scale rose from 52 during the control period to 64 at the twenty-fourth week of semistarvation.

In summary, this subject's latent personality weaknesses were amplified and brought to the surface by the stress. He did not have the strength to carry out

Table 5. T Scores and Codes of Successive Tests on Case No. 232

Test	Hs	D	Hy	Pd	Mf	Pa	Pt	Sc	Ma
C	43	46	61	52	59	58	38	42	47
	MMPI Code: 3–564/92 18:7								
S12	68	70	76	62	63	56	49	52	52
	MMPI Code: 32'154–689/7								
S24	68	78	80	68	62	63	63	67	58
	MMPI Code: 3″2'148 675–9								

the program or the capacity to decide unequivocally to get out of the unpleasant situation. Thus he developed an experimentally induced neurosis characterized by such symptoms as indecisiveness, self-depreciation, feeling of guilt, restlessness, nervous tension, compulsive gum chewing, and eating off the diet.

Case No. 233. This case is somewhat similar to the preceding one (No. 232). The central feature is the probable eating off the diet.

The two subjects were close friends. Both were athletic, less intellectual and less cultured than the average members of the group. This man was also addicted to excessive gum chewing, and he failed to lose weight in spite of drastic reductions in his diet. Because of this his data were not used in the final group analysis although the subject remained in the experiment and was used for independent short-term biochemical observations.

There was only indirect evidence that this man's failure to lose weight was due to dietary violations. He denied eating any unauthorized food although he admitted that he was unable to control his gum chewing because of his nervousness. He appeared very depressed but was inarticulate in both the interviews and the diary in which he generally wrote much less than the average subject. The subject had feelings of inferiority and lacked self-confidence; he described himself as disorganized, lacking in planning, and a procrastinator; he wet the bed until the age of fifteen, was shy and poorly socialized until much later.

The MMPI showed a striking rise early in the semistarvation period (Table 6); the control profile was normal. In this case the changes in the MMPI profile present a more correct picture of the semistarvation neurosis than would have been obtained on the basis of diaries and interviews in which the subject was hopelessly inarticulate.

Table 6. T Scores and Codes of Successive Tests on Case No. 233

Test	Hs	D	Hy	Pd	Mf	Pa	Pt	Sc	Ma
C	48	51	49	42	61	41	47	54	60
	MMPI Code: 59–82/317 46								
S12	68	87	65	51	67	41	54	56	54
	MMPI Code: 2" '153–8794/6								
S24	68	89	69	56	58	48	60	65	54
	MMPI Code: 2" '3187–549/6								

Case No. 130. The subject had a history of personality difficulties when he entered the experiment; these became aggravated during the stress. The final result, however, appears to have been a net gain.

This 24-year-old pretheological student was born and largely raised in India where his parents were missionaries. His background history is filled with evidence of adjustment difficulties which led him to change schools many times. In childhood the subject suffered from terrible nightmares: "To this day [they] send shivers down my back just to think of them." He struggled with autoeroticism and feared that he had stronger sex desire than most people. Yet in spite of marked neurotic qualities the subject has a good record of accomplishment.

He describes himself as having few close friends, being shy, submissive, and having a marked inferiority complex. In recent years he has had several periods of mild depression alternating with periods of mild elation. Just prior to his admission to the experiment he worked as an orderly in a mental hospital. At first he was in an up swing; he enjoyed his work; he founded and edited an institutional publication. The elated phase was soon followed by a depression which lasted several months and was more severe than the preceding ones.

The history of this cyclothymic disorder nearly caused his nonacceptance for the experiment. It was finally decided to include him because of his assets. He had insight into his problem, gave evidence of strength of character, had a good record of accomplishment in spite of his personality handicaps. He gave the clinical impression that he would be able to complete what he started.

Objectively, the patient did very well during the entire experiment. He had the usual physical symptoms and slightly more than his share of irritability and hostility, the latter being expressed especially toward one of the generally unpopular men (No. 29). The subject experienced a number of periods in which his spirits were definitely high; he associated this with discovering that he could "take" the stress of the experiment better than many of the men toward whom he had previously felt inferior. These elated periods alternated with times in which he suffered "a deep, dark depression." None of these mood swings, either up or down, lasted more than a few days.

Toward the end of the starvation stress the subject felt that he had reached the end of his rope. He expressed the fear that he was going "crazy" (subject No. 20 was the only other subject to express this fear). He felt that he was losing his inhibitions. He looked pained and depressed much of the time. On many occasions during the last three or four weeks of semistarvation he had impelling desires to smash or break things. At no time, however, were these impulses carried into action. In rehabilitation he was in the lowest caloric group (the other groups receiving from 400 to 1200 more calories). He carried on in spite of the resulting slow rate of rehabilitation. As time went on, his mood swings lessened in intensity and frequency.

After the experiment was all over, the subject felt he had been personally strengthened by the ordeal. "It undressed us. Those who we had thought would be strong were weak; those who we surely thought would take a beating held up best."

Four profiles of the MMPI are presented (Table 7). The prestarvation profile shows an elevation on the psychotic end. This is consistent with his cyclothymic pattern. At the end of semistarvation the profile shows an added neurotic response of considerable severity. In other words, the whole personality was involved. By the twelfth week of controlled refeeding there is a noticeable improvement in those symptoms which were brought out by the semistarvation stress. By the thirty-third week of rehabilitation, that is, after twenty-one weeks of complete freedom, his scores on the psychoneurotic scales of the MMPI are as good or better than his prestarvation values. In addition, there is a striking improvement in the scores obtained on the psychotic scales of the inventory. This suggests that the experience of having gone through the experiment had significant therapeutic value for the subject, although the permanency of this improvement cannot be predicted on the basis of the information available.

Case No. 29. In this case the experimental neurosis took the form of severe social deterioration. The subject also suffered from moderately severe paresthesias.

The 33-year-old professional actor came from an economically secure urban background. His mother dominated the family and tended to favor the subject over his older sister. In speaking of his childhood and adolescence he referred to himself as "mother's little helper." He played with dolls during much of his childhood and always heartily disliked fighting. He believes that he had some romantic interest in girls before the age of 11; from 12 to 13 he went through a period of hero worship and from the age of 13 he had definite bisexual leanings. After finishing elementary school he overcame his earlier traits sufficiently to play football for eight years, yet he claims to have been afraid of physical contact in spite of successfully holding a position on the varsity team. He did graduate work in drama and took up the theater as his profession.

Table 7. T Scores and Codes of Successive Tests on Case No. 130

Test	Hs	D	Hy	Pd	Mf	Pa	Pt	Sc	Ma
C	51	67	44	58	75	48	76	79	60
	MMPI Code: 875'29–41/63								
S24	72	93	68	52	67	52	62	80	62
	MMPI Code: 2°8"1'35 79–46								
R12	67	80	59	53	65	48	68	81	67
	MMPI Code: 82" '7195–34/6								
R33	53	48	53	40	69	59	52	53	61
	MMPI Code: 59–61387/24								

When this man entered the experiment he was pleasant, polished, and well poised. During standardization he was well accepted in spite of his theatrical manners. He was confident of his ability to withstand the semistarvation stress. This subject began to show his semistarvation neurosis in the early weeks. He lost his composure, and developed marked irritability and egocentricity. He continually dramatized his suffering even when out in public, much to the annoyance and embarrassment of the other subjects. He became easily the most unpopular member of the group, a fact which many of the men showed openly. This undoubtedly increased his stress since he was sensitive to the feelings of others.

His personality deterioration was more severe than in the majority of the cases. The D score on the MMPI went up over three standard deviations from the mean and there was an elevation in the "psychotic" scales of the inventory (Table 8).

During the thirteenth week the subject began to experience tingling and burning sensations in the anterior aspects of both thighs. For a few weeks he had a similar but less definite "dry" sensation on the underneath area of the penis. These abnormal sensations gradually increased in area and intensity throughout the remainder of the twenty-four weeks of semistarvation. At their height the burning pain on the thighs was very distressing.

Neurologic examinations revealed no positive findings aside from abnormal response to superficial sensory stimuli in the anterior and lateral aspects of both thighs. Testing with a pin and cotton elicited "burning" sensations which were much more intense in the very center of the disturbed areas. The latter were bilaterally symmetrical and their boundaries shaded off gradually into the surrounding normal parts. By the fourth week of rehabilitation there was a marked diminution in the intensity of the paresthesias. By the twelfth week of rehabilitation they were still further reduced although the area remained about the same.

Table 8. T Scores and Codes of Successive Tests on Case No. 29

Test	Hs	D	Hy	Pd	Mf	Pa	Pt	Sc	Ma
C	43	49	58	56	99	53	50	56	62
	MMPI Code: 5°'9–34867/21								
S24	70	83	70	66	85	62	73	78	65
	MMPI Code: 52"8713'496								
R12	60	59	72	69	92	56	60	67	68
	MMPI Code: 5°"3'498 17–26								
R33	48	51	55	66	82	50	49	51	61
	MMPI Code: 5" '49–3286/71								

The sensory disturbances in this case are somewhat suggestive of meralgia paresthetica except for the more widespread distribution. The personality deterioration was very marked and the emotional distress may have played a role in the importance assigned to these symptoms by the subject.

Case No. 101. This man developed mild paresthesias in addition to the usual semistarvation changes.

The subject, age 30, gave the impression of being a stable, mature, well-integrated individual with a sense of dry humor and a matter-of-fact outlook on life. He had been an active church worker and had held a number of positions of leadership in the Boy Scouts and church groups. This work occupied his attention almost to the complete exclusion of interests in the opposite sex. His history gave little evidence of neurotic traits in his personality make-up. After completing high school, he took up the printing trade and followed this occupation for several years. He entered college at the age of 24 and graduated at 28.

In semistarvation he suffered a marked physical deterioration. During the last weeks of semistarvation his weight picture was complicated by the development of edema. His gross body weight was decreasing too slowly and his diet was cut drastically. He was acutely unhappy and felt sure that the Laboratory was making a mistake and that he was in physical danger. He became extremely depressed and worried about himself. For example, now that sexual urges were absent, he was free of his long-standing habit of masturbation; he feared that the habit would return when he was rehabilitated.

During the twenty-second week of semistarvation he began to experience burning and tingling in the left thigh. This difficulty gradually increased and for a time involved the right thigh also. It gradually subsided during rehabilitation. (He was in the top group receiving a 1200 Cal. supplement.)

Neurologic examinations were entirely negative except for paresthetic areas on the anterior aspects of each thigh. These areas, which covered approximately one third of the anterior aspect of the thigh, were irregular in outline and the

Table 9. T Scores and Codes of Successive Tests on Case No. 101

Test	Hs	D	Hy	Pd	Mf	Pa	Pt	Sc	Ma
C	42	58	50	37	76	45	47	43	42
			MMPI Code: 5′–23/76819:4						
S24	62	72	56	49	69	57	56	54	46
			MMPI Code: 2′51–6378/49						
R12	53	72	49	45	80	50	59	53	56
			MMPI Code: 5″2′–7918 6/34						

boundaries shaded gradually into normal skin. The subject was readily able to distinguish sharp from dull. The intensity of his subjective sensations varied greatly from time to time. The routine recheck toward the end of controlled rehabilitation revealed a return to normal except for small vaguely outlined areas which were slightly "dull" to touch; these were not noticed spontaneously.

The MMPI (see Table 9) during control was normal. The semistarvation profile indicates the typical semistarvation neurosis; the relatively high D (72) and the low Hy (56) adds weight to our clinical impression that the paresthesias were not hysterical (contrast with profile on subject No. 5).

In summary, this subject suffered severely; he developed a full-blown neurosis which was characterized especially by irritability, impatience, and concern over previous masturbation. The disturbance in skin sensation appears to have had a physiologic basis and constituted an additional source of stress. Although the paresthesias were more disturbing and less well tolerated during periods of depression and irritability, they did not appear to have the characteristics of a psychogenic disturbance.

Case No. 5. This subject developed neurologic symptoms, probably hysterical in origin.

This 29-year-old man came from a rugged background. His parents were mill-hands who lived in poverty most of their lives. The subject was raised in the slums and was often placed in boarding homes while his mother worked. There was no religion in the family. The father showed no interest in the home and the brother had many traits of a psychopath. The subject was ashamed of his father and had no close feelings for his brother.

As the patient matured, he appears to have made a fairly good adjustment to life, emancipating himself from home influence. After some deliberation and conflict he chose the ministry as his vocational goal. In temperament he appeared extroverted. He was highly intelligent and had ability as an actor. On the surface he appeared easygoing and good-natured, but he was restless and often became tense. Most of his Civilian Public Service experience was in the mental hospitals where he served as an attendant. This contact stimulated his interest in psychiatric disturbances and led him to an unceasing psychologic analysis of himself and of others. He was a person who had strong feelings and who developed strong likes and dislikes. Although he tried to be objective, his personal antipathy toward the interviewer to whom he was first assigned was so intense that a change was necessary.

The subject was overweight and was required to lose weight during standardization (from 83.6 Kg. to 80.8 Kg.). Since he was still above normal weight for his age and height, his weight loss was placed at 29 per cent as compared with 24 per cent for the group average. During the first half of semistarvation he developed the characteristic physical symptoms common to the group, but he suffered less psychologically. He was so elated over the happy progress of a new and promising love affair that he thought and talked of little else.

Midway through semistarvation the girl broke off their engagement. Not only was this in itself a severe blow, but he now became fully aware for the first time of the disquieting effects of the starvation stress. His dreams about food became more intense. His depression and irritability were marked. He was impatient and strongly resented the restrictions incidental to the experiment.

During the next four weeks he continued to be in a turmoil over his unhappy romance. They saw each other often since they both participated in the activities of the University Theater where they had met originally. As time went on, the subject became better able to control his outward behavior and feelings, and he found some solace in the company of his ex-fiancée's sister.

In the eighteenth week he reports in his diary that his spirits were much improved but that he began to experience some difficulty in walking: "My right foot seems unhinged at the ankle. When I step on my heel, the toe comes down with a slap as if I had no control of the muscles." At the same time he noted a transient numbness of the right thumb. Two days lated he noted for the first time that he was able to converse with his ex-fiancée without emotional distress. "No feeling aroused at all. She might just as well have been any one of a dozen other girls I know fairly well."

This same day he reported to the staff his new physical complaints. The symptoms included "numbness" near the base of the index finger of the right hand, and hypesthesia on the anterior aspects of both legs, extending from below the knee to the toes. He also complained of a peculiar weakness of the right ankle which "gave way" unexpectedly. All these symptoms recurred intermittently.

Neurologically, the subject's condition was objectively normal on all three occasions on which the subject was examined. He was able to distinguish sharp from dull and to recognize light touch at all times. The hypesthetic area on the hand and the sensory disturbance of the left leg disappeared permanently in a few days while the other symptoms gradually faded out over a period of ten weeks. The record of the routine neurologic examination made during the fourth week of rehabilitation indicates that though the hypesthesic area on the right leg was still reported as present, the subject stated that it no longer attracted his attention. At no time did any of these symptoms cause real discomfort to the subject, and he did not show concern over them. He reported their presence in a matter-of-fact way as a part of the experimental routine.

That the neurologic symptoms experienced by this subject were hysterical in nature is supported by the negative objective neurologic findings, and the vague outline, indefinite localizations, and intermittent character of the sensory disturbances. They were preceded by a period of relative emotional calm in reference to his love affair. The subject, who had studied abnormal psychology in college, considered the condition as probably hysterical although he was puzzled as to how one so worldly and sophisticated as himself could have hysteria.

The MMPI was normal during control (Table 10). The semistarvation profile, obtained after he had had symptoms for about five weeks, shows the typical elevation on the neurotic end of the curve with the peak on Hy of 78.

Although it seems unlikely, it can be argued that there may have been neurologic, nutritional, or other physiologic factors responsible for the development of the sensory complaints. Even if this were so, it is our opinion that these became the focus for the hysterical conversion that still plays an important role in the production of the final clinical picture.

Table 10. T Scores and Codes of Successive Tests on Case No. 5

Test	Hs	D	Hy	Pd	Mf	Pa	Pt	Sc	Ma
C	52	48	64	63	65	64	41	47	48
	MMPI Code: 5364–1/2987								
S24	66	72	78	62	71	53	51	57	50
	MMPI Code: 325'14–8679								
R12	47	58	68	60	69	59	39	47	57
	MMPI Code: 53 4–629/18:7								

Case No. 20. This subject suffered a pronounced personality deterioration culminating in two attempts at self-mutilation.

The subject was 28 years of age; he came from a wealthy urban home. His father died when the subject was 14 years of age, but he left a considerable fortune. His mother exerted a dominating influence over her children. Her second marriage turned out unhappily, ending in divorce but only after the stepfather had wasted the family fortune. The brother, age 31, has been a long-standing problem whose academic, occupational, and marital ventures were failures. The sister, age 30, has remained at home in order to be a companion to her mother. It is important to note that the subject's family matters remained complicated, unsettled, and distressing to him during the time that he was participating in the experiment.

He graduated from college at the age of 23. In spite of personal assets he showed a peculiar immaturity for his age and background, expressed in exaggerated standards of himself, vocational indecision, underdeveloped sex life, dependence on his family, and restlessness.

The subject developed the semistarvation neurosis in marked degree. He suffered considerably from hunger, weakness, irritability, and moroseness. His eating habits became annoying to others. Since he had appeared at the start as *the* strong man who could "take it," the personality changes were especially distressing to him. He was hurt by his drop in popularity.

In the fourteenth week he felt that he had had about all he could take. Only the approaching end of semistarvation some ten weeks away enabled the subject to hold together. Yet his strength of character was being shaken by the temptation to escape from the stressful situation. For a time his determination rallied. He wrote that even if he developed tuberculosis he would insist on remaining in the experiment for the benefit of medical science. Shortly thereafter he attempted to burn his bridges by committing himself to an extra two-month period of further experimentation after the end of twelve weeks of controlled refeeding.

On the last day of semistarvation he collapsed on the treadmill. Although this would not have been considered unusual in view of the subject's physical weakness, he suffered an acute emotional upset because he felt that he had failed to live up to the standards which he set for himself.

While the subject was making such a struggle to appear strong during the semistarvation stress, he had failed to anticipate that the twelve-week rehabilitation period might be little better than the preceding starvation. It was his bad luck that he was assigned to the next to the lowest caloric group. The going was tough for him and the thoughts of continued participation in the experiment were becoming unbearable.

At the end of the first week of rehabilitation he injured his left hand when his automobile slipped off the jack. One finger was torn three-fourths off at the distal phalanx and required outpatient surgical care. He made it appear that this was an accident but confided the truth to one staff member. In order to get out of the experiment he had attempted to mutilate himself; he had done an incomplete job because he lost his nerve at the last moment. The injury was not serious enough to warrant his release from the experiment. His psychologic tension was not relieved after the accident or following his confession.

The next week his diary indicated that he was painfully aware of the fact that he no longer could hold up during this unexpected continuation of the stress, let alone appear as a strong man.

While he was in this unhappy state of mind, his sister came to visit him. Their visit started off badly as there were many troublesome family affairs to be discussed. The next day, in spite of this additional stress, his spirits lifted remarkably. That evening he and his sister went to the home of a friend. While his sister had dinner with their hosts, the subject went into the yard to chop wood as he had often done before. He somehow managed to chop off three fingers of his left hand. He was given emergency surgery in the Student Health Service at the University Hospitals where he remained for five days.

On the day following the accident the subject, while mildly distraught, talked freely and indicated his partial insight into the psychodynamics involved. The following is a verbatim record of an interview:

I've always thrown myself into everything I did and have done it very hard. Afterward I have reacted with fever and collapse and have been babied by my mother. I have recently had the stress of this pneumonia and then the last month of semistarvation was very tough, especially the edema. On top of that I've had a difficult home situation. My brother is a rotter. I owe it to my mother and sister to spend time at home. I asked to be taken off the list of those going abroad since my mother's affairs are more important. Then rehabilitation started. I had looked to six months of starvation as a job to be done and I did it. But then I had no chance to relax and rest and let down. When rehabilitation started, I was still hungry. It was really more starvation. In fact, I suffered from more hunger because I could not take food out [to make "sandwiches"] as I had before. I was blue over the whole thing. I was in a weird frame of mind. I thought that there was only one thing that would pull me out of the doldrums, that is release from C.P.S. I decided to get rid of some fingers. Ten days ago I jacked up my car and let the car fall on these fingers. It missed them all except it crushed the end of one finger [same hand]. That's not normal. It was premeditated. Since then I have begun to worry about my state of mind. I have also worried about the family; my brother's wacky, my sister's very worried over my mother, and maybe there's something wrong with me too. I've always been able to sleep, but not last week; I tossed and turned. I tried to do some reading but all I could do was think of home. I had so little control over my mind that I was afraid I would lose it. One morning at breakfast I came closer to an act of violence than I ever had before. Someone across the table — I can't remember who — will never know how close he came to having a tray smash down on his head. He'd done nothing. I just wanted to be at my mother's and not at the breakfast table in Shevlin Hall. It was all going on in my mind. I just felt that I had cracked. Finally, in bed at night I tried to be as objective as I could and I've managed to force myself to stick until July 29 [end of semistarvation]. On the last day of semi-starvation, well, I didn't finish it . . . I only lasted ten seconds on the treadmill and that upset me and I bawled for a half hour and then more. I was so disappointed to flop at the last test . . . As for this [referring to the loss of the fingers], I don't know. I had made up my mind to stick it through to October 20. I felt I'd be de-mobilized by the end of my leave. I felt there'd be no point in this at this time when the war is over. How silly it had been to drop a car on my fingers, I thought. I cer-tainly had no idea I'd do this [sic!]. I am now back at the place I was; that is, I'd like to get a 4-F and go home. I'm afraid, what will I do next?

Although the subject was kept on the same caloric level, he did receive in the hospital a few variations in diet items (e.g., fruit). He appeared to enjoy the experi-ence immensely. The bed rest, attention, and freedom from routine during a few days of hospitalization appear to have satisfied his immature, dependent needs and to have served as a satisfactory substitute for home and his mother.

After the release from the hospital, the subject was persuaded to remain in the experiment and was able to carry on during the remaining two months. The pain suffered may have served as punishment for failing to perform up to expected standards and for the desires to leave the experiment; it may have expiated his sense of guilt. Also, he was being slowly rehabilitated physically and was approaching the end of the regimentation imposed by the experiment and the C.P.S. assignment.

In subsequent interviews he almost completely repressed the purposeful nature of the accident. Although he could not clearly explain or describe exactly how it happened, he gave "rational" suggestions: he was "too weak," had poor control, it was uncomfortable to hold the ax with both hands because of the sore fingers on the left hand (previously smashed in the auto-jack incident), the ax must have hit a branch, etc. He argued strongly that the accident had no personal motivation, yet he did make this comment: "I wasn't myself for two weeks. I may be more valuable to the experiment than if I hadn't done it." From this time on he carefully avoided all mention of the accident, though he continued to talk and write freely on every-thing else. He was puzzled over a newly acquired aversion for psychology and psy-chologists; this appears to have been a defense against self-revelation.

It is of psychologic interest that the pattern of self-mutilation appears to have been suggested by an experience two years earlier which he never once mentioned while at the Laboratory. At a previous C.P.S. assignment he gave first aid to one of his close friends who had lost several fingers in a buzz saw; this friend was subse-quently given a 4-F classification and released from C.P.S.

The MMPI profile taken during standardization is normal, while the one taken at the end of semistarvation is severely neurotic in type (Table 11). At the second week of rehabilitation the D score has further increased by nearly one standard deviation and, more significantly, the psychotic end of the profile has shown a marked rise. Such a profile indicates that the subject is under a severe stress which he is not able to handle. This profile was obtained four days after his first accident and six days before his second one. The scores at the twelfth week of rehabilitation indicate a slow return toward normality.

Table 11. T Scores and Codes of Successive Tests on Case No. 20

Test	Hs	D	Hy	Pd	Mf	Pa	Pt	Sc	Ma
C	44	56	52	62	78	54	47	52	52
			MMPI Code: 5'4–26389/71						
S24	82	104	88	48	71	56	62	67	38
			MMPI Code: 2°31″5'87–6/4:9						
R2	74	113	82	70	73	73	82	83	48
			MMPI Code: 2°837″1564'/9						
R12	72	87	85	57	72	59	54	60	44
			MMPI Code: 23″15'8–647/9						

In summary, subject No. 20 displayed in a severe degree the usual personality changes of "semistarvation neurosis." The physical deterioration conflicted sharply with his pattern of always being the strong man. By expecting rapid rehabilitation, he misgauged the duration of the stress; because of his "all or none" pattern he was particularly unprepared for this and was unable to make the necessary psychologic adjustment. In addition he suffered severely from a conflict between the desire to escape from the painful situation and the desire to save face. The psychologic situation was further complicated by distressing home conditions. All this led to a severe emotional conflict.

The first attempt to solve this conflict was through deliberate self-mutilation (smashing his hand). After this abortive attempt he was disgusted with himself, miserable, and depressed. The second "accident" appears to have been brought about by more unconscious mechanisms. The action, while not providing a solution of the underlying problems, did have a therapeutic effect which enabled the subject to complete the experiment.

Discussion

The Nature of Personality Changes in Starvation. Except for the presence of clinical edema, the anatomic and physiologic changes resulting from semistarvation were essentially similar in all subjects. In the psychologic and social aspects the individuals varied to a greater extent, although there was enough similarity in the response to the stress that we may speak of "semistarvation neurosis." The greater variation of the psychologic manifestations of starvation was due to etiologic complexity of the behavioral responses, large individual differences in basic personality make-up, and, most importantly, less uniformity imposed by the experimental regimen in this area.

The behavioral, emotional, and social manifestations of starvation may be looked upon as psychosomatic phenomena in the broad sense; that is, they are the results of a complex interaction between anatomic, physiologic, individual-psychologic, and social-psychologic factors. In view of the psychopathologic effects of vitamin deficiencies it may be noted that the diet was fully satisfactory as far as the vitamins, and especially the vitamin B complex, are concerned.

Behavioral changes often represented useful or necessary adjustments. Thus loss of strength and endurance, accompanied by irritability and general discomfort, are partially compensated for by decrease in physical activities and reduced social contacts. For example, attempts to participate in such activities as dancing resulted in painful fatigue; the subjects learned to avoid this type of experience as they became aware of their increasing physical debility. A decreased body temperature was compensated for by the use of more clothing and bed covers, by the reveling in hot showers, and by the demand that food be very hot. Physiologic changes affecting the hormonal system such as decreased activity of the sex glands (and possible other glands) modified the character and intensity of the sex "drive." Compiling of recipes and poring over cookbooks may be considered as one of the mechanisms compensating for prolonged hunger.

Similarity to Natural Starvation. The basic picture presented by our subjects during semistarvation is essentially comparable to that seen in "naturally" occurring famine [r25]. This was clearly evident in the anatomic and physiologic effects — weight loss, emaciation, weakness, reduced basal metabolism rate and pulse rate, edema, etc. The psychologic effects of starvation, such as hunger, intense preoccupation with food, irritability and depression, and social introversion observed in the Minnesota experiment have also their parallels in famine.

This indicates that the fact that the subjects were conscientious objectors did not distort the psychophysiologic relationships between decreased food intake and behavior. We wish to emphasize that in the standardization period the subjects were clinically completely normal. Their underlying character and personality were approximately those which one could find in good average citizens of comparable age, intelligence, education, and social economic background. However, there were significant differences in the area of attitudes toward problems of social ethics and, in particular, of participation in military activities.

Factors Unique to the Minnesota Experiment in Contrast to Natural Starvation. There were a number of factors alleviating the stress of semistarvation, incidental to the controlled conditions under which it was conducted. The subjects were provided with good physical care. They had comfortable, healthful living quarters, adequate clothing, and sanitary facilities. They had opportunity to participate in the curricular and extracurricular activities at the university and had their own educational program focused on training men for European relief; their recreational facilities were excellent. Their food was controlled and there was no struggle for existence. The subjects were secure in the knowledge that their food would be served and that it would be available regularly. More importantly, they knew that the starvation phase would end after six months and that rehabilitation would follow. They were given competent medical supervision and were free from the political and social turmoil that commonly accompanies naturally occurring starvation.

On the other hand, some of the provisions and restrictions imposed by the experimental regimen increased the severity of the stress as compared with naturally occurring starvation. The subjects voluntarily starved in the midst of plenty and were unable to improve their nutritional condition by personal effort and ingenuity. The limitation of personal freedom required by the experimental program was in itself a hardship.

There was a natural, strong conflict between the desire to continue to participate in the experiment and to gain all the satisfactions resulting from it on the one hand, and the desire to escape from the painful situation. Although the men committed themselves at the start, there was no other but moral pressure to keep them in the experiment. Actually, the only formal penalty would have been a transfer to another C.P.S. camp. It was a particular strain on the character of the subjects that a large measure of responsibility for conforming to the experimental regimen was placed directly on them. It should be noted that the subjects were allowed to go freely to the homes of friends, into restaurants for black coffee, etc. About midway in the semistarvation period it became necessary to establish a buddy system in order to lessen this strain. The buddy system in time became a powerful source of irritation in itself.

The "Experimental Neurosis" Resulting from Semistarvation. To a large extent the same stresses of semistarvation were shared by all the subjects. An attempt had been made to adjust the desired weight loss in such a way that the weight decrement would take into account the "nutritional status" at the start of the semistarvation period, and thus to equalize the physical stress inherent in the loss of weight The subjects shared the same living quarters and were exposed to the same experimental regimen. The resulting behavioral changes, summarized by the inadequate term of "semistarvation neurosis," were necessary and universal; hence, they may be considered as "normal" reactions under the given circumstances although they markedly deviated from the prestarvation pattern of behavior.

In addition to the commonly shared neurotic symptomatology, some subjects manifested forms of behavior deviating not only from the prestarvation condition but also from the general patterns of simple "semistarvation neurosis." A response to the semistarvation regimen was considered as "abnormal" if it appeared to be inefficient, unusual, exaggerated, or contrary to the main purpose of the experiment.

Excessive gum chewing was one of the reactions which may be considered as an "inefficient" mechanism. It was started in an attempt to alleviate hunger and nervous tension, but it was continued compulsively in spite of the fact that it failed to give the desired result and, in addition, caused a sore mouth and an unnecessary expenditure of funds. This symptom occurred in great intensity in four subjects; two of these failed to adhere to the semistarvation diet.

The subject who chopped off his fingers certainly showed a reaction which was both inefficient and unusual; it was a roundabout way to achieve the end in mind. The hysterical sensory disturbances in subject No. 5 can be also classified as unusual.

The personal antagonism created by subject No. 29 represented a reaction of the rest of the group to an exaggerated irritability. Some of the mannerisms and ritualistic eating habits, such as interminable "souping" of food, belong also to the category of exaggerated responses.

Eating off the diet was contrary to the purpose of the experiment. A strict adherence to the dietary regimen was an essential criterion of conformity to the social values of the subject group, and those who did not adhere to the agreed restrictions exhibited a behavior pattern similar to ordinary antisocial activity. It should be emphasized that with one or two exceptions this did not consist in a rational act of procuring food such as one might obtain in a restaurant. On the contrary, the subjects' inefficient and neurotic approach to the solution of the problem of hunger is shown by the fact that those who broke the diet ate garbage, raw rutabagas, infinitesimal amounts of food, or in other ways attempted to minimize their behavior discrepancies and expiate their guilt.

Why did some men develop these abnormal behavior patterns? Generally one may attempt to interpret the behavior differences in the light of psychophysiologic constitution, past history, and present situational factors. In some of our cases we were able to interpret the abnormalities of behavior in these terms. In other instances the mechanisms were not completely clear.

The fact that under the experimental stress of semistarvation the individual differences increased is demonstrated also by the rise in the standard deviations of the individual scores on the neurotic scales of the MMPI. Thus the standard deviation of the hypochondriasis scores for the 32 men who completed the experiment increased from 3.4 in control to 6.6 at the end of the semistarvation period. For depression the corresponding values are 6.5 and 12.1, for hysteria 6.1 and 8.2.

Ex post facto it appeared that men with a more stable personality make-up showed minimal deterioration while those with latent personality weaknesses developed more severe symptoms; however, it should be acknowledged that we would have been unable to predict, with any degree of certainty before the start of the stress, which individuals would develop "abnormal" reactions.

Summary

Thirty-six men recruited from the Civilian Public Service camps volunteered for an experiment on semistarvation and subsequent nutritional rehabilitation. The men lost on the average about one fourth of their original body weight, and exhibited profound changes in a number of physiologic functions.

All subjects developed emotional and personality symptoms of "semistarvation neurosis" varying in intensity from mild to severe. In the majority of cases these symptoms receded during the following twelve weeks of controlled rehabilitation. On follow up, after an additional period of twenty-one weeks of unrestricted rehabilitation, the men were back to their prestarvation normal. Thus the psychologic disturbances, induced by the semistarvation regimen and relieved on refeeding, can be considered as an experimental psychoneurosis.

In the present paper, attention was focused on nine subjects selected because they exhibited symptoms of special interest from the neuropsychiatric point of view.

Two men suffered from paresthesias of probable physiologic origin. One had sensory and motor disturbances, probably hysterical in nature.

Another subject suffered a psychogenic accident.

In four men the reaction to the stress took the form of a character neurosis. The disintegration manifested itself by inability to adhere consistently to the diet. Under the moral and social pressures to conform to the experimental regimen, one of these four developed a pathologic reaction bordering on psychosis; this cleared rapidly upon his release from the experiment.

One subject had a history of previous personality difficulties, cyclothymic in character. These were exaggerated by the stress but clinically did not reach clearly pathologic intensity. When nutritionally rehabilitated this man appeared to have benefited psychiatrically from the successful participation in the experiment.

One case, exemplifying those subjects who completed the experiment with minimal personality deterioration, was included to provide a contrast with men who developed more frank neuropsychiatric symptoms.

J. BROZEK AND NANCY K. KJENAAS

✦

ARTICLE 52 *Item Analysis of the Psychoneurotic Scales on the MMPI in Experimental Semistarvation*

THE MMPI was part of an extensive battery of tests used in a starvation-rehabilitation experiment to follow personality changes through a semistarvation period of six months and a controlled rehabilitation period of three months. The subjects in this experiment were 32 young men, considered physically and psychologically normal, selected from a larger group of conscientious objectors who volunteered for the experiment. In the course of six months of semistarvation the group lost an average of about one fourth of their prestarvation body weight and developed the classical physical and psychological [r90] symptoms of semistarvation.

The over-all MMPI results have been reported elsewhere [526 (see VIII, 51)]. In summary, before the start of semistarvation the mean scores for the group were within the normal range on all the MMPI scales. As semistarvation continued, there was a significant elevation of scores on the scales of the neurotic triad (Hs, D, Hy). This elevation tended to decrease steadily during the rehabilitation period. The pattern of elevation at the end of the semistarvation period was similar to that found by Leverenz [386 (see VII, 42)] in a group of 28 diagnosed cases of depression and by Gough [234 (VI, 38)] in a group of 24 cases diagnosed as moderate psychoneurosis.

The Present Problem

The standards for the MMPI were derived from a large normal group and from carefully selected samples of psychiatric patients [300 (see II, 5), 301 (II, 7), 420 (II, 6), 423 (see II, 9)]. Both the normal and the psychiatric groups were considered to be *physically* normal. The group of semistarved subjects was definitely not comparable in physical condition to the groups on which the MMPI was standardized. This difference poses the problem whether the score elevations observed in this experiment have the same interpretative significance as they would have in a physically normal group.

Information on the psychoneurotic effects of physical disorders in psychiatrically normal groups is limited. It has been found that the presence of physical illness elevates the Hs score slightly. Fifty patients in the general wards of the University of Minnesota Hospitals who were free from obvious psychiatric disturbances had

484

a mean standard score of 58 on the Hs scale; the presence of physical symptoms alters the personality pattern only moderately in the direction of hypochondriasis [420 (see II, 6)]. This conclusion is supported by the data of Leverenz who found a median Hs score of 53 for 105 patients in surgical wards [386 (see VII, 42)]. In their original article on the depression scale, Hathaway and McKinley [301 (see II, 7)] reported scores from a group of 229 patients in hospital wards who did not require psychiatric attention; the men had a mean standard D score of 60, the women averaged 55.

In the semistarvation experiment, the mean Hs score was 63. It was accompanied by marked elevations of scores on the other two psychoneurotic scales (D = 74, Hy = 70). It is important to note that all three of the elevated scales (Hs, D, Hy) contain a large number of somatic complaint items. In order to determine the relative contribution of the somatic and other items to the total scores, an item analysis was made of the responses on the Hs, D, and Hy scales in the control period and in semistarvation. As another approach to the problem of psychological interpretation of the semistarvation changes in the Hs, D, and Hy scales, a comparison was made between the frequencies of abnormal answers to a given item obtained for the MMPI psychiatric criterion groups and the semistarved subjects.

Classification of the Items

In order to determine the kind of items which contribute importantly to the score elevations, it seemed desirable to divide the total pool of items for the three scales into four categories: somatic, psychic, corrective, and subtle. These terms do not imply an absolute classification of the items and merely serve as convenient labels. Out of the total pool of 117 items, 39 were classified as somatic, 40 as psychic. It is obvious that a *rigid* separation of somatic and psychic items is not possible, and the present division is to be understood as a gross segregation to aid in the item analysis.

The corrective items were added to the preliminary D scales by the authors of the MMPI to decrease, or correct, the number of spuriously high D scores. The corrective items showed little increase in frequency from normals to depressed patients but were present in clinically nondepressed persons who had high D scores. There are 11 correction items on the D scale [301 (see II, 7)].

The term "subtle" has been used by some writers to designate a group of items not concerned with complaints but reflecting a defensive or self-deceptive attitude in the subjects. These items fall largely on the hysteria scale. On these items, the hysteria patients tend to give the apparently "normal" response more often than do the normals. The following are representative subtle items (and answers): "I think most people would lie to get ahead." (False) "It is safer to trust nobody." (False) "At times I feel like swearing." (False)

The 27 items here classified as subtle were checked against the list of Wiener and Harmon [645 (see IV, 22)] who have been interested in the relative contribution of "obvious" and "subtle" items to the total scores on several of the MMPI scales. Of our 27 items, 25 (93 per cent) were included in Wiener and Harmon's list.

Results: Over-All Changes in the Psychoneurotic Scores

As background for a more detailed analysis of the change in MMPI scores under conditions of semistarvation, the mean standard scores on the hypochondriasis, depression, and hysteria scales are given in Table 1.

Table 1. Scores on the Psychoneurotic Scales of the MMPI in Different Phases of a Semistarvation Rehabilitation Experiment [a]

Scale	C		S12	S24		R6	R12	R33
	Mean	SD	Mean	Mean	SD	Mean	Mean	Mean
Hs	45.7	3.4	58.2	63.0	6.6	55.8	54.1	44.0
D	54.2	6.5	64.8	73.9	12.0	66.6	65.7	51.0
Hy	59.0	6.1	65.8	70.0	8.2	66.5	64.9	59.6

[a] C refers to the control (prestarvation) values, S12 and S24 to the 12th and 24th week of semistarvation, R6, R12, and R33 to the respective weeks of rehabilitation. N = 32, except at R33 where N = 20.

The data indicate a pronounced rise in scores on all three scales during semistarvation, followed by a gradual return to normal values during nutritional rehabilitation. The change was interpreted as a nonspecific neurosis, with depression as the dominant feature. In contrast with the general rise in the psychoneurotic scales, the scores on the psychotic scales did not change importantly during semistarvation. For the purpose of a more detailed analysis the items on the Hs, D, and Hy scales will be pooled.

Results: Direct Item Analysis of the Semistarvation Changes

In evaluating each item, two frequencies (f, F) were taken into account: the number of men who answered a particular item in the abnormal direction in the control period (f) and during semistarvation (F). The *actual increase* $(F-f)$ from control to semistarvation in the number of men with abnormal responses may be expressed as the percentage of the total possible increase in the number of subjects giving such a response, $(N-f)$. This value will be designated as Δ. Mathematically,

$$\Delta = 100 \times \frac{(F-f)}{(N-f)}.$$

The distribution of the Δ values is given in Table 2. All the positive values denote an increase in the frequency of abnormal responses to a particular item during semistarvation. The negative values indicate a trend toward fewer abnormal answers during semistarvation; all these latter changes were small and were, therefore, grouped together. The median of the distribution is 9, with a Q_3 (the third quartile) of 29. A more or less arbitrary value of $\Delta \geqq 30$ was chosen as separating the less sensitive from the more sensitive items. The 29 items which changed in the abnormal direction to this extent or more are listed in Table 3 where they are divided into the four categories discussed above. These 29 items will be referred to hereafter as the "significant" items.

Table 2. Frequency Distributions of Δ Values of Various Groups of Items
from the Scales of the Neurotic Triad

Δ Values	All Items	Somatic	Psychic	Corrective	Subtle
96–100	1	1	0	0	0
91–95	2	2	0	0	0
86–90	2	1	1	0	0
81–85	1	1	0	0	0
76–80	0	0	0	0	0
71–75	2	0	1	1	0
66–70	2	0	0	0	0
61–65	3	1	1	1	0
56–60	2	1	0	1	0
51–55	0	0	0	0	0
46–50	4	1	2	0	1
41–45	4	2	1	0	1
36–40	4	3	1	0	0
31–35	2	1	1	0	0
26–30	6	3	1	1	1
21–25	2	1	1	0	0
16–20	8	0	4	2	2
11–15	12	3	8	0	1
6–10	9	7	2	0	1
0–5	17	10	4	0	3
Negative	35	2	11	6	16

The data were evaluated by calculating (1) the proportion of significant items in the four item categories (somatic, psychic, corrective, and subtle), (2) the relative contribution of each of the four item categories to the group of 29 significant items, and (3) the proportion of the total items on the Hs, D, and Hy scales which were found to be significant.

In Table 2 the Δ values are also plotted for each of the four item categories. The distributions for the somatic and psychic items are similar, with the median value in both cases falling in the class interval 10–14. The corrective and subtle items, on the other hand, changed in the abnormal direction in fewer of the subjects, the median Δ value being close to zero for both distributions.

The proportion of significant and nonsignificant items in the four item categories is indicated in Table 4. More than a third (36 per cent) of the somatic items were among those designated as significant. The percentage of significant items in the other categories was smaller.

How are the 29 significant items distributed among the four item categories? Using the frequencies given in Table 4, we obtain the following percentages: 48 per cent of the significant items ($\Delta \geqq 30$) were somatic, 32 per cent psychic, 10 per cent corrective, and 10 per cent subtle.

Table 5 presents an analysis of the total number of items in the four categories, tabulated separately for the three scales. The 29 significant items were broken down in the same way. All the figures have been converted to percentages to facilitate comparison. It should be remembered that some of the items are scored on more than one of the scales. It is apparent that the 100 per cent contribution of somatic items to the elevation of Hs scores has no special significance, since *all* the items in the Hs scale are somatic complaints.

Table 3. Hs, D, and Hy Items Which Showed a Marked Increase from Control to the 24th Week of Semistarvation in the Frequency of Abnormal Responses (N = 32)

Item Identification	Percentage of Possible Increase, Δ	Scales
Somatic Items		
A-5. I do not tire quickly. (False)	97	Hs, Hy
C-17. I am about as able to work as I ever was. (False)	94	Hs, D, Hy
A-3. I have never felt better in my life than I do now. (False)	92	D, Hy
A-40. I feel weak all over much of the time. (True)	88	Hs, D, Hy
A-42. I have had no difficulty in keeping my balance in walking. (False)	80	Hs, Hy
G-23. At times I am full of energy. (False)	62	D
A-47. Parts of my body often have feelings like burning, tingling, crawling, or like "going to sleep." (True)	59	Hs
A-16. I seldom or never have dizzy spells. (False)	48	Hs, Hy
A-2. I am in just as good physical health as most of my friends. (False)	44	Hs, D, Hy
B-27. I wake up fresh and rested most mornings. (False)	42	Hs, Hy
A-4. I am neither gaining nor losing weight. (False)	38	Hs, D
B-20. I have had no difficulty in starting or holding my bowel movements. (False)	37	Hs
A-55. My hands and feet are usually warm enough. (False)	36	Hs, Hy
B-10. I hardly ever notice my heart pounding and I am seldom short of breath. (False)	33	Hs, Hy
Psychic Items		
A-24. My judgment is better than it ever was. (False)	85	D
F-42. I have difficulty in starting to do things. (True)	70	D
B-36. I dream frequently about things that are best kept to myself. (False)	67	D
I-27. I find it hard to keep my mind on a task or job. (True)	64	D, Hy
I-37. I certainly feel useless at times. (True)	48	D
E-41. I enjoy many different kinds of play and recreation. (False)	45	D
F-44. I have had periods of days, weeks, or months, when I couldn't take care of things because I couldn't "get going." (True)	42	D
C-48. I like to flirt. (False)	37	D
B-2. I cannot understand what I read as well as I used to. (True)	32	D
Corrective Items		
B-8. I have never vomited blood or coughed up blood. (True)	71	D
B-6. I do not have spells of hayfever or asthma. (True)	60	D
B-3. I sweat very easily even on cool days. (False)	57	D
Subtle Items		
C-42. I like to read newspaper articles on crime. (False)	69	Hy
E-3. I feel that it is certainly best to keep my mouth shut when I'm in trouble. (False)	46	Hy
F-5. I wish I were not so shy. (False)	40	Hy

Table 4. The Relative Proportion of the Total Number of Significant Items in Different Item Categories

Type of Item	Total No. of Items	Significant Items [a]	Non-significant Items	Total
Somatic	39	14 (36%)	25 (64%)	100%
Psychic	40	9 (23%)	31 (77%)	100%
Corrective	11	3 (27%)	8 (73%)	100%
Subtle	27	3 (11%)	24 (89%)	100%

[a] The term "significant" denotes items in which Δ ≥ 30.

488

Table 5. The Proportion of the Total Number of Hs, D, and Hy Items in the Four Categories, Compared with the Proportion of the Significant Items

Category	Hs		D		Hy	
	Total	Signif.	Total	Signif.	Total	Signif.
Somatic	33 (100%)	12 (100%)	11 (18%)	6 (33%)	26 (43%)	10 (71%)
Psychic			33 (55%)	9 (50%)	9 (18%)	1 (7%)
Corrective			11 (18%)	3 (17%)		
Subtle			5 (9%)	0 (0%)	25 (42%)	3 (22%)
Totals	33 (100%)	12 (100%)	60 (100%)	18 (100%)	60 (100%)	14 (100%)

The changes in the D scale under semistarvation are of particular importance for the present discussion since depression was the dominant feature of the "semi-starvation neurosis." The mean score on the D scale after 24 weeks of semistarvation was 73.9, the highest mean elevation observed (see Table 1). It may be noted (see Table 5) that the psychic items not directly concerned with bodily complaints constituted one half of the significant items on this scale. This finding indicates that the elevation of the mean depression score is not brought about primarily by an increase in somatic complaints.

Results: Indirect Item Analysis by Comparison with Psychiatric Groups

Comparison of the percentage frequencies of abnormal answers in the starvation group with psychiatric groups should further clarify the nature of the personality changes which took place in the course of experimental semistarvation. Since we are interested primarily in items which have changed in semistarvation, only the significant items, listed in Table 3, were considered in Table 6. The figures indicate the percentages of subjects in the different groups who answered a given item in the abnormal direction.

The similarity between the experimental subjects in the control period and MMPI normal males is striking. There are five items (A-4, C-48, F-42, I-27, E-3) which were answered abnormally by the group at the control period more frequently than by the MMPI normal group. The excess of False answers to item A-4 ("I am neither gaining nor losing weight") is accounted for by the attempt made during the control period to reduce weight in those men who were overweight and to increase the weight of those subjects who were below their standard weight. The reasons for the differences on the other four items are not as clear.

Comparison of the semistarved subjects with the psychiatric criterion groups (hypochondriasis, reactive depression, manic-depression, and hysteria) reveals again a remarkable general similarity in the percentage of the abnormal answers to the significant items. Several items were answered in the abnormal direction by a very large proportion of the experimental subjects. Most of these items are clearly related to the stress. They indicate lack of endurance (A-5), weakness (A-40), difficulty in walking (A-42), decreased capacity for work (C-17), inability to enjoy vigorous recreation (E-41), and decreased sex interest (C-48). Other closely related complaints are those of decreased initiative (F-42), inability to concentrate (I-27), and lack of confidence in one's judgment (A-24).

At this time it may be instructive to consider answers given by the experimental

Table 6. Percentage Frequency of Abnormal Responses for Various Items of the MMPI [a]

Item Identi-fication	MMPI Normals	Experimental Group in Control Period	MMPI Abnormals				Experimental Group after 24 Weeks of Semistarvation
			Hs	RD	MD	Hy	
Somatic Items							
A-2	11	0	56	60	52	60	44
A-3	50	41		4	4	0	3
A-4	14	56	68	72	48		72
A-5	17	9	68			80	97
A-16	22	9	56			33	53
A-40	6	0	52	52	68	47	88
A-42	8	6	32			47	81
A-47	23	9	80				63
A-55	11	13	36			60	44
B-10	32	16	56			60	44
B-20	18	6	44				41
B-27	20	25	56			87	56
C-17	9	3	68	56	72	67	94
G-23	90	81		60	60		69
Psychic Items							
A-24	37	38		72	16		91
B-2	9	3		60	48		34
B-36	18	9		4	8		3
C-48	30	59		16	4		37
E-41	7	9		36	44		50
F-42	24	38		40	60		81
F-44	16	19		60	76		53
I-27	7	22		20	60	20	72
I-37	44	34		64	76		66
Corrective Items							
B-3	42	22		40	44		9
B-6	16	16		28	8		6
B-8	18	22		24	12		6
Subtle Items							
C-42	42	59				87	88
E-3	27	59				73	78
F-5	35	31				40	19

[a] Comparison was made of the experimental groups (N = 32) during the control period with Hathaway and McKinley's group of 139 normal males. Also, the values for the experimental group during the 24th week of semistarvation were compared with four psychiatric criterion groups–hypochondriasis (Hs), reactive depression (RD), manic-depression (MD), hysteria (Hy). The number of patients was 25, 25, 25, and 15, respectively.

subjects in a complaint inventory, specially designed for the experiment. Whereas only 3 per cent of the subjects reported at the control period that they felt down-hearted frequently, in semistarvation the percentage increased to 62 per cent; similarly, during semistarvation the men complained that they found the experimental life a strain much of the time, were frequently bored with people, preferred to be left alone, and became impatient when interrupted. It is evident both from the MMPI results and from the complaint inventory that semistarvation resulted in definite and pronounced personality changes. Such a conclusion would agree with the behavioral observations of the "semistarvation neurosis" [r59, 526 (see VIII, 51)].

Summary and Conclusions

Analysis was made of the responses to the items constituting the psychoneurotic scales (Hs, D, Hy) of the MMPI, in order to determine the type of items which contributed to the observed score elevations. The inventory was administered during the control period and after six months of semistarvation. In view of the marked morphological and physiological changes in the subjects, it was felt that the contribution of somatic complaint items might be disproportionate.

For purposes of analysis, the items on the Hs, D, and Hy scales were separated into four categories: somatic, psychic, corrective, and subtle. An item was considered significant if there was an increase of 30 per cent or more from control to semistarvation in the percentage of subjects who answered the item in the abnormal direction.

Somatic complaint items comprised 48 per cent of the significant items; psychic items comprised 32 per cent. The corrective and subtle items contributed a total of 20 per cent to the group of significant items. An analysis of the clinical scales taken separately shows that the somatic items contribute most of the elevation on the Hy scale. On the D scale, however, 50 per cent of the significant items were psychic.

An attempt was made to determine whether the items contributing to the observed score elevations in the semistarved subjects are the same items which contribute to the elevation of scores in neurotic patients who had no physical pathology. On the whole, the percentage frequencies were strikingly similar.

The major conclusion concerns the character of the psychological changes resulting from prolonged experimental semistarvation. There were no fundamental differences between the kind of answers given by the semistarved subjects and those given by patients with a clinical diagnosis of psychoneurosis. This indicates that the semistarved men suffered from an actual, though temporary, personality disturbance, which may be described as a mild psychoneurosis.

A. L. ANDERSEN AND L. J. HANVIK

ARTICLE 53 *The Differential Effect of Frontal and Parietal Brain Lesions on MMPI Profiles*

THIS paper is the outgrowth of a psychometric study of patients who had suffered focal brain damage and in whom the locus of the lesion had been ascertained either by surgery, e.g., in cases of brain tumor, or, in gunshot wound cases, by X-ray demonstration of metallic foreign bodies in the brain. The patients studied were all male patients at the Minneapolis Veterans Administration Hospital.

The results reported here are concerned only with the MMPI profiles of the following two subgroups of brain-damaged patients: sixteen cases with frontal lobe lesions and twenty-seven cases with parietal involvement. In the first group the lesions were, in all cases, confined to the frontal lobes, but the second group was a somewhat more mixed group in that some of these patients had lesions which extended to more than one lobe, though in all cases the common denominator of "parietal involvement" was present. With respect to laterality, there were approximately the same number of right and left hemisphere lesions.

Problem and Method

The analysis described herein was performed to test the hypothesis that there are no significant differences between the MMPI profiles of the patients with frontal lobe lesions and the profiles of those patients with lesions involving the parietal lobe.

In analyzing the differences between the two groups, two methods were employed: (1) mean T scores for each group were obtained on all scales, and tests were done to determine the statistical significance of the differences which appeared; (2) profiles were "coded" by the ranking method described by Welsh [617 (see III, 13)] and the mean ranks for all scales were computed for each patient group. The results obtained by these methods are presented in Tables 1 and 2.

Discussion of Results

Inspection of Table 1 shows that the mean T score on the K scale is significantly higher for the group of patients with frontal lobe lesions. However, on the F, D, Pt, and Si scales the parietal involvement group had significantly higher mean T scores.

492

Table 1. T-Score Means and Codes for Two Brain Damaged Groups

Group	?	L	F	K	Hs	D	Hy	Pd	Mf	Pa	Pt	Sc	Ma	Si
Frontal lobe cases (N = 16)..	50	54	52	61	60	55	61	55	52	54	55	59	52	46
MMPI Code: 31–8 247659/0 K–LF?														
Parietal lobe cases (N = 27)..	50	51	58	51	70	69	65	56	49	54	65	64	58	53
MMPI Code: 1'2 378–9460/5 FKL?/														

Table 2. Mean Ranks of Each MMPI Scale in Two Brain Damaged Groups

Group	Hs	D	Hy	Pd	Mf	Pa	Pt	Sc	Ma	Si
Frontal lobe cases (N = 16)....	4.3	5.6	3.4	5.4	5.9	5.7	6	4.4	6.3	8
Parietal lobe cases (N = 27)....	3.6	3.2	4.2	6.2	7.8	7.3	4	4.8	6.3	7.6

With respect to variability, the following differences were noted: on the L scale, the frontal lobe group is significantly more variable; on Hs, Hy, and Si, the parietal involvement group is the more variable. A possible reason for the greater variability of the parietal involvement group on the clinical scales is that this group is a more variable group with regard to location of brain damage. For the frontal lobe cases all had lesions exclusively in the frontal lobe, while the parietal lobe cases showed overlapping of lesions into other lobes and were thus not as pure a group neurologically.

An interesting fact is that the differences in mean T scores which have been referred to above suggest that the patients with parietal involvement have more severely disturbed personalities than do the patients with frontal lobe lesions. In addition to and complementing this difference in severity, there is also a difference between the two groups in *type* of personality involvement. The mean profile for cases of frontal lobe injury exhibited a V-shaped neurotic triad (i.e., the depression score is below those of hypochondriasis and hysteria). There is also a secondary elevation on the schizophrenia scale. The "composite" profile code of the frontal lobe cases (using Welsh's method of coding) is 31–8 247659/0 K–LF?. From this profile, one might conjecture the mean personality type of the frontal group to be capable of description somewhat as follows: accepting, nonirritable, not anxious, affable, easygoing, and possessed of a relatively low general level of aspiration. This description does, in fact, fit the most common clinical picture observed among the individual patients in this group.

The mean profile for the patient group with parietal lobe involvement is quite different from the profile just described. Here, the neurotic triad scores present an *inverted* V shape and the secondary peak is on the psychasthenia scale rather than on the schizophrenia scale as is the case in the frontal lobe group. When we consider individual cases, a higher proportion of markedly abnormal profiles are found among the parietal involvement group. Profiles capable of being interpreted as normal are far more common among patients with frontal lobe damage than among patients with parietal involvement.

The Welsh profile code for the parietal group is 1'2 378–9460/5 FKL?/. This profile might be interpreted as reflecting an "anxiety neurosis" type of personality: i.e., rigid, worrying, pessimistic, hyperactive, precise, and detail-bound. As a group, the patients making up this parietal involvement group appear more sensitive to anxiety-producing environmental situations than are the frontal lobe patients or normal individuals without brain damage. This sensitivity and the general anxiety-prone personality type are clinically observable in many individual cases in the parietal involvement group. This type of personality is rare, if not nonexistent, in the frontal lobe group of patients.

The differences observed between these two localization groups suggest the presence of some cerebral localization of the reaction patterns which influence the behavior of an individual in response to his environment and which are reflected on MMPI records. Of interest in this connection, for the purposes of comparison, are the mean MMPI profiles published by Hovey [330 (see VI, 40)]. His composite profile for cases of dissociative-conversion reaction has a marked resemblance to that presented in this paper (Table 2) for cases with frontal lobe damage. Hovey's composite profile for cases of anxiety neurosis, on the other hand, resembles the profile presented herein (Table 2) for cases of brain damage with parietal involvement.

Summary

The results of a study of MMPI profiles of patients suffering focal brain damage are presented. Characteristic T-score and pattern differences are shown between patients with frontal lobe lesions and those with parietal involvement. The former group is shown to have both psychometric and clinical indications characteristic of the hysteroid type of reaction pattern; the latter group most closely resembles patients suffering with anxiety neurosis.

A. H. CANTER

◆————————————————————————————————

ARTICLE 54 *MMPI Profiles in Multiple Sclerosis*

A CAREFUL examination of the American literature on multiple sclerosis, as Sugar and Nadell [r157] have recently pointed out, reveals a paucity of material dealing with the mental or emotional symptoms of that disease. The meeting of the Association for Research in Mental and Nervous Disease in December 1948, which was devoted to a discussion of the various aspects of the disease, served to emphasize not only our relative lack of information about multiple sclerosis but, particularly, the need for research studies which might add to our understanding and ultimately to its control.

The present report of research is part of a more comprehensive and continuing investigation begun in early 1948 at the Veterans Administration Mental Hygiene Clinic, Brooklyn Regional Office, which was described in a previous publication by Canter [r30]. The purpose of the present report is to study the psychological aspects of multiple sclerosis as revealed by the MMPI in order to determine whether the data reveal any reliable personality patterns associated with the disease.

Many previous studies of the MMPI have been concerned with the demonstration of statistically significant differences between various diagnostic groups. In these studies, patterns characteristic of each group have been obtained by constructing a profile from the average standard scores found on each of the nine personality scales. Admittedly, these "average profiles" have limited clinical value in the treatment and understanding of the individual patient. Descriptive studies of multiple sclerosis, however, must first be made prior to attempting cross-validation studies, or studies which can be of direct value in the treatment of individual patients. As was previously indicated, this present report is concerned primarily with identification of the personality patterns associated with multiple sclerosis.

Subjects

The subjects of this study are 33 of the patients comprising the experimental group of multiple sclerotics described in detail in a previous study [r30]. In general, the group constitutes a fairly large and representative sample of the World War II veterans in the early stages of the disease process. The mean age of the group was approximately 32, and the duration of the acute symptoms ranged from one to eight years, with an approximate average of four years. In all the cases sufficient organic damage exists to make the medical diagnosis of multiple sclerosis certain.

495

Procedure

The group form of the MMPI was administered as part of a battery of psychological tests in the preliminary phases of the study of multiple sclerotics. The patients were informed at the outset of the initial testing that the purpose of the psychological examinations was to secure data on multiple sclerosis which might contribute to a better understanding of the disease. As previously described, the experimental group revealed a maximum amount of motivation and was uniformly cooperative in complying with the testing procedure. Of the 33 patients who took the MMPI initially, 21 patients received a retest within one week of the date exactly six months later. Twelve members of the experimental group did not receive the retest at the exact six-month date because of administrative difficulties. There is no reason to believe that the cases for which retests are available differ significantly from the entire group of cases.

To increase the value of the objective data, a clinical team of a neuropsychiatrist, a clinical psychologist, and a psychiatric social worker were asked to write independently a "brief impression" gained from the inspection of the average profile of the 33 multiple sclerotics. These impressions were not made with the purpose of attempting a complete personality description or evaluation, but simply to indicate what appeared (to the judges) to be the significant personality trends revealed by the profiles.

Results

The data necessary for answering the problems of this investigation are set forth in Table 1. Records were, of course, examined and analyzed individually, but the material has been combined into one profile for simplicity of presentation. This procedure involves obscuring qualitative differences, but because of relatively narrow ranges of scores on the component personality scales, the technique is not seriously in error.

Table 1. T-Score Means, Standard Deviations, and Codes of Initial and Retest Results

Group	?	L	F	K	Hs	D	Hy	Pd	Mf	Pa	Pt	Sc	Ma
Initial (N = 33)													
Mean ..	50.4	54.5	55.7	57.8	81.2	79.4	75.3	59.2	55.4	53.2	63.0	63.6	55.1
SD	1.9	3.9	5.7	8.4	12.9	12.8	10.0	11.5	8.7	9.2	16.0	14.4	9.2
					MMPI Code: 1"23'87–4596 KFL?/								
Retest (N = 21)													
Mean ..	50.4	52.6	53.3	54.2	79.0	78.8	76.6	59.0	53.5	51.6	61.4	62.1	52.1
SD	1.9	3.7	5.0	8.4	12.7	12.7	9.3	10.2	9.1	9.2	14.9	14.1	9.3
					MMPI Code: 123'87–4596 KFL?/								

A comparison of the two profiles reveals that their general shape is quite similar. There is a small, but general, regression of the mean scores on the component scales in the direction of the general population norms, which might be attributed to the slight clinical improvement of the group as a whole in their acceptance and adjustment to the disease process. However, this trend revealed by the retest is more apparent than real. A statistical analysis (the t test of the difference in means) fails to reveal any significant changes of the means in the component scales upon re-examination.

Excerpts of the impressions of the significant personality trends noted by the "clinical team" working independently were as follows:

The MMPI curve is an over-all mildly elevated curve indicating a pervasive maladjustment. The Hs and D, as the highest scores, suggest preoccupation with physical functioning is tinged with hopelessness. With the Hs higher than the Hy score, the indication is that physical preoccupation is a relatively malignant one and is not balanced by tension-relieving dependence or conversion. The slight elevation of the Pt and Sc scores indicates ego-disorganizing processes and may be a warning of future development.

This looks like the curve of a person reacting to situational stress such as injury or chronic disease. It would seem that the Pt and Sc elevations must represent an attempt to deal with anxiety centering around conflicts having to do with body image and capacities (Hs). The D, which is not significantly high, suggests a feeling of apathy and hopelessness rather than a true clinical depression. This would suggest that deep-seated dependency needs do not seem a factor, and a retreat into invalidism is not an acceptable way out. The Hy is not sufficiently elevated to suggest a conversion solution. There is apparently much free-floating anxiety about self and health that the ego has to handle. The significant aspect of this curve for therapy is the high Pt and Sc, which reveal a way of handling anxiety that may threaten the ego sufficiently to precipitate a psychotic break.

There is apprehension over health, depression, some irritability, and aggressiveness leading to some difficulty in social adjustment. There is a tendency to act immaturely and unrealistically with a desire for dependency. Excessive drinking and/or speech difficulty may be present. There is a low level of drive or motivation.

Discussion

An inspection of the profiles in Table 1 and an examination of the impressions of the three "judges" indicate that the elevation of Hs, D, and Hy are noteworthy. The elevation of these three scales, as well as the profile of the remaining scales, indicates the "neurotic triad" which the authors of the MMPI suggest as characteristic of the "greater portion of these persons not under medical care who are commonly called neurotic, as well as individuals so abnormal as to need psychiatric attention." This type of curve suggests the "typical" personality configuration in which the person reacts to stress with depression and is further characterized by lack of self-confidence, tendency to worry, narrowness of interest, and introversion.

It is beyond the scope of this paper to review in detail, or to examine, the various concepts and theories concerning the etiology of multiple sclerosis or the "dynamics" of the personality structure. It is of interest to note that the present findings tend to support the common clinical observation of the presence of a "neurotic overlay" in multiple sclerosis. It is of further interest to note that according to the case histories of this veteran population of multiple sclerotics, approximately 65 per cent had received a diagnosis of some type of hysteria prior to the development of overt neurological symptoms which could be identified and prior to the clear establishment of a diagnosis of multiple sclerosis.

Grinker, Ham, and Robbins [r66] have pointed out that neurotic manifestations often obscure the first evidence of the central lesions, causing many false diagnoses of hysteria for the entire syndrome. Grinker *et al.* indicate that these neurotic mani-festations have been considered as a problem in differential diagnosis, and that only rarely has attention been given to the possibility that the disturbance may not only be the concomitant or result of the damage to the nervous system, but also an important factor in the etiology. In Sugar and Nadell's study [r157], wherein special emphasis was placed on the emotional affective symptomatology, the changes in the emotional content or prevailing mood were considered an important diagnostic sign. They suggest that the affective disturbances in mood and behavior commonly noted are consistent with the patient's previous personality make-up. Although the present study is in agreement with their finding that disturbances in mood and behavior are of importance in understanding the multiple sclerotic patient, it is at variance with their findings insofar as it suggests that the prevailing mood and the emotional content are in the direction of depression. Examination of personal diaries and other autobiographical material submitted by several patients in con-junction with the broader phases of the continuing work on multiple sclerosis clearly shows that dysphoria is the predominant mood for a majority of this sample popula-tion of multiple sclerotics. One factor possibly explaining the difference in the present findings and those of Sugar and Nadell is the shorter average duration of illness in our patients. The patients in this study had been ill on an average of ap-proximately four years at the time of initial examination, whereas the patients in the Sugar-Nadell study had been ill for an average of 10.8 years when examined.

The findings revealed by the MMPI profiles are not surprising in view of the impairment of functioning brought about by the disease process. Generally it has been observed that the patients have difficulty in accepting the disease and its progressive limitations. There is a frequently expressed attitude that physical strength and health are considered necessary for confidence and accomplishment, and that conflict between desires and ability to perform permeates the personality. There is, furthermore, an ambivalence concerning the future role in life, producing indecisiveness and feelings of insecurity which are often reflected in relatively poor emotional control and social adjustment. These psychological factors, of course, should be considered in any treatment program of multiple sclerosis.

The value of the present MMPI study, or any other psychometric measure, is not so much in obtaining proof of the obvious, as it is in establishing more objective-ly and precisely the nature and degree of the personality characteristics associated with the disease. A final note of caution to be kept in mind is that psychometric measures do not pretend to furnish a neurological diagnosis, nor do they determine whether or not a person is a multiple sclerotic.

Summary

The personality characteristics associated with multiple sclerosis as revealed by the MMPI profiles are presented and discussed. The personality characteristics revealed are a reaction of depression, preoccupation and concern about bodily func-tions, feelings of hopelessness and insecurity, as well as tendencies toward inde-cisiveness, narrowness of interests, and introversion. Difficulty in accepting the disease and its progressive limitations, and ambivalence and insecurity concerning the future, are often reflected in relatively poor emotional control and social adjust-ment.

L. J. HANVIK

◆ ─────────────────────────────────────

ARTICLE 55 *MMPI Profiles in Patients with Low-Back Pain*

ALTHOUGH the literature relating to the subject of low-back pain is extensive, perusal of this literature has indicated that the standard techniques of clinical psychology have not been widely used to aid in evaluating the functional elements in patients with this syndrome. The following study is an attempt to see if patients whose complaint of low-back pain is deemed psychogenic in origin present a characteristically different picture psychologically from patients with like physical symptoms but whose symptoms are known to be produced by organic disease. The patients studied here were all patients at the Minneapolis Veterans Administration Hospital whose primary reason for hospitalization was low-back pain.

Problem

This investigation was undertaken to determine if, and to what extent, the MMPI can be used in differentiating between patients with "functional" low-back pain and patients who likewise have low-back pain but in whom there is evidence of the presence of organic disease.

In the selection of cases, two criteria were followed: (1) Back pain must have been the primary reason for hospitalization. (2) The pain originated or appeared to originate in the back, in the spinal column, or in close proximity thereto, from the lowest thoracic vertebrae to the coccyx. There may have been, and frequently was, other pain (radiated or associated), but the source and basis of pain was deemed to be the lower back.

The subjects were all male inpatients admitted to the above-mentioned hospital with the complaint of back pain as defined above. The group actually constituted two clinical groups:

1. Thirty proved "organic" cases of low-back pain; all of these were patients with protruded intervertebral disc, and in all but two of these the evidence of the presence of disc was surgical, i.e., a disc was removed at operation. In the other two cases the diagnosis of disc was based on X-ray evidence (spinogram) and characteristic history, plus evidence of correctly distributed pain.

2. Thirty cases with no clear-cut organic findings, i.e., the general physical and neurological examinations were essentially negative.

499

The groups were equated for age (within five years), socioeconomic group (1940 census classification), marital status, intelligence (within Stanford-Binet categories, since the measure of intelligence used was the Stanford-Binet Vocabulary), and race (all white).

The following methods were used with the MMPI to test the hypothesis that the two clinical groups were not significantly different with respect to their test scores and patterns: (1) t tests for the significance of differences between mean T scores of the two groups on the MMPI scales; (2) pattern analysis of the MMPI coded profiles for the two groups; (3) test of the ability of experienced clinicians to separate the MMPI profiles into the correct groups in a manner significantly different from chance.

Results

An inspection of Table 1 will show that certain marked differences exist between the MMPI profiles of the two groups of patients.

Table 1. T-Score Means, Standard Deviations, and Codes of Two Groups of Low Back Pain Cases

Group	K	Hs	D	Hy	Pd	Mf	Pa	Pt	Sc	Ma	Si
Organic cases (N = 30)											
Mean ...	53.9	57.9	57.5	56.6	49.0	48.2	46.9	48.5	47.5	47.5	48.5
SD	7.4	11.8	8.2	9.4	11.4	7.4	7.0	7.8	7.9	7.5	7.6
				MMPI Code: 123/4075986 KLF?/							
Functional cases (N = 30)											
Mean ...	58.5	73.3	62.8	69.4	57.5	48.6	50.7	56.4	55.2	53.0	46.4
SD	9.8	11.1	9.9	8.7	7.9	8.6	10.1	7.8	6.4	9.3	7.5
				MMPI Code: 1'32–47896/50 KLF?/							
t	2.04	6.23°°°	2.20°	8.20°°°	3.32°°	0.36	1.68	3.90°°°	4.11°°°	1.30	0.20

° Significant at the .05 level.
°° Significant at the .01 level.
°°° Significant at the .001 level.

Table 1 illustrates that the "composite" profile for the 30 functional patients shows a fairly clear-cut "conversion-V" or "depressive valley" [234 (see VI, 38)] configuration; i.e., hypochondriasis and hysteria are both elevated and depression is low, relatively. This V-shaped pattern has aptly been termed the "conversion-V" because it is so frequently observed to occur in the records of conversion hysteria patients and because it so clearly portrays the essential elements of the hysterical adjustment where there are conversion features: e.g., the existence of physical symptoms along with indifference (low D) or apparent dissociation of the affective reactions. This type of record quotes the patient as saying, in effect, "I have numerous bodily complaints but I am relatively unworried, not depressed." The composite profile for the organics, it can be seen, does not show this pattern but, instead, is somewhat of a straight line, with Hs, D, and Hy approximately equal.

When mean T scores of the two groups are compared (see Table 1), a number of significant differences are found: the mean T scores on Hs, Hy, Pt, Sc, and Pd show very significant differences; the groups are also significantly different on the

D scale, though the difference is somewhat less pronounced than on the five scales previously mentioned. The functional group, it is noted, has the higher scores on all these scales.

Analysis of the profile codes for the two groups, though it could not be carried out in statistical terms, also revealed differences: for example, D moves downward in importance as one progresses from the organic through the functional group of cases. Hy moves to the fore in rank as one progresses in the same direction.

After it was established that statistically significant differences exist between the MMPI scores for the two clinical groups, it was thought desirable to get an idea of the extent to which these differences could be used by clinicians in differentiating the profiles of the two groups by inspection. A profile-sorting experiment was therefore carried out with the aid of four clinical psychologists, all experienced in the clinical use of the MMPI. Only one judge had any knowledge at the outset that the sorting had anything to do with the low-back study, and that judge did only the "second sorting," to be explained subsequently. The other three judges sorted the profiles twice.

For the first sorting the judges were instructed in this manner:

These are curves of males ($N = 60$) from the ages of 20 to 55, median age 35. Sort them into piles of diagnostic categories as follows:

1. Essentially normal
2. "Normal" with physical disease
3. Simple adult maladjustment
4. Psychoneurosis:
   a. Reactive depression
   b. Hysteria
      i. Anxiety
      ii. Conversion
   c. Psychasthenia
   d. Neurasthenia
   e. Hypochondriasis
   f. Anxiety state
   g. Mixed
5. Manic-depressive:
   a. Manic
   b. Depressed
   c. Mixed
6. Schizophrenia:
   a. Simple
   b. Hebephrenic
   c. Catatonic
   d. Paranoid
7. Paranoid
8. Involutional Psychosis
   a. Melancholia
   b. Paranoid
9. Psychosis with psychopathic personality
10. Organic psychosis (e.g., paresis)

11. Psychopathic personality
   a. Asocial, amoral (Pd syndrome)
   b. Pathologic emotionality
   c. Pathologic sexuality

Record the case numbers after the diagnostic category in which you think it belongs.

After each of the three judges had performed this first sorting on the 60 MMPI profiles, he was given the following instructions for the second sorting:

These are all cases of veterans in the VA Hospital with the major complaint of low-back pain. Of these 60 curves, there are 30 of each of two groups of cases: (1) male veterans with low-back pain having no demonstrable organic finding upon thorough physical study; (2) male veterans with low-back pain and a surgically confirmed prolapsed intervertebral disc. About half of these were tested as much as ten days after surgery, the rest were tested before surgery. Sort into two piles, one "functional" and one "disc." You may use or ignore your previous sorting as you see fit.

Examination of the results of the first sorting indicated that the psychotic categories (Nos. 5 to 10, inclusive, above) were largely ignored by the judges. That is, although the judges had no information whatever as to the character of the sample (other than the sex and age range), they were able to conclude correctly from the MMPI profiles that the patients represented thereby (1) were not psychotic, (2) had a sizable number of "normals" among them, and (3) had a large number of neurotics among them, particularly hysterical and hypochondriacal individuals. This fact is especially significant in view of the fact that the sorting was "blind," a condition which does not prevail in the actual clinical situation.

Table 2 summarizes the results of the second sorting and indicates how well the four judges were able to sort the profiles into the categories "functional" and "organic." An inspection of the table reveals that all except one of the judges were able to sort the profiles significantly better than chance; and the total correct sortings for the four judges (including the one who failed to sort the profiles significantly better than chance) yielded a chi square with a probability of .001.

Table 3 shows that when three or four judges independently agreed as to whether a given profile should be called "functional" or "organic," the accuracy of the sorting increased, so that the difference from chance was even more highly significant statistically.

We can conclude from the profile-sorting experiment that experienced clinicians can distinguish with good accuracy the MMPI profiles of patients with functional low-back pain from those of patients in the organic group. This is the case in spite of the fact that supplementary information and cues which are frequently available in the clinical setting were lacking in the present experiment.

As will be noted from the instructions given for the second sorting, some of the patients were tested before surgery and some afterward. By means of an item analysis and significance tests, the MMPI profiles of the group tested prior to surgery were compared with those of the group tested afterward in order to see if there were any differences. All tests indicated that there were no significant differences.

A word should perhaps be added here concerning individual differences in the ability to sort MMPI profiles. It is, of course, essential that an individual shall have

Table 2. Results of "Second Sorting" of MMPI Profiles of 30 Organic Cases of Backache and 30 Functional Cases of Backache

Judge	Percentage Called Correctly	Chi Square	Probability
A	77	9.187	<.01 a
B	73	6.909	<.01
C	70	5.000	<.03
D	57	0.536	Chance
Four judges combined	69	18.306	<.001

a Chi square for the .01 level is 6.635.

Table 3. Chi Square Using Only Cases on Which Four or Three of the Judges Independently Agree as to the Sorting

Agreement	N a	% b	Chi Square	Contingency Co-efficient	Probability
Four judges ..	29	83	12.461	.548	<.001
Three judges ..	52	75	13.019	.447	<.001

a N equals the number of cases which fit the criteria (i.e., the number of cases on which four or three judges independently agreed as to the category into which they should be sorted).

b "%" equals the percentage of correct hits (i.e., the percentage of N correctly called when we consider only those cases on which four or three judges independently agreed as to the sorting).

had practice clinically in dealing with a considerable number and variety of MMPI profiles. The judges employed in the sorting experiment just described, for instance, have all had abundant experience in the use of the MMPI in diagnosis and have all viewed numerous profiles of neurotic, psychotic, and normal individuals. Even so, there appear to be differences in skill, and these differences have consistently exhibited themselves in a series of sorting tests like the one reported here.

For example, Judge D (see Table 2), whose sorting level was apparently "chance" in this experiment, was found to have been at or near the bottom in proficiency in at least two other sorting problems where his results were in competition with those of from three to five other judges. Moreover, this is true notwithstanding the fact that Judge D has had at least as much clinical experience with the MMPI as any judge with whom he has been "in competition." There are other instances known to the author in which certain experienced judges consistently ranked low or high in sorting in competition with others. It would thus seem that sorting, or, better, "evaluation" of MMPI profiles is a clinical activity or skill requiring good judgment sharpened by experience and that, even among psychologists who have had approximately the same amount of clinical experience with the test, there appear to be marked individual differences in the level of skill attained.

Summary

A study was done to determine if the MMPI could be used in differentiating between cases of presumed psychogenic backache and backache cases in which there was definite evidence (surgical in all except two cases) of herniated intervertebral disc.

There were statistically significant differences between the two groups on the following six scales: Hs, D, Hy, Pd, Pt, and Sc. The functional patients scored higher on all of these scales. When the mean T scores for all patients in the functional group were plotted, the resultant profile was neurotic in type, showing the "conversion-V" configuration, which features elevations on Hs and Hy, with D relatively low and a mild rise on Pt.

Profile-sorting experiments revealed that judges could distinguish the profiles of members of the two groups in a manner significantly better than chance.

Therapy

THERE has been a great need for research on problems of therapy for emotional disorders, but efforts to study these procedures systematically have been hampered by the ambiguities and low reliability of standard diagnostic procedures. To evaluate alternative therapeutic techniques one must apply them to groups which have been matched for kind of illness, degree of involvement, and prognostic potential. There is also the need to follow up this initial matching with careful application of criteria reflecting kind and degree of change that are independent of the therapy process, the patient, and the therapist himself. Since little progress can be made in this difficult area by isolated research workers, there is an equally compelling need for a common basis of comparison by means of which different workers can collate their findings and determine the generality of their conclusions. Since this comparison must be as precise as possible, the basis of comparison must be communicated in quantitative as well as qualitative form. The papers that have been collected in this section furnish evidence on the suitability of the MMPI for these purposes.

In article 56, Gallagher offers evidence that the MMPI does reflect changes concomitant with brief psychotherapy although his design does not allow him to conclude that these changes are attributable to the therapy per se. The MMPI score changes are related, however, to nontest behavior of the clients which is indicative of various degrees of improvement.

Barron in article 57 demonstrates a significant relationship between pre-therapy MMPI scores and subsequent ratings of degree of improvement in psychotherapy. His material furnishes evidence on the role of personality integration in the patient's capacity to benefit from psychotherapeutic efforts.

In article 58, Kaufmann studies a group of cases which were rated as improved during six months of outpatient therapy in a student health service. He contrasts his score changes on the patient group with the stability of the MMPI scores on a group of normal students without known psychiatric involvement. Although it is important to know that mere retesting on the MMPI does not in itself lead to score decrements, his lack of a control group with equally high MMPI elevations vitiates to some extent the results of his analysis. Evidence on this latter point is furnished by Rosen's [498] study of tests administered one to two days apart on a sample of VA hospital psychiatric cases in which he found impressive stability on the two testings. Further support may be found in Roseman's paper [684] where a control was used.

The results which Schofield reports in article 59 help round out this picture by showing among other things that mere exposure to psychiatric therapy does not necessarily bring down elevated MMPI scores. He is also able to show the differential effects of hospitalization alone versus hospitalization combined with electro-convulsive therapy on roughly comparable groups of psychotic patients. The reader is referred to the more complete reports of Schofield's analyses [535 and 536] for discussion of the item studies which had to be excluded from the present volume because of space limitations.

Pearson develops a useful prognosis index in article 60 which has borne up well in subsequent validational studies. This work could well mature into sets of indices which would provide a basis for assignment of cases to different therapeutic regimes in installations where there is a wide range of cases and alternative therapies are available.

In the last article in this section, Feldman is able to demonstrate further the use-fulness of MMPI scores in predicting therapeutic outcome as well as provide evi-dence that the test on readministration tends to corroborate clinical ratings of the effect of therapy.

The lack of appropriate control groups in all these studies points up the cogent need for further research devoted to these problems. The usefulness of the MMPI as a basis for matching before therapy has not yet been realized. Little has been done in exploring the exciting possibility of using the test findings on the therapists them-selves as part of the prediction formulas in combination with data from the patients assigned to them.

The articles in this section came from the following sources: article 56 from J. J. Gallagher, MMPI changes concomitant with client-centered therapy, *Journal of Consulting Psychology*, 1953, 17, 334–338, and Manifest anxiety changes concomitant with client-centered therapy, *Journal of Consulting Psychology*, 1953, 17, 443–446; article 57 from F. Barron, Some test correlates of response to therapy, *Journal of Consulting Psychology*, 1953, 17, 235–241; article 58 from P. Kaufmann, Changes in the MMPI as a function of psychiatric therapy, *Journal of Consulting Psychology*, 1950, 14, 458–464; article 59 from W. Schofield, Changes in responses to the MMPI following certain therapies, *Psychological Monographs*, 1950, 64, No. 5 (Whole No. 311) and A further study of the effects of therapies on MMPI responses, *Journal of Abnormal and Social Psychology*, 1953, 48, 67–77; article 60 from J. S. Pearson, Prediction of the response of schizo-phrenic patients to electroconvulsive therapy, *Journal of Clinical Psychology*, 1950, 6, 285–287, and J. S. Pearson and W. M. Swenson, A note on extended findings with the MMPI in predicting response to electroconvulsive therapy, *Journal of Clinical Psychology*, 1951, 7, 288; and article 61 from M. J. Feldman, The use of the MMPI profile for prognosis and evaluation of shock therapy, *Journal of Consulting Psychology*, 1952, 16, 376–382. We are indebted to the authors and to the publishers of the journals for permission to reproduce these articles in this form.

J. J. GALLAGHER

ARTICLE 56 *MMPI Changes Concomitant with Client-Centered Therapy*

THE problem of how to evaluate psychotherapy seems often to be complicated by the larger problem as to what the goals in therapy are, or should be. Nowhere is this problem more evident than in the recent article by Eysenck [r55] who reviewed the literature on evaluation of psychotherapy and came to the tentative conclusion that the available evidence fails to support the notion that psychotherapy facilitates recovery from neurotic disorders. To reach this interesting conclusion, Eysenck had to accept as equal or nearly equal the judgments of a great number of psychiatrists and physicians as to what constitutes *cure* or *improvement.* He is probably right in stating that his conclusions will be looked on with a skeptical eye, although he assumes that it will be the result of an emotional block on the part of the skeptics rather than any methodological weakness leading to his own conclusions. It should be clear by now that "success in psychotherapy" is a value judgment concept, a fact which makes it difficult to find a definition acceptable to everyone. The real problem to the science of psychology is that the many discussions and vituperative arguments as to what therapy should be have not advanced us too much further in our search of what therapy is.

Since the MMPI has been a popular diagnostic instrument, research has been mainly confined to differential diagnostic studies [277, 341, 400, 436 (see V, 31), 456, 509], although some investigations have been completed on MMPI changes as a result of various shock therapies [114, 276, 291, 470].

It has, as yet, seen limited use as a tool for evaluation of psychotherapy. Rashkis and Shaskan [487] used the MMPI to evaluate group psychotherapy of a permissive nature. Using a T score of over 70 as a measure of deviation from the normal on 22 psychiatric battle casualties and 15 anxiety state patients, they found the greatest changes in the direction of improvement in the D, Hy, Hs, and Pt scales. The Pd scale remained unchanged and the Ma scale showed a tendency to increase.

Schofield [535 (see IX, 59)], reasoning that a measure of personality deviation should also measure changes in therapy, compared four groups of women undergoing different types of therapy with pre-therapy and post-therapy MMPI scores. He also attempted to develop a scale of items from the MMPI which would predict amenability to therapy.

There were two groups of neurotic women, one treated on an outpatient basis and the other hospitalized, and two groups of psychotic women, one group having electroshock treatment and the other having no shock treatment. These groups were different from the population used in the present study in that they had limited education and average intelligence, were older, and were all women.

The outpatient neurotic group that was being treated by junior medical students showed no significant changes on post-therapy MMPI's. The hospitalized psychoneurotics showed significant differences on the Hs, Hy, and Pd scales and a general lowering effect on the whole profile. The hospitalized psychotics who had no shock treatment showed no significant changes on the post-therapy tests, while the psychotics who underwent shock treatment showed changes on the F, Hs, D, Hy, Pd, Pt, and Sc scales. A group of nonhospitalized normal women showed no significant changes on tests which were given with the same general time lapse as those of the therapy groups.

Schofield's attempt to establish a predictive scale for therapy was not successful, as there was too much overlap on the scale between the much improved and the slightly improved group. He attributed his lack of success to a "lack of a reliable clinical criterion of patients' responses to therapy."

Wiener and Phillips [646] studied the changes of the MMPI on a patient undergoing modified psychoanalysis (one hour a week). During a period of eight months there was noticed a strong drop in the D, Pt, and Sc scales and a moderate drop in the Hy and Pa scores. It was also noted that the K score went up and that these changes remained when the patient was re-examined a year after therapy was discontinued.

Mosak [680] reported the results of 28 clients who had undergone client-centered psychotherapy for an average number of fifteen interviews. He reported that the post-therapy MMPI results indicated significant decreases on the D, Sc, Hs, Hy, and Pa scales. The individual profiles showed the same pattern as was observable on the pre-therapy tests with a general drop in scores on all the scales. The Bell Adjustment Inventory, also given to the same clients, showed significant improvement in the feelings toward the self and toward others.

Profile Analysis of Therapeutic Outcome

The writer would suggest that there is another and more profitable way of approaching this problem, namely, to demonstrate empirically what changes do take place as a result of a particular type of therapy. Thus, objective evidence will be available, regardless of whether or not it is acceptable to various critics, as to what a therapy does do as distinguished from what its followers feel it should do.

Problem. The present problem is to determine whether there were any changes in the results of the MMPI after a group of college students had undergone client-centered therapy. All the cases, predominantly college students who came to the Psychological Clinic for aid in their personal adjustment, were minutely examined by the members of a group research project in psychotherapy. Interviews were recorded and transcribed, pre-tests and post-tests were administered, therapists' ratings and various judges' ratings were obtained, etc. The present study deals with the MMPI results and their relationship with other measures of progress in treatment.

Hypotheses. The following hypotheses were tested in the present study:

1. Changes that take place as a result of any type of psychotherapy should be reflected in subsequent changes in the results of personality tests. As there is a change in the direction of health in the individual, there should be a corresponding depression in the scores that represent maladjustment.

2. It was expected that the greater the move to health in the individual, the greater the expected change in the personality tests toward health. Thus, a positive correlation between change in maladjustment scores on the MMPI and the criterion measures of success in psychotherapy was expected.

Subjects. The 41 subjects involved in this study were all students of the Pennsylvania State College who came to the Psychological Clinic between September 1949 and August 1950, either by request of various agencies or upon their own volition, to obtain aid in their personal adjustment. All these subjects were counseled by advanced graduate students in clinical psychology who had been trained in client-centered therapy. No attempt was made to diagnose these cases prior to therapy except that persons judged as prepsychotic or psychotic on the basis of initial contacts were transferred to the staff psychiatrist. The median number of therapy interviews was between five and six, although some cases were seen for a much longer period of time.

Figures obtained from the registrar of the college for the year 1949–1950 showed that the group who came for therapy was representative of the total college population for the semester enrolled, in age (mean = 21.75) and sex (75 per cent males). There was a higher proportion of liberal arts students in the therapy group than in the general college population. No evidence was available to suggest why this was so.

Raw MMPI scores of 202 randomly selected college students were used as a typical college normative group with which to compare the therapy population. The mean raw score for each of the MMPI scales was obtained and then converted into a T score so that some comparison would be possible. It would have been desirable to have a control group of maladjusted students who did not undergo psychotherapy. However, practical considerations militated against such a procedure at this time.

Procedure. A battery of tests consisting of the Rorschach, the MMPI, and the Mooney Problem Check List was given to each of the subjects before the beginning of the therapy interviews or, at the latest, before the second therapy interview. The post-therapy tests were given after an agreement was reached by the therapist and client that the therapy contacts should end.

In order to correlate the change on the MMPI with other measures of success, a maladjustment scale was developed to give one score which would represent the amount of deviance from the normal in each case. To obtain this score the deviant scores on all the items of the Hs, D, Hy, Pd, Pa, Pt, and Sc scales were summed. The Mf and Ma scales were not included because norms on college students revealed these scales to be unduly elevated. The procedure of summing the individual items was used in preference to summing the T scores, since some items appear on more than one scale and would be unduly weighted by such a procedure.

The Therapy Criterion Measures. A multiple criterion for evaluating client-centered psychotherapy with college students was developed by Tucker [r163], using the cases in the present group. This multiple criterion consisted of four measures:

1. A 29-item Therapy Rating Scale scored by the therapist following the end of contacts with the client.

2. The same Therapy Rating Scale scored by judges who read at least 60 per cent of the transcribed interviews including the first and last interviews.

3. A 14-item Client Rating Scale which the client filled out at the time he took the post-therapy test battery.

4. The ratio of negative to positive feelings in the final interview as compared with the ratio of negative to positive feelings in the first interview.

These four criterion measures were combined into a total criterion score by weighting each measure according to the ratio of its summed intercorrelation with the other three measures. All the rating scales were constructed especially for this study by members of the group research project. For further information concerning the reliability of judges' ratings, the construction of rating scales, etc., the reader is referred to Tucker's original work [r163].

Table 1. T-Score Means, Standard Deviations, and Codes of Two Testings of the Therapy Group Compared with a Random College Sample

Group	F	K	Hs	D	Hy	Pd	Pa	Pt	Sc	Ma	Si	Mal [a]
Pre-therapy (N = 41)												
Mean ..	57.9	53.1	55.2	67.1	60.7	62.5	56.7	67.5	64.4	57.2	59.9	86.6
SD	7.7	6.5	12.9	12.5	10.9	13.5	8.3	8.5	12.7	8.0	11.3	17.5
				MMPI Code: 72843–0 961								
Post-therapy (N = 41)												
Mean ..	55.5°	55.3°	51.7°	60.9°°	59.5	61.2	55.2	63.5°°	62.2	59.0	55.0°°	79.4°°
SD	6.9	8.9	9.3	12.5	8.6	10.0	9.3	11.8	11.7	7.7	10.0	18.0
				MMPI Code: 7842–39 601								
College sample (N = 202)												
Mean ..	57	53	47	50	56	53	53	47	49	57	...	...
SD	9	8	4	6	6	9	8	14	11	11	...	...
				MMPI Code: 93 46 2/8 17								

[a] Mean raw scores.
° The difference between pre-therapy and post-therapy is significant at the .05 level of confidence.
°° The difference between pre-therapy and post-therapy is significant at the .01 level of confidence.

Results. The results were as follows:

1. Table 1 shows significant differences between pre-therapy and post-therapy mean T scores on the F, K, Hs, D, Pt, and Si scales. There was also a significant difference between groups on the maladjustment scale constructed especially for this study. These mean changes include, of course, a great variety of individual changes. Some cases showed a 30 to 40 T-score improvement on certain scales while others, surprisingly enough, showed an upward surge in their profiles. It was the opinion of most therapists handling such cases that such an upward surge was

indicative of a breakdown of defenses and the individual's greater awareness of his problems, rather than an indication of a sudden turn to greater maladjustment.

2. All the scales, with the exception of K and Ma, showed a tendency to be lower on the post-therapy test. This finding agrees with Mosak, who reported a general lowering of all scales as a result of therapy.

3. Despite a considerably lower mean score on post-therapy results, the mean T scores of the therapy group were still considerably higher than those of the random sample group of college students. This would seem to suggest that a sizable amount of improvement might still be profitably made with the therapy group It must be remembered that the post-therapy tests were given immediately after therapy had been completed. There seems to be some evidence [r38], to suggest that further change and improvement in the client takes place for a period after therapy has been completed.

4. The scales generally regarded as the character or behavior disorder scales, Hy, Pd, and Ma, showed the least tendency to change as a concomitant of client-centered therapy. Conversely the feeling or discomfort scales, D, Pt, and Hs, showed the greatest tendency toward change. It should be noted that the character and behavior disorders have been traditionally the group considered least susceptible to any kind of psychotherapy and this may be more evidence supporting that clinical finding, rather than a specific failing of client-centered therapy.

Table 2. Correlation of MMPI Maladjustment
Change Score with Client-Centered
Therapy Criteria [a]

Criterion Measure	Maladjustment Change Score
Therapist Rating Scale	.15
Judge Rating Scale	.33
Client Rating Scale	.58°°
P-N Feeling Ratio	.44°
Multiple criterion	.41°

[a] N = 30.
° Significant at the .05 level.
°° Significant at the .01 level.

5. Table 2 shows the correlation of MMPI maladjustment change scores with the various criterion measures developed by Tucker. Although there is a positive correlation with all four criterion measures, only the Client Rating Scale and the Positive-Negative Feeling Ratio showed significant correlations with the maladjustment change scores. This would seem to represent another example of the phenomenon mentioned previously by Tucker [r163] and Gallagher [213], that the client's evaluation of his progress and the psychologist's judgment of the client's progress are fairly independent of each other. Since the MMPI is, by and large, a measure of self-evaluation, we would expect fairly high correlations between MMPI changes and Client Rating Scales and Positive-Negative Feeling Ratios. Similarly, we might expect low correlations between the therapists' and judges' ratings and the MMPI change scores, and this is what happened.

Discussion. The results of the present study seemed to indicate that there were some changes, as measured by the MMPI, taking place in a group of college students concomitant with client-centered therapy. It should be noted also that considerable changes took place despite two unfavorable factors present in this study: first, the use of relatively inexperienced therapists, and, second, a shorter number of interviews than is generally accepted as necessary to accomplish real change in a client.

Also of interest was the fact that some scales were more susceptible to change than others. Generally it was the mood or feeling scales which showed the greatest change in the direction of health, while the behavior or character disorder scales showed the least amount of change toward health. While this is generally true of all types of psychotherapy, consistent results along this line would suggest that those patients who show initially high scores in the behavior disorder scales might profitably be handled in some other fashion than by being submitted to psychotherapy, in this case, client-centered psychotherapy.

Another finding of interest was that there seem to be two different and relatively independent frames of reference toward success in psychotherapy: the client's frame of reference in which he estimates change that has occurred within himself, and the therapists' frame of reference in which they estimate the amount of change that has taken place within the individual. While we, as psychologists, would like to believe that our expert opinions are more accurate and more realistic in the evaluation of actual change, it does not necessarily follow that this is so. Some further study in which the opinions of both client and therapist are checked against some observable behavioral change in the client would do much to clear up this problem.

The existence of such different frames of reference would pose a particular problem for client-centered therapy, for if the client is to have the final and irrevocable decision as to when he will leave therapy, he may often leave a rather frustrated therapist behind, who feels that the client has escaped therapy with only some anxiety reduction rather than a permanent solution or adaptation to his problem. Certainly some effort needs to be made to bring these frames of reference into closer conjunction with each other.

Analysis of Anxiety Measures

It is rather difficult to get even tentative agreement among various schools of thought on the goals of therapy; however, practically all disciplines mention the diminution of anxiety stress as an important subgoal. Certainly the removal of anxiety without a subsequent change in the ability of the individual to adapt is of limited value. It is equally true that without anxiety-stress reduction there is little real chance that a patient will be able to adapt himself more efficiently. It was felt by the writer that a constructive approach toward the merging of objectives of various schools of therapy would be obtained by measuring the effectiveness of each school in attaining the measurable subgoals that they claim to achieve by their methods.

The hypotheses were these:

1. College students undergoing client-centered therapy will show significant decrease in anxiety stress following such therapy.

2. There should be a relationship between reduction in anxiety and therapy success. Therefore, a relatively high correlation would be expected between reduction in anxiety-stress scores and success in therapy.

The measures used in the present study were as follows:

1. The Taylor Anxiety Scale. This scale was not used in its entirety since many of the present subjects finished only 366 of the total MMPI items. This necessitated using only 34 out of the total of 50 items.

2. The Winne Neuroticism Scale. This scale was included because of its high imputed relationship with the Taylor scale, and to find out if "neuroticism" in this case was synonymous with anxiety stress.

3. The Welsh Anxiety Index. This scale was in reality a combination of the standard scales already in use on the MMPI. This score was obtained by the formula:

$$AI = \frac{Hs + D + Hy}{3} + (D + Pt) - (Hs + Hy)$$

Since this scale requires no scoring other than the original scales of the MMPI, it could obviate the use of the Taylor and Winne scales if its predictive ability were the same or better than those scales.

4. The Welsh Internalization Ratio. This was obtained by the following formula:

$$IR = \frac{Hs + D + Pt}{Hy + Pd + Ma}$$

This measure was included to see whether the Internalization Ratio would change in the expected direction, toward externalization. As can be seen by the formula, the higher the score the greater the internalization.

The standard t test of significance was used to determine the significance of the differences between the pre-therapy and post-therapy measures. The differences on each of the preceding scales were correlated by the Pearson product-moment r method with a multiple criterion for success in psychotherapy to see which of the measures predicted best to that criterion. Correlations were also calculated between the individual measures which went to make up the multiple criterion and pre-therapy to post-therapy differences on the anxiety-stress scales.

Results. These were the results of the study:

1. Table 3 shows that all the scales used in the present study reveal a difference in the predicted direction between pre-therapy and post-therapy scores that is significant at the .01 level of confidence. Of particular interest is the change in the Welsh Internalization Ratio in which the group shows a definite trend toward externalization following client-centered therapy.

2. Table 4 reveals the correlations between anxiety-stress change scores and the therapy-success criterion measures. As might be expected, the various anxiety-stress measures show a moderate to high agreement among themselves. It is clear that they are measuring somewhat the same quality, but they could hardly be used interchangeably on the basis of the present findings. Of particular interest is the high correlation between the Taylor scale and the Winne scale, confirming previous

findings. One might think that this could be accounted for on the basis of considerable item overlap in the two scales. However, a check revealed that only 6 of the 34 items on the Taylor scale also appear on the Winne scale.

3. The correlations between anxiety-stress changes and the therapy-success measures show considerable variation. The Taylor scale seems to agree with these measures most adequately, although the Winne scale shows a significant agreement with every measure but the Client Rating Scale.

Table 3. Differences between Pre-Therapy and Post-Therapy Anxiety-Stress Scores

Measure	N	Mean	SD	Measure	N	Mean	SD
Taylor Anxiety				Welsh Anxiety Index			
Pre-therapy	42	17.28	6.18	Pre-therapy	42	80.60	24.78
Post-therapy	42	13.76°	6.13	Post-therapy	42	70.40°	24.60
Winne Neuroticism				Welsh Internalization			
Pre-therapy	41	9.85	4.28	Ratio			
Post-therapy	41	7.97°	3.82	Pre-therapy	42	105.76	15.86
				Post-therapy	42	98.41°	15.53

° The difference between pre-therapy and post-therapy scores was significant at the .01 level of confidence.

Table 4. Intercorrelations of Anxiety-Stress Changes and Criteria for Therapy Success [a]

Measure	Winne Neuroticism	Welsh Anxiety Index	Welsh Internalization Ratio	Multiple Criterion	Therapist Rating	Judge Rating	Client Rating	P-N Ratio
Taylor Anxiety	.62	.49	.38	.54	.35	.47	.48	.49
Winne Neuroticism		.30	.58	.54	.51	.45	.21	.42
Welsh Anxiety Index			.71	.28	.08	.28	.42	.21
Welsh Internalization Ratio				.40	.13	.33	.16	.37

[a] For .05 level of confidence, r = .355; for .01 level of confidence, r = .456.

4. The Welsh Anxiety Index and Internalization Ratio did not fare so well, showing relatively low agreement with many of the criteria measures. One is forced to conclude from this that the scales designed specifically to measure neuroticism and anxiety stress are better predictors of therapy success than are combinations of previously used MMPI scales.

Discussion. The results of the present study seem to show rather clearly that there is a decrease in anxiety stress concomitant with client-centered therapy. As was stated previously, this result will have more meaning when placed beside other studies which show behavioral changes and perceptual differences as a result of therapy. Also important would be the same type of comparison done by members of an opposing theoretical and therapeutic orientation.

One may reasonably ask if the high correlations obtained between anxiety scales and therapy criterion measures were not due largely to the therapy measures depending upon observation of this very stress reduction. On the Client Rating Scale and the P-N ratio this might be of relatively great consequence; however, on the therapists' and judges' rating scales the emphasis in judgments was placed on development of insight, planning behavior, understanding of self, etc. Thus we can say with some confidence that these correlations are a result of concomitant rather than similar behavior.

Summary

Forty-one college students who underwent client-centered therapy from advanced graduate students in clinical psychology were given a pre-therapy and post-therapy battery of tests, one of which was the MMPI. The purpose of the present study was to determine if there were any changes in the MMPI concomitant with the application of therapy and to see how well the changes on the MMPI compared with a multiple criterion of success in therapy.

The results showed significant differences in the direction of health on six of the MMPI scales with the greatest differences being shown on the feeling or mood scales, while the least differences were shown on the character and behavior disorder scales. The MMPI maladjustment change scores showed significant correlations with measures of self-rating of success in therapy and of change in ratio of positive and negative feelings from the beginning to the end of therapy.

An attempt was made to see if there were anxiety-stress changes, as measured by various MMPI anxiety scales, from pre-therapy to post-therapy. Comparisons were also made between the change in stress measures from the pre-therapy test to the post-therapy test and the various therapy-success criterion measures.

It was found that, although all four measures showed a significant decrease in stress from pre-therapy to post-therapy, two of the measures, the Taylor Anxiety Scale and the Winne Neuroticism Scale, showed the highest amount of agreement with the therapy-success measures.

ARTICLE 57 *Some Tests Correlates of Response to Psychotherapy*

THIS paper reports certain personality and intelligence test correlates of changes in psychological morbidity in thirty-three adult psychoneurotics following six months of psychotherapy in the outpatient service of a state psychiatric clinic. These findings are part of the results of a study of somewhat broader scope, in which psychotherapy was considered as a special case of personal interaction in general, and in which therapeutic relationships and outcomes were rationalized in terms of the personality structures of therapists as well as of patients [42].

The present paper, in addition to being restricted to a report on the test results of patients only, will adopt by choice a somewhat narrow conception of response to psychotherapy. The criterion variable can be best characterized as an answer to the question "Did the patient improve or not?" where the word "improve" means some fairly general changes in state from bad to good. Examples of such changes are these: (1) the patient feels better, is more comfortable, takes more interest in life, and the like; (2) important interpersonal relations are straightened out a bit; (3) physical symptoms have been relieved or cured; (4) important health-tending decisions have been made; (5) there has been an increase in insightful remarks and behavior.

The judgment as to whether or not improvement had occurred was made by two expert observers (heads of departments at the Langley Porter Clinic) who had not had any part in the conduct of therapy. Each therapist made a formal presentation before these two judges of every case he had handled; prior to the presentation the judges had read all the material concerning the patient which had been recorded in the clinical chart.

In the instruction to the judges it was emphasized that the crucial variable was *not* general level of functioning of the patient at the conclusion of the therapy, but rather the *change in state* which had occurred between beginning and end of therapy. Further, it was made clear to the judges that part of their function was to evaluate the therapist's involvement in his own account of the therapeutic process, and to weigh that factor in coming to a best estimate as to the degree of change which had actually occurred.

On the basis, then, of two main sources of information (formal presentation of

516

the case by the therapist, and an evaluation from the clinical chart), the expert raters assigned cases, first of all, into two main categories, those who had shown definite improvement and those who had failed to improve or who had improved only slightly. They were in close agreement on this crude categorization, differing on only 2 of the 33 cases which were studied and rated. In addition, they assigned ratings on a 100-point scale to each case, so that the total sample was ranked in terms of the variable "improvement." The correlation between the two independent sets of ratings was .91. The two disagreements were resolved by averaging the scale ratings. The final classification included 17 patients in the improved group, 16 in the unimproved.

Some Illustrations of Criterion Behavior

It is of some interest to examine the kinds of incidents and outcomes which the judges considered indicative of improvement or lack of it. Here is a partial list of such incidents and outcomes, abstracted from the clinical charts of these patients.

Illustrations of improvement were these:

1. A woman patient who had been frigid through four years of marriage which terminated in divorce now established an intimate relationship with another man in which for the first time she experienced orgasm in sexual intercourse.

2. A man who entered therapy in a very depressed, anxious, and physically upset state, and whose troubles centered on his relations with his foreman on a construction job (a relationship in which he was outwardly submissive and cooperative but inwardly enraged), finally learned to "stand up to" the foreman and express his feelings. There was a clear advance in his feelings of independence and self-esteem, and toward the conclusion of the therapy the patient left his former job and started a business of his own.

3. A woman with menstrual difficulties related to unconscious hostility toward her husband because of his disregard of her own wishes in sexual intercourse became conscious both of her anger and her retaliative tactics, with consequent disappearance of the menstrual difficulties and a more candid and unmartyred relationship with her husband.

4. A woman who had been recently divorced after an extremely traumatizing marriage and who entered therapy in a state of tremendous agitation and anxiety, so incapacitating that she could not sit in the lobby of the clinic or cross a street or look anyone in the face, gradually lost her phobias, experienced a great reduction in anxiety, and became able to associate comfortably with other people.

5. A man suffering from severe gastric disturbances which he considered unrelated to any emotional problems entered therapy upon the strongly worded advice of the internist. His dissociation of affect from the death of his mother and subsequent disturbing childhood years in an orphanage was gradually broken down and he re-experienced his own sense of forsakenness and finally came to terms with it, crucially aided by the support and understanding of the woman therapist.

Lack of improvement was considered shown in these incidents:

1. A very dogmatic and dominating man who entered therapy at the insistence of his wife (who complained of his overbearingness with her and their three children) proved too overbearing for the young woman therapist as well. The therapist was unable to handle the negative countertransference which developed, and the therapeutic interaction became simply a battle, with consequent lack of improvement in the patient.

2. A woman of forty, who had never been married and who suffered from continual headaches and disturbing sexual impulses which she attempted to suppress, found herself obliged to terminate therapy for some good reason precisely after the hour at which the therapist had told her he would give her a physical examination on the occasion of their next appointment.

3. A man with a history of homosexuality attempted to seduce his male therapist, who responded with anger as well as some anxiety. The patient did not return.

4. A psychopathic young man who had a long history of rebelliousness, brushes with the law, and employment instability entered therapy because, he said, he happened to be passing by the clinic and wondered what it would be like to be a patient. He liked it for a while, especially as he happened to be assigned to an attractive woman therapist, but after a few months he hitchhiked off in a southerly direction, leaving a chatty farewell note for the doctor in which he addressed her by her first name.

5. An engineer of extremely masculine appearance and manners complained of a "psychic malfunction" and wanted "a few treatments to get at the nuclear material and get the thing cleared up." His therapist insisted on taking a nondianetic, unhurried approach to the matter, which annoyed the patient, who nevertheless remained in therapy in the expectation that something would eventually happen.

One might summarize the kinds of outcomes in the improved group as follows: (1) The patient generally reported a feeling of well-being at the conclusion of therapy, in contrast to depression and anxiety at its start; (2) specific symptoms, such as headaches, frigidity or impotence, gastric disturbances, menstrual difficulties, and skin disorders, tended to be relieved or totally cleared up; (3) in some cases there were significant changes in the direction of more mature interpersonal relations, especially with parents, parent-substitutes, or spouses.

The failures in psychotherapy could often be traced to the inability of the therapist to handle some particularly difficult problem. Perhaps with more experienced psychotherapists some of the patients who did not improve would have made progress; however, there seemed little doubt that the cases which were marked down as therapeutic failures were basically the more difficult problems. As we shall see later from the test results, it was generally the more disturbed individuals who did not improve.

Test Correlates of Improvement

The test battery given these patients before psychotherapy began consisted of a shortened form of the Wechsler-Bellevue Intelligence Scale, the MMPI, the Rorschach Psycho-Diagnostic and the Ethnocentrism Scale (in Form 60 of the University of California Public Opinion Study scales). The patients themselves were all receiving psychotherapy for the first time, and they began the course of treatment just at the time that their therapists were starting a six-month period of service in the outpatient clinic. The therapists were psychiatric residents who had had little experience in intensive psychotherapy.

Most of the patients had one hour of treatment a week for six months. Of the 33 patients, 12 were men and 21 were women. They ranged in age from 20 to 45. All but 3 of them were high school graduates, but only 2 were college graduates. As a group they could probably be characterized as lower middle class socioeconomically. Two thirds of them were gainfully employed.

All the testing was done by the experimenter. Conventional controls were exercised to prevent contamination in the prediction of outcome from the tests. The controls were as follows: (1) Only the experimenter knew the test results. The psychotherapists were informed of this condition before the experiment began, and were told that they would be given information concerning the testing only if in their judgment it was essential to the diagnostic formulation and the handling of the case. In three cases such information was requested by the therapist during the course of the therapy. The information given was not comprehensive, but was in response to some specific point. These cases were retained in the sample in spite of their being exceptions to the general rule, for their exclusion would be as likely a source of contamination as their retention. (2) The judges of outcome had no knowledge of the test results. (3) The test protocols were identified by a code number rather than by name, so that clinicians who attempted to predict outcome had no knowledge of the patient beyond that afforded by the test results themselves.

The design of the present study, so far as prediction of outcome is concerned, is a replication of some earlier work by Harris and Christiansen [292], who used in an almost identical clinical setting a similar criterion of outcome of therapy and the same clinical tests, except that they did not employ the ethnocentrism scale. It is therefore in some respects a cross-validation of their findings, or at least it offers further evidence on some of the questions they discussed. Their results will therefore be compared with the present findings whenever such comparisons seem relevant.

The Wechsler-Bellevue Intelligence Test. An abbreviated form of the Wechsler scale, consisting of the Comprehension, Similarities, Block Design, and Digit Symbol subtests, was used. Harris and Christiansen, using the same subtests, had found no significant relationship between improvement and intelligence. In this sample, however, the two variables were associated positively, the Pearsonian r being .46, which is significant at the .01 level. The mean of the improved group was 122; that of the unimproved group was 112.

The mean IQ of the total sample was 117, as compared with a mean of 108 in the Harris-Christiansen study. An important difference between the two samples so far as method of selection is concerned should be noted: The Harris-Christiansen sample consisted of already hospitalized persons who were given psychotherapy because of delayed recovery from physical disease, surgery, or accident, whereas almost all the patients in the present study had elected on their own initiative to seek psychotherapy at the clinic, and in their waking hours went about the business of life in an upright position. This difference might well account for the IQ difference between the samples, as well as for the fact that these self-referred patients were a good standard deviation above the general population mean in intelligence. Simply being aware of the fact that psychotherapy is to be had and that it makes sense to seek it when you are in personal difficulties is probably related positively to general intelligence and cultural sophistication.

It is also to be expected on theoretical grounds that greater effectiveness of cortical functioning (which presumably reveals itself on the Wechsler-Bellevue) should be associated with a factor of modifiability in personality structure. Intelligence certainly involves the ability to cognize relationships adequately, including emotional relationships, and to correct one's cognitions on the basis of new evidence. It would seem that in this sample, at any rate, the more intelligent patients were better able to use the psychotherapeutic relationship to induce desired personality changes.

The MMPI. The MMPI analysis may be divided into three main sections: (1) group differences between the improved and unimproved cases on the MMPI scales; (2) prediction of outcome from MMPI profiles by clinical psychologists skilled in the use of the test, as well as by certain rational indices or rules for mechanical sorting of the profiles; (3) development and cross-validation of a prediction scale. Enterprises 1 and 2 will be reported in this paper; the development and cross-validation of a prediction scale will be reported separately, however, since it involved work with a number of other samples and raised some test-specific questions which are not properly within the scope of this paper [44 (see IV, 26)].

Table 1. T-Score Means and Codes of Two Criterion Groups

Group	L	F	K	Hs	D	Hy	Pd	Mf_M	Mf_F	Pa	Pt	Sc	Ma
Improved (N = 17)	52	60	54	59	65	63	72	62	48	57	62	66	56
MMPI Code: 4'82 37–169 F-KL													
Unimproved (N = 16)	52	64	49	62	71	68	69	67	47	66	71	74	61
MMPI Code: 827'43619 F–L/K													

Group comparisons on the usual diagnostic and validity scales are shown in Table 1. Only on the paranoia scale was there a significant difference between the means of the improved and unimproved groups (t of 2.6, p < .02). The unimproved group profile is consistently higher on almost all scales, however, and the peak is at schizophrenia, with the average T scores for psychasthenia and depression also being greater than 70. The sorts of individuals who earn profiles like this are usually schizoid; in *An Atlas for the Clinical Use of the MMPI* [307], most of the 8724 profiles carry a diagnosis of reactive depression with underlying schizoid trends. This fits well with the observation by Harris and Christiansen that poor prognosis is generally associated with what they call "subclinical psychotic trends," referring to a more severe ego dysfunction than the first clinical impression seems to indicate. Depression and anxiety are salient features of the clinical picture in almost all patients who seek psychotherapy in the outpatient clinic; but the patients who fail to improve are those in whom paranoid and schizoid features underlie the psychoneurotic symptoms. A reasonable guess would be that their personal difficulties are more chronic and characterologically based, in contrast to the more acute and situation-linked problems of the patients who improve.

The 33 individual MMPI profiles were also given to clinical psychologists for prognostic evaluations. Eight clinicians independently attempted to predict outcome from the profiles, having no other information concerning the patient beyond age and sex. Each clinician sorted the 33 records into two groups, predicting either that the case would be improved or that it would be unimproved. Of 264 (8 × 33) such classifications, 164 (62.12 per cent) were correct. The sum of the eight values of chi square was 20.46, which for 8 df yields a p less than .01. The three best sorters had a pooled accuracy percentage of 69.7 per cent. All the sorters were more often correct than in error, but it should be pointed out that an average accuracy of

62 per cent when 50 per cent would be expected by chance is a fairly modest achievement in clinical prediction. Even the best of the MMPI analysts would be well advised to be tentative in their prognostic formulations.

Rational indices and rules for mechanical sorting produce substantially the same accuracy of prediction as do sortings by clinicians; actually, such indices are slightly more effective. Two fairly simple and obvious mechanical predictors were put to the test. The first of these employed the rule that for any profile with all scores within the normal range (i.e., greater than 30, less than 70) improvement should be predicted. Ten profiles met this requirement, and 9 of these cases had in fact improved. Twenty-four of 33 profiles (73 per cent) were thus classified correctly (chi square of 8.1, $p < .01$). Exceptions were then allowed in the general rule: e.g.. profiles with only D or with only D and Pt greater than 70 would be called improved. Both exceptions led to an accuracy of prediction between 75 and 80 per cent.

In addition to these sorting rules, a simple index of subclinical psychotic trends was defined by summing the scores of four scales (F, Pa, Sc, and Ma) usually found elevated in psychosis. This index correlated .40 with outcome as it had been rated on a 100-point scale.

It is of some interest that the same indices which predicted response to psychotherapy worked equally well in another setting, with a sample apparently quite different from the patient sample at this clinic. In a study of personal effectiveness in male graduate students in their final year of work for the doctorate, ratings were obtained from faculty members on certain dimensions such as originality and personal soundness. The averaged faculty ratings on personal soundness for 40 such students correlated −.4 with the index defined by the sum of F, Pa, Sc, and Ma, and had a contingency of .52 with a mechanical sorting of the MMPI profiles using the rule that all profiles having no clinical scale elevation (except D) of 70 or above should be called sound, while all others should be called unsound.

The "personally sound" graduate students were different from the "personally unsound" students in the same way that patients who profited considerably from psychotherapy differed from patients who profited little or not at all. As one would expect, however, there was a difference in absolute level of adjustment; the distribution of scores on the prognosis for psychotherapy scale [44 (see IV, 26)] showed a clear progression in group means from the unimproved patients through the improved patients and the unsound graduate students to the sound graduate students.

What these relationships indicate, it would seem, is that the patients who are most likely to get well are those who are not very sick in the first place. Another way of putting this is to say that patients who are more integrated to begin with are better able to use the psychotherapeutic relationship to solve whatever problems brought them into therapy. A corollary of this is that the potential gains from therapy should increase as therapy progresses, at least up to the point where the critical problem for the patient is to become genuinely independent of the therapist. By that time, of course, the therapeutic process has become internalized, and personality problems have been brought "into the ego," to be dealt with rationally and objectively.

The Rorschach Psychodiagnostic. The Rorschach analysis was carried out according to the same general design as the MMPI analysis, with the exception that no prognostic scale was developed. Average profiles were determined for the improved and unimproved groups, using the Klopfer-Kelly conventions for the scoring and nomenclature of determinants. Individual scores on the Harris-Christiansen Rorschach Prognostic Index [292] were computed, and the relationship of outcome to that index was calculated. Finally, the test protocols, including both content of responses and profiles of determinants, were given to clinicians for sorting.

All the Rorschachs were administered by the experimenter, with all the verbalizations and relevant behavior of the patient being recorded. The tests were scored independently by the experimenter and by one other clinical psychologist who had had several years of experience in both the scoring and the interpretation of the Rorschach. The experimenter himself had had approximately three years of clinical experience with the test, in addition to a graduate course in its scoring and interpretation. The two independent scorings showed a high degree of agreement; discrepancies were reconciled in a conference on review of the scoring. The improved and unimproved groups did not differ significantly on any Rorschach determinant, or on any of the important ratios, such as W, D, Dd, plus S, M: sum C, and so on. This finding is consistent with Rorschach results in the graduate student sample previously referred to; in that study no significant relationship was found between any Rorschach determinant or combination of determinants and the criterion variable, personal soundness.

The Harris-Christiansen Prognostic Index correlated .00 with improvement. As Cronbach [r39] has pointed out, most empirical Rorschach indices fail to hold up under cross-validation, so that this is not a surprising finding.

Somewhat contrary to the expectation of most persons who have worked with the test, however, is the finding that experienced Rorschach interpreters were not able to predict outcome of therapy on the basis of the Rorschach evaluation. Four clinicians, all of whom were highly trained and experienced, both in the use of the test and in general clinical practice, attempted the sorting task. They had at hand all the responses of the patients, as well as a summary of the scoring in terms of the usual ratios and profile of determinants. Only one of the four sortings approached significance, and that was in the negative direction; that is, the sorter was more often wrong than right in predicting outcome.

The Ethnocentrism Scale. Certain theoretical considerations had led to the inclusion of the ethnocentrism scale in the test battery. Levinson [388] had found, in a study at this same clinic, that ethnocentric patients showed a personality syndrome of a sort which would be resistant to change through psychotherapy. High-scoring patients were described by her as having the following characteristics: "rigid, constricted personalities . . . stereotyped, conventionalized thinking . . . undifferentiated egos . . . narrow range of experience, emotionally and intellectually . . . weak interpersonal relationships, expressed in terms of dominance-submission." The low-scoring patients, on the other hand, were marked by their "desire to be loved and fear of being rejected . . . expressed directly in interpersonal relations and in a very personalized way . . . the frequency with which low scorers discuss their relationships to others is striking."

These considerations suggested the hypothesis that patients who scored high on the ethnocentrism scale would be less likely to enter deeply into the sort of personal interaction which occurs in psychotherapy. From the very beginning of therapy they would find it necessary to narrate the comings and goings of their somatic complaints, and to minimize the importance of their psychological problems as the cause of their somatic disturbances. According to this notion, ethnocentric patients would tend characteristically to isolate affect and to avoid psychological self-examination; they would be strangers to their own inner life.

While the psychological formulation itself was not checked on in any detail in the present study, the hypothesis that it led to (i.e., that ethnocentrism would be negatively related to improvement) was confirmed. The correlation of the E scale with improvement ratings was —.64, making it the best single predictor employed in this study.

Several reservations, however, should be noted. In the first place, scores on the E scale are negatively related to intelligence, which can be presumed to be a somewhat more basic psychological variable than ethnocentrism. As Gough [246] has pointed out, many of the items in the E scale are written in such an extreme fashion that a person of some intelligence and education could not agree with them, even though the sentiment expressed might win his approval if the form of its statement were less clearly irrational. Since improvement is correlated positively with intelligence in this sample (.46), one would expect a negative relationship between improvement and ethnocentrism on the basis simply of their common relationship to intelligence.

When intelligence is partialed out, however, some relationship remains. The coefficient of partial correlation between ethnocentrism and improvement, with intelligence held constant, is —.34. Partialing intelligence out in this manner is not strictly correct, of course, except in a mechanical way; actually, some underlying emotional-cognitive variable such as rigidity, which is complexly related both to intelligence and to ethnocentrism, may be accounting for a large part of the correlation of both of those measures with the capacity for psychological change as shown by improvement in therapy.

There is one other reservation to be noted. Four of the psychotherapists in this study were Jewish, a fact which might have affected both the ethnocentric patient's attitude toward them and their attitude toward the ethnocentric patient. In several of the therapeutic interactions, such patient attitudes came out into the open, and were dealt with therapeutically; and in at least one case the therapist admitted candidly to the psychologist that his own response to the patient's anti-Semitism was disruptive of the relationship.

In spite of these reservations, however, the relationship between ethnocentrism and capacity for psychological change through psychotherapy is a striking one, and if confirmed would be of some theoretical importance. It may, indeed, have implications for social communities as well as individuals, and would suggest that the social organization which fosters prejudice might well be forfeiting the kind of emotional flexibility which is necessary if in time of crisis it is to cure its own ills.

Summary

Change in psychological morbidity as a consequence of six months of psychotherapy was studied in a sample of 33 adult psychoneurotics who were treated in the outpatient service of a state psychiatric clinic. Changes for the better might be summarized as follows: (1) The patient generally reported a feeling of well-being at the conclusion of therapy, in contrast to depression and anxiety at its start; (2) various psychosomatic symptoms tended to be relieved or cured; (3) significant interpersonal relations were established on a more mature basis.

Patients were rated on the degree of their improvement by two skilled judges who evaluated both the interview-by-interview account of the therapy in the clinical chart and the therapist's report in conference on the course and outcome of the therapy. Ratings of degree of change for the better were then correlated with various psychological tests.

The chief test correlates are these: (1) intelligence is positively associated with change; (2) level of integration at the beginning of therapy is positively associated with change (i.e., those who are better off to begin with are likely to improve the most); (3) ethnocentrism is negatively related to change.

P. KAUFMANN

ARTICLE 58 *Changes in the MMPI as a Function of*
Psychiatric Therapy

GENERALLY, one of the consequences of successful psychotherapy is a change
in the patient's pattern of adjustment. The scores on any personality inventory
which describes patterns of adjustment should therefore change as a function of
psychotherapy. This study attempts to determine such a relationship. The MMPI
was selected as a test which measures an individual's adjustment.

The MMPI has been used in a wide variety of situations. Personality differences
of various occupational groups have been studied [298, 400, 603]. Gough [234 (see
VI, 38)] and Meehl [436 (V, 31)] have investigated profile patterns for use in clinical diagnosis. The possibility of deliberate deception has been studied by Gough
[235] and Hunt [339].

A number of investigations similar to the present study have been carried out
by Carp [113], Pacella and co-workers [470], and Rashkis and Shaskan [487]. This
study differs from prior investigations in one or more of the following respects. A
different population was sampled. The treatment which the patients received was
conference therapy. A control group was used, and measures of statistical significance were applied.

Method

The Clinic. This study was conducted in conjunction with the neuropsychiatric
service of the Department of Student Health and Preventive Medicine of the University of Wisconsin. The neuropsychiatric service cares for the neurological and
psychiatric cases among the students of the university.

The MMPI along with various other psychometric tools is used whenever the
therapist feels that these instruments could help in a preliminary differential diagnosis, aid in determining the severity of the disorder, or offer suggestions for the
therapeutic approach. Final diagnoses are based primarily on material obtained in
the conferences with the patients rather then on psychometric results. In most cases
the psychometric tests are administered at the beginning of therapy; occasionally,
however, it is felt that one or more of these tests might have a disturbing effect on
the patient. In such cases the tests are administered whenever the therapist judges
the patient can profitably be subjected to them. All tests are taken voluntarily.

The following progress ratings, assigned by the therapist at the conclusion of therapy, are used: improved, temporarily improved, unimproved. Criteria by which clinical progress is estimated are set forth in another publication [r165].

The Instrument. The individual card form of the MMPI was administered to each subject. Standard instructions were used with the special exhortation to classify as few items as possible in the Cannot Say category. This deviation from standard procedure was necessary because it had been the practice at the clinic for some time.

Patient Subjects. All patients who were under treatment during the academic year 1947–48, who had taken the MMPI during the early part of their therapeutic sessions, and whose therapist saw no objection to a retest, were asked to repeat the MMPI. Since only a very small number of these patients received a progress rating other than improved, the improved cases alone were chosen as subjects for this study. A description of this group in terms of sex, age range and average, and range and average of the interval between tests is found in Table 1. Thirty-four of these patients were diagnosed as anxiety tension state, and the remaining 17 were distributed among the following diagnostic groups: adolescent reaction, 1; compulsive state, 5; phobia, 1; hysteria, 3; manic-depressive state, incipient, 1; dementia praecox, incipient, 1; dementia praecox, developed, 2; depression state, 2; psychopathic personality, 1.

Table 1. Description of Groups

	Patients			Controls		
	Male (N = 27)	Female (N = 24)	Total (N = 51)	Male (N = 33)	Female (N = 21)	Total (N = 54)
Age in years						
Range	19–32	18–27	18–32	19–33	18–30	18–33
Mean	23.4	21.8	22.6	23.2	22.5	22.9
Interval between tests in months						
Range	2–14	2–13	2–14	1–8	1–8	1–8
Mean	6.5	6.4	6.4	4.8	5.6	5.1

Control Subjects. These subjects were drawn from the student body of the University of Wisconsin, largely from Psychology 1 classes. They were matched with the patients as far as possible for number, age, sex, and interval between tests. Table 1 describes this group. None of these subjects was under psychiatric therapy at the time of his first test or underwent such treatment between the first and second test.

Results

Statistical Analysis. The statistical analysis used in this study consists of comparisons of the central tendencies of patients and controls on both pre-test and post-test and the changes between pre-test and post-test in patients and controls. The differences of change from pre-test to post-test in patients and controls were also computed and tested for significance. The t test of significance was used throughout the comparisons. The .01 level of confidence was accepted as indicative of statistical significance. In order to determine the homogeneity of the changes obtained, correlation coefficients between pre-tests and post-tests on each scale were computed for both the patient and control groups. All these measures are based on K-corrected T scores.

Significance of Comparisons. Means and standard deviations computed for the scores on each scale for the pre-tests and post-tests of the patient and control groups are presented in Tables 2 and 3 respectively. The difference measures given in the same tables were computed in the following manner. The difference between each pre-test and post-test score was calculated for each patient on each scale by subtracting the former from the latter. Means and standard deviations of these differences were then computed.

1. The results of the comparisons of the pre-tests and post-tests of the patient group are shown in Table 2. Those scales which in the comparison between pre-therapy patients and their controls showed the greatest amount of differentiation proved to be the most modifiable scales as a function of therapy.

2. Table 3 shows the pre-test vs. post-test comparisons for the control group. The difference on the Ma scale reaches the .05 level, and the difference on the K scale reaches the .01 level of confidence.

3. Table 4 shows the comparisons between patients and controls on their respective pre-tests. Except for the L scale, the Mf scale in the case of females, and the Ma scale, all differences reach the .05 level of confidence. Differences on the K, F, Hs, D, Hy, Pd, Mf for males, Pt, and Sc scales are significant at or beyond the .01 level of confidence. The D, Pt, Sc scales show the greatest differences, ranging from 15 to slightly more than 20 scale points. Except in the case of the K scale and the Mf scale for females all these differences are in the direction of higher T scores for the patients. The reverse tendency in the K scale and the Mf scale for females will be discussed later.

4. Table 4 also shows the comparison of patients and controls on their respective post-tests. There are six scales which in this comparison show significant differences at or beyond the .01 level of confidence. These differences are in the pathological direction for the patient group. In comparing these differences with the corresponding differences between the pre-tests of the two groups, however, it will be noted that the scales which show a significantly more pathological picture in the post-test do so to a lesser degree than in the pre-test; in other words, while the post-tests of the patients are still significantly different from corresponding tests of the control group, they differ less than the pre-tests.

5. Table 4 also presents the comparison of differences in change from pre-test to post-test between patient and control groups. These results agree fairly closely with those of the comparison of the pre-test vs. post-test scores in the patient group, except that for the K and Pa scales the differences in this comparison are not significant because the control group changed in the same direction as the patients.

Correlation of Pre-Tests and Post-Tests. Among the controls all correlation coefficients between pre-test and post-test scores are significantly different from zero at the .01 level of confidence. These coefficients generally tend to be somewhat lower than those reported by the authors of the scale. The coefficients for the patient group are lower than those for the control group but, excepting those for the Mf scale, are significantly different from zero at the .01 level of confidence; the coefficients for the Mf scale are significant at the .05 level of confidence. This is due at

Table 2. T-Score Means, Standard Deviations, and Codes of Pre-Tests and Post-Tests of Treatment Group

Test	?	L	F	K	Hs	D	Hy	Pd	Mf_M	Mf_F	Pa	Pt	Sc	Ma
Pre-test (N = 51)														
Mean	51.6	51.4	58.2	51.1	63.1	69.8	65.9	61.0	67.9	46.7	57.7	70.9	70.0	56.6
SD	3.9	2.8	7.2	8.3	15.4	13.4	12.2	12.3	8.9	8.2	9.9	14.5	15.0	10.6
						MMPI Code: 78'2314-69 F'PLK/								
Post-test (N = 51)														
Mean	51.3	51.2	54.9	56.6	57.5	60.3	63.3	60.5	64.0	48.7	54.5	62.6	61.7	55.3
SD	4.7	3.3	6.7	8.2	11.1	12.1	9.5	10.4	10.0	9.2	8.3	10.4	10.6	10.6
						MMPI Code: 378'42-196 KFPL/								
M_{diff}	-.3	-.2	-3.4	5.5	-5.8	-9.5	-2.7	-.7	-3.8	2.0	-3.2	-8.4	-8.3	-.9
SE_{diff}	5.4	3.0	7.3	8.5	12.1	14.1	10.1	10.8	10.1	9.5	8.3	14.2	14.2	11.4
t value[a]	.38	.48	3.29**	4.65**	3.41**	4.80**	1.87	.43	1.97	1.03	2.78**	4.21**	4.17**	.54

[a] All t values are based on 50 df except Mf_M (26 df) and Mf_F (23 df).
** Significant at or beyond the .01 level of confidence.

Table 3. T-Score Means, Standard Deviations, and Codes of Pre-Tests and Post-Tests of Control Group

Test	?	L	F	K	Hs	D	Hy	Pd	Mf_M	Mf_F	Pa	Pt	Sc	Ma
Pre-test (N = 54)														
Mean	50.3	51.1	53.3	56.2	51.1	49.4	56.0	53.7	60.5	51.2	53.4	54.7	55.0	55.8
SD	1.3	2.5	5.4	8.0	6.2	10.8	7.5	8.4	10.8	9.7	7.6	9.5	9.5	11.2
						MMPI Code: 3'987461/2 KFL?/								
Post-test (N = 54)														
Mean	50.2	51.2	52.8	59.4	50.0	48.2	54.6	53.2	60.6	52.9	52.0	55.3	55.3	52.6
SD	.8	2.7	5.4	9.1	7.1	9.7	7.9	8.6	13.0	9.4	8.6	10.4	9.3	10.6
						MMPI Code: 783'4961/2 KFL?/								
M_{diff}	-.1	.1	-.6	3.3	-1.2	-1.4	-1.4	-.4	.1	.5	-1.4	.6	.4	-3.0
SE_{diff}	1.1	2.6	5.3	6.6	6.5	8.7	5.8	8.1	9.3	6.3	7.5	7.9	8.0	9.1
t value[a]	.48	.31	.78	3.60**	1.30	1.21	1.79	.39	.07	.35	1.39	.54	.40	2.41*

[a] All t values are based on 53 df except Mf_M (32 df) and Mf_F (20 df).
* Significant at or beyond the .05 level of confidence.
** Significant at or beyond the .01 level of confidence.

Table 4. Significance of Differences between Means of Patient and Control Groups on Pre-Test, Post-Test, and Changes between Pre- and Post-Tests

	Pre-Test		Post-Test		Change between Pre-Test and Post-Test	
	Difference	t [a]	Difference	t [a]	Difference	t [a]
?	−1.3	2.28°	−1.1	1.68	− .2	.30
L	− .3	.57	0	0	− .3	.57
K	5.1	3.18°°	2.8	1.64	2.2	1.47
F	−4.9	3.94°°	−2.1	1.77	−2.8	2.24°
Hs	−12.0	5.25°°	−7.5	4.12°°	−4.7	2.46°
D	−20.4	8.52°°	−12.1	5.60°°	−8.0	3.49°°
Hy	−9.9	5.00°°	−8.7	5.08°°	−1.2	.74
Pd	−7.3	3.54°°	−7.3	3.89°°	− .2	.11
Mf_M	−7.4	2.81°°	−3.4	1.09	−3.9	1.54
Mf_F	4.5	1.65	4.2	1.48	1.5	.60
Pa	−4.3	2.47°	−2.5	1.51	−1.8	1.16
Pt	−16.2	6.73°°	−7.3	3.56°°	−8.9	3.96°°
Sc	−15.0	6.09°°	−6.4	3.27°°	−8.7	3.85°°
Ma	− .8	.37	−2.7	1.24	2.1	1.04

[a] All t values are based on 103 df except $Mf_M = 58$ df, and $Mf_F = 43$ df.
°Significant at or beyond the .05 level of confidence.
°° Significant at or beyond the .01 level of confidence.

least in part to the smaller number of cases, since the Mf scale coefficients were computed separately for males and females.

Discussion

The results summarized in the above section may be conveniently discussed in terms of the clinical usefulness of the individual scales.

The Cannot Say Scale. The difference between patient and control group pre-tests reaches only the .05 level of confidence. The difference between the two groups is less than two scale points, and there is considerable overlap. Thus, for a group of this kind, the differentiation of the scores on this scale is not large enough to be useful from a clinical point of view.

The Lie Scale. Since no statistically significant differences appeared on this scale in any of the comparisons, the scale did not prove useful for clinical differentiation in this study.

The K Scale. The patient group scored significantly lower than the control group on this scale in the pre-test. This significant difference between the two groups disappeared in the post-tests. This was not simply due to an increase in the scores of the patients, but rather to a greater increase in the scores of the patients than in those of the controls, for the controls also showed a significant change in the same direction as the patients.

Since a low K score indicates a self-critical attitude [424 (see II, 11)], it may be concluded that both groups showed a tendency to move away from self-criticism under the conditions of this investigation. It is not necessarily true, however, that the dynamic meaning of these changes is the same for both groups, although there is no statistical difference in amount of change between the two groups. In designating the meaning of a high K score, McKinley and his co-workers [424] refer to it as defensive. In terms of the design and the results of this study, such a designation is probably adequate for the control group, for it would imply that there were no systematic adjustment changes in this group which would bring about such a shift, but rather a changed attitude toward the test, a "test-wiseness," which would result in the differences obtained. A defensive attitude may be one of the factors producing the change in the patient group, but it seems reasonable to consider some other possible contributing influences.

A group of psychiatric patients may reasonably be expected as a function of emotional disturbances to be more critical in a self-blaming sense than a normal group. Since guilt feelings are often a powerful factor in emotional maladjustment, it is easy to see why such patients should present themselves in a more self-critical manner than normal individuals. Moreover, aggression directed against the self, which in the most severe instances may result in self-mutilation or self-destruction, may in a milder case express itself in increased self-criticism. Lastly, it is not inconceivable that patients who willingly submit to psychotherapy may want to impress the therapist with the seriousness of their difficulty. While this may not be a matter of crude deception, it may nevertheless be a factor in increasing the intensity of the patients' self-criticism. It is not clear how closely akin such an attitude is to deliberate malingering; in any case it might be of interest to point out that Hunt [339] found that subjects who deliberately tried to fake a pathological picture on this inventory obtained low K scores. The removal of one or more of these factors with the patient group may therefore be a contributing cause for the shift in this scale with the patients examined in this study.

Since the K factor shows a statistically significant difference between the patient and the control group on the pre-test, it seems reasonable to conclude that this scale may have clinically diagnostic value in its own right. Further work needs to be done for a more specific determination of its diagnostic significance and relationship to other psychiatric syndromes.

The F Scale. The fact that the F scale showed a significantly higher mean score for the patients than for the control group, and was furthermore significantly modified as a function of psychiatric therapy, suggests that this scale is a general indicator of psychiatric disorder. It is thus more than a validity scale, the function for which it was originally devised. This is in agreement with other investigations. Hathaway and McKinley [303] as well as Kazan and Sheinberg [357] have found that a high F score is suggestive of severe psychiatric disease.

The Hypochondriasis Scale. This scale appeared quite sensitive in differentiating patients from control subjects. The scores of the patients were sufficiently modified as a function of therapy that the difference between the mean scores of their pre-tests and post-tests is significant at the .01 level of confidence. However, this change was not as large as the corresponding change in various other scales. Thus, while the Hs scale proved to be of value in differentiation, it did not appear to be the most discriminating scale in this group of patients.

The Depression Scale. In general this proved to be the most discriminating scale, as well as the most sensitive scale to change. In spite of the fact that Hathaway and McKinley [301 (see II, 7)] point out that this scale measures a very unstable trait, often radically changed within 24 hours, the controls showed very little systematic change between the two tests. As is apparent from a study of many profiles, this scale generally tends to be among the highest for psychiatric patients. In Gough's [234 (see VI, 38)] diagnostic patterns, this scale has one of the highest mean scores in the profiles of all his diagnostic groups.

It is reasonable to expect that a scale which indicates "poor morale, lack of hope in the future, and dissatisfaction with the patient's own status generally" [301] should yield an abnormal score in psychiatric patients capable of handling the inventory. It is equally reasonable to expect that as a patient develops insight and learns to solve, meet, or accept his problems, or alters his attitude toward them [r165], his poor morale and hopelessness should subside.

The Hysteria and Psychopathic Deviate Scales. While these scales discriminated well between patients and controls on the pre-test, they proved to be among the least modifiable scales as a function of therapy. It may therefore be concluded that in a group like this the Hy and Pd scales have some general diagnostic value, but do not reflect clinical improvement. Since only a few patients in this group were diagnosed as hysterics, and one as psychopathic deviate, these data do not yield information as to the possibility of using this scale as a gauge for clinical improvement of patients with these disorders.

The Masculinity-Femininity Scale. Since males and females were treated separately on this scale, with consequent reduction in number of cases, there is a general tendency for differences not to reach statistical significance. On the pre-test the male patients scored sufficiently above the controls to reach significance. This difference was reduced after therapy, so that in the post-test the two groups were no longer significantly different.

Dynamically speaking, one might suggest that the male patients, generally having more feminine interests than the controls, are a less self-assertive group than the controls. One might further suggest that to a certain extent they are more easily subdued by adverse circumstances. While more feminine interests for the males might be reflected in less masculine behavior and thus contribute to sexual problems in the total maladjustment picture, an interpretation of the elevated scores in terms of homosexual trends seems unjustified.

None of the comparisons made on the female patients proved significant. They showed some tendency, which with a greater number of cases might have reached significance, to have lower scores than the controls. Since a low score on the Mf scale for a female indicates an interest pattern which tends in the feminine direction more than average, this slightly lower score might also point up a tendency toward lack of self-assertion.

The Paranoia Scale. This scale did not discriminate between the two groups, although the difference between patients and controls on the pre-test almost reached statistical significance. Various partial explanations may be given for this. First, none of the patients included in this group was diagnosed as a paranoid, so that it may be assumed that suspiciousness and paranoid trends were not the predominant symptom of any of these patients. Moreover, as the authors of the inventory point out, a number of paranoid individuals can disguise their suspiciousness very skillfully [303], a factor which would minimize the sensitivity of the scale for differential diagnosis.

Since there was only a small difference between the two groups on the pre-test, i.e., the patients' mean score was not very far above that of the controls, it is easy to understand why the patients' scores on this scale were not greatly modified as a function of therapy. Nevertheless, this change reached statistical significance.

The Psychasthenia Scale. Along with the D scale, this scale proved to be one of the most sensitive scales in all the comparisons made. A later article will discuss its differentiating power between mild and more severely disturbed psychiatric cases, the function of the scale which seems to be most outstanding. The data from the entire patient group suggest that this scale differentiates psychiatric patients from normals effectively. In a group of this kind it might be used as a gauge of clinical improvement.

The Schizophrenia Scale. Since this scale shows the highest correlation with the Pt scale [424 (see II, 11)], it is easy to see why the comparisons on this scale are essentially the same as those on the Pt scale. In a group similar to this, therefore, the scale may serve as a gauge of clinical improvement.

The Hypomania Scale. This scale did not prove discriminating between patients and controls, nor did it show any appreciable modification as a function of therapy. The low differentiating power of the scale may be considered as being partly due to the fact that no patient diagnosed as a fully developed manic was included in the study. Moreover, the authors of the inventory indicate that the validity of this scale is not conclusive [423 (see II, 9)].

Retest Correlations. The fact that the correlation coefficients on all scales are significantly different from zero adds evidence to that obtained from the significant shifts between the two tests that the differences obtained were generally systematic. For the controls it is not easy to account for the considerably lower coefficients than those reported by the authors of the test. One possible partial explanation might be that these authors had a large proportion of their subjects repeat the test after a relatively short period of time. Furthermore, if their group included many cases with extremely deviant scores, they might have received higher correlation coefficients due to the wider range of scores. Without definite data on these conditions, however, the above suggestions can only be offered as very tentative hypotheses. One other explanation suggests itself. Many of the post-tests in this control group were taken shortly before final examinations began. The increased tension may very well have influenced different subjects differently, thus producing relatively large though somewhat unsystematic changes between tests. For the patients it is reasonable to expect that retest correlations would be lower than those of the controls, because it would be expected that intervening therapy would affect the patients differentially.

Summary

An investigation was conducted for the purpose of studying changes in the MMPI as a function of psychiatric therapy. The sample of patients consisted of 51 students who received, primarily, conference therapy in the neuropsychiatric service of the Department of Student Health and Preventive Medicine of the University of Wisconsin. All these patients were rated improved by their therapists. The MMPI was administered at the beginning and at the end of therapy. A comparable control group not under psychiatric therapy was tested and retested at intervals similar to those of the patients.

The following results were obtained:

1. The patient group obtained higher mean scores on all scales except the K scale, and the Mf scale in the case of females.

2. The D, Pt, and Sc scales were found to be the most sensitive in differentiating the patient and control groups as well as the most modifiable ones as a function of therapy. The Hs scale, and the Mf scale in the case of males, showed the same tendencies as the above scales but to a considerably lower degree. The K score increased for both groups with repeated administration of the test; the increase for the controls, however, was smaller. The F scale differentiated between patients and controls and was modified as a function of therapy. The Hy and Pd scales tended to differentiate between groups but proved resistant to modification with therapy among these patients. The Pa and especially the Ma scale did not prove to be of appreciable value in any respect in this study.

3. The reduction in patients' scores as a function of therapy was in no case great enough to obtain a mean score equal to that of the control group on the respective scale, although in the case of a number of scales the differences on the post-test were not significant, whereas the corresponding pre-test differences had been.

4. No significant changes from pre-test to post-test mean scores occurred in the control group except on the K scale.

ARTICLE 59 Changes Following Certain Therapies as Reflected in the MMPI

THREE influences stimulated the present study: the intensive demand for more and better psychiatric services, the attempts to formulate new systems of psychotherapy, and the very recent but increasing efforts to establish objective criteria for the evaluation of therapeutic endeavors. Specifically, this study is concerned with an exploration of certain of the theoretical and practical problems involved in the measurement by means of a structured personality inventory of therapeutically induced changes in personality.

This paper presents an investigation of some of the problems arising in the application and interpretation of such evaluations, particularly as they furnish data on the effectiveness of given therapies.

The histories of the major psychiatric therapies have followed a certain pattern. In brief, there has been an initial enthusiastic announcement of the new technique accompanied with or followed shortly by figures on recovery which have represented not merely a sizable improvement over those for earlier therapies but which have approached the 100 per cent point so closely as to suggest a specific cure. Later reports on the technique from other clinics and sometimes from the clinic of origin have shown considerably lower frequencies of recovery. Thus, Sakel in first publishing on insulin shock therapy of schizophrenia claimed 87.9 per cent remissions. This figure has not been duplicated by any other workers.

There are undoubtedly many factors involved in the explanation of divergencies between comparable figures for recovery rates in two clinics as well as for the failure of originally very high rates of remission in a given clinic to be maintained in further studies. A considerable part of divergence in interclinic statistics is probably due to differences in the systems (or lack of system) by which the status of patients is evaluated both before and after a course of therapy. Most commonly such evaluations are characterized by subjectivity, with little concern that the evaluation of the patient before and after therapy be on the same schedule of variables. In extreme form, this type of evaluation of a patient's progress is expressed in terms of the fact that his diagnosis at time of admission to the hospital was "schizophrenia—paranoid type" and that he was noted at the time of discharge to be free of hallucinations. There would be many observations and facts concern-

534

ing the patient which went into the diagnosis and yet which, in the form of a diagnosis, would not be available as a basis for evaluating his status when discharged. Likewise, there could be many observations concerning the patient at the time of discharge which would be relevant to predictions of his adjustment at home and at work and yet which would not be properly weighed and communicated by recording only that his hallucinatory behavior had ceased. *Evaluations of this gross type permit recognition of the most obvious degrees of improvement, i.e., abatement of severe symptomatology, but they are not sufficient for detection of improvement in the patient's personality with respect to those inadequacies in social adjustments and diurnal habits which served as the first clues to his illness.* From this point of view, the maximal efficacy of a given therapy for a given patient could not be ascertained at the time of his discharge from the hospital but only after he had returned to a normal, noninstitutional environment and only in terms of the quality of his adjustments in that environment. Furthermore, the observations and evaluations of his post-therapy behavior would have to be ordered to the same method of recording as was used to depict his status prior to therapy. Limitations of time and money have generally prohibited the attainment of this ideal paradigm for the validation of a therapeutic procedure. The next best approach demands that the status of the individual be thoroughly measured in terms of such observations as are possible immediately prior to the start of a course of therapy and immediately upon the completion of that course. It is equally important in this more circumscribed evaluation of the patient's progress that his status before and after therapy be measured with respect to the same variables.

It may be argued that no matter how rigorous the procedure of investigation, the "pure" effects of shock therapy, for example, may not be determined since such therapy is always imbedded in a certain setting and administered by personnel whose effects on the patients cannot be held constant. It may further be argued that the effects assignable to shock are inextricably mixed with the effects of the less dramatic psychotherapeutic efforts of the physician. With regard to this last point, it must be recognized that the ancillary therapeutic programs developed for the patient receiving convulsive therapy are probably as diverse as the theories proposed to explain the mechanics (or dynamics) of shock as therapy. This source of discrepancy should be remembered when it is necessary to explain different measured effects in different clinics when the same (?) therapy has been applied.

With regard to the complicating effects of other psychotherapeutic efforts (e.g., interviews) accompanying a major medical therapy, it should be recognized that the clinic in which the decision to apply a convulsive therapy is *not* accompanied by a reduction (either planned or unplanned) in the number of hours spent by the physician in personal contacts with the patient is probably rare. When a gross procedure of the nature of electroshock seems a promising approach with a given patient, the therapist probably feels some justification in reducing his contacts with that patient so as to afford more hours to those patients for whom no "specific" therapy is available. In short, the effects of a therapy such as electroshock are probably open to evaluation in a more pure form than would at first appear to be the case.

The design and carrying through of investigations of the above nature must necessarily await the development of adequate techniques for the thorough descriptive assay of the individual personality. It has been only within the last decade that clinical psychology has offered an instrument having the essential virtues of psychiatrically oriented variables empirically validated and quantitatively expressed. This instrument is the MMPI.

The wide use of the MMPI by psychiatrists, clinics, and general physicians attests to its success in a diagnostic role [56, 449 (see VII, 43)]. It is interesting to note that only recently has there been a sign of appreciation of its potential value in measuring the effects of a given course of therapy [276, 449, 470]. That there should be such a lag in the use of a basically diagnostic instrument for the evaluation of change reflects a general failure on the part of psychiatrists and psychologists to recognize that the determination of the patient's condition at any time after hospitalization or the onset of therapeutic interviews cannot be usefully made except on the very same variables the assessment of which served as the basis for hospitalization or the onset of therapy. The clinician should be no less willing to accept supportive information for his post-therapy evaluation than he was to seek assistance in the original problem of diagnosis.

The major assumption underlying the investigation reported here is that an instrument of demonstrated validity in the measurement of personality deviations of psychiatric import is of equal validity for the evaluation of personality changes and of the therapeutic operations deemed responsible for those changes. It is not assumed, however, that a direct evaluation of change in personality, or of the efficacy of a therapy, is possible through the single study of score changes. Rather, it is believed necessary to determine whether there are patterns of change in scores on a multivariable instrument which are characteristic for given patients under given regimens and to discriminate, on as objective a basis as possible, between those changes in the personality assay which are therapy-related and those which are merely chance. Further, it is believed necessary to evaluate the extent of the relationship between changes in item response and associated score changes.

In the event that an individual completes a personality questionnaire such as the MMPI on two different occasions, certain analyses may be made of any differences which are observed in the resulting profiles. It may be asked if the two profiles differ in a degree which would appear to approach significance. More specifically, this question relates to whether the two scores obtained on each single scale of the profiles differ by such an amount as exceeds that for which the hypothesis of no true difference (between the means of hypothetical populations of first-profile and second-profile scores) is tenable. For simplicity in reference, this is the problem of *status-score change*. The observed differences between the various pairs of status scores constitute *change-scores*.

The investigation began with a careful check of the approximately 7000 records in the MMPI research files at the University of Minnesota to obtain the names of all persons, normals and patients, to whom the inventory had been administered on at least two occasions. For all cases, available information on education, occupation, marital status, place of residence, etc., was recorded in addition to the interval, to the nearest five-day unit, between the two administrations of the MMPI. No inpatients were included in the study unless a check of their hospital record revealed that they had been discharged "improved" or "recovered" and that the two MMPI profiles had been obtained within the limits of a single hospitalization, and the length of this hospitalization was recorded in addition to the above information. The hospital charts of the patients were also checked carefully to determine the exact nature of the therapy which the patient had received, and particular note was made of the use of electroshock.

A post-admission MMPI is obtained routinely on all patients admitted to the psychopathic unit of the University of Minnesota Hospitals. With the beginning of this study in September 1946 a special effort was made to collect post-therapy, pre-discharge MMPI records on all patients. Most of the patients comprising the "psychotic-shock" group for this study were obtained in this manner.

The psychopathic unit has a total of only thirty-five beds of which six are in a separate ward for grossly disturbed patients. While the number of beds available to men and women patients on the general psychiatric ward are approximately equal, the actual number of women hospitalized per year greatly exceeds the number of men. The first section reports findings on female patients and the second reports data on males.

Female Groups

The normal cases fall into two groups: the first is composed of nineteen female night-school students, half of whom took the individual form of the MMPI first and one week later took the group form, the other half taking the two forms in reversed order with a one-week interval between them. The second group is composed of 23 females selected from the files because they had two MMPI records. The mean interval between the two tests for this second group was 136.4 days; the median interval was 47.5 days. This indicates the marked positive skewness which characterized the distribution of inter-test intervals. The mean age of the first group was 32.1 years, with a standard deviation of 7.3; the mean age of the second group was 26.3 years, with a standard deviation of 4.4. The difference in the mean ages of the two groups is not significant ($t = .998$) nor is the difference in the variances significant ($F = 2.727$). The MMPI test and retest means and standard deviations for the two normal groups are given in Table 1. Only one of the test-retest differences in mean score is statistically significant; this difference occurs on the Pt scale in the night-school sample ($t = 3.35$; $p < .01$). The test-retest correlation for the Pt scores in this group is .783, the highest of such correlations in this group for any of the clinical scales. If we may assume — on the basis of the very marked tendency in both groups of normals for the second test means on the clinical scales to be lower than the original means and on the basis of similar findings in other studies which have indicated a tendency for the "adjustment scores" of normals to change in the direction of improvement—that there exists an as yet unanalyzed factor making for a regression toward the norm in the personality measure of normals, even in the absence of originally extreme scores, then the appearance of such a factor would be maximized in the test-retest difference of those scales having the greatest reliability. This explanation of the change on the Pt scale shown by the night-school students is offered in the absence of evidence of any more obvious factor which might account for the observed difference. It will be noted from Table 2, which presents a summary of descriptive statistics for the normal and clinical groups, that the combined normal group is characterized by a high incidence of individuals with high school education or better, from metropolitan areas.

Table 1. T-Score Means, Standard Deviations, and Codes of Test-Retest Findings
on Two Groups of Normals

Group	?[a]	L[a]	F[a]	K	Hs	D	Hy	Pd	Pa	Pt	Sc	Ma
Night-school (N = 19)												
Test 1												
Mean	12.6	3.2	3.4	55.2	48.0	51.4	52.1	54.0	53.8	52.1	53.1	51.4
SD	9.7	2.2	3.1	8.6	5.4	8.8	6.8	8.8	10.2	6.6	7.5	8.2
				MMPI Code: 4683729/1 KF?/L								
Test 2												
Mean	17.3	3.4	2.6	56.3	46.0	49.0	50.9	52.9	50.6	48.7	51.5	49.0
SD	19.0	2.2	3.2	8.6	5.7	7.3	7.8	9.2	9.3	6.8	8.4	8.7
				MMPI Code: 4836/2971 K?/FL								
File-random (N = 23)												
Test 1												
Mean	20.4	3.4	3.0	57.9	46.3	47.0	50.4	49.6	50.2	47.8	52.2	48.4
SD	17.8	2.3	2.0	7.8	7.8	10.0	8.6	7.1	8.6	7.2	7.8	9.4
				MMPI Code: 836/4 9721 K?F/L								
Test 2												
Mean	21.9	3.6	2.4	59.0	45.4	45.3	48.2	49.2	51.0	47.2	50.7	49.2
SD	20.4	2.0	1.8	7.8	5.7	7.6	8.4	8.5	7.0	7.8	6.2	10.8
				MMPI Code: 68/4937 12 K?/FL								

[a] Raw scores.

Table 2. General Descriptive Statistics for the Five Samples Tested

Group [a]	Number	Age Mean	Age Range	Days in Hospital [b] Mean	Days in Hospital [b] Range	Days between MMPI's Mean	Days between MMPI's Range	% Single	% H.S. [c]
Normals	42	28.9	21–46			61.6	2–1060	78.6	95.0
OPD	25	32.1	17–56	5.8	2–18	80.6	5–330	32.0	63.2
PN	24	26.9	17–39	52.0	20–114	33.4	5–75	41.7	34.8
PS-NS	13	35.8	20–57	64.4	15–106	33.8	5–65	38.5	30.8
PS-S	20	43.2	20–59	50.6	23–90	27.2	5–40	30.8	83.3

[a] OPD = 25 outpatients; PN = 24 hospitalized neurotics; PS-NS = 13 hospitalized psychotics who received neither insulin nor electroshock therapy; PS-S = 20 hospitalized psychotics treated with electroshock.

[b] The figures in this column for the OPD group refer to the number of clinic visits in the interval between the two MMPI's.

[c] Percentage of group with high school education or better.

The clinical groups are four in number: 25 outpatients; 24 hospitalized neurotics; 13 hospitalized psychotics who did not receive any type of convulsive therapy; and 20 psychotics who received electroshock therapy. Table 3 presents the composition of the clinical groups by diagnosis.

The two MMPI records of each subject were tallied on a common form in such a way as to indicate the actual response (True, False, Cannot Say) of the subject to each item on each of the two testings. From these combined records, it was possible to determine for each individual the total number of changed responses, the number of changes by direction of change, and the number of changes per general type of item. These data for the individuals were then combined to permit determination of group statistics.

The mean score of each group on each of the validity and clinical scales of the MMPI was determined for the first and second tests and the reliability of the differences between the test and retest means of each group was determined by statistical analysis.

Table 3. The Composition of the Clinical Groups by Diagnosis

Group and Diagnosis	Number	Group and Diagnosis	Number
OPD (N = 25)		PS-NS (N = 13) continued	
Psychoneurosis (mostly mixed)	22	Manic-depressive, circular	1
Schizophrenia, simple	1	Agitated depression	1
Hypomania	1	Schizophrenia, simple	1
Undiagnosed	1	Schizophrenia, catatonic	1
PN (N = 24)		Recurrent depression	1
Psychoneurosis, mixed	13	Psychosis, undiagnosed	3
Psychoneurosis, hysteria	4	PS-S (N = 20)	
Psychoneurosis, hypochondriasis ..	2	Manic-depressive, depressed	4
Psychoneurosis, psychasthenia	1	Involutional melancholia	8
Psychoneurosis, reactive depression	4	Involutional paranoia	2
PS-NS (N = 13)		Schizophrenia, paranoid	2
Manic-depressive, depressed	3	Schizophrenia, hebephrenia	1
Manic-depressive, manic	2	Schizophrenia, undetermined	1
		Paranoid condition	2

In view of the small N for each of the patient groups, the present study can only be considered as exploratory rather than definitive, a search for support or refutation of specific hypotheses, rather than a basis for final establishment of conclusions.

The means and standard deviations of each of the groups on each of the validity and clinical scales of the MMPI, for both administrations of the inventory, are given in Table 4. It will be noted with respect to the clinical variables that there is a general tendency for the mean scores on the second administration to be lower than those for the first. Exceptions to this occur on the Pd scale in the outpatient (OPD) group, on the Mf scale in the hospitalized neurotic (PN) group, and on the D and Hy scales for the psychotic patients who did not receive electroshock therapy (PS-NS). None of the mean score differences of the combined normal group is statistically significant nor is any of the OPD group. The mean F-score difference in the normal group has a $p < .02$.

In the PN group, the second test means on the Hs, Hy, and Pd scales are significantly lower than the original means ($p < .01$ in each case).

The PS-NS group shows no significant mean differences on any of the clinical scales. The difference between the two K-score means is significant at the .01 level.

The sample of psychotic patients who received electroshock therapy (PS-S) shows a reliable decrease of mean score on the Hs, D, Hy, Pd, Pt, and Sc scales. The mean difference on the Pa scales has a probability of less than .02.

With respect to the validity scales, it should be noted that there is a consistent tendency for the F-score mean to be smaller on the second test, while the reverse

Table 4. T-Score Means, Standard Deviations, and Codes of Test-Retest Findings
on Several Diagnostic Groups

Group	?ᵃ	Lᵃ	Fᵃ	K	Hs	D	Hy	Pd	Mfᵇ	Pa	Pt	Sc	Ma
Normals (N = 42)													
Test 1													
Mean	17.0	3.2	3.2	56.6	47.1	49.0	51.6	51.6		51.8	49.8	52.6	49.8
SD	15.2	2.2	2.6	8.3	6.9	9.8	8.0	8.2		9.5	7.2	7.6	9.0
MMPI Code: 8634/7921 K?F/L													
Test 2													
Mean	19.8	3.4	2.6	57.8	45.7	47.0	49.4	50.8		50.8	47.9	51.0	49.1
SD	19.9	2.1	2.6	8.3	5.7	7.7	8.2	9.0		8.2	7.4	7.2	9.8
MMPI Code: 846/39 721 K?/FL													
Outpatients (N = 25)													
Test 1													
Mean	14.8	4.4	7.0	51.3	74.4	73.5	76.2	61.3	48.8	61.2	69.5	69.8	55.9
SD	19.0	2.2	4.0	9.0	13.4	13.4	11.2	12.2	12.1	10.6	11.4	12.8	11.9
MMPI Code: 312'87 46–9/5 F–KL?													
Test 2													
Mean	8.0	4.2	6.2	52.4	70.1	72.7	73.1	66.2	48.8	59.7	68.4	67.3	55.0
SD	8.0	1.6	3.4	8.2	12.6	9.0	12.4	14.8	9.8	9.4	13.6	13.2	10.5
MMPI Code: 321'784–69/5 FKL?/													
Neurotics (N = 24)													
Test 1													
Mean	14.2	4.6	6.1	52.2	74.9	71.8	77.2	63.6	42.8	62.5	66.6	69.2	55.2
SD	18.6	2.6	3.9	9.8	13.4	8.3	10.8	13.2	8.9	10.6	11.8	12.4	12.7
MMPI Code: 312'8746–9/5 FKL?/													
Test 2													
Mean	11.6	4.2	5.2	53.4	66.5°°	67.6	69.2	60.5	46.2	59.1	65.8	67.0	55.8
SD	12.4	2.4	5.0	8.5	12.4	9.7	11.3	11.0	10.6	10.2	12.7	14.4	12.6
MMPI Code: 328174–69/5 FKL?/													
Psychotics, no shock (N = 13)													
Test 1													
Mean	27.4	4.3	10.9	44.6	58.6	64.9	62.0	58.8		70.0	66.2	70.0	59.0
SD	23.4	2.2	9.4	6.9	13.3	11.0	12.0	14.4		12.3	11.4	16.3	18.0
MMPI Code: 68'723–941 F–L?/K													
Test 2													
Mean	11.4	4.5	6.6	52.5°°	57.8	66.7	63.1	58.1		66.0	63.4	64.8	53.3
SD	9.3	1.3	6.7	6.8	11.2	7.3	10.4	6.8		14.4	8.6	15.6	17.8
MMPI Code: 26873–419 FKL?/													
Psychotics (N = 20)													
Test 1													
Mean	14.4	4.6	8.2	52.1	62.8	74.4	65.2	72.0	49.4	70.2	70.9	72.2	56.2
SD	13.6	2.4	6.0	7.2	10.7	10.8	13.5	15.8	10.0	14.2	17.2	19.7	12.2
MMPI Code: 284 76'31–9/5 F–KL?													
Test 2													
Mean	23.0	3.7	4.0°°	50.7	53.0°°	58.2°°	55.7	57.6	49.4	59.2	57.6°°	59.8°°	52.5
SD	23.4	2.0	2.5	6.9	12.8	9.1	12.2	13.3	9.2	19.4	15.3	15.7	12.3
MMPI Code: 68247319/5 FK?/L													

ᵃ Raw scores.

ᵇ The N's on which Mf scores are based are outpatients = 20; neurotics = 13.

°° Differences between means are significant at .01 level.

540

holds for the K score except for the PS-S group. None of the mean differences for these two variables is reliable, however.

From Table 2, it may be seen that the normal group is characterized by a higher proportion of single persons and persons with a high school education or better than characterizes the clinical groups. From Table 4, it appears that these selective factors have not unduly influenced the "normality" of this group insofar as the clinical scales of the MMPI are concerned. The two profiles follow the 50-score line closely and there is not the elevation on the Hy scale to be expected in a college group. Furthermore, the test-retest reliabilities for the various scales in the combined normal group closely approximate those reported for normals in the literature.

In working with personality scores in which deviation is permitted in one direction only, in which experience with like measures indicates a general phenomenon of regression in the direction of "normality" (i.e., lower scores) with a simple passage of time, and in which the expected direction of change for patients receiving specialized therapy is toward lower scores on a retest, we would expect the retest scores of patients to show a reduced range and to find this reduced range reflected in lower test-retest correlations than are found with normals tested over a similar interval. In general these expectations are borne out by the results in Table 5, which show a tendency for the test-retest correlations to be lower for the patient groups than for the normals. In view of this argument, it may be considered more proper to consider test-retest correlations in patients who have had therapy as indices, at least in part, of therapeutic efficacy rather than as reliability coefficients. The small size of the samples in this study precludes testing the significance of the differences between these coefficients but their values are reflected in the tests of the reliability of the differences in corresponding means since they enter into the determination of the standard error of the difference between means for the test and retest scores. In this respect, it should be noted that Darley [r41] interpreted his test-retest coefficients, which were considerably lower than the corrected odd-even reliabilities for his measures, as gauges of "trait stability," representing a nonreducible combination of actual change in his subjects plus errors of measurement.

The similarity of the profiles for the OPD and PN groups (Table 4) is notable. The pre-therapy and post-therapy profiles for both of these groups show the general form which has been described as "typical" for neurotics [241 (see VI, 38)]. In

Table 5. Test-Retest Correlations of Each Group on Each Scale

Group	?	L	F	K	Hs	D	Hy	Pd	Mf	Pa	Pt	Sc	Ma
Normals (N = 42)	.718	.810	.749	.663	.724	.734	.682	.569		.585	.701	.594	.783
OPD (N = 25)	.430	.556	.797	.580	.657	.424	.664	.568	.827	.367	.708	.796	.746
PN (N = 24) ..	.884	.596	.687	.763	.536	.570	.617	.605	.589	.498	.475	.608	.819
PS-NS [a] (N = 13)	.334	.852	.375	.105	.220	.707	.436	.375		.052	.147	−.303	.608
PS-S (N = 20)	.434	.555	.384	.353	.908	.486	.555	.431	.343	.580	.496	.660	.456

[a] The coefficients for the PS-NS group are product-moment r's corresponding to computed rho's as given in Table 45, p. 362, Garrett, *Statistics in Psychology and Education*, 2nd edition.

terms of such typical profiles, the elevation on the neurotic triad for these groups would suggest that they were composed of so-called mild psychoneurotics. The height of the secondary elevation on the Pa, Pt, and Sc scales, however, is greater than that to be expected in mild psychoneurotics and suggests that both the outpatient and the hospitalized groups were composed of rather severe problems. This might explain at least partially the ineffectiveness of the outpatient therapy in reducing the neurotic triad although the relatively small number of therapy sessions intervening between the two profiles (see Table 2) is undoubtedly a factor also.

"Therapy" as provided by the OPD clinic requires definition. The patients have their most frequent and extensive contacts (for history-taking, therapeutic interviews, etc.) with "junior clerks." These are junior medical students who are assigned to the psychiatric service for a ten-week period. In their OPD activity, they work in close alliance with the psychiatric residents and are supervised by the senior staff psychiatrists and clinical associates. While the patients are seen regularly (weekly or biweekly) by the junior clerks, they are seen only occasionally by a staff psychiatrist.

The rise in the mean Pd score of the OPD group, contrasted with the significant decrease in the same score for the hospitalized neurotics, presents an intriguing problem of explanation. One hypothesis which might explain these relationships is based on the relative "social acceptance" of the neurotic symptomatology experienced by the outpatient versus the inpatient. In the case of the outpatient, the probing of the therapist to uncover possible conflictual material which might have an etiologic role and his apparent discounting of the gross symptomatology may result in a sensitizing of the patient to the quality of his social adjustments to the extent that, with later administrations of the MMPI, he becomes a "plus-getter" on those items of the Pd scale which pertain to family and social adjustments, while his neurotic symptoms are relatively unaffected. The lower mean scores on the L and Hy scales for the second administration of the MMPI to the OPD group, while not significantly different from the original means, are in accord with this hypothesis.

In the case of the hospitalized neurotic, both the severity of symptoms which justified intramural therapy and the fact that hospitalization occurred mean that the therapist and the patient alike may legitimately note the progress of therapy in terms of the amelioration of gross symptomatology and there is less of the subtle pressure on the patient to continue to uncover interpersonal conflicts.

It is interesting to note that with psychotic patients, the ordinary regimen of the psychiatric ward in the absence of electroconvulsive therapy is not adequate to achieve a significant reduction of the mean scores on the psychotic scales. While all the psychotic scales in Table 4 show reductions in mean score, there is a slight though not significant increase in the mean scores for the D and Hy scales. The relative "mildness" of the profiles plus the fact that these patients did not receive electroshock suggests that they were borderline or mild psychotics with extensive neurotic coloring and this fact may account for the apparent shift from psychotic to neurotic symptomatology. Concomitant with this shift, there is an increase in defensiveness or control as revealed in a mean K-score increase of 7.90 ($t = 3.000$, $p < .01$).

In Table 4 the two mean profiles for the group of psychotic patients who received electroconvulsive therapy are of interest not only because of the marked changes they reveal but because of the stability shown by the Mf and Ma scales. The stability of these two scales in a group which shows so much change on the other clinical variables is of great importance as evidence for the selective sensitivity of the MMPI in reflecting therapy-induced changes. Had all the MMPI scales shown significantly reduced means following electroshock therapy, it might be argued that all that was being measured was a gross tendency to response change as a result of the confusion and memory defects associated with EST and that specific personality changes were masked. The differential change reflected in the profiles of Table 4 argues for the efficiency of the MMPI as an instrument for detecting the particular results of special therapies.

In summary, the data on the mean pre-therapy and post-therapy profiles reveal no significant changes for the OPD group, reliable improvement in the Hs, Hy, and Pd scores for the sample of hospitalized neurotics (PN), no significant changes for the psychotics who received no electroshock therapy (PS-NS), and reliable improvements on the Hs, D, Hy, Pd, Pt, and Sc scores for the psychotics treated with electroshock (PS-S).

The sample of psychotic patients treated with electroshock, though a very mixed group, was composed largely of depressions and involutional melancholias. The average number of *grand mal* treatments received by these patients was between six and seven, and the interval between their two MMPI's was slightly less than one month. This group showed a significant post-shock reduction of their mean scores on all the MMPI clinical scales with the exception of masculinity-femininity and hypomania. Those means which were highest before therapy in this group were on the depression, psychopathic deviate, psychasthenia, and schizophrenia scales, and it was on these scales that the greatest change occurred.

The sample of hospitalized neurotics had a mean initial profile practically identical with that of the outpatient sample. However, after a mean interval of approximately one month, the same as the median interval for the outpatient group, the profile for the hospitalized neurotics showed a significant decrease of the hypochondriasis, hysteria, and psychopathic deviate scores. It must be remembered that all patients in three hospitalized groups were discharged as "improved" or "recovered." It may be concluded that improvement in the personality pattern of neurotics under the general regimen of the psychiatric ward is shown in a significant reduction of hypochondriacal and hysterical symptomatology as measured by the MMPI. Apparently, this form of therapy does not suffice to reduce any marked degree of depression as reflected in the MMPI D score. The ineffectiveness of hospitalization alone to cure depressive states in a neurotic syndrome can only be judged with respect to the interval of intramural therapy represented in our sample, namely, approximately one month.

Within the limits of our small sample of psychiatric outpatients and the nature and number of psychiatric interviews intervening between the collection of the two MMPI records, it would not appear that outpatient therapy of the type afforded by the university clinic suffices to affect a significant change in the mean scores of such patients on any of the clinical scales. The outpatient sample consisted almost wholly of psychoneurotics of mixed type who had an average of five clinic visits between their tests. No clinical evaluation of the nature of their response to therapy was available. The data of this study would indicate that such patients require more intensive therapy than that afforded by the outpatient clinic or a greater number of therapy interviews (or both) before they will show a favorable response. This conclusion is presented with certain reservations. It may be argued that improvement in the outpatient group occurred in areas of attitude, self-evaluation, and personal relationship not sampled by the MMPI. It may further be argued that the validity of the MMPI as a measure of therapeutically derived changes in personality has not been sufficiently established to warrant its application as the sole criterion in evaluating such changes. However, in the absence of other criteria and with consideration for the validity of the MMPI as a picture of the patient's pretherapy status, the data of the present study do not yield evidence of improvement in the psychiatric status of the outpatients.

Male Groups

The subjects used in this section, all males, were selected so as to be as directly comparable as possible to the subjects of the previous section except for sex. Data will be reported for four groups: University of Wisconsin student controls, University of Wisconsin student outpatients, psychoneurotic patients who were hospitalized but received no electroshock therapy, and psychotic patients who received electroconvulsive therapy (ECT). Certain gross descriptive data for these male subjects are presented in Tables 6 and 7. In the case of the patient groups, as was true for the female study, all hospitalized subjects were considered improved at the time of discharge. No uniform progress data were available on the hospital clinic outpatients.

Table 6 reveals that the Wisconsin male controls and clinic patients are somewhat younger than the female normals and outpatients of the previous section. Also, the intervals between the two MMPI administrations in these male groups are roughly twice the length of those which obtained for the comparable females. The male hospitalized neurotics of this study differ from the hospitalized female neurotics of the original analysis in being an average of ten years younger, in being hospitalized for a much shorter period, and in having a briefer interval between the two MMPI's. The male psychotics of this study treated with ECT are somewhat younger than the comparable female sample, have a slightly longer interval between MMPI's, and a very similar mean length of hospitalization. The average

Table 6. Gross Descriptive Data for the Male Subjects

Group [a]	N	Age		Days in Hospital		Days between MMPI's		% Single	% H.S. Education [b]
		Mean	Range	Mean	Range	Mean	Range		
UWC	27	23.4	17–33			144.3	32–236		
UWP	24	23.3	19–29			182.4	53–395		
PN	10	36.4	17–55	27.5	9–63	22.0	4–59	30	70.0
PS-S	22	39.2	18–68	49.5	17–115	34.6	5–84	50	36.4

a UWC = University of Wisconsin students, nonpatients; UWP = University of Wisconsin student outpatients; PN = nonhospitalized psychoneurotics treated in the University of Minnesota Outpatient Clinic; PS-S = psychotics hospitalized at the University of Minnesota Hospitals and treated with electroconvulsive therapy.

b High school education or better.

number of ECT treatments administered to the patients of this study was approximately ten, which is an average of about three more than were received by the female sample. With respect to the variables of age, length of hospitalization, and interval between the pre-therapy and post-therapy MMPI profiles, it is clear that the male subjects of this study show divergence from the central tendencies of the previously reported female samples, but these divergences are not great.

Table 7 reports the diagnostic composition of the three male clinical groups. The outpatient group shows a marked concentration of anxiety states and obsessive-compulsive syndromes and is therefore very different from the corresponding female sample. The hospitalized neurotics show good diagnostic similarity to the corresponding females. The male psychotics who received ECT are likewise very similar in diagnostic composition to the comparable female sample.

Table 7. Composition of the Clinical Groups by Diagnosis

Group and Diagnosis	Number
UWP (N = 24)	
Anxiety tension state	15
Compulsive-obsessive	4
Hysteria	2
Depression	1
Schizophrenia, incipient	1
Adolescent reaction	1
PN (N = 10)	
Psychoneurosis, mixed	3
Psychoneurosis, reactive depression	5
Psychoneurosis, psychasthenia	2
PS-S (N = 22)	
Schizophrenia, paranoid	7
Schizophrenia, mixed	2
Manic-depressive, depressed	6
Involutional melancholia	5
Paranoid condition	2

In considering the findings as to profile and item changes associated with the particular therapies of the male groups of this study and in comparing these changes with those that obtained in the previous investigation of females, the above similarities and differences of major aspects of the comparable samples must be kept in view.

Table 8 shows the mean pre-test and post-test profiles of the four groups. Those mean differences having statistical reliability are indicated directly on the profiles. From Table 8 it may be noted that seven of the nine scales show a mean tendency toward lower scores in the control students after an average interval of five months. The changes are slight and for the most part not reliable. In the case of the Hy and Ma scales, however, the controls show a reliable, though very small, decrement in scores. On the Hy scale, the mean decrease in score amounts to less than two raw score points ($M = 1.82$), but the test-retest consistency of scores on this scale in the control group was apparently so high that the associated standard error of the mean difference is quite small ($SE_{diff} = .582$), and the resulting critical ratio indi-

Table 8. T-Score Means and Codes of Test-Retest Findings on Several Diagnostic Groups

Group	?	L	F	K	Hs	D	Hy	Pd	Mf	Pa	Pt	Sc	Ma
Controls (N = 27)													
Test 1	50	50	50	54	53	52	58	54	61	52	55	54	57
Test 2	50	50	50	58	50	49°°	56	51	58	52	55	53	54°
Outpatients (N = 24)													
Test 1	50	50	58	51	71	75	69	62	67	58	78	74	57
Test 2	50°°	50	53°°	57°	59°°	65°°	64°	63	65	57	64°°	64°°	58
Hospitalized neurotics (N = 10)													
Test 1	50	50	54	55	63	75	65	64	59	60	71	66	56
Test 2	50	50	58	49	59°	78	66	67	60	62	73	66	62
Psychotics, shock (N = 22)													
Test 1	50	50	62	52	64	79	64	68	62	66	78	77	57
Test 2	50	50	58	54	51°°	62°°	52°°	58°°	54°°	57°°	61°°	62°°	52°°

MMPI Codes (in order):
- Controls Test 1 — MMPI Code: 5–39 748126 K?LF/
- Controls Test 2 — MMPI Code: 53798641/2 K?LF/
- Outpatients Test 1 — MMPI Code: 7281'354–69 FK?L/
- Outpatients Test 2 — MMPI Code: 253784–196 KF?L/
- Hospitalized neurotics Test 1 — MMPI Code: 27'8341 6–59 KF ?L/
- Hospitalized neurotics Test 2 — MMPI Code: 27'438 695–1 F?L/K
- Psychotics Test 1 — MMPI Code: 278'46135–9 F–K?L
- Psychotics Test 2 — MMPI Code: 287–465391 FK?L/

° The difference between means is significant at the .05 level.
°° The difference between means is significant at the .01 level.

cates the change, though slight, to be stable. Likewise, the mean change in raw scores on the Ma scale was 1.33 points; the standard error of this difference was .622. In general, the test and retest profiles of the male controls of this study are very similar to those of the female normals in the earlier study.

Table 8 also presents the mean pre-therapy and post-therapy profiles of the Wisconsin student-patient group. Again, a very consistent trend to lower scores on retest is observed with the mean changes in this treated group of neurotics being of greater magnitude than was found in the normals. Changes on the Pd, Mf, Pa, and Ma scales are not statistically reliable. The mean test-retest score decrements among the remaining clinical scales are all highly reliable. It may be noted that the mean scores show a distinct change in the direction and degree of slope of the F − K differential. This is very similar to changes in these scales found to be associated with successful therapy of the female subjects. The changes in the mean K scores and F scores are statistically reliable. It appears that by virtue of diagnostic considerations, nature and extent of therapy, and length of therapy, the male student-outpatient group shows more extensive personality alterations than are reflected in the post-therapy MMPI profiles of the female psychiatric outpatients, who showed no reliable changes on any of the scales after an average of five visits to a large outpatient psychiatric clinic.

The effect of an average of one month of hospitalization in a small, well-staffed, and well-equipped psychiatric unit on the MMPI profiles of male neurotics is shown in Table 8. The consistent tendency to lower retest scores, even in the absence of markedly extreme values initially, is seen again. The changes in mean score are very small and, with the exception of that on the Hs scale, not reliable. The mean change in raw score on Hs was 1.7 points; the standard error was .650. In comparing these data with those obtained from hospitalized female neurotics, it is interesting that they also produced their only reliable mean change on Hs.

Table 8 demonstrates the effects of an average of ten ECT treatments over a mean interval of 35 days on the MMPI profiles of male psychotics. Again, the marked changes are very similar to those found with female patients treated with ECT. The changes in mean clinical scores of the profiles are significant at the .01 level except for the Ma scale. In the previous study of females, all clinical scales except Mf and Ma showed highly reliable changes following ECT.

In general, the group changes in the MMPI profiles of these four samples of males show good agreement with the changes shown by comparable female groups of the earlier study. The particular behavior of the profiles of specific therapy groups may not be attributed simply to selective sex factors. Stability of group profiles in the normals of both sexes appears to be very good, with reliability of certain scales approaching a magnitude which generates statistical confidence in very small changes in mean scale score.

The finding of marked changes in the group standings of the male student-outpatients, with reliable improvement indicated on five of the nine clinical scales following therapy, requires comment in view of the failure of the female outpatients to show significant changes on any of the variables. The male subjects were younger by an average of nearly ten years and, by virtue of their selection, were undoubtedly brighter than the female clinic patients. Furthermore, the interval between MMPI's and the extent of therapy contacts were generally greater for the males. All four of these variables, age, intellect, interval, and intensity of treatment, favor the males and would support greater anticipation of favorable changes in the male records than in the female. Finally, the greater accessibility of the student counseling center and the more effective coordination of efforts possible within the campus environment as contrasted with the clinic, which must treat people far from their home base, is to the comparative detriment of the efforts of the hospital clinic. In consideration of these variables, we would be led to be relatively optimistic as to how the MMPI might reflect response to therapy in the student center, and relatively pessimistic as regards the outpatient clinic. The data fit these considerations. Furthermore, recognizing these sources of group-to-group variance, we may not conclude that male patients improve while females do not, or that the type and extent of psychotherapy available through a hospital outpatient clinic is basically ineffective. In this regard, it must be further noted that all members of the male outpatient sample had been clinically appraised to be "improved," but no such appraisal of progress was available for the female outpatients.

In summary, we find that in a situation in which we would anticipate positive response to therapy and improved psychiatric status and where there is clinical judgment of improvement, the MMPI gives good evidence of the therapeutic change. In situations in which we have some reason to doubt therapeutic efficacy and there is no clinical judgment of uniform patient improvement, the MMPI remains unchanged. These findings support the hypothesis that the MMPI may be used as a measure of response to therapy.

J. S. PEARSON

◆───────────────────────────────

ARTICLE 60 *Prediction of the Response of Schizophrenic Patients to Electroconvulsive Therapy*

THE value of the MMPI [303] in predicting the response of psychiatric patients to electronarcosis therapy has been demonstrated by Harris *et al.* [291]. Hales and Simon [276] in a similar study of insulin shock therapy found some prognostic significance in the results from the MMPI although the evidence was not conclusive.

Method

In an attempt to extend and confirm some of the findings of these studies the case histories of 60 white male veterans, patients on the psychiatric ward at the Minneapolis Veterans Administration Hospital, were examined. These cases comprised a group of which each member had completed a course of three or more electric shock treatments between November 1948 and May 1949.

Thirty-nine of this number had taken the MMPI within seven days before the first EST treatment. Of the remainder, some were unable to sort the test item cards because of the severity of their illnesses and in other cases it was deemed necessary to begin treatment so soon after admission that a pre-shock record could not be obtained. No attempt was made to control such factors as previous electric shock series and/or insulin treatments, coramine injections, and insulin used concurrently with the electroshock treatments.

Judgments of "good" and "poor" results of shock treatment for the cases on whom the MMPI was available were made on the basis of the psychiatrist's statements relating to EST in the discharge summary or, in a few cases where patients were still in the hospital, upon the verbal report of the psychiatrist in charge. Statements indicating any degree of improvement whatsoever were considered as evidence of a "good" result regardless of the final evaluation of the total hospital result. These statements were of this general sort: "after the fifth treatment there was considerable improvement in the man's mental status. . . . At the end of the shock therapy it was seen that the man was markedly improved. . . ."

The result was rated as "poor" if no change or a change for the worse was observed. These judgments were based on statements such as these: "Electric shock therapy was instituted with 15 treatments being given. There was no noticeable

548

change. . . ." ". . . he received 16 such treatments, these treatments apparently bringing out more pathology. In the last day or so he has been assaultive. . . ."

It should be emphasized that these judgments were based solely on the effectiveness of EST per se insofar as this could be determined. In some of the cases rated as "good" result, the benefits were quite transient and the progress of the illness necessitated commitment to long-term treatment in hospitals for psychotics while in a number of the cases rated "poor," the total hospital result effected a satisfactory return to society. The reasons for establishing the criteria for the result of treatment on these bases were, first, that it seemed desirable to consider the immediate and directly observable effects of shock and, second, that no adequate basis existed for separating the long-term results of shock from the long-term results of an active "total push" hospital program.

Attempts were then made to discover factors in the MMPI profiles which might enable the prediction of the result of the shock therapy. Of the 39 records 10 were eliminated because they constituted a group of involutional psychoses, psychotic depressive reactions, and mixed psychoneuroses for whom the result of shock therapy was uniformly good and it was readily apparent that their clustering on certain scales would spuriously raise the discriminatory powers of the test. It was likewise apparent that the factors involved in differential response to EST as defined by our criteria for "good" and "poor" results were related to the clinical picture of schizophrenia. Accordingly, the remaining cases, 29 in number, were considered. Of this group 16 were classified as responding poorly to EST and 13 classified as having made a good response. The "poor" group included 15 cases of schizophrenia: 10 paranoid type, 2 catatonic, 2 simple, and 1 hebephrenic. The remaining case was diagnosed "dissociative reaction with depersonalization." Of the 13 cases in the "good" group, 9 were diagnosed paranoid schizophrenia, 2 catatonic, and 2 were termed "depressive reaction in a basically schizoid personality."

Results

By tabulating a number of combinations of the MMPI scale values, three variables appeared to differentiate the two groups well beyond the level of chance expectancy (less than .01, according to the test of chi square).

The indications from the MMPI were that the result of electric shock therapy was poor when (1) the T score on the D scale was greater than 84 or less than 55; (2) the T score on the Sc scale was greater than 84; and (3) the total number of the nine original clinical scales with T scores of 80 or above was four or more.

Combining these indicators permits prediction of the result of EST in 72 per cent of the cases in this sample if none or one of the signs positive is considered to indicate a favorable prognosis for response to shock. With cutting at that level, EST would have been recommended for six patients who did not benefit from it and contraindicated for only two patients who did actually respond well.

Moving the cutting point up to all three signs positive as indicative of poor result eliminated the two cases where shock was falsely contraindicated, and 44 per cent of the cases where the treatment was unavailing were still correctly identified.

An independent sample of 15 cases was obtained between May and August 1949. Rated according to the same criteria, 8 were judged to have made a good response to EST. Of these, 7 were diagnosed schizophrenia, paranoid type, and 1 schizophrenia, hebephrenic type. Of the 7 cases in the "poor" group, 4 were of the paranoid type, 2 simple, and 1 catatonic.

The prognostic indicators held up as well in the cross-validation sample as in the original group; thus it appears that the MMPI quite definitely reflects some factor or factors related to the differential response of schizophrenic patients undergoing electric shock therapy.

The distributions of the two samples with respect to the MMPI signs are combined in Table 1 where it may be seen that 11, or 48 per cent, of the cases which made a poor response are identified by their MMPI profiles as different from the entire group having made a good response.

Table 1. Combined Distribution of Original and
Cross-Validation Groups

Number of Signs Positive	Number of Patients	
	Good Response	Poor Response
0	14	3
1	4	5
2	3	4
3	0	11

In clinical terms as judged from interpretation of the MMPI scales, the patients who made a good response to EST were characterized by a moderate to severe degree of depression in conjunction with symptoms such as hallucinations, ideas of reference, and other abnormalities associated with the diagnosis of schizophrenia. The group which made the poor response, on the other hand, was characterized by an inappropriate freedom from depression in the cases where the depression scale scores fell below T score 55 (this is in agreement with the finding of Harris *et al.*) and in the cases where extreme elevations of the depression scale were noted, by a chaotic state perhaps best described as an abandonment of the struggle to retain contact with reality. The extreme elevation of the Sc scale and the over-all elevation of the profile in terms of the number of scales with T scores above 80 found to be indicative of poor result are likewise thought to reflect this chaotic state rather than a mere increase in the number of psychotic symptoms.

With regard to the application of the findings of this investigation, the suggestion seems warranted that the MMPI may be used effectively as a screening device with schizophrenic patients for whom electric shock therapy is being considered and that patients for whom all three of the signs enumerated above are positive be given some other form of treatment. It is the impression of the writer that a large proportion of the group responding poorly to EST subsequently did well on insulin although unfortunately this impression could not be subjected to systematic investigation.

If nearly half of the patients who receive no benefit from EST can be identified by this means without falsely contraindicating the treatment in cases where it might be effective, the various economies involved and the slight but definite incidence of adverse effects from EST seem to indicate the use of the test in the manner described.

Follow-Up Group °

An analysis of the pre-treatment records of 10 male and 23 female psychotic patients at the St. Peter State Hospital was carried out with respect to the prognostic signs discovered in the earlier section. The 33 cases, all first admissions, were rated by ward nurses as to the degree of improvement following electric shock therapy. The following breakdown with respect to diagnosis and results of therapy was observed: Ten patients were rated as "unimproved." This group included five paranoid schizophrenics, four schizophrenics of the hebephrenic type, and one psychopathic personality with psychosis. Three patients were rated as "slightly improved," including two schizophrenics of the paranoid type and one hebephrenic. Seven patients were rated as "moderately improved," including three paranoid schizophrenics; one psychopathic personality with psychosis; one involutional psychosis; one manic-depressive, manic; and one manic-depressive, mixed. Thirteen patients rated as "marked improvement" included two paranoid, three simple, and one hebephrenic schizophrenics; three involutional psychoses; two manic-depressives, manic; and two manic-depressives, depressed.

While the small cell frequencies made a legitimate statistical analysis of the 4 x 4 fold contingency table impossible, inspection of the ungrouped data revealed that cases for whom all three prognostic signs were positive generally were rated "unimproved" following treatment, those with one or two signs positive improved slightly or moderately, and those for whom none of the three signs were positive generally were rated "marked improvement." One case for whom a poor response to treatment was predicted since all three prognostic signs were positive actually was rated as moderately improved. This one instance differs with the findings from the veterans hospital group where no one for whom all three prognostic signs were positive was rated as having made an improvement. Folding this distribution into a 2 x 2 fold table yielded a chi-square value of 9.91 significant at the .01 level and a contingency coefficient of .48.

A scoring key for the MMPI had previously been developed by item analysis of the two groups of patients utilized in the earlier study. When applied to the groups from which it was derived this scale gave a very remarkable separation, and we were hopeful that it might prove more valuable in predicting response to treatment than the signs reported. However, when this scale was applied to the St. Peter State Hospital groups the results were most disappointing—the difference between the means for the "unimproved" and "marked improvement" groups barely approached statistical significance and the dispersion of individual cases indicated the scale to be useless in individual prediction.

Summary

The pre-treatment MMPI records of 29 male psychiatric patients were analyzed with respect to psychiatrists' estimates of the patients responses to electric shock therapy. These cases all bore psychiatric diagnoses of schizophrenia or closely

° Data for this analysis were obtained with the assistance of W. M. Swenson, senior psychologist, St. Peter State Hospital, St. Peter, Minnesota.

related disorders. Three signs were found which enabled better than chance prediction of response. These signs indicate a poor response when the score on the depression scale lies above 84 or below 55, when the score on the schizophrenia scale lies above 84, and when the total number of scales with T scores of 80 or above is greater than three. A cross-validation group of 15 cases yielded the same results as the original sample.

Further evidence has been found that the MMPI may be of use in predicting the response of psychotic patients to electric shock therapy. Item analysis leading to the development of a new and specific scoring key proved less fruitful than examination of scores on the nine original clinical scales. The evidence is thought to support the use of the MMPI as a screening device for schizophrenic patients and to determine that when all three of the signs are positive, electric shock is contraindicated.

ARTICLE 61 *The Use of the MMPI Profile for Prognosis and Evaluation of Shock Therapy*

HATHAWAY and McKinley [302] originally designed the MMPI to serve as a diagnostic tool for a number of separate clinical syndromes. The empirical findings of Schmidt [528 (see VI, 39)] and Gough [234 (VI, 38)], among others, indicated the usefulness of various patterns of scores on the subscales as an aid to diagnosis. Harris and his associates [290, 291, 292] broadened the scope of profile analysis on the MMPI by discovering typical patterns of scores related to prognosis. With slight variations (chiefly in the magnitude of the scores) their findings were consistent for such diverse groups as neurotics treated by brief psychotherapy and psychotics treated by various types of shock treatment. The pre-treatment scores of groups who subsequently responded poorly to therapy in contrast to groups who responded favorably contained higher average scores on the psychopathic deviate (Pd), psychasthenia (Pt), and schizophrenia (Sc) scales. These signs were found in all groups studied; other prognostic signs were educed which were more specific to a particular group. Subsequently other studies [114, 276, 470] presenting data on the prognostic value of the MMPI profile have appeared in the literature. The discrepancies in the results of these various studies are marked. Without some clarification of these divergent findings, the prognostic use of the MMPI profile would seem to be limited.

Carp [114], for example, concluded that high scores on the psychotic scales of the MMPI were favorable signs for insulin treatment of schizophrenia. In his study the unimproved group had average scores well within normal limits on both Pt and Sc. Hales and Simon [276], using a small sample, reported findings somewhat similar to those of Carp. Pacella, Piotrowski, and Lewis [470], on the other hand, found that the average pre-shock scores of both improved and unimproved schizophrenics were so similar that the test could have little prognostic value.

The writer believes that the results and conclusions of the present study may furnish a basis for reconciling the apparent contradictions reported by previous investigators. Thus this study may clarify the prognostic use of the MMPI profile.

The Low-Profile Group

The discrepant results among the previous prognostic studies may be a function of a number of factors such as (1) unreliability stemming from small-sized samples;

(2) unreliable ratings of improvement at the termination of treatment; (3) use of a broad twofold rating of improved and unimproved obscuring differences which might appear in a threefold classification; and (4) inclusion of records with all scores within normal limits concealing differential patterns. Perhaps the last-named factor is most important. In most aspects of measurement, proper scientific procedure demands the inclusion of all cases. Slavish adherence to such a dictum, however, can in some situations produce grossly misleading results. Experience with the MMPI leads the author to believe that misses, i.e., records in a clinical group with all T scores below 70, should be excluded in any attempt to work out the average profile for a particular clinical group. The inclusion of the "misses" may very well lead to meaningless averages in the sense that the profile is not characteristic of the scores obtained by subjects in the group who have elevated profiles, i.e., the test "hits." Inclusion of test misses in psychotic groups especially seems likely to produce distorted averages. An undue proportion of psychotic "test misses" seem to have all T scores within normal limits and to be supernormal in just those aspects of the test which are important for prognosis, namely on Hs, Pt, and Sc. When the scales are not K-corrected on the records of these test misses, their T scores on these scales tend to be well below 50 and the raw scores, of course, are very low—often zero to two points on Hs and three to nine points on Pt and Sc. Thus the inclusion of test misses in the analysis of groups of psychotics is likely not only to lower the average magnitude of the scores but also to alter markedly the shape of the profile. Carp's data [114] illustrate the point made in the preceding discussion. In his unimproved group all T scores on Sc are below 70 or above 90. Further his unimproved group seems to contain an undue proportion of supernormal profiles, judging from results on Pt and Sc where 14 of 22 cases have T scores below 50.

In the present study 15 per cent (40 out of 224 cases) of the records had all scores within normal limits. These records were not included in the analysis. It seems probable that previous prognostic studies contained varying proportions of test misses thus leading to the discrepant results. These cases are not "test misses" in the usual sense of the word. Rather the ability of some psychotic patients to achieve extremely low scores on those scales heavily loaded with bizarre symptomatic items appears to be related to the personality structure of these respondents. It may be significant that in the present study approximately half of these cases were diagnosed as paranoid schizophrenics. These subjects seem to be worthy of intensive study in their own right to determine in what way they differ from schizophrenics with elevated MMPI profiles. At any rate their ego structure is sufficiently intact to permit them to deny most symptoms. Their suspiciousness works too well, however, for their supernormal profiles as described above allow the clinician to differentiate these cases from neurotic test misses who are much less likely to have such consistently low scores on Hs, Pt, and Sc.

Selection of Cases

The present study included the MMPI records of all patients at the Langley Porter Clinic who were given a test before shock treatment between the years 1943 and 1948. This study contained some of the same records used in the studies by Harris et al. [290, 291], but this sample is much larger than in any of the previous studies. Also an attempt was made to eliminate some factors which might lower both the validity and the reliability of the data. Thus a number of cases were eliminated from consideration because of the following restrictions:

1. As already mentioned, records were not used which did not contain at least one T score of 70 or over (other than masculinity-femininity, Mf).

2. Psychiatric ratings of improvement were obtained both at the termination of treatment and in follow-up periods. Cases with inconsistent ratings were discarded, e.g., recovered at the end of treatment but unimproved six months later.

3. Also eliminated were records which contained excessively high scores on two indices of internal validity, a T score over 70 on the ? index and a raw score over 19 on the F scale.

The final sample contained 184 cases tested before treatment was instituted. Post-treatment records were also available for 56 cases. The pre-shock records were divided into three groups called *recovered, improved,* and *unimproved.* The groupings were based upon psychiatrists' ratings of improvement at the termination of treatment and upon follow-up reports of at least six months' duration. The use of a threefold classification of improvement as well as the use of follow-up studies would seem to enhance the possibility of achieving greater validity and reliability in this study.

The data presented in Table 1 indicate that the groups used were not unusual in any respect. The unimproved group is somewhat younger while the recovered group tends to be somewhat more intelligent. A more detailed summary of the personal characteristics of the groups is presented elewhere [200].

Table 2 presents the distribution by diagnosis and type of shock treatment. It can readily be seen that the groups are not equal in these respects. While it would

Table 1. Personal Characteristics of the Prognostic Groups

Group	N	Average Age	Sex		Average Pre-Shock Intelligence [a]	
			M	F	N	Mean
Recovered	82	38.0	36%	64%	48	111
Improved	40	34.5	28	72	14	107
Unimproved	62	31.5	48	52	30	103
All cases	184	35.0	39%	61%	92	108

[a] Based upon four subtests, Similarities, Comprehension, Block Design, and Digit-symbol, of the Wechsler-Bellevue Scale.

Table 2. Distributions within Prognostic Groups by Diagnosis and Type of Shock Treatment

Group	N	Diagnosis [a]			Type of Shock Treatment		
		Aff.	Schiz.	PN	ES	EN	I
Recovered	82	64%	29%	5%	75%	10%	15%
Improved	40	38	42	20	55	12	33
Unimproved	62	16	54	27	41	18	41

[a] Percentages do not add up to 100 because several cases were not assigned a definite diagnosis.

have been desirable to equate the prognostic groups in terms of age, intelligence, sex, diagnosis, and type of shock treatment (electric shocks (ES), electronarcosis (EN), and insulin (I) were used), such procedures were not feasible with the present-sized samples.

Results on Prognostic Groups

Two analyses were made of the pre-shock scores. First the scores of the prognostic groups were analyzed without respect to diagnosis. Then separate analyses were made to compute the average profile of the affective disorders (the affective disorders included cases diagnosed as manic-depressive, depressed; involutional melancholia; manic-depressed, manic—most of the cases, however, were manic-depressive, depressed) and schizophrenic groups within each prognostic category to determine if prognostic signs differ according to diagnosis. For the first analysis the mean T scores on the pre-shock records of each of the three prognostic groups were tabulated without respect to diagnosis. Table 3 indicates some systematic differences between the three groups on their MMPI profiles which may be of prognostic value. The important findings may be summarized as follows:

Table 3. T-Score Means, Standard Deviations, and Codes of Preshock Tests on Various Outcome Groups, with Significance Levels of Mean Differences

Group	L [a]	F [a]	K	Hs	D	Hy	Pd	Mf	Pa	Pt	Sc	Ma
Recovered (N = 82)												
Mean	5	8	55	64	84	70	64	56	68	68	66	52
SD	2	5	9	13	16	12	11	11	12	10	13	12
MMPI Code: 2″3′67814–59 F–KL												
Improved (N = 40)												
Mean	4	10	49	66	81	69	71	55	68	73	76	62
SD	2	6	6	12	18	12	12	12	11	9	13	14
MMPI Code: 2″874′3619–5 F–L/K												
Unimproved (N = 62)												
Mean	4	11	49	67	85	69	74	51	73	76	80	61
SD	2	6	8	14	16	12	12	13	12	10	14	13
MMPI Code: 28″746′319–5 F–L/K												
p values (based on CR)												
Recovered vs. improved	.01	.05	.01				.01			.01	.01	.01
Recovered vs. unimproved	.01	.01	.01				.01	.05	.05	.01	.01	.01
Improved vs. unimproved								.05	.05			

[a] Raw scores.

1. The average profile of the recovered group is quite different from both the improved and unimproved groups who have quite similar profiles.

2. Scores on the "neurotic triad," Hs, D, and Hy, do not differentiate the groups.

3. The most discriminating scales are Pd, Pt, Sc, and Ma.

4. The recovered group has significantly higher scores on L and K and significantly lower scores on F than either of the other two groups.

Nine of the 12 scales (excluding only Hs, D, and Hy) differentiate significantly at the .05 level or higher between the recovered and unimproved groups. Thus the present results are quite contrary to Carp's findings [114] in that a poor prognosis for shock therapy accompanies high scores on those scales of the MMPI which reflect the most severe types of psychiatric disorders. It should be noted that the scales were not K-corrected. At the time the data were collected, K was not in general use. Inspection of the data, however, indicates that the use of K would reduce the differences obtained in the present study; hence the accuracy of predictions of response to shock therapy would be reduced.

In the second analysis the mean T scores were computed on the basis of diagnosis within each prognostic group. Table 4 indicates that affective disorders and schizophrenics have markedly similar MMPI profiles when analyzed on the basis of response to shock treatment. In other words, the pre-shock MMPI profile of a recovered schizophrenic tends to be more similar to that of a recovered affective disorder than to an unimproved schizophrenic. However, a few trends emerge from the data which might aid the clinician to make a more accurate prognosis when the diagnosis is known. It appears to be an unfavorable prognostic sign for a patient diagnosed as an affective disorder to be overly concerned with bodily functions as shown by high scores on Hs. Affective disorders score consistently higher than schizophrenics on the D scale in each prognostic category, but there is very little

Table 4. T-Score Means, Standard Deviations, and Codes of Pre-Shock Tests for Each Outcome Group (Divided into Schizophrenic and Affective Disorder Diagnosis)

Group	L[a]	F[a]	K	Hs	D	Hy	Pd	Mf	Pa	Pt	Sc	Ma
Recovered												
Schizophrenic (N = 24)												
Mean	5	10	53	65	79	67	66	55	74	69	71	56
SD	3	4	9	14	14	11	12	11	12	11	12	13
MMPI Code: 268'7<u>341</u>–<u>95</u> F-<u>LK</u>												
Affective (N = 52)												
Mean	4	7[••]	55	62	85	71	63	56	65[••]	67	65	52
SD	2	4	9	11	17	11	11	11	12	10	13	12
MMPI Code: 2"3'7<u>68</u> <u>41</u>–59 F-KL												
Improved												
Schizophrenic (N = 17)												
Mean	3	11	47	64	71	65	70	56	67	68	75	69
SD	2	5	6	13	16	12	14	12	9	9	13	13
MMPI Code: 824'976 <u>31</u>–5 F-/<u>KL</u>												
Affective (N = 15)												
Mean	4	10	49	69	89[••]	72	70	58	67	76[•]	76	59[•]
SD	2	5	6	11	17	11	10	10	12	7	11	10
MMPI Code: 2"7<u>834</u>'16–<u>95</u> F-<u>L/K</u>												
Unimproved												
Schizophrenic (N = 34)												
Mean	3	14	48	63	80	65	78	62	74	75	83	63
SD	2	6	9	11	17	11	12	14	11	11	13	12
MMPI Code: 82"476'3<u>195</u> F'/KL												
Affective (N = 10)												
Mean	4	10[•]	49	72[•]	93[•]	71	70	57	73	77	75	58
SD	2	5	5	13	20	11	13	11	12	9	12	15
MMPI Code: 2[•]"786<u>134</u>'–<u>95</u> F-<u>L/K</u>												

a Raw scores.
° Significant at the .05 level.
°° Significant at the .01 level.

difference between the scores of the diagnostic groups on the Sc scale within each prognostic category.

Discussion

The present study presents fairly conclusive evidence in support of the prognostic value of the MMPI profile for shock therapy. The writer can only conjecture that the discrepancies in the results of this study with those of previous studies arise from differences in methodology, chief of which is the inclusion or exclusion of the test misses. The study raises a question about possible personality differences between those patients who respond well and those who respond poorly to shock treatment. The overt symptomatology appeared extreme enough to lead to a psychiatric diagnosis of psychosis in most of these cases. Yet the average profile of the recovered group resembles that of less severely disturbed neurotics who responded favorably to psychotherapy [292]. It could very well be the case that patients can manifest rather bizarre symptoms at times even though their underlying ego structure is fairly intact. From an analysis of the actual items of the MMPI which differentiate the prognostic groups, the writer has suggested elsewhere [200] that patients who recover with shock treatment perceive the possibility of satisfactory interpersonal relations even before therapy while the converse is true of those who remain unimproved.

This study also suggests that prognostic groupings cut across conventional diagnostic categories. At least for the most severely disturbed patients, a classification system based upon prognosis may effect a more homogeneous grouping than one based upon diagnosis. If this assertion is valid, it would follow that studies of other variables in relation to the prognostic categories, e.g., scatter on the Wechsler-Bellevue and degree of concretization of thought, would reveal higher correlations than can be demonstrated with diagnostic groups.

Evaluation of Treatment

Previous studies using post-shock MMPI profiles to evaluate the results of treatment agree fairly well [114, 276, 470]. Improved groups have average T scores well within normal limits on all scales, while unimproved groups tend to have as high post-shock records as their pre-shock records, or even higher. Some interesting results were obtained by Pacella, Piotrowski, and Lewis [470] who gave two post-shock tests, the first a week after the end of treatment, the second four to eight weeks later. After one week their group of affective disorders had average T scores below 50 on most scales but on the second testing their scores tended to increase somewhat. The schizophrenic group which improved, however, had average T scores around 50 on most scales on the first post-test which tended to become supernormal (around 40) on the second test. The schizophrenic group who remained unimproved had T scores on the first post-test which matched their pre-shock profile fairly closely, but on the second post-test their scores became even higher. While the interpretation of these findings is not obvious in terms of concomitant behavioral changes, the results make it imperative for similar investigations to report the time of post-treatment testing.

The data in the present study are too limited to warrant an extensive analysis. Only 56 post-shock records divided evenly between the recovered and unimproved groups were collected. The tests were administered to most patients about one week after the last shock treatment. The mean T scores were computed for the two groups without respect to diagnosis. Table 5 illustrates that the post-shock records differentiate the groups even more clearly than did their preshock tests. Only 5 of the 28 recovered patients had T scores of 70 or over on their post-shock tests. The highest T score was 78 and in most of these five cases the D score was an isolated peak. In contrast 25 of the 28 unimproved records had at least one T score of 70 or more. Also the K score tended to be fairly high in the recovered group. It may be that patients who are rated "recovered" after shock treatment still have severe conflicts which are denied and suppressed. If the records had been corrected for K, the average differences in the profiles would be smaller. Thus the uncorrected profile can serve as a fairly valid index of response to shock treatment. It is unfortunate that post-test results were not obtained on the improved group. It can be surmised that they would retain their intermediate position, thereby increasing the difficulty of using the MMPI profile to evaluate response to shock treatment.

Table 5. T-Score Means and Codes of Post-Shock Tests on Two Outcome Groups

Group	L	F	K	Hs	D	Hy	Pd	Mf	Pa	Pt	Sc	Ma
Recovered (N = 28)	50	50	58	48	57	56	53	52	50	47	48	48
					MMPI Code: 23 456/1897 KLF/							
Unimproved (N = 28) ...	50	64	52	60	76	64	68	57	65	68	70	59
					MMPI Code: 28'47 63 1–95 F–KL							

Summary

1. On the basis of post-treatment clinical ratings, the pre-treatment MMPI records of 184 patients were divided into three prognostic groups, recovered, improved, and unimproved.

2. The profiles of the three groups differed significantly on a number of scales. High scores on the psychotic, psychopathic deviate, and F scales accompanied a poor prognosis for shock therapy; high scores on the L and K scales accompanied a favorable prognosis. Scores on neurotic scales did not differentiate the groups.

3. The patterns observed in the groups as a whole did not change appreciably when the groups were analyzed further on the basis of diagnostic categories.

4. Post-treatment MMPI profiles reflected response to therapy quite accurately.

General Personality

ALTHOUGH the MMPI was originally developed in a psychiatric setting for the express purpose of providing scores on traits "commonly characteristic of disabling psychological abnormality" [303, p. 2], it was inevitable that the test would be used with more or less normal persons as well. This extension was explicitly anticipated and exploratory work in this area carried out by the Minnesota group. "Although the scales are named according to the abnormal manifestation of the symptom complex, they have all been shown to have meaning within the normal range" [303, p. 2]. It is with this latter area of application that the articles included in this section deal.

In article 62 Black uses a peer nomination method to identify subgroups of college women. These subgroups are shown to differ from each other and from college women in general. Although the sociometric ratings were not chosen to test specific scales or psychiatric dimensions, the study points out interesting and useful meanings of the clinical scales.

Goodstein in article 63 also deals with the MMPI at the college level. He collates average profiles for male college students to demonstrate that regional or local norms for these populations are unnecessary. But he does argue that the differences between scores of people in general and the college means call for new norms in university screening work.

In article 64 Barron examines more closely some findings related to hostility and aggression found among air force officers who had scored high on the ego-strength scale [44 (see IV, 26)]. This important study is one of the first to relate childhood experiences to present scores on an MMPI scale. It is to be hoped that further investigation of etiological implications of scales and configurations will be undertaken.

The utility of the MMPI as a screening device with candidates for the priesthood is assayed by Bier in article 65. On the basis of his findings he suggests methods of reducing the item content for this specialized use and advocates modified norms. Quite rightly, he points out that the validity of such an abbreviated and altered test would have to be established empirically by further research.

Hovey in article 66 takes up the relation between different levels of elevation on MMPI scales and ward-practice ratings of psychiatric nursing students. With this group, the optimal level is not always found to fall at the T-score mean of Minnesota norms. The large number of cases required for this type of analysis is a restriction on the technique, but the need for this information is crucial.

The material reported in this section is encouraging in its reflection of the usefulness of scores varying within the lower ranges of the clinical scales. It was, of course, possible that scales constructed for more gross separations would prove in-

560

sensitive to smaller differences in personality manifestations. This likelihood has been confuted by the findings of these workers. They have demonstrated differences within the normal groups and dependable relationships with constructs which are not usually part of psychiatric nosology. However, the conclusion reached by several of these authors that specialized norms will have to be constructed for these populations is not one with which we would agree. Our interpretation is that there are inferences which can legitimately be made from a specified score value of an MMPI scale regardless of the relative frequency or infrequency of this score value in the group under consideration. A standard normative group forms the only defensible reference for score comparison. With Aumack, we can only conclude that "the uncovering of sub-group variations within normative data may function to refine the test for further and more complicated relativistic evaluations" [30, p. 80].

The articles in this section came from the following sources: article 62 from J. D. Black, The interpretation of MMPI profiles of college women, Ph.D. dissertation, University of Minnesota, 1953; article 63 from L. D. Goodstein, Regional differences in MMPI responses among male college students, *Journal of Consulting Psychology*, 1954, 18, 437–441; article 64 is an original manuscript prepared for this volume; article 65 from W. C. Bier (S.J.), A comparative study of a seminary group and four other groups on the MMPI, *Studies in Psychology and Psychiatry from the Catholic University of America*, 1948, 7, 1–107; and article 66 from H. B. Hovey, MMPI aberration potentials in a nonclinical group, *Journal of Social Psychology*, 1954, 40, 299–307. We are indebted to the authors and to the publishers of the journals for permission to reproduce these articles in this form.

◆————————————————————————————————

ARTICLE 62 *MMPI Results for Fifteen Groups of Female College Students*

IN TRYING to investigate the validity of a personality test in any so-called normal population, the problem of finding reliable criteria that are also practically meaningful and useful is extremely difficult. It is virtually impossible to arrange for several counselors or psychologists to become sufficiently acquainted with two hundred women to rate them reliably on characteristics one might be interested in. In the present study, one attempt to surmount this difficulty was to employ nomination by peers to find subgroups of girls who presumably possessed certain characteristics to an unusual degree. A "secret ballot" (part of the procedures described in III, 17) was used to accomplish this. No attempts were made to supply definitions for these characteristics. It was felt that they were in sufficiently common use to be readily understood and that to confine the ratings to the experimenter's definitions of the terms would have less practical value, though it might have increased the amount of significant differentiation among the groups.

When the nominations were tabulated, the three or four girls in each residence receiving a substantial plurality of nominations for any category were chosen for that particular criterion group. The number of girls "elected" to each of the fifteen groups varied from 12 to 25, the smaller N's occurring when nominations were very scattered or in the categories for which girls found it difficult to make choices. Since the fifteen groups consist of a total of 273 names, it will be obvious that some girls appear in more than one group.

Mean profiles and codes for each of the groups and the composite group were computed and these are reproduced in Table 1. The group means on eleven MMPI scales were compared with the total means and in 26 cases, representing about 16 per cent of the 165 comparisons made, they were significantly different at or beyond the .05 level (see Table 2). The most useful scales in this differentiation are 6 (Pa), 7 (Pt), and 8 (Sc); the least valuable is 9 (Ma) (see Table 3).

The mean profile obtained from this Stanford sample of undergraduate women is compared with the largest and most representative samples of college women from the literature in Table 4. Although the samples differ in whether or not K corrections were made, in time of testing, in selectivity of the groups (college within the university, student leaders, psychology classes), nevertheless the median

562

profile from all of these additional groups shows substantial correspondence with the profile obtained in the present study.

The profiles within each nomination group were classified by high points and the distributions of primary peaks are reported in Table 5. The very small N's on which these percentages are based make it difficult for even large differences to attain significance.

Table 1. Raw Score Means, Standard Deviations, and Codes for Fifteen Criterion Groups

Group	F	K	Hs	D	Hy	Pd	Mf	Pa	Pt	Sc	Ma
Most likable (N = 25)											
Mean	3.3	15.7	12.6	17.6	20.3	19.0	37.3	9.6	26.8	24.6	18.7
SD	1.79	4.24	1.75	2.44	3.70	3.47	3.42	2.22	3.67	3.40	4.44
			MMPI Code: 69378 4/152								
Most shy (N = 18)											
Mean	5.3	17.1	13.8	22.1	22.4	21.2	37.1	11.4	30.9	28.9	18.8
SD	4.63	4.10	4.14	4.96	6.22	4.97	3.49	3.47	5.83	5.19	4.39
			MMPI Code: 678–32491/5								
Most career-minded (N = 15)											
Mean	2.6	15.2	11.4	18.9	19.7	18.5	36.7	8.7	25.5	23.9	18.1
SD	2.22	5.56	3.22	3.97	3.45	2.55	4.27	2.57	5.07	5.19	4.89
			MMPI Code: 968375/241								
Most independent (N = 21)											
Mean	5.3	14.5	12.5	20.7	20.9	20.5	36.6	9.4	26.7	25.8	18.5
SD	4.51	4.36	4.18	3.89	5.43	4.60	5.43	3.31	5.71	6.14	4.90
			MMPI Code: 82346975/1								
Most naive (N = 16)											
Mean	4.6	17.9	14.1	21.5	22.9	22.2	38.3	11.0	29.7	28.3	18.9
SD	5.02	4.82	4.63	4.66	5.59	4.04	3.37	2.75	5.82	6.44	3.91
			MMPI Code: 68437 921/5								
Doesn't fit in (N = 18)											
Mean	5.6	15.1	12.3	19.4	20.4	20.9	37.2	9.3	26.6	26.7	19.8
SD	4.86	3.81	4.71	5.62	5.78	4.58	5.48	3.38	6.00	6.61	3.31
			MMPI Code: 984637 2/15								
Best leader (N = 18)											
Mean	2.9	15.4	12.6	18.3	21.7	19.3	38.5	9.5	25.9	23.7	18.4
SD	1.58	3.88	1.26	2.77	3.48	3.48	4.49	2.46	3.57	2.38	3.68
			MMPI Code: 369 847/125								
Most aggressive (N = 18)											
Mean	3.3	15.7	12.5	18.3	20.4	20.4	37.1	8.4	25.4	24.4	20.1
SD	2.21	4.65	2.77	3.02	4.05	3.84	3.10	2.27	4.13	4.26	3.01
			MMPI Code: 9438 67/152								
Most athletic (N = 20)											
Mean	2.8	15.2	11.4	18.2	20.8	19.8	34.0	8.7	25.5	24.0	20.6
SD	2.32	5.25	1.92	3.20	3.92	3.52	4.41	3.05	5.20	4.62	3.52
			MMPI Code: 953 4687/12								
Most tense (N = 17)											
Mean	4.0	15.5	13.2	20.9	22.5	21.5	38.6	10.7	29.4	26.1	19.4
SD	2.85	3.38	2.84	6.47	2.14	4.59	4.52	2.14	6.06	5.21	3.96
			MMPI Code: 67349821/5								
Least mature (N = 19)											
Mean	3.5	17.1	13.3	20.5	20.2	22.0	38.7	9.3	27.9	26.8	19.7
SD	2.48	3.05	3.31	5.84	3.18	4.75	4.83	2.30	5.79	5.16	3.94
			MMPI Code: 489 76 231/5								
Most sensitive (N = 12)											
Mean	3.6	17.2	13.7	24.9	23.4	23.0	39.5	11.2	32.1	28.3	17.8
SD	2.60	3.76	2.74	3.97	4.29	2.28	3.28	2.01	4.50	4.66	2.88
			MMPI Code: 2746–83 19/5								

Table 1. continued

Group	F	K	Hs	D	Hy	Pd	Mf	Pa	Pt	Sc	Ma
Best conversationalist (N = 14)											
Mean	3.1	17.3	13.0	17.5	24.1	22.2	38.1	9.6	26.8	26.0	20.8
SD	1.39	3.71	1.81	3.09	3.45	3.69	4.44	1.91	3.27	2.75	2.72
MMPI Code: 9–34 6871/52											
Most sociable (N = 19)											
Mean	2.6	16.8	12.3	18.5	22.1	19.7	38.9	9.8	27.2	25.1	18.9
SD	1.53	4.01	1.65	2.78	5.16	3.13	2.79	2.38	3.25	2.81	2.32
MMPI Code: 369874/125											
Least interested in dating (N = 19)											
Mean	4.8	15.5	13.1	20.4	20.4	20.5	36.6	10.0	27.1	26.7	18.4
SD	4.98	4.83	4.36	4.27	5.26	4.98	5.14	3.80	5.95	6.05	4.19
MMPI Code: 68 49372 15/											

Table 2. Significant Scales for Nominated Groups

Scale	Total Mean	Group Mean	p	Scale	Total Mean	Group Mean	p
Most Likable				*Best Leader*			
D	51	46.6	.01	Sc	55.5	50.8	.02
Hy	56	52.8	.05	*Most Aggressive*			
Pd	54.5	50	.02	Pa	55	51.5	.05
Most Independent				Pt	55	50.5	.05
F	52	56	.05	*Most Athletic*			
K	58	54	.02	K	58	55.5	.05
Most Shy				Hs	50.5	47	.02
Pa	55	60	.01	Mf	47	51	.0001
Pt	55	59.8	.02	Pt	55	50.5	.05
Sc	55.5	59.8	.02	Sc	55.5	52	.05
Most Naive				*Most Sensitive*			
Pa	55	59	.05	D	51	61	.01
Most Career-Minded				Pa	55	59.8	.05
Hs	50.5	46.5	.05	Pt	55	61	.01
Pd	54.5	49	.02	*Best Conversationalist*			
Sc	55.5	50.9	.05	D	51	46.5	.05
Doesn't Fit in							
F	52	57	.02				
K	58	55	.05				

Table 3. Number of Times Each Scale Significantly Differentiated Nominated Groups

Scale	No.	Scale	No.
F	2	Mf	1
K	3	Pa	4
Hs	2	Pt	4
D	3	Sc	4
Hy	1	Ma	0
Pd	2	Total	26

Table 4. Mean MMPI Profiles in Fifteen Studies of College Females

Group	K	Hs	D	Hy	Pd	Mf	Pa	Pt	Sc	Ma
Stanford, all classes and majors (N = 206) [66]	58	50.5	51	56	54.5	47	55	55	55.5	56
MMPI Code: 398674 21/5										
Minnesota, General College freshman (N = 366) [89] ...	...	46.7	49.9	52.9	53.8	53	52.2	48.3	49.2	54.7
MMPI Code: 94536/2871										
Utah State Agricultural College freshmen (N = 310) [175] ..	51	48	47	51	51	51	55	52	52	54
MMPI Code: 69 78345/12										
Pennsylvania State College (N = 115) [209]	a	50.8	50.8	56.1	54.6	48.4	53.5	54.6	56.2	59
MMPI Code: 983 47612/5										
Western College, all students (N = 407) [277]	...	45.6	46.9	52.4	48.5	54.7	51.5	48.4	48.7	52.3
MMPI Code: 5396/48721										
Minnesota, SLA freshmen (N = 489) b	55.5	49	49	53	54	48	54	54.5	54	54.5
MMPI Code: 794683/125										
Wisconsin freshmen (N = 760) b	55.5	50	50	54.5	54.5	50	54.5	54.5	55	55
MMPI Code: 893467 125/										
Montana State freshmen (N = 249) b	54.5	50	49	53	54	50.5	55	55.5	55	55
MMPI Code: 768943 51/2										
New York colleges, music and general subjects (N = 185) [401]	...	47.1	48.4	52.7	49.7	50.3	52.2	48.7	51.4	54.6
MMPI Code: 9368 5/4721										
New York colleges, nursing and liberal arts (N = 155) [401]	...	45.8	46.9	52.3	49.6	53.9	50.3	46.6	48.4	54.8
MMPI Code: 9536/48271										
Minnesota, General College students (N = 151) [501] ...	56.3	48.7	49.9	53.7	56.6	50.9	52.2	54.5	55.6	57.5
MMPI Code: 948 7365/21										
Maine, sophomores in psychology classes (N = 166) [563]	a	50	49	54	53	51	50	53	55	58
MMPI Code: 98347 516/2										
Pennsylvania State College (N = 172) [571]	...	46	51	55	53	49	53	49	50	57
MMPI Code: 9346 28/571										
Minnesota, sorority members (N = 808) [653]	57.8	50.6	49.5	54.5	54.8	49.3	53.3	54	54.5	57.4
MMPI Code: 9438761/25										
Minnesota, leaders in student affairs (N = 475) [653]	58	50	48.3	54.5	54.3	48.6	54.3	53.1	54.5	57.4
MMPI Code: 9384671/52										

a K was added but its value was not reported.

b From an unpublished paper by Donald P. Hoyt, Student Counseling Bureau, University of Minnesota.

Table 5. Code Distributions for Nominated Groups

Group	1's	2's	3's	4's	5's	6's	7's	8's	9's	N's
All girls	1.9%	7.8%	15.0%	13.6%	7.8%	12.6%	10.2%	5.3%	25.7%	206
Most likable	4.0	.0	20.0	8.0	8.0	20.0	12.0	4.0	24.0	25
Most independent ...	.0	9.5	19.0	9.5	14.3	4.8	9.5	9.5	23.8	21
Most shy	.0	11.1	5.5	16.7	.0	5.5	16.7°	16.7a	27.7	18
Most naive	.0	12.5	18.7	18.7	.0	6.3	18.7	6.3	18.7	16
Most career-minded ..	.0	6.7	13.3	.0a	13.3	6.7	6.7	13.3	40.0a	15
Doesn't fit in with group	.0	11.1	.0a	16.7	11.1	5.5	5.5	11.1	38.8a	18
Best leader	.0	5.5	16.7	11.1	.0	33.3°°	11.1	.0	22.2	18
Most tense	.0	11.7	11.7	5.9	.0	11.7	17.6	5.9	35.3	17
Most aggressive	.0	.0	16.7	16.7	.0	22.2a	.0a	5.5	38.8a	18
Least mature	.0	10.5	21.0	15.8	.0	5.2	10.5	.0	36.8	19
Most athletic	.0	10.0	10.0	10.0	10.0	5.0	10.0	.0	45.0°	20
Most sensitive	.0	25.0°	16.7	33.3°	.0	.0a	16.7	8.3	.0°	12
Best conversationalist	.0	.0	28.5a	14.3	.0	7.1	.0a	.0	50.0°	14
Most sociable	.0	.0	21.0	15.8	.0	26.3°	10.5	5.2	21.0	19
Least interested in dates	5.2	.0	.0a	15.8	15.8	10.5	10.5	15.8°	26.3	19

a Differences are to be noted, though not established as statistically significant.

° Significantly different from "all girls" at the .05 level.

°° Significantly different from "all girls" at the .01 level.

Test Findings

Most Likable. The mean profile of this group is similar in general contour to that of all girls but has a somewhat lower over-all elevation. The most liked girls turn out to be significantly lower on scales 2 (D), 3 (Hy), and 4 (Pd). Standard deviations for this group also tend to be markedly lower, which is a little surprising in view of the fact that apparently each woman was choosing the girl she liked most. It suggests that, regardless of our own personality patterns, we tend to see the same people as most likable.

In viewing mean profiles, it is important of course to keep in mind that they are not the profiles of any single individual. The individual profiles naturally show appropriate variation. Nevertheless, it is worth pointing out, perhaps, that not a single one of these likable girls received a T score greater than 54 on 1 (Hs), only one exceeded $T = 51$ on 2, one had a 5 (Mf) above 59, only one an 8 above 60. The suggestion is that certain scales are perhaps crucial in determining whether or not one is eligible to be called "most likable." The distribution of code percentages for the girls in this group is virtually identical with that for all girls. It appears that no single MMPI scale or profile pattern measures "likableness," but that any of several elevations tends to exclude college women from nomination as likable.

Most Independent. The mean profile for this group also follows the general pattern for the total group, except that the 3 loses its prominence and there is a negative rather than positive slope on the validity scales, with F exceeding K. It is on these two scales that significant differences are found between the independent girls and women in general. Since the F scale measures basically a disposition to say things that very few people say, one can surmise that this is one defining property of the independent person, at least in the college residence. Interestingly enough, the large standard deviations of this group on almost all scales suggest that girls are seen as independent who deviate markedly in either direction on MMPI variables. This is particularly striking on the 5 scale, where there is a small cluster of girls obtaining scores above $T = 70$, only one with a score between 70 and 49, and another group with its center at $T = 45$. There is thus a bimodal distribution of very "masculine" interests and typically "feminine" ones. The mean profile of these independent girls is somewhat similar to that of the girls who "do not fit in with the group." There is actually some overlap in the nominations for these two groups, but not enough to account for the similarity in their profiles. The code distributions of the group are not significantly different from the modal distribution.

While independence is ordinarily considered a desirable characteristic, it appears that girls who stand out among their peers as "most independent" are not necessarily socially well adjusted. The essence of independence in this group appears to be the ability or willingness to be different, as it were, all of which is suggested by the high F, the low K and 3, and the tendency of the group to have an abnormally large range of scores on all scales.

Most Shy. The girls nominated in this category show pronounced differences from the women in general, both in mean profile and in code distribution. There is a clear-cut elevation of the psychotic scales, 6, 7, and 8 all being significantly higher than the total group mean. The lowest 6 score for any of the group is 47, and the lowest 7 and 8 are, respectively, 45 and 44. These figures emphasize that almost the entire distribution of scores on these three scales lies above $T = 50$. One third of the group have profile codes starting with a 7 or 8, more than twice as many such codes as are found in the total group. The high 8 for this group would of course be anticipated theoretically. The lack of self-assurance and the insecurity which are implicit in the 7 might also be expected to accompany marked shyness, but the elevation of the 6 is less predictable. Except on K and 5, the standard deviations of this group tend to be larger than or about the same as those for the total group. As a group, then, the shyest girls in a college population show a clear-cut tendency to receive their highest scores on the three psychotic scales and those scores will, in general, be significantly above the mean of the girls in general.

Most Naive. The mean profile for these girls is markedly similar to the "most shy" group except for the slightly higher 4 score. They are differentiated from the women in general at a statistically significant level by the 6 scale, on which they are four T-score points higher. In retrospect, it seems probable that the women found great difficulty in defining naiveté or that the definitions of individuals varied considerably. There is a wide range of scores on almost all scales; for example, on 1, which ordinarily has a small standard deviation, the range of scores is from 40 to 78. The range on 7 and 8 is about the same. On 5, the range is narrower, only one girl scoring higher than 53 and most of them falling at or below the total group mean. There appears thus to be an association between naiveté and femininity, or at least a lack of naiveté in more masculine women.

Clinically, naiveté is sometimes associated with 3 [598], but as the term is used by these college women at any rate there is no substantiation for this clinical impression. Furthermore, the presence of higher Pa scores in this group suggests that our conception of the 6 scale may require revision.

Most Career-Minded. The flattest mean profile of all fifteen groups is achieved by those girls designated "most career-minded." It is below the total group mean on every scale except 5 and all but one of the clinical scales lies between $T = 47$ and $T = 52$. On three of the scales the mean scores are significantly lower in the statistical sense: 1, 4, and 8. Except for the K and 9 scales, the standard deviations tend to be generally lower or the same for the career-minded girls. This is particularly striking on scale 4 where all but one score falls between 43 and 52. The most noticeable differences in profile code distributions are that 40 per cent have codes beginning with a 9 and none have codes starting with 4. Furthermore, only one of the 9's is a 94.

The general picture of these girls, seen by their peers as career-oriented, is one of being well organized, clear-thinking, and perhaps more energetic and determined than average. As a group, their MMPI's suggest somewhat less anxious, more optimistic and secure persons than average. In this respect, they sound similar to the cadet nurses whom Lough [401] compared with women students in liberal arts and teaching curriculums and found to deviate in a similar direction. Another way of stating the findings on this group is that their mean scores tend to approach the adult means on every scale (except 1 and 2) more closely than do the mean scores of Stanford women in general.

Girls Who "Don't Fit in with the Group." The mean profile of these girls is distinguished principally by the increased F and lowered K scores, giving a negative slope such as was found with the "most independent" girls. As a group, they achieve a wide distribution of scores on virtually all the scales, only K showing a smaller standard deviation than the total group. On the code distribution, they are noteworthy only because of an absence of 3's and because nearly 40 per cent of the profiles have a 9 peak. The group as a whole is not characterized by an extreme number of high scores; for example, there is only one 7 score above 70, only two 8 scores above 67.

It appears that none of the MMPI scales is particularly related to the problem of not fitting into the college dormitory, or, putting it another way, there are numerous personality characteristics which may cause a girl to be seen as not fitting into the group. The fact of her not fitting in may be suggested by the negative slope in the F-K axis, but this does not, of course, reveal the reasons for her difficulty. In studying the individual profiles of this group, however, one discovers that two thirds of them have one or more scales which exceed 70 or are below 40 and all but two have scores above 65 or below 40. It may be worth noting that, although the significance of very low scores on some scales may be obscure, such a score is deviant and may therefore suggest that its recipient will have difficulty winning acceptance by her peers.

Best Leaders. The mean profile of the best leaders is lower than the total group profile on all scales except 6, where it is equal. Only one of these discrepancies achieves statistical significance, i.e., Sc. The group is remarkably homogeneous, all the standard deviations being small. Indeed, only two scores in the entire group exceed 70, one on 5 and one on 9. Only 13 out of the total of 162 scores exceed $T = 60$. Excluding scale 5, only seven scores are below forty. These girls, then, seen by their peers as the best leaders, are characterized by a remarkable tendency to score near the adult mean of the MMPI scales. Some interesting comparisons with Williamson's data on Minnesota student leaders [653] are possible. The mean profile of his women leaders, which is included in Table 4, is almost identical with the Stanford women-in-general profile, and thus tends to be somewhat higher than the mean profile of our best leaders. Williamson found many significant differences between his women leaders and freshmen women and, except for being lower on 2, his leaders were *higher* in every case than the freshmen.

However, a glance at Table 4 will show that (except for K and 6) his leaders had scores identical to or *lower* than those of sorority members at the University of Minnesota, and it would seem more appropriate to make this comparison. Thus, Williamson's findings are similar to those in the present study in that mean scores of leaders tend to be the same or lower than those of their peers. There is a tendency, however, for the Stanford "best leaders" to be closer to the adult means than Williamson's group.

In the data on profile codes, there is the interesting finding, significant at the .01 level, that one third of the leaders have profiles with a peak on 6. These are predominantly 63 and 64 codes. Otherwise, the high points are distributed pretty much in modal fashion. A *peak* on 6 tends to be associated with leadership among these college women but a *high* score on 6 tends to be associated with shyness. A study of the distributions of 6 scores for the most shy versus the best leaders reveals that 72 per cent of the former exceed the mean of the latter group on 6. Furthermore, while none of the leaders score higher than T = 65, one third of the shy girls score 67 or higher, yet only 5.5 per cent of them had a peak on 6. Obviously, these facts also mean that the shy girls tend to have higher scores on other scales than the leaders, but this does not make the findings with respect to 6 a statistical artifact. Other groups (e.g., career-minded girls) have also lower over-all profiles but a *reduced* incidence of 6 peaks.

To summarize, it may be safe to say that a modest elevation of 6, especially when it is a profile's peak, may point to leadership potentialities in a college woman, while more extreme elevations (or a modest elevation where Pa is not the peak), may be associated with shyness and lack of aggressiveness. These findings emphasize the intricacies of scale 6 and the importance of profile analysis.

Most Tense. The mean profile for this group shows no significant differences from the modal profile of the population studied. Scales 6 and 7 are slightly higher but unstably so. Nor does the distribution of profile codes show any differences approaching significance. The reasons for these negative findings are not known. Actually, of all the categories for which nominations were sought, this seemed a priori most likely to provide a characteristic MMPI pattern. Clinically, the existence of tension is clearly associated with certain scales, especially 2 and 7, and it is surprising that this association is not verified in this study as it has been in studies with abnormal populations. In retrospect, it seems possible that a layman's use of the word "tension" or "tense" is somewhat less precise than the clinician's. The presence of high scores on some of the scales, for example 9, suggests perhaps the Stanford women included in the tense group many who were hyperactive or restless but whose tension was not associated with obvious anxiety. The MMPI does not distinguish in any consistent way the girls in this population described as "most tense," although it may be of significance that none of the girls in this group received Mf scores above 60 and only one earned an Mf above 55.

Most Aggressive. The mean profile of the most aggressive girls is distinguished from that of their peers by significantly lower scores on 6 and 7. They are homogeneous relative to the total group, virtually all the standard deviations being low. The general profile shows lower mean scores on all the scales except 4 and 5, which are at the mean of the total group, and 9, which is higher. The result is a 943 profile code. In general, these aggressive girls are not characterized by deviant profiles; there are only two scores over 70 and, except for 9, only four others over 65. There are almost no scores below 40 on any scale. The girls seen as most aggressive then are, in MMPI terms, generally well-organized individuals, optimistic, free from much of the insecurity, shyness, and sensitivity that characterize many college women, perhaps a little more energetic and less susceptible to social pressure than women in general. It is interesting to compare the means of the most aggressive girls with the best leaders: the latter have higher 6 and lower 9 scores but otherwise the profiles are similar. It would appear that the best leaders are not also seen as most aggressive by their peers. (There is an actual overlap of five girls of the eighteen in these two groups.)

Substantially more than half of the most aggressive girls have their MMPI peaks on 6 or 9. In fact, all but one of the eighteen have profile codes which begin 3, 4, 6, or 9. Since the means of these scales are not above the total means (except for 9), this code distribution is obviously achieved by generally lower scores on 1, 2, 7, and 8 — the principal indicators of tension, anxiety, depression, i.e., the neurotic picture. The high percentage of 6 codes, together with the lower mean 6 score, reinforces the suggestion made about 6 in discussing the leaders.

It is obvious that no single MMPI variable measures either leadership or aggressiveness. Among the population studied here, it appears that the women seen as aggressive or as good leaders are distinguished more by the absence of those insecurities and anxieties which, modest though they may be, prevent the girls in general from giving a less self-conscious and uninhibited expression of their personalities. The personalities are organized in the typical adult fashion: they are more mature.

Least Mature. The group nominated as least mature showed no statistically significant differences from the total group. The profile code is slightly different, having a primary elevation on 4, and the mean 3 and 5 scores are slightly lower, the mean 4 score slightly higher than for the population as a whole. There is no stable deviation in the distribution of codes for this group. The distribution of 4 scores is interesting, almost all of them being concentrated between T= 53 and 63, only three of them falling below T = 53. Other than this tendency for immaturity to be related to the 4 score, the profiles of these girls did not differ from the population of Stanford women. Theoretically one might expect the impulsivity and selfishness of the 4 to be identified as immaturity in this population, but it is an association which is only suggested in this part of the study.

Most Athletic. The mean profile of this group has a 95 code and, as such, contrasts sharply with the modal profile and with virtually all the others, since 5 is ordinarily one of the two or three lowest scales. Interestingly enough, there are more significant differences between the most athletic group and the girls in general than for any other of the nominated groups. These girls are significantly lower on K, 1, 7, and 8, and significantly higher on 5. These rather general differences in personality characteristics as measured by the MMPI should emphasize that athletic tendencies in a girl have much broader implications than may sometimes be appreciated. In general, the athletic girl is seen to have a more masculine pattern of interests, to be more confident and energetic, and to be freer than her peers from concern about health or bodily function, and from anxieties, insecurities, self-consciousness and sensitivity.

The most athletic girls in this population do not deviate above 70 on any scale except 5 or 9. In spite of the fact that the group as a whole differs significantly from its peers on so many scales, only two of the athletic girls are also included in the group which does not fit in. (One of these earned a 9 score of 73, the other a 5 score of 74.) On the other hand, only two are also seen as most likable, and only two are included in the most aggressive group. Seven of them overlap with the group described as "least interested in dating." In general, although they are different from their peers, they are neither rejected by them nor extremely popular with them, and although their interests are more masculine, they are not seen as particularly aggressive. The profile codes reveal that nearly half the group has a primary elevation on 9, with the remaining codes generally scattered. This would seem to substantiate the clinical impression that many girls with peaks on 9 are fond of physical activity. It is worthy of mention that only two of the girls have a primary peak on 5 itself. Nevertheless, the higher mean 5 score, which is achieved partly through the absence of any low 5 scores (only one is below 45) points to the clear relationship between high scores on this variable and athletic or physical activity interests.

Most Sensitive. The twelve most sensitive girls give a mean profile that is totally unlike the population profile or any of the other group profiles, except perhaps the most shy girls. With four scores at or above 60 and two others almost reaching that point, it has the highest over-all elevation. In spite of the small N, three of the differences are significant: the higher 2 and 7 at the .01 level, the higher 6 at the .05 level. The standard deviations tend to be generally smaller and on some scales there is almost no spread. For example, all but one of the 4 scores fall between 53 and 67 while none of the 8 scores falls below 49 and only two are above 61. On scale 5, there is again an interesting dichotomous distribution — seven of the group have T scores between 37 and 41, inclusive, while the remaining five score between 51 and 57. It will be readily noted that each of these clusters is almost equidistant from the total population mean of 47. On over half the sensitive group, then, 5 is quite low while on the remainder it is above the population mean.

The girl who is seen as sensitive in the sense of being easily hurt is characterized, on this test, by depression and discouragement, anxiety, insecurity, tension, shyness, and uncertainty. There is also a slight tendency, apparently, for the girls in this group to deviate from their peers on the interest scale, particularly in the direction of femininity. The relatively higher 4 score is interesting and somewhat surprising. While we perhaps do not ordinarily think of the 4 as being easily hurt, he does tend to be defensive in many situations and defensiveness is certainly a clue to sensitivity. Thus we may have in this group two kinds of hypersensitive people — those who react intropunitively, with depression, anxiety, and withdrawal, and another which may react extrapunitively with defiance or tactless, diffident, or vindictive responses.

Some support for this hypothesis appears in the distribution of code frequencies for the sensitive girls. One fourth of them have a primary elevation on 2 while one third have a similar elevation on 4. There are no 24's although there are two 42's. This concentration of primary peaks on 2 and 4 as well as the absence of any profile with peaks on 9 is significant at the .05 level.

In any event, the mean MMPI profile of the sensitive girls is clearly distinguished from profiles of other groups although sensitivity is apparently measured by a number of scales just as it is expressed in a variety of ways.

Best Conversationalists. This category was included because it seemed somewhat less subjective than some of the others and more closely related to a specific aspect of behavior, yet probably possessing broader implications. There was apparently some wisdom in this choice because the group does give a profile which differs from the total group mean profile in predictable fashion. The best conversationalists as a group have a lower 2, and higher 3, 4, and 9 scores, though only the first of these differences is significant statistically. The group is relatively homogeneous. More than three fourths of the best conversationalists have a profile code beginning with 3 or 9, especially 9, and it is also interesting that every one of the group has a 3, 4, or 9 as one of the first two numbers of its code. There is a high incidence of 93's and 94's.

Actually, the absence of 2 and the presence of 3 and 9 appear to be crucial elements in being considered a good conversationalist. Not one of the girls has a 2 above 55, all have a 3 score between 50 and 70, and all but one have 9 scores above 55. The best conversationalists, then, appear to have the need for social approval which is associated with scale 3 clinically, to have in some cases the "absence of social fear" [439] which characterizes many 4's, and to have some of the self-confidence, energy, enthusiasm, and expansiveness which are associated with 9. In addition to this there is an absence of the depression, discouragement, and subjective distress of the depressed person.

Most Sociable. There were no significant mean score differences for the most sociable girls. This may emphasize the superiority of categories like best conversationalist which are more intimately tied to specific behavior. The sociable girls have slightly lower 5 and 2 scores but these differences are not known to be reliable. It may be significant that none of them had a 5 score above 53, though the mean score of the Mf is only slightly below the total mean. The code percentages do show some interesting trends, one of which is significant statistically: one fourth of the girls have profiles with 6 as the high point, and the remainder of the high points are scattered, with preference for 3's and 9's. Here again we have the phenomenon of a primary elevation on 6 pointing to abilities in dealing with other people though the 6 score itself apparently should not be high. Only one of this group of sociable girls had a 6 score above 65. In any event, the MMPI's of the most sociable girls suggest certain trends but show few clear-cut differences from the population here studied in general. Sociable behavior would appear possible through the presence or absence of a number of different MMPI factors.

Least Interested in Dating. This category was another attempt to provide an opportunity for rating a specific aspect of behavior. Unfortunately, this one was somewhat less successful in providing a homogeneous group and certainly in revealing any characteristic MMPI scores for girls who are not interested in dating. One reason for the heterogeneity was suggested by the fact that at least some of the girls nominated for this group were uninterested in dates because they were engaged to boys at other colleges. In any event, the scores have a tremendous range on almost all scales, e.g., scale 1 scores range from 35 to 78, 6 scores from 35 to 75, 8 scores from 40 to 78. There is clearly a higher incidence of deviancy in both directions in this group and a statistically significant tendency for profiles to have a primary elevation on 8, though this peak characterizes less than one fifth of the profiles. There is also a tendency for an absence of primary peaks on 3 and, indeed, the 3 and 4 scores tend to have a narrow range, especially in the upward direction. As a group, the girls described as least interested in dating have a higher incidence of maladjustment on certain MMPI scales than the other groups but the present study establishes no particular relationship between any scale or scales and interest in dating.

Summary

The findings of the present study clearly demonstrate that college women classified by their peers according to certain commonly used descriptive phrases obtain MMPI scores and profile patterns which in many cases differentiate them from college women in general at Stanford. This result is especially significant because none of the categories studied was designed to have particular reference to any particular MMPI scale. It would have been possible to obtain sociometric ratings for factors such as "most depressed," "most hypochondriacal," "most masculine." Such ratings might, indeed, have provided a more direct validation of the individual MMPI scales within a "normal" population. Yet the opportunity to study the test performances of girls classified according to behavior of desirable as well as undesirable types, behavior which occurs with considerable frequency in a college population, and behavior which is not necessarily related to any specific psychopathological syndrome — this opportunity seemed too significant to sacrifice merely to establish that there are, in a college population, persons who deviate on both ratings and tests of conventional psychiatric difficulties.

Nevertheless, one consequence of this decision has been that the evaluation of the MMPI performance of these criterion groups is not a conventional validity study. While it would have been possible to develop specific hypotheses about the MMPI scores these various groups would obtain, and then to test these hypotheses, this procedure was not followed, principally because it would really have been more a test of the intuitive skill of the experimenter than a validation of the MMPI. In most cases, the differences that were found are consonant with clinical expectation; in cases where they are not, which principally involve scale 6, the explanation seems to lie in our ignorance of the operation of that scale within the normal population, for its behavior is quite consistent in the four cases where it differentiates groups.

In any event, though we have not been bound by the requirements of a rigorous validation study of individual MMPI scales, it seems entirely within the meaning of these data to say that the test differences between the fifteen sociometric groups and the women-in-general do constitute a preliminary validation of the MMPI with this population. In only two of the fifteen cases are there no statistically significant differences between the population and the subgroup in some aspect of MMPI performance.

L. D. GOODSTEIN

◆―――――――――――――――――――――――――――――――

ARTICLE 63 *Regional Differences in MMPI Responses among Male College Students*

THE usefulness of any psychometric instrument depends, at least in part, upon the applicability of the available norms. The blind application of a test valid for one population to a different type of group often leads to serious errors of interpretation. The use of the MMPI with college populations has been criticized on two points. First, college students tend to be more deviant than the general population in their MMPI responses and, second, local or regional norms are thought necessary for each college or geographical region. Brown [89], Cottle [146], Gilliland and Colgin [225], and others have urged the development of local norms while Tyler and Michaelis [599] among others have actually constructed such local norms.

Black [66 (see X, 62)] has taken a somewhat contradictory position. He collected, from the literature, MMPI data on a large group of college females, a total N of 5014, at fifteen different colleges and universities. Although he did not use an over-all test of significance, he concluded, "these data suggest that there is a characteristic profile for college women which does not differ from college to college. It is certainly true that some of the differences are statistically significant, but that they are of little practical significance" [66]. The purpose of the present paper is to test further the notion that local or regional norms are necessary for interpreting MMPI profiles of college students by examining the data available on college males.

Procedure

One group of subjects, consisting of 408 randomly selected male freshmen, had been tested at the State University of Iowa with booklet form of the MMPI. From the published literature and from unpublished studies available to the author, seven additional groups were selected as meeting the following criteria:

1. Subjects randomly selected or 100 per cent sampling technique used. The inclusion of data that had been obtained through administration to students in special curriculums or to preselected groups of students, e.g., student leaders, might lead to a confounding of the results and were not included.

2. N > 100. Relatively large samples were seemingly more free of bias.

3. Means and standard deviations reported for all nine clinical scales with K

574

correction where appropriate. As the K correction is now routinely used, those studies without the K correction were not included.

Results

The means, the standard deviations, and the number of cases on the nine clinical scales and the K scale for the eight schools are presented in Table 1. The agreement among the scale means of the eight samples is very striking. The largest difference between any two means on a single scale is 7.8 T-score units on the Mf scale. With the exception of the differences on the Mf scale, none of the differences exceeds 4.9 T-score units, which would be less than half a standard deviation according to the original standardization data. The smallness of the differences when raw scores are used is even more striking. Only the Mf scale has a difference between any two means of over 4 raw score units. The median range difference in raw score units is only 1.9.

The data from these eight colleges were then placed into three groups based upon geographical regions: the eastern group, including the University of Maine and the Pennsylvania State College; the midwestern group, including the universities of Iowa, Minnesota, and Wisconsin; and the western group, including Montana State College, Utah State College, and the University of New Mexico. To provide an over-all test of significance these data were analyzed by a Lindquist [r98] Type I analysis of variance design in which the regions were a "between subjects" factor, while the nine clinical scales and the regions × scales interaction were "within subjects" factors. As shown in Table 2, only the obtained F for the scales was significant, indicating that the means on the nine clinical scales were not equal. The obtained F's for regions and the regions × scales interaction did not exceed unity. There is no evidence to support the notion that geographical differences are significant determinants of MMPI means.

To test the importance of these geographical regional influences, a similar analysis was then performed with the standard deviation data. The variability data were also divided into three groups in the same manner as the mean data and the identical analysis of variance design was used. While such data do not usually fulfill the assumptions about normality necessary for an analysis of variance, recent empirical evidence would indicate that slight deviations from normality are of little consequence and may be ignored [r98].

As may be seen in Table 3, only the obtained F for scales was statistically significant, which would indicate that the variability of the nine clinical scales was not equal. The D and Pt scales have the largest variances while the Hy, Hs, and Pa scales have the smallest variances. The F's for regions and the regions × scales interaction were less than unity. On the basis of this analysis, therefore, we may conclude that the variances are not significantly dependent upon regional influences.

Discussion

An inspection of the means for the eight schools reveals that no one group was consistently higher or lower than any other group. The patterning of scores would seem to be more a function of chance fluctuation than due to the operation of any cultural or environmental factors. The obtained differences over regions would

Table 1. T-Score Means, Standard Deviations, and Codes for Various College Groups Arranged According to Geographical Region

Group	K	Hs	D	Hy	Pd	Mf	Pa	Pt	Sc	Ma
East										
Maine										
(N = 316) [563]										
Mean	a	53.0	53.0	55.0	55.0	59.0	50.0	56.0	55.0	60.0
SD	a	8.5	12.1	7.7	10.8	10.6	9.1	12.6	12.2	11.1
MMPI Code: 9–5 7348 126										
Pennsylvania State										
(N = 121) [117]										
Mean	a	53.4	53.5	56.3	57.0	59.6	52.2	58.0	57.1	60.2
SD	a	8.3	11.8	7.7	9.5	8.6	9.6	10.8	8.9	9.6
MMPI Code: 9–5 7843 216										
Midwest										
Iowa (N = 408) [232]										
Mean	15.3	53.0	53.0	56.0	57.0	58.0	54.0	56.0	57.0	58.0
SD	4.8	8.2	11.6	8.2	9.8	10.8	7.9	12.8	11.6	11.0
MMPI Code: 594837 612/										
Minnesota										
(N = 1321) [653]										
Mean	14.4	51.1	51.8	54.2	56.6	56.9	52.6	56.8	56.9	58.1
SD	4.6	8.1	10.3	7.3	9.7	9.7	8.6	10.4	10.8	10.3
MMPI Code: 958743621/										
Wisconsin										
(N = 1422) b										
Mean	14.5	51.2	52.2	55.0	56.0	59.0	53.0	56.7	56.0	58.0
SD	4.4	7.2	10.5	7.7	9.7	10.6	7.9	9.4	10.1	10.6
MMPI Code: 59 7483 621/										
West										
Montana State										
(N = 456) b										
Mean	14.2	50.5	52.5	54.5	56.0	58.0	54.1	56.9	56.9	59.0
SD	4.5	10.0	12.1	7.8	9.6	10.2	8.0	10.1	8.9	9.6
MMPI Code: 95 784 3621/										
New Mexico										
(N = 149) [465]										
Mean	16.4	54.1	53.9	57.8	58.1	62.7	53.4	56.8	57.2	59.2
SD	9.4	8.7	10.5	7.8	10.4	9.9	7.8	10.2	10.5	10.0
MMPI Code: 5–94387 126										
Utah State										
(N = 842) [175]										
Mean	13.8	51.5	50.2	52.9	54.3	54.9	53.0	53.6	52.4	55.8
SD	4.4	7.1	9.0	7.9	8.8	9.1	9.0	9.5	10.7	9.2
MMPI Code: 954763812/										
Group median										
Males (N = 5035)										
Mean	14.5	52.3	52.8	55.0	56.3	58.5	53.0	56.7	56.9	58.7
SD	4.6	8.3	11.1	7.8	9.8	10.1	8.3	10.3	10.8	10.2
MMPI Code: 95 8743621/										
Females										
(N = 5014) [66]										
Mean	15.5	48	48	54	54	51	53	53	54	55
MMPI Code: 9348675/12										

a K added but its value not reported.

b From an unpublished paper by Donald P. Hoyt, Student Counseling Bureau, University of Minnesota.

Table 2. Analysis of Variance of Means

Source	df	MS	F
Between subjects ...	7	11.37	
Regions	2	1.69	
Error (b)	5	15.25	
Within subjects	64	67.55	
Scales	8	46.71	56.72 [a]
Regions × scales..	16	1.45	1.63
Error (w)	40	.89	
Total	71		

[a] p < .01.

Table 3. Analysis of Variance of Standard Deviations

Source	df	MS	F
Between subjects ...	7	2.34	
Regions	2	2.13	
Error (b)	5	2.43	
Within subjects	64	1.87	
Scales	8	10.81	18.02 [a]
Regions × scales..	16	.57	
Error (w)	40	.60	
Total	71		

[a] p < .01.

seem to be of such little consequence that the development of regional norms is unnecessary.

It is important to note that the mean T scores on all nine clinical scales are above the expected mean value of 50. This finding is in support of the notion that college students, as a group, are more deviant in their responses to the MMPI than the general adult population used in the standardization of the instrument. These results, however, should not be interpreted to mean that the MMPI cannot be useful in evaluating the adjustment of college students, but rather support the idea that separate norms for college students as a group are not only desirable but essential.

In this regard it is interesting to note that, if 70 is used as the cutting score, approximately 15 per cent of our total group of 5000, or 750, have "abnormal" scores on the Ma scale. Extending this criterion to the other scales, we identify approximately 7 to 10 per cent of our group as abnormal on each of the Pd, Mf, Pt, and Sc scales. Without allowing for any overlap, that is, a single subject scoring above 70 on more than one scale, we would have identified approximately half of our 5000 male college students as abnormal by such a procedure. While this, of course, may be a valid "diagnosis," the capacity of our college mental hygiene facilities certainly demands a more rigorous screening instrument. Seemingly the usefulness of the MMPI as a screening test in the collegiate setting would depend upon the development of new cutting scores.

The consistency in the pattern of scores among the eight schools also seems worthy of note. The peaks on Ma, Mf, Sc, Pt, Pd, and Hy suggest that there is a characteristic profile for college males. They appear to be more feminine in their interests, to be more active, less inhibited, but more worrying than the male population in general. This diagnostic picture would seem to be validated by clinical observations in the classroom and on the campus as well as in the counseling office.

We may then compare our typical profile for college males with that obtained by Black [66] for college females. This comparison is shown in Table 1. In each case the points are based upon the median mean; in our study the median is of eight colleges, in Black's study it is of fifteen colleges. The total N's, however, are very similar, 5035 for our sample, 5014 for Black's.

The differences between these two profiles are rather interesting. The males are higher on all the clinical scales with the exception of Pa where the points almost coincide. The largest differences are on the Mf, Ma, Pt, D, and Hs scales. The women are below the expected mean value of 50 on the Hs and D scales while the men, as noted before, are consistently above 50. The women are higher on the K scale, indicating a somewhat more defensive attitude. The effect of this higher K value, however, is to reduce the differences betwen the sexes on K-corrected scales as the higher K results in higher values on five of the nine scales.

While it may not be obvious upon first glance, there is a good bit of similarity between these two profiles. If we exclude the Mf and Pa scales from consideration, the profiles then appear quite similar with peaks on Ma and Sc and valleys on Hs and D, although the female profile is, of course, lower. It is rather surprising to note that, while college males are considerably more feminine in their interests than males in general, college females are *not* more masculine in their interests than women in general. The reasons for this finding and the possible implications for the future adjustment of these individuals are left to conjecture. The differences between these profiles would suggest that, in using the MMPI in a college setting, separate norms are necessary for males and females.

Summary

The present study has been a comparison of the results of MMPI administration to large groups of male undergraduates at eight different colleges and universities for regional differences. When the mean scores were subjected to an analysis of variance, the results indicated that there were no significant regional differences. An analysis of variance for the standard deviations also showed no significant regional differences. The obtained differences are apparently of such little consequence that the development of regional or local norms seems unnecessary.

While there is a characeristic profile for the college male that differs little from college to college, it is markedly different from the characteristic profile of the noncollege male and from the characteristic profile of the college female. New norms would appear necessary in using the MMPI as a screening test in clinical work with university populations.

✦ ————————————————————————————————

ARTICLE 64 *Ego-Strength and the Management*
of Aggression

THIS paper concerns itself with some observations incidental to the validation of
an MMPI scale which purports to measure strength of the ego (the Es scale)
[44 (see IV, 26)]. Most of the correlates of the scale seem to fit in well with the
concept of ego-strength as one generally finds it used in the psychoanalytic literature; in the present study, however, in which the subjects are healthy, well-functioning men of generally superior abilities, there appeared as significant correlates
of the ego-strength scale a cluster of traits seemingly more related to egocentrism:
competitiveness, marked power-orientation, and disregard of the rights of others.
The aim of this paper is to report these findings and to seek to give some theoretical
account of them.

By way of background, validity information concerning the scale may be considered briefly. The Es scale was constructed originally for the purpose of predicting
response to psychotherapy, and for this it appears to have substantial predictive
efficiency, producing correlations of .38, .42, and .52 against rated outcome in three
cross-validating samples [44]. It consistently has high negative correlations with
the MMPI clinical symptom scales, as indeed a measure of ego-strength should
have. Thus it is related positively to the ability to recover from psychological distress, and negatively to the tendency to develop psychiatric symptoms.

The scale also correlates positively with measured intelligence. In some half-
dozen samples [r11, 44], in which the measures of intelligence included the Wechsler-Bellevue, the Miller Analogies, the Primary Mental Abilities Test, the Wesman
Personnel Classification Test, the Terman Concept Mastery Test, and the Idea
Classification Test, the Es scale correlated from .35 to .45 with those measures.

Other aspects of ego-strength find representation among the reported correlates
of the scale. In studies using the living-in assessment method, which permitted observations of the subjects through three days of informal social interaction and in
many lifelike situational tests, the Es scale correlated significantly with ratings
of such dimensions as vitality, drive, self-confidence, poise, and breadth of interest
[r11]. In a study of courage and fighting ability under enemy fire (in infantry
combat in Korea), the scale achieved excellent discrimination between fighters
and nonfighters, the fighters scoring higher on Es [675]. In group psychotherapy

579

[678], the scale has been found to have positive relationship to active participation in the group process. In still another study [651], it has been reported to be the only MMPI scale correlating positively with favorable aspects of functioning, such as W and M, on the Rorschach test.

In the present study, the scale was found to correlate positively with independence of judgment in a group situational test based on the Asch experiment [r11], with resistance to illusion, and with ability to orient oneself in darkness in a situation [688] in which there is not only a minimum of external support but also a deliberately introduced distorting influence (the Witkin rod and frame experiment). Es was also correlated positively with several tests of social judgment, and negatively with the fascism scale [r3]. These findings are reported in detail elsewhere [47], and are cited here only by way of indicating that the ego-strength scale may be presumed to have sufficient validity and consistency so that the unexpected findings to be described below may properly be considered as requiring explanation in terms of the theory of ego development.

Sample and Method of Study

The men who constituted the sample for study in this investigation were 100 United States Air Force officers, of the rank of captain. They were observed for three days in a program of living-in assessment at the Institute of Personality Assessment and Research in Berkeley.

The majority of these men were combat veterans, and many of them had been decorated for valor during World War II. Of the 100, 96 were married, and most of these were fathers as well. In general, the sample was well above average in personal stability, intelligence, and physical health. This fact, of course, showed itself on the Es scale: the average T score for the sample was 63, with a standard deviation of 5.7.

In an effort to achieve a personality description of each subject which would allow room for the expression of clinical inference and which would at the same time be readily amenable to statistical analysis, a set of 76 Q-sort statements descriptive of personal functioning was assembled. These 76 statements were used by each staff member at the conclusion of the three days of living-in assessment to sum up his impressions of each person studied; the statements were sorted on a nine-point scale, the frequencies at each point being such as to make the final distribution conform closely to the normal curve. The objective was to obtain an ordering of the traits according to *saliency within the person*, rather than to order the persons in relation to one another on a given dimension. These staff observer Q-sorts were then composited for all staff raters (ten in all). It is thus the averaged staff judgments with which the individual subject is finally characterized.

These Q-sort descriptions were of course given without knowledge of the objective test performances of the subjects. No rater knew the Es scores of any of the subjects at the time he did the Q-sort.

A word concerning the method of study may be appropriate here. The distinctive feature of living-in assessment as a research instrument is that it provides a great variety of informal social interaction, in which the psychological staff members sit down to meals with the subjects, participate in a social hour before dinner, and are fairly called participant observers. In addition, considerable emphasis is placed upon situational tests, and also upon interviews, group discussion, improvisations, charades, and the like. Thus the social characteristics of the subjects have much opportunity to manifest themselves, and the raters are in a position to observe significant behavior.

Results with the Q-Sort

The relationship between Es scores and each one of the 76 Q-sort statements was determined. A total of 40 of the 76 statements proved to be correlated to a statistically significant (.05 level) degree with Es. (This was an unusually large number of Q-sort correlates for an MMPI scale in the present study; most of the standard clinical indicators on the MMPI were significantly correlated with only two or three Q-sort items, the average for the entire test being fewer than 5 per scale.)

A Tryon-type cluster analysis of the entire Q-sort item-pool was carried out to discover what communities of variance existed among the items. This cluster analysis is reported elsewhere [r21]. In listing the 40 Q-sort items correlated with the Es scale, we have grouped variables according to their own intercorrelations; that is, clusters of interrelated items are presented together.

Cluster I. Items Descriptive of General Effectiveness
1. Efficient, capable, able to mobilize resources easily and effectively; not bothered with work inhibitions.
2. Derives personal reward and pleasure from his work; values productive achievement for its own sake.
3. Is self-reliant; independent in judgment; able to think for himself.
4. Is an effective leader.
5. Is counteractive in the face of frustration.
6. Takes the initiative in social relations.
7. Communicates ideas clearly and effectively.
8. Is persuasive; tends to win other people over to his point of view.
9. Is verbally fluent; conversationally facile.

Cluster II. Items Descriptive of Aggressiveness, Power-Orientation, and Disregard of the Rights of Others
1. Takes an ascendant role in his relations with others.
2. Is competitive with his peers; likes to go ahead and to win.
3. Emphasizes success and productive achievement as a means for achieving status, power, and recognition.
4. Is aggressive and hostile in his personal relations.
5. Manipulates people as a means for achieving personal ends; opportunistic; sloughs over the meaning and value of the individual.
6. Is rebellious toward authority figures, rules, and other constraints.
7. Is sarcastic and cynical.

Items in clusters not substantially represented among Es scale correlates
1. Is masculine in his style and manner of behavior.
2. Is active and vigorous.
3. Prefers action to contemplation.
4. Undercontrols his impulses; acts with insufficient thinking and deliberation.

The Q-sort items which have a significant (.05 level) negative association with Es are these:

Cluster III. Items Descriptive of Personal Inferiority, Lack of Inner Resources

1. Lacks social poise and presence; becomes rattled and upset in social situations.
2. Lacks confidence in his own ability.
3. Is unable to make decisions without vacillation, hesitation, or delay.
4. Would become confused, disorganized, and unadaptive under stress.
5. Is suggestible; overly responsive to other people's evaluations rather than his own.
6. Is rigid; inflexible in thought and action.
7. Has a narrow range of interests.
8. Has slow personal tempo; responds, speaks, and moves slowly.
9. Tends not to become involved in things; passively resistant.
10. Is pedantic and fussy about minor things.

Cluster IV. Items Descriptive of Excessive Conformity and Personal Constriction

1. Overcontrols his impulses; is inhibited; needlessly delays or denies himself gratification.
2. With respect to authority, is submissive, compliant, and overly accepting.
3. Conforming; tends to do the things that are prescribed.
4. Tends to side-step troublesome situations; makes concessions to avoid unpleasantness.
5. Is stereotyped and unoriginal in his approach to problems.
6. Is self-abasing; feels unworthy, guilty, humble; given to self-blame.
7. Is pessimistic about his professional future and advancement.

Items in clusters not substantially represented among Es scale correlates

1. Sympathetic; feels for and with other people.
2. Respects others; is permissive and accepting; not judgmental.
3. Is effeminate in his style and manner of behavior.

Discussion of Q-Sort Results

Most of the results from the use of the Q-sort technique are quite consistent with findings from other procedures and from other studies. High scorers on Es, it would seem, are effective and independent people, with easy command over their own resources. They are intelligent, stable, and somewhat original, and they make their presence felt socially. Men who score high are appropriately masculine in their style of behavior. Low scorers, on the other hand, are confused, unadaptive, rigid, submissive, and rather stereotyped and unoriginal; low scorers among men tend to be somewhat effeminate as well.

This much is readily assimilable to the concept of ego-strength as it is generally used by psychologists. The observations which are the central concern of this report, however, point either to inadequacies in the scale or to some theoretical difficulties in relation to the concept itself. The Q-sort items in Cluster II appear to describe certain features, in the characters of at least some high scorers, which are not usually associated with strength of the ego. There is a good deal of aggression, perhaps even unethicality and destructiveness, implied in these items. There are at least some persons among the high scorers who are hostile and competitive, rebellious toward authority, opportunistic and manipulative, and sarcastic and cynical. If one thinks of a strong ego as one which is well integrated with a rational superego, then these persons might be considered to be improperly classified by the scale. Briefly, they appear to be manifesting more egoism than ego-strength.

The essential question here has to do with the existence and the management of aggression and hostility. Broadly speaking, hostility may be turned either inward, against the self, or outward, against objects; in an effective person, theory would hold, it is turned inward, in the service of the superego, to just the extent necessary for easy socialization; and outward, in the service of the ego, to just the extent necessary for the vigorous prosecution of one's own interests in gaining goods and prospering in life. Excesses in either direction would presumably characterize the weak ego; either extreme intropunitiveness or rampant hostility which draws retaliation is an inefficient solution in the management of aggression.

However, there is an economic consideration which must be borne in mind, and which may be crucial in explaining the present finding. Individuals differ in the amount of hostility and aggression which they carry about with them, and which it is the business of the ego to handle effectively. In persons with an excess of hostility, originating perhaps in more than the usual amount of frustration and disharmony in childhood, it might be expected that the question essentially resolves itself into this: will hostility be turned characteristically against the self, with the ego adopting a masochistic position in relation to the superego, or will the hostility be turned characteristically against objects other than the self?

The externally directed aggressiveness which we have observed in some high scorers on Es might then be explained as an economic solution, and a mark of greater rather than less ego-strength, if indeed it can be shown that these persons were subjected in childhood to experiences of frustration and disharmony, more so than what one finds in other high scorers on the scale. Fortunately, there are some data which bear on this hypothesis, and which permit at least a partial check on it. Each person studied had been interviewed for two hours by a psychiatrist concerning his background, with particular attention to childhood history. The interviewer, at the conclusion of the study, then rated all subjects relative to one another, using a nine-point scale, on various psychiatric variables, including one called "pathogenicity of childhood." This was defined as "the presence in childhood of circumstances which commonly produce mental illness or psychological upset." (The interviewers, it should be mentioned, did not see the subjects at any time except during the interview, and knew nothing of objective test performances or of the assessment staff's reactions to the subjects.)

To check the hypothesis that "hostile" high scorers on Es had more pathogenic childhoods, average scores of each subject on the Q-sort items in Cluster II were determined. Then all subjects who had earned T scores of 60 or more on the Es scale were ranked in terms of their Cluster II scores. This group consisted of 61 subjects. The top and bottom third of these (20 in each group, high Cluster II scorers being *more* aggressive and low scorers *less*) were now selected for comparison on life-history background factors, particularly the rating on pathogenicity of childhood. The latter comparison is presented in Table 1.

Considered in relation to the total sample, high scorers on both Es and Cluster II have had more pathogenic childhoods than the average subject, while persons who score high on Es but low on Cluster II have had less than the average amount of difficulty in childhood. The difference is statistically significant when the two groups are compared with one another. The interpretation seems justified that persons high on ego-strength, who nevertheless manifest considerable hostility toward others, are those who actually have more aggression in themselves to manage as a result of disturbing events in childhood.

Results supporting this interpretation are obtained when specific background information from the life-history interviews is considered. The interviewers, immediately upon the conclusion of each interview, used an "interview check list" to record what they had learned of the subject and his background. The 267 check list items were analyzed for differences between high Es scorers who were *high* and those who were *low* on Q-sort Cluster II. Thirty-three items showed differences significant at the .05 level. An over-all description based on this analysis is given below.

Table 1. Comparison of High Ego-Strength, High Aggressiveness
S's with High Ego-Strength, Low Aggressivness S's on
Ratings of Pathogenicity of Childhood

Item	Subjects High on Es, Low on Aggressiveness (Cluster II)		Subjects High on Es, High on Aggressiveness (Cluster II)
Mean	4.4		5.8
SD	2.11		1.99
F		4.45	
p		<.05	

Lows on Cluster II (hostility and aggression) were warmer in relating to the interviewer, were dressed both more comfortably and more inconspicuously, and appeared to be both more masculine and more reserved. Highs were described as more assertive, more self-assured, and more verbose. Highs also appeared more military, and held themselves straighter. As children, the lows were quieter, and tended more to play with other boys. The highs were more aggressive, and their play was described as more rough-and-tumble. The highs expressed negative affect toward their parents, while lows had more positive affect, and were more dutiful as children. The lows were more often described as having had stable homes. The highs, on the other hand, reported much more family friction. Highs describe their mothers more often as practical, while lows describe their mothers as warm and home-making. No differences emerged in the description of the father. In general, however, the lows idealized their parents more. To the lows, religion was personally meaningful and important, and they spoke favorably of it more often than did the highs. Highs had more often been separated or divorced from their wives. Highs also had more frequently had premarital intercourse with their wives.

The over-all picture from the life-history interview would seem to support the generalization that aggressiveness in persons of excellent ego-strength stems from life circumstances marked by relatively greater discord in the home during childhood, and friction in significant personal relations.

Summary

The ego-strength scale of the MMPI was used in a "living-in assessment" study of 100 military officers. Scorers on the scale had previously been found to be associated positively with a wide variety of valued personal traits, such as intelligence,. personal stability, independence of judgment, secure sense of reality, and ease and effectiveness in social situations. An unexpected finding that some high scorers on the scale were notably aggressive and hostile was explained in terms of the economic management of hostility engendered by disturbing childhood circumstances. The more aggressive subjects who had earned high scores on the scale reported more instability and family friction in their homes during their childhood, and they also expressed more negative feelings toward their parents; the less aggressive high-scoring subjects came of homes marked more by stability and warmth.

ARTICLE 65 *A Comparative Study of Five Catholic College Groups on the MMPI*

THE present study is an attempt to learn in detail something about the psychological factors which make for adjustment in a very specialized form of life, namely, among students for the priesthood. Personality evaluation and measurement have been much advanced in the last fifteen years, but virtually nothing is yet known of the extent to which general findings and general norms would have to be modified when applied to special vocational groups. The present investigation is directed toward discovering a preliminary answer for one such group, i.e., seminary students.

Personality measurement has fallen considerably short of the achievement reached in the field of intelligence and even of aptitudes. Nevertheless, personality measures applied in school, industry, and counseling have proved genuinely helpful, especially if not too much is asked of them in their present stage of development and their results are interpreted with reasonable reserve. This moderate but real success suggests the possibility of their profitable adaptation in the selection and evaluation of candidates for the priesthood.

Some such attempt would appear to be justified, if not indeed demanded. A recent study [r28], based on the accumulated records of two minor seminaries, the one embracing a period of forty, the other of fifty-seven years, reports that of the 2500 entrants to the two institutions no better than 25 to 35 per cent actually completed the seminary course and were ordained to the priesthood. In evaluating the numbers here quoted, it must be remembered that they include the minor as well as the major seminary. (The minor or junior seminary includes four years of college-preparatory high school and two years of classical college study. The major seminary includes the last two years of college with emphasis on Scholastic philosophy, and four years of theology.) In the case of one of the two minor seminaries referred to by Burke, 57 per cent of the 1341 entrants left by the end of the fourth year, i.e., two years before entering the major seminary. This indicates that, were the major seminary alone considered, the numbers here quoted would be reduced by more than a half. Nevertheless, the essential point is that the number of those who leave after having once begun the course of seminary studies is large, and it seems possible that the unfitness of some at least of these candidates could be detected at the very outset with considerable saving in time, money, and human energy. Such a

586

goal certainly is the desire of the candidate himself no less than of the seminary director.

The seminary certainly demands a very specialized way of life, and it is possible that the general norms of adjustment, made on a basis of the population at large, would have to be so modified when applied to this special group as to be substantially inapplicable. If, on the other hand, the essential applicability of such a test to the seminary group is demonstrated, there may still be important areas in which modification of the general norms is called for. If there prove to be areas of adjustment in which the seminary group differs significantly from the general population, it is important that a seminary candidate be judged, in respect to his mental health, by these modified norms, for this is the specialized way of life to which he proposes to apply himself. It can scarcely be doubted that what is unsatisfactory adjustment in one way of life may be very acceptable in another. It may be that a person would score poorly in adjustment if judged by general norms but may yet adjust very well to seminary life. The specific problem of this study is thus seen to be part of the larger problem of the extent to which general standards and general norms have to be modified for special vocational groups.

In the present investigation the attack upon the problem indicated has been made in terms of one particular personality test, the MMPI, which was chosen as the most promising instrument in the field.

The Subjects

The primary purpose of the present study was to determine to what extent the general norms of the MMPI would prove applicable to a seminary group. In other words, the author was seeking to discover what areas of personality adjustment or mental health might distinguish or uniquely specify the seminary group. This information, it was anticipated, would be revealed in the most striking light if a seminary group was compared with several other groups made as comparable to the seminary group as possible.

Vocational groups most similar to the seminary group would be found, it seemed, among professional students. Hence groups of medical, dental, and law students were secured for comparison with the seminary group. Finally a college group was included, and that for three reasons: (1) The validity studies of Hathaway and McKinley, as well as subsequent investigations, indicated certain special features relative to college groups; and since we were concerned with possible modifications of general norms, inclusion of a college group appeared desirable. (2) Since college is a least common denominator among professional students, the inclusion of this group might act as a general control and a sort of base line for comparison. (3) We were interested ultimately in the possible adaptation of the MMPI as a help in evaluating the psychological adjustment and mental health of candidates for the priesthood, and the college group approximates more closely than any of the others the general status of the seminary candidate at time of application.

The Seminary Group. The MMPI was administered to 188 seminary students. Of these, the records of three respondents were discarded because they did not meet the norms on the three qualifying scales of the inventory. This procedure of eliminating those records not satisfactory on the qualifying scales was followed for all the groups. Work has been done throughout this investigation with standard scores, and according to the test norms, those records were considered nonqualify-ing whose scores on these scales were more than two standard deviations above the mean. When the score on one of the qualifying scales rises above this critical level, it does not, in the opinion of the authors of the test, automatically invalidate the record, but it does call for caution and individual interpretation. Since the present study concerned itself only with group results, individual evaluation could not be given, and such records had to be dropped from the population.

Four additional tests had to be dropped from the seminary group because the respondents did not give their ages, which were required, as explained below, in order to equate the groups on this basis. Ten more were eliminated because they were minor seminarians.

The seminary group employed in the study thus numbered 171. These were drawn from the ranks of diocesan seminarians and from three religious orders, all major seminarians, engaged in the study of either philosophy or theology in prepara-tion for the priesthood. They were geographically well distributed, being drawn from the East, the Midwest, and the Far West. The author considers, therefore, that this seminary group is a good representative sampling of students for the priesthood.

The Medical Group. Tests were administered to 264 medical students. Of these the records of 5 were dropped on the basis of their scores on the qualifying scales of the MMPI. Of the remainder, 25 were eliminated because they were non-Catholics. This appeared necessary. Since all the seminary group were Catholics, difference of religion, if this appeared in the other groups, might be a factor making for differences on the MMPI scales between the seminary and the other groups. In keeping, therefore, with the fundamental pattern of studying groups as similar to the seminary group as possible, the non-Catholics were eliminated from all the other groups. For the same fundamental reason, since all the seminarians were unmarried, the married men were dropped from the other groups. Because they were married, 26 additional students were withdrawn from the medical group. This left a medical group of 208, the subjects of the present study. The geographical dis-tribution as indicated by home state is good, and there is no reason to think that this is not a reasonably representative cross section of medical students.

The Dental Group. MMPI tests were given to 206 dental students. Of these 3 had to be eliminated on a basis of qualifying scores, 58 because they were not Catholics, and 24 because they were married, leaving 121 as the subjects actually used in the study. Again the geographical distribution by home state is good, and there is no indication that this is not a representative group of dental students.

The Law Group. In this group 162 tests were administered. Of this number 6 had to be eliminated for qualifying scales, 57 because they were non-Catholics, and 44 because they were married, leaving but 55 in the group which could be used in the present study. The number which could actually be employed in the law group was disappointingly small, but it was impossible to secure more because the testing was done during the war years when the rosters of law schools were much depleted. The seminary population was untouched by the draft during the war, and medical and dental students were largely unaffected, because the army and navy simply inducted medical and dental students and left them at their stud-ies. The picture was different in law schools, which were substantially affected by the draft, and when, in addition, unmarried students were required as in the present case, the task of getting any large number at that particular time proved impossibly difficult.

In addition to the small size of the law group, it is probably not well representative of the ordinary peacetime law school population. But neither for that matter is the swollen postwar law school population of today. The author either, therefore, had to drop the law group entirely, or employ what he had been able to get and look upon the results as suggestive rather than representative or definitive in any sense. The latter alternative was chosen. Though there are only 55 in the law group, they are drawn from eight different law schools, in the East, Midwest, and Far West. From this point of view the sampling is good.

It may be pointed out that the limitation of our medical, dental, and law students to unmarried men does not restrict their representativeness. The married professional student is not typical; he is a war and postwar product.

The College Group. This was the largest group, 464 college students taking the inventory. Of these, 17 had to be eliminated on the basis of qualifying scales, 76 because of religion, and 2 because of failure to furnish age data. This left a college group of 369.

The college group too was somewhat affected by the war situation. There were a large number of freshmen and sophomores in the group, since the upper classmen had for the most part been drawn off by the draft. This tended to make the college sample younger than would ordinarily be the case, but despite this fact it is undoubtedly more representative of a normal college population than would be the present veteran-filled college classes.

This process of elimination accomplished the purpose of providing groups as comparable to the seminary group as possible on all counts. All the groups employed in the study were composed of men who were both Catholic and unmarried. There was the least common denominator of college with respect to education; the further educational diversity was but a reflection of divergent vocational training, and therefore part of the picture of occupational difference. The common denominator of college education did much to induce automatically a relative homogeneity of socioeconomic background. The same factor operated likewise to produce a rough equation of the groups on a basis of intelligence. There was no ceiling, as is evident, in this respect in any of the groups, but there was in all a common lower level. It is well known that the successive stages of the educational system act as very effective eliminators of the less able intellectually, so that a certain minimal level of intelligence — naturally higher than the population at large — is characteristic of all college groups. There remained, however, marked differences of age between the groups. Such differences could not be controlled experimentally, but the groups were equated statistically on the basis of age by a covariance technique. This equation left the only major difference between the groups a vocational one, which was the pattern of investigation the author had set out to achieve.

Results

Most of the 1284 tests given in the course of this investigation were administered anonymously. Since the author was not interested in the individual but only in the group results, this seemed the better procedure. Many of the items of the questionnaire are of a distinctly personal nature, and a frank answer is frequently not flattering to the individual. The cloak of anonymity offered a better guarantee that the questions would be answered with the requisite frankness.

With anonymity in administration of the tests two consequences followed. First, the qualifying scales of the MMPI assumed great importance, for they gave the only guarantee that the test record could be accepted at its face value. The author considers the incorporation of qualifying scales into the inventory as a distinct advance in personality test construction. For this reason too the test norms were held to resolutely in this respect and all records were excluded which did not meet the demands of even one of the qualifying scales. It is a tribute to the cooperativeness of our respondents that only 34 records out of 1284, less than 3 per cent of the total, had to be rejected on this basis.

A second result of conducting the tests anonymously was the necessity of securing all pertinent information at the time of administration, as any subsequent check for such a purpose was precluded.

The results of the analysis of covariance are given in Tables 1 and 2. Table 1 gives the experimental and adjusted means, together with differences between them, for each of the groups on each of the MMPI scales. Likewise included in this table is the standard deviation for each group on each of the scales, based, however, not on the adjusted means, but on the means of the experimental population.

Table 1 reveals that on the first seven of the MMPI scales for the first four groups the effect of controlling for age variation is to lower the experimentally determined score. The dominant effect, therefore, of correcting for age differences is to bring the scores of our groups nearer to the test norms for the general population. The effect, on the contrary, for the college group on these same scales is to raise the experimental score. In the last two scales the opposite effect takes place. Here the first four groups show a rise in the corrected over the experimental mean, the college group a decline.

Hathaway and McKinley [301] had early noted an age difference on the MMPI with a clear tendency for higher scores at higher age levels. The present results appear to bear out this observation. In correcting for age differences one notes the tendency for the scores of the older groups to be lowered and those for the youngest group to be raised. Such a tendency is in accord with these earlier findings.

Table 1 likewise reveals the varying extent to which age differences influence the individual scales. The general average correction for age differences is 0.593. The D scale shows an average age correction of more than twice that amount, namely, 1.187; while the Pd scale shows hardly any influence at all, 0.010. On the basis of these results, therefore, D appears more than one hundred times more subject to the influence of age differences than the Pd scale. These scales represent the extremes in this respect, the others ranging in between.

A significant feature of Table 1 is the consistent manner in which the means for the present groups rise above the mean of the general population as established in the test norms. Table 1 reveals that 89 per cent of the group means on the MMPI scales are above 50. This observation is true whether the experimental or the adjusted means are considered.

An analysis of the number of scale deviations large enough to fall, according to the norms of the MMPI, in the area of the abnormal will furnish evidence of the

Table 1. Experimental and Adjusted Means, Differences between Them, and Standard Deviations for Each Group

Item	Hs	D	Hy	Pd	Mf	Pa	Pt	Sc	Ma
				Seminary					
			MMPI Code: 5–39672841						
Experimental mean	51.088	53.421	57.012	52.298	63.439	54.333	53.924	53.099	54.661
Adjusted mean	49.948	51.347	55.528	52.281	62.104	53.691	53.792	53.786	56.030
Difference ...	−1.140	−2.074	−1.484	−0.017	−1.335	−0.642	−0.132	0.687	1.369
SD [a]	8.14	11.74	7.72	9.78	9.52	7.27	8.95	7.70	8.44
				Medical					
			MMPI Code: 9543 678/21						
Experimental mean	46.707	48.543	54.067	54.769	58.231	52.125	51.457	50.875	59.312
Adjusted mean	46.520	48.203	53.824	54.766	58.012	52.020	51.435	50.988	59.537
Difference ...	−0.187	−0.340	−0.757	−0.003	−0.219	−0.105	−0.022	0.113	0.225
SD	5.33	9.53	6.70	10.39	9.39	10.05	9.05	8.12	9.27
				Dental					
			MMPI Code: 9354 786/12						
Experimental mean	48.099	47.083	53.397	52.967	53.231	50.901	51.380	51.091	59.289
Adjusted mean	47.770	46.484	52.969	52.962	52.846	50.716	51.342	51.289	59.684
Difference ...	−0.329	−0.599	−0.428	−0.005	−0.385	−0.185	−0.038	0.198	0.395
SD ./.......	6.52	10.93	7.13	9.56	9.54	7.91	9.50	8.91	10.45
				Law					
			MMPI Code: 953426781/						
Experimental mean	51.327	53.891	57.564	54.073	59.000	53.200	52.454	51.764	59.400
Adjusted mean	50.574	52.522	56.584	54.062	58.119	52.776	51.584	52.218	60.304
Difference ...	−0.753	−1.369	−0.980	−0.011	−0.881	−0.424	−0.870	0.454	0.904
SD	6.90	12.68	7.57	8.19	9.26	9.08	11.28	9.72	8.32
				College					
			MMPI Code: 9534786 2/1						
Experimental mean	49.902	50.518	53.900	53.737	54.859	52.528	53.187	53.106	57.653
Adjusted mean	50.756	52.071	55.011	53.750	55.859	53.009	53.286	52.591	56.628
Difference ...	0.854	1.553	1.111	0.013	1.000	0.481	0.099	−0.515	−1.025
SD	7.44	11.01	8.18	10.30	10.29	8.09	9.84	9.37	10.00
				Differences					
Total	3.263	5.935	4.760	0.049	3.820	1.837	1.161	1.967	3.918
Average	0.653	1.187	0.952	0.010	0.764	0.367	0.232	0.393	0.784

[a] The standard deviations are calculated for the experimental population.

departure of the subjects of the present study from the norms set up for the population at large.

It will be seen from Table 3 that 5.3 per cent of the scales are abnormal, only slightly more than the amount expected on statistical grounds. In evaluating this figure, however, one important point must be taken into consideration. Statistically it is expected that about as many will fall short of the mean by more than two standard deviations as will exceed it by the same amount. In the present case, however, this symmetrical distribution is by no means attained. The MMPI does not provide for extreme deviations below the mean to the same extent to which provision is made for deviations above the mean.

Table 2. t Ratios Giving Statistical Significance of Adjusted Means of Table 1 [a]

Group	Hs	D	Hy	Pd	Mf	Pa	Pt	Sc	Ma
				Seminary					
Medical	−4.737[b]	−2.789	−2.173	2.395	−4.045	−2.050	−2.382	3.083	3.562
Dental	−2.615	−3.749	−2.836	0.570	−7.953	−3.172	−2.151	−2.391	3.225
Law	0.576	0.694	0.897	1.143	−2.623	−0.748	−1.486	−1.150	2.891
College	1.246	0.717	−0.736	1.580	−6.889	−0.934	−0.570	−1.469	0.678
				Medical					
Dental	1.559	−1.377	−0.984	−1.570	−4.611	−1.444	−0.085	0.299	0.135
Law	3.814	2.609	2.396	−0.462	0.072	0.631	0.102	0.923	0.530
College	6.968	4.086	1.802	−1.166	−2.534	1.445	2.227	2.103	−3.517
				Dental					
Law	2.459	3.400	2.926	0.673	3.309	1.604	0.155	0.650	0.400
College	4.066	4.884	2.566	0.748	2.935	2.772	1.935	1.414	−3.059
				Law					
College	0.180	−0.286	−1.433	−0.215	−1.596	0.204	1.228	0.293	−2.666
				Total					
.05 level	0	0	1	0	0	1	2	1	0
.02 level	1	0	2	1	1	0	1	1	0
.01 level	5	6	2	0	7	2	0	1	6

[a] $t_{05} = 1.960$; $t_{02} = 2.326$; $t_{01} = 2.576$
[b] − indicates difference in favor of better adjustment for the comparative over the standard group.

Table 3. Number and Percentage of Abnormal Scales by Groups

Group	Individuals Having Abnormal Scales		Abnormal Scales	
	Number	Percentage	Number	Percentage
Seminary	69	40.3	103	6.7
Medical	61	29.6	83	4.4
Dental	34	28.1	49	4.5
Law	18	32.7	32	6.5
College	102	27.6	173	5.2
Total	284	30.7	440	5.3

On only five of the nine MMPI scales is it possible to secure a standard score under 30. On the other four scales, optimum adjustment as measured by the inventory is assigned a standard score above 30. By actual count in the population employed in the present study only 8 out of the 440 abnormal scales were abnormally low. All the rest were abnormally high, i.e., in the direction of maladjustment. In other words, the number of abnormally high scales in our population is more than twice the statistical expectancy. On purely statistical grounds it would be expected that about one in forty of the MMPI scales would have a standard score in excess of 70. In the present study the observed frequency of scores above 70 is about one in sixteen. This difference is certainly significant and confirms very strikingly the unmistakable tendency of the subjects to score higher than the population at large upon which the MMPI was standardized.

The evidence here presented confirms and extends what has previously been reported on the deviant tendencies of such college-educated populations.

The seminary group manifests the same deviant tendencies as the general population of the study, though in a more marked degree than the other groups. This is indicated by the differences between the seminary and the other groups on the MMPI scales. If the .05 level of significance is accepted, 55 per cent of the differences between the seminary and the other groups are significant; 40 per cent of such differences are significant at the .01 level. Of these statistically significant differences 80 per cent are in the direction of greater deviation, i.e., poorer adjustment, for the seminary group. In other words, the seminary group is the most deviant portion of an already deviant population.

Table 3 gives further evidence that the seminary group is the most deviant of the population. The seminary group has the highest percentage of abnormal scales, whether we consider the percentage of individuals having one or more scales in the abnormal range (and this for the seminary group is 40 per cent), or whether we consider the percentage of abnormal scales directly, which in the case of the seminary group is 6.7 per cent. This last figure is approximately three times the frequency expected on statistical grounds, and, taken with the other evidence, marks the seminary group as unmistakably departing from the general population as indicated in the test norms.

Since the inventory does not directly yield any total adjustment score, the author was compelled to estimate a total adjustment score for each of the subjects of the study. This score for each of the subjects was secured by simply adding the T scores for each of the scales. The MMPI is so constructed that on all the scales satisfactory adjustment is indicated by low scores, poor adjustment by high scores. The tendencies, therefore, of all the scales are in the same direction, and hence the higher total score would be indicative of poorer general adjustment and the lower score of more satisfactory adjustment.

One check was made to test the validity of the assumption that the tendencies of all the scales were in the same direction by calculating and constructing a table of intercorrelations on all the MMPI scales for the total population of the study.

Only 3 of the 36 intercorrelations are negative (all are found on the Ma scale) but only 2 of the 3 are statistically significant. These negative intercorrelations, few and low as they are, clearly do not disturb in any essential way the underlying tendencies of the intercorrelation table which are all positive and hence in the same general direction. The author considers, therefore, that the total adjustment score gives a general, over-all picture of adjustment and that, as a consequence, the higher it is, the poorer the general adjustment; the lower, the better the general adjustment.

When a total adjustment score was obtained for each individual, it became no more than a routine operation to arrange each group in an ordered series from the best to the poorest in adjustment. The extremes of the population appeared to furnish the purest examples of good and poor adjustment, where the tendencies in each case were likely to appear in clearest detail. Accordingly the bottom and top 27 per cent of each group were cut off on a basis of the total adjustment scores.

A covariance analysis was applied to these two portions of the population for the inter-group differences on each of the MMPI scales. A summary of the number of inter-group differences which are significant at the three levels of confidence, the .05, the .02, and the .01, has been made and is presented in Table 4. It should be remarked that in all three analyses the differences were calculated on a basis of group means adjusted for age differences.

Table 4. Number of Differences Attaining Significance at Different Confidence Levels for the Total Groups and for the Well-Adjusted and Poorly Adjusted Portions of the Population

MMPI Scales	Total Groups			Well-Adjusted Portion			Poorly Adjusted Portion		
	$p < .05$	$p < .02$	$p < .01$	$p < .05$	$p < .02$	$p < .01$	$p < .05$	$p < .02$	$p < .01$
Hs	0	1	5	2	2	2	1	2	3
D	0	0	6	1	2	0	1	1	4
Hy	1	2	2	1	0	1	2	0	1
Pd	0	1	0	0	0	0	2	1	1
Mf	0	1	7	2	0	6	0	0	5
Pa	1	0	2	0	0	3	0	0	0
Pt	2	1	0	0	1	3	2	1	0
Sc	1	1	1	0	0	4	2	1	1
Ma	0	0	6	0	0	2	0	0	4
Total	5	7	29	6	5	21	10	6	19

One fact emerges clearly from these data, especially as summarized in Table 4. There are fewer significant inter-group differences in the well-adjusted and the poorly adjusted portions of the population than there are when the groups are treated as a whole.

It may be said, therefore, that the well-adjusted and poorly adjusted portions of the experimental group form, each of them, relatively homogeneous populations. This is true despite the fact that in each case the population is composed of five different vocational groups. Of the two, the well adjusted clearly form the more homogeneous population. Here, as pointed out above, are found the smallest number of significant inter-group differences. In this portion of the population, too, the standard deviation on every one of the MMPI scales is smaller than it is for the total population. With the poorly adjusted population, on the contrary, only three out of the nine scales have standard deviations smaller than those found for the total groups.

The impression begins to form that adjustment — at least in its markedly better or poorer form — is something quite basic, which cuts across the relatively more superficial occupational and vocational lines. This conclusion is much strengthened by a consideration of Table 5, which presents in terms of t ratios the significant differences between the means of the well-adjusted and the poorly adjusted portions of each group.

The inter-group differences as revealed in the well-adjusted and poorly adjusted portions of the population are exceeded many times over by the differences between the well-adjusted and poorly adjusted portions of the same group. Well-adjusted seminarians are shown to differ far more from poorly adjusted seminarians than they do from well-adjusted medical, dental, law, and college students. Psychological adjustment emerges as something basic transcending purely vocational lines. Good personality adjustment is found to mean, to a very large extent, the same thing in the seminarian as it does in the members of the other occupational groups comprising the present study, and the same is true of poor or unfavorable adjustment.

Table 5. t Ratios Giving the Significant Differences between the Means of the Well-Adjusted and Poorly Adjusted Portions of Each Group [a]

Group	Hs	D	Hy	Pd	Mf	Pa	Pt	Sc	Ma
Seminary	9.980	8.373	5.519	9.018	7.022	5.782	12.363	10.903	2.411
Medical	6.343	6.097	3.373	12.406	9.353	7.752	13.090	12.838	7.137
Dental	6.827	5.784	3.315	8.287	5.761	6.834	10.643	10.463	6.126
Law	5.151	5.540	2.035	5.478	4.694	5.298	8.758	8.798	1.949
College	16.182	14.048	9.920	11.500	14.030	10.594	19.143	18.470	7.170
Total population	21.262	18.821	11.941	21.366	19.556	16.631	29.617	28.390	11.649

[a] $t_{05} = 1.960$; $t_{02} = 2.326$; $t_{01} = 2.576$.

This, the author believes, is the answer to the first question which this investigation was designed to answer. Are seminarians so special a group that the norms of personality adjustment or mental health, established for the population at large, are inapplicable to them?

The answer to this question on the basis of the present evidence is No! The MMPI will serve as a substantially suitable instrument in the testing of seminary adjustment because it is accomplishing essentially the same thing, giving essentially the same differentiation in the seminary group as it is in the others. The seminarian does not present a substantially different picture of good and satisfactory, or poor and unsatisfactory adjustment, from that given by the members of the other occupational groups studied. When, however, nearly a third of the total number of differences attain significance at the .01 level, they demand serious consideration.

Table 6 presents in summary form these data. The next to last row of Table 6 gives for all groups combined the percentage of the total number of differences attaining significance at each of the three levels of confidence. The last row of the table presents the same data for the seminary group alone. A comparison of these two rows reveals that the seminary group surpasses the other groups in the number of areas of adjustment which stand revealed as significantly different. These, we may say, are the areas of adjustment uniquely specifying the seminary group, and there are more of these areas of special adjustment for the seminary group than for the others. This fact is borne out in the two rows referred to by a direct comparison of the .01 levels for the total groups and for the well-adjusted portion of the population. In the former case the general percentage is 32.2, the seminary, 38.9; and in the latter instance the 23.3 of the general percentage is doubled for the seminary group, becoming 44.4. If we now cumulate the general percentages for the analysis of total groups, combining the percentages significant at the .01, the .02, and the .05 levels, we get a total of 45.5 per cent of the differences which attain significance by the most lenient criterion (the .05 level). A similar cumulation for the seminary group gives 55.5 per cent of the differences significant by the same criterion. Similarly, in the well-adjusted analysis, a cumulative total of the general percentage gives 35.5 per cent significant differences; the same for the seminary group again gives 55.5 per cent. In the analysis of the poorly adjusted portion of the population, the cumulative totals are practically the same for the general percentage (38.9) and for the seminary group (38.8). This indicates clearly that there are a number of areas of adjustment which uniquely specify the seminary group.

Table 6. Number of Differences Attaining Significance at Different Confidence Levels for Each of the Experimental Groups

Experimental Group	Total Group			Well-Adjusted Portion			Poorly Adjusted Portion		
	$p < .05$	$p < .02$	$p < .01$	$p < .05$	$p < .02$	$p < .01$	$p < .05$	$p < .02$	$p < .01$
Seminary	3	3	14	1	3	16	3	4	7
Medical	4	4	11	1	0	8	4	2	11
Dental	1	3	15	4	3	5	4	3	8
Law	0	2	8	4	2	5	4	1	3
College	2	2	10	2	2	8	5	2	9
Total	10	14	58	12	10	42	20	12	38
Percentage of total	5.5	7.8	32.2	6.7	5.5	23.3	11.1	6.7	21.1
Percentage of seminary group	8.3	8.3	38.9	2.8	8.3	44.4	8.3	11.1	19.4

There remains one further point which appears worthy of presentation and which serves to distinguish the well-adjusted and poorly adjusted portions of the population from the total groups. Intercorrelations of the MMPI scales for the well-adjusted and poorly adjusted portions of the population show 18 negative correlations in the table of the well-adjusted portion of the population out of a total of 36 correlations, exactly half. There are 12 negative correlations, or one third of the total, in the table of the poorly adjusted portion of the population. This large number of negative correlations, especially in view of the very small number in the table of the total population, calls for some explanation.

The author believes that the explanation lies fundamentally in terms of the compensation which inevitably takes place in the sphere of personality adjustment, whereby a high score on the one scale may in very large part be compensated for, if other portions of the personality profile are favorable. This is the fundamental reason why it is unsafe to attempt an interpretation of adjustment on the basis of a single score, even though high, on an individual scale, without taking into account the entire personality profile.

The negative correlations found are indices, in the interpretation suggested here, of the extent to which such compensatory influences operated in the population of the present study. While a certain number of the compensatory influences observed may be explained by the natural opposition between traits, the author suggests that an appreciable portion cannot be explained in this way and are due to the unifying power of the personality, whereby deficiencies in one area are supplied by more or less conscious cultivation of other areas. This suggested interpretation may have some kinship with the "successful compensation" of which Adler made so much and which he erected into his system of individual psychology.

The larger number of negative correlations in the well-adjusted portion of the population reveals that compensatory influences, of the kind indicated, were more at work here than among the poorly adjusted, even though in the latter instance too this tendency was very appreciably present. In other words, more poor scores on individual scales were compensated for by the well adjusted than good scores lost by the poorly adjusted. Very good adjustment appears to involve a considerable integration of the total personality. Poor adjustment does not appear to be so total an affair. Generally poor adjustment does not seem to be incompatible with rather good adjustment in certain restricted areas of personality.

Where the negative correlations are most in evidence and where, according to the interpretation suggested, the compensatory influences are at a maximum, the average intercorrelations are found to be lowest. The average intercorrelation for the well-adjusted portion of the population, where the largest number of negative correlations is found, is .1832, and for the total groups, where there are very few negative correlations, the average correlation coefficient rises to .3148. The relatively low intercorrelation coefficients obtained throughout this investigation are in keeping with other MMPI findings and are an indication that the MMPI scales are measuring largely different and relatively independent phases of personality adjustment.

When the several groups are compared on the MMPI scales (see Table 7), the greatest inter-group differences for the seminary group are found on the Mf scale. Here 10 out of the 12 differences attain significance at the .01 level. On the same criterion of significance, the Ma and Sc scales are next in importance, with Hs, D, and Pa following closely thereafter. In the last three scales, one third of the differences are significant at this level, and this result, as we have seen, is about the average for the entire population of this study.

Following this viewpoint in interpretation, Table 7 reveals the seminary group as unique in its personality adjustment to an extent meeting the highest criterion of significance (.01 level) in six or seven of the nine MMPI scales. In terms of the MMPI scales, therefore, these appear to be the areas of adjustment in which modifications of the general norms should be considered if this test is to be employed with seminary groups. As indicated previously, the entire experimental population shows in accentuated form the general tendency of college and college-educated groups to score higher on the MMPI scales than the general population on which the test norms have been based. If the seminary group is differentiated to the extent indicated above from other groups in an already deviant population, it is an a fortiori argument that the differentiation from the general population is even greater and hence that the modification of these general norms is even more necessary.

It is necessary to explain here that Table 7, which sums up the statistical significance of the differences between the seminary group and the other groups, cannot be interpreted without some reference to the absolute scores of the seminary group on the MMPI scales. These scores for the total seminary group are given in Table 1. This table reveals that the seminarians score above the mean of the population on all nine of the MMPI scales. In the view expressed here these absolute scores constitute more basic data than are given by the inter-group differences. Had we chosen other groups to compare with the seminary group, the inter-group differences would have been changed, but the scores of the seminary group on the MMPI scales would have remained the same. However, these basic scores do not tell us much about the adjustment specific to the seminary group. On the supposition that a representative group of seminary students are as well adjusted for their way of life as a cross section of the general population for theirs, these scores create a presumption of unfairness to the seminary group and carry the suggestion, therefore, that some modification be allowed in interpreting these scores for such a group. The author has considered that the areas of adjustment specific to the seminary group would be revealed most significantly by the inter-group differences. This conviction has guided the plan of the entire investigation, and it is consistent, therefore, to allow the inter-group differences to receive the stress in interpretation.

Table 7. t Ratios Giving Statistical Significance of the Differences between the Means of the Seminary and the Other Groups on the MMPI Scales [a]

Group	Hs	D	Hy	Pd	Mf	Pa	Pt	Sc	Ma
				Total Group					
Medical	−4.737	−2.797	−2.173	2.395	−4.045	−2.050	−2.382	3.083	3.562
Dental	−2.615	−3.749	−2.836	0.570	−7.953	−3.172	−2.151	−2.391	3.225
Law	0.576	0.694	0.897	1.143	−2.623	−0.748	−1.486	−1.150	2.891
College	1.246	0.717	−0.736	1.580	−6.889	−0.934	−0.570	−1.469	0.678
				Well-Adjusted					
Medical	−3.593	−0.274	0.144	−1.073	−4.049	−2.755	−3.536	−5.560	−0.814
Dental	−2.282	−2.448	−0.544	−1.031	−6.499	−3.571	−3.628	−4.644	−0.726
Law	0.710	−0.505	1.753	0.267	−2.619	−1.677	−2.455	−3.037	1.330
College	−2.421	−0.487	−1.303	−1.678	−7.561	−3.373	−3.809	−6.424	−2.658
				Poorly Adjusted					
Medical	−5.076	−2.610	−2.188	1.266	−1.866	−0.990	−2.486	−2.540	3.324
Dental	−2.399	−2.600	−1.724	−0.092	−5.395	−0.924	−1.961	−1.564	3.553
Law	−0.199	0.467	0.122	0.520	−1.339	0.888	0.277	0.842	1.883
College	−0.196	0.822	0.262	−2.331	−3.418	−1.170	−1.622	−2.109	0.325
				Total					
.05 level	1	0	2	0	0	1	2	1	0
.02 level	2	1	0	2	0	0	3	2	0
.01 level	4	4	1	0	10	4	3	5	6

[a] — indicates difference in favor of better adjustment for the other group in question over the seminary group. $t_{05} = 1.960$; $t_{02} = 2.326$; $t_{01} = 2.576$.

It is interesting to note, however, how these two lines of evidence coincide in picking out the Mf scale as the one on which the seminary group manifests the most divergence both from the general test norms (Table 1) and the scores of the other groups (Table 7). Mf is the masculine-feminine interest scale and is built upon the assumption that men and women have characteristic patterns of interest and that these interests may be interpreted as indices of masculine and feminine tendencies. The concept here, as in the other MMPI scales, is that this tendency — possessed within proper limits — is a necessary component of the normally adjusted personality, but that its excess — in the direction of the interest pattern characteristic of the opposite sex — may become a disabling personality disorder. The present results indicate that this is the least suitable of the scales for use with a seminary group and, in this connection, offer an interesting commentary upon and confirmation of the earliest work of Terman and Miles [r160]. These authors did the pioneer work in masculinity-femininity tests and report very unfavorable scores for seminary students.

All the differences given above between the seminary group and the other groups are in terms of the MMPI scales. The information here afforded remains in rather general and global terms. The author wished to explain and specify somewhat further the meaning of these differences in personality adjustment. It was decided that the most satisfactory way of accomplishing this end would be to descend from the scales of the MMPI to the individual test items and to submit these to an analysis.

The item analysis was made on the well-adjusted and the poorly adjusted portion of the population, the same 27 per cent showing the best and the same 27 per cent showing the poorest adjustment as furnished the subjects for the preceding analysis. This choice was motivated by the same design which had dictated the original division into well-adjusted and poorly adjusted portions of the population, the conviction, namely, that in these extremes of the population the clearest and most revealing pictures of good and bad, or satisfactory and unsatisfactory, adjustment would be found.

The item analysis was restricted to the first 366 items as they are found in the new group form of the MMPI. These 366 items in the new group form contain 16 duplications so that actually the analysis was made on 350 of the original 550 items. These are the only items which have been incorporated into any of the MMPI personality scales thus far published, and it appeared that the purposes of the item analysis would best be served by restricting the scope of this analysis to correspond with the covariance analysis previously discussed. The latter analysis, as is evident, was in terms of the MMPI scales.

The first step in the item analysis was a simple tally of the number of True, Untrue, and Cannot Say responses for each item. The percentage of responses falling in these three categories are presented in Table 8. This table reveals a marked trend in which all groups agree. The well adjusted consistently mark fewer of the items True and more of them Untrue than the poorly adjusted. This fact seems logical and understandable. If the MMPI is designed to test for personality adjustment, it is evident that many items in the inventory would necessarily deal with personality disorders. More of the items characteristic of maladjustments would be true of the poorly adjusted. One wonders, however, if there may not be another tendency at work. Some of the maladjusted are characteristically suggestible to an extent that the mere proposal of an idea is sufficient for them to ascribe it to themselves. The hypochondriac is an instance in point. Typically he has every ill which is mentioned. A tendency toward suggestibility may be so widespread among the poorly adjusted as to be truly characteristic.

The next step in the item analysis was to make a study of the items showing the greatest inter-group differences in adjustment. To accomplish this end, the author had to take the items one by one, and the groups pair by pair, and determine for each item and each pair the percentage difference. Clearly the items which yielded, on a basis of this comparison, the greatest percentage differences were the items giving the most differentiation in adjustment between the two groups. Out of the 350 items so compared, the 40 giving the greatest inter-group differentiation were selected for further study. Similar tables were prepared for the other groups.

Table 8. Percentage of Responses Falling in the True, Untrue, and Cannot Say Categories

Group	Well-Adjusted Portion			Poorly Adjusted Portion		
	True	Untrue	Cannot Say	True	Untrue	Cannot Say
Seminary	39.2	58.7	2.1	43.7	55.0	1.3
Medical	38.4	60.6	1.0	45.2	54.2	0.6
Dental	38.8	59.7	1.5	45.6	53.7	0.7
Law	38.6	59.8	1.6	44.5	54.6	0.9
College	38.0	59.8	2.2	45.4	53.2	1.4

It is worthy of note that the 160 items reduce to 72 different items. In terms of items, then, this is the place where the differentiation in adjustment between the seminary and the other groups is to be found.

We may well ask to what extent the 72 items thus found to specify the adjustment of the seminary group would be discovered among the items differentiating the other groups in the same way. The analogous case for the medical group yielded 113 different items; for the dental group, 107; for the law group, 92; and for the college group, 103. If now these five tables are put together, a composite table is obtained which gives for all groups combined the relative discriminatory value of all the items which have qualified between any two groups as among the 40 most discriminatory items. This table provides a summary for the entire experimental population of the power of the MMPI items to differentiate on the basis of adjustment among the five different vocational groups comprising the present study.

The author went on to deal with the most discriminatory items in the poorly adjusted portion of the population, and, proceeding in the manner indicated above, derived a table for this portion of the population analogous in all details to that for the well-adjusted groups. Then the author proceeded in the same way to study the least discriminatory items, taking, as before, pair by pair for comparison, the 40 items which gave the least percentage difference between the groups. Thus, the tables for the least discriminatory items were constructed. Again a separate study was made of the well-adjusted and poorly adjusted portions of the population, and in each case the end result was a composite table.

One thing more was needed to complete the design of the item analysis. This was a study of the power of the MMPI items to differentiate between the well-adjusted and poorly adjusted portion of each group. All that has been described up to this point has dealt with inter-group differentiation; now we turn to the question of intra-group diversification.

The extent to which the results of the item analysis furnish a check on the validity of the MMPI scales will first be considered.

It was previously noted that for the well-adjusted portion of the population, the

Mf scale clearly gives the largest number of inter-group differences, and in Table 9 this is also the scale which contains the highest percentage of most discriminatory items and a relatively small percentage of least discriminatory items. The same scale gives the greatest number of inter-group differences for the poorly adjusted part of the population, and again this is the scale which has the highest percentage of most discriminatory items. The correspondence for the Pa scale is also good, but for the rest it must be admitted that the correspondence between Table 9 and the previous tables appears indifferent at best.

Table 9. The Four Summary Tables of the Item Analysis, Grouped According to the Scales to Which the Items Belong

Scale	No. of Items in Scale	Well-Adjusted Portion				Poorly Adjusted Portion			
		Most Discriminating		Least Discriminating		Most Discriminating		Least Discriminating	
		No.	Percentage	No.	Percentage	No.	Percentage	No.	Percentage
Hs	33	7	21.2	21	63.6	9	27.3	28	84.8
D	60	25	41.7	23	38.3	30	50.0	39	65.0
Hy	60	28	46.7	26	43.3	27	45.0	36	60.0
Pd	50	24	48.0	21	42.0	32	64.0	25	50.0
Mf	60	37	61.7	19	31.7	39	65.0	38	63.3
Pa	40	10	25.0	24	60.0	11	27.5	28	70.0
Pt	48	11	22.9	23	47.9	22	45.8	31	64.6
Sc	78	13	16.7	54	69.2	30	38.5	51	65.4
Ma	46	28	60.9	11	23.9	24	52.2	25	54.3
Average			38.3		46.6		46.1		64.1

It is possible to pick out one factor which prevented a closer correspondence between the results obtained by the two methods. The analysis made on the basis of the scale derivations employed means adjusted for age differences among the groups. In the case of the item analysis no such modification was possible, and the unadjusted experimental results had to be employed. It is inconceivable, however, that age differences alone could have produced the inconclusive correspondence between the two methods. It seems necessary to conclude that items which fall neither among the least nor among the most discriminatory according to the criteria also contribute appreciably to the adjustment profile.

One further point is deserving of remark. It will be noted in Table 9 that the average percentage is notably greater for the least discriminatory items. This increase follows as a natural consequence from the larger number of items found in the composite tables for the least discriminatory items. It will be remembered that in each case the 40 items were selected which gave the greatest or the least percentage difference between the groups, when the latter were compared pair by pair. These 40 most discriminatory items become, for all groups combined, 133 different items for the well-adjusted portions of the population, and 151 for the poorly adjusted. A like number of 40 least discriminatory items become 163 different items for the well-adjusted, and 229 (considerably more than half of the total of 350) for the poorly adjusted portion of the population. This is clear confirmation of what has previously been noted, namely, the considerably greater homogeneity of the well-adjusted portion of the population.

A study was made of the items which differentiated most between the well-adjusted and the poorly adjusted portions of each group; and likewise of the items which gave the least such differentiation. This information is recast in Table 10.

Table 10. Items Giving the Most and Least Discrimination between the Well-Adjusted and Poorly Adjusted Portions of Each Group, Arranged According to the Scale to Which the Items Belong

Scale	No. of Items In Scale	Most Discriminating Items		Least Discriminating Items		Percentage Difference	Percentage of Total
		No.	Percentage	No.	Percentage		
Hs	33	6	18.2	12	36.4	18.2	54.6
D	60	25	41.7	24	40.0	1.7	81.7
Hy	60	24	40.0	21	35.0	5.0	75.0
Pd	50	26	52.0	20	40.0	12.0	92.0
Mf	60	20	33.3	29	48.3	15.0	81.6
Pa	40	7	17.5	20	50.0	32.5	67.5
Pt	48	31	64.6	6	12.5	52.1	77.1
Sc	78	28	35.9	30	38.5	2.6	74.4
Ma	46	12	26.1	14	30.4	4.3	56.5
Average percentage			36.6		36.8		73.4

Table 10 may be compared with Table 5 which gives the significance ratios for the differences between the well-adjusted and poorly adjusted portions of each group. It will be observed that scale Pt, which shows in Table 5 the largest ratio for the total population, is also the scale which has in Table 10 the highest percentage of most discriminatory items. It is worthy of note that here the average percentage of least discriminatory items is not appreciably greater than the average for the most discriminatory items. In other words the proportion of least discriminatory items is less here than in the inter-group differences, and consequently the effective proportion of most discriminatory items is greater. This fact would appear to confirm, and to a certain extent to explain, the previous findings to the effect that the well-adjusted portion of any group differ more from the poorly adjusted portion of the same group than they do from the well-adjusted portion of other groups.

It appears legitimate to conclude that, other things being equal, the more satisfactory MMPI scales are those with the higher percentage of most discriminatory items. Put another way, these would appear to be the scales which furnish the best discrimination between the well adjusted and the poorly adjusted, and thus most effectively accomplish what is the basic task of any adjustment inventory. This, it must be admitted, is not an adequate criterion, and it is an intrinsic one in the sense that the original division of the population into well adjusted and poorly adjusted was made on the basis of the MMPI scores. It is, however, an independent criterion since it is derived from an analysis of the items directly without reference to the scales, so that it may legitimately be considered as a check on the scale results. On the basis of this criterion, the Pt scale appears to very good advantage, since 64.6 per cent of the scale is made up of most discriminatory items, and only 12.5 per cent of the total number of scale items consist of the least discriminatory items. This finding assumes special interest in view of the remark of Meehl and Hathaway that "The Pt scale has never been considered very satisfactory" [441 (see I, 2)]. On the same criterion, Pa appears to poor advantage with only 17.5 per cent composed of most discriminatory items and 50.0 per cent of least discriminatory items. This 50.0 per cent is likewise the highest percentage of least discriminatory items found in any of the scales. Worthy of note is the surprisingly large portion of the total number of items supplied by these most and least discriminatory items, the average being 73.4 per cent, and reaching in the Pd scale 92.0 per cent of the total.

The previous conclusion was that the vocational groups employed in this study were about two thirds in agreement on their adjustment, and about one third different. In terms now of the items which give the greatest inter-group differentiation, there is considerable overlap. The items which give marked differentiation, for instance, between the seminary group and the medical, are, to a considerable extent, the same items which serve to differentiate the seminary group from the dental. Even in the diversity manifested among the groups, there is considerable agreement — to speak paradoxically. In other words, the diversity is there but its causes — in terms of the items producing it — are largely the same. The burden of inter-group differentiation in adjustment is carried by relatively few items.

One further tendency is manifested. There is a greater percentage of overlap among items in the well-adjusted than in the poorly adjusted portion of the population. This observation confirms the fact previously reported, on several different lines of evidence, of the greater homogeneity of the well-adjusted part of the population.

We may now inquire what is the adjustment, in terms of the test items, which serves to specify the seminary group and to distinguish it from the other groups? The answer to this question is twofold: the between-group differences, and the within-group differences.

Limitation of space prevents the presentation of tables, but it is possible, nevertheless, to indicate to what extent the same items serve to differentiate the seminarians, whether well or poorly adjusted, from those in the other groups. The 40 items which give the greatest differentiation between the seminary group and each of the other groups reduce to 72 different items. Of these 72 items, 37, or 51 per cent, are found also among the items which serve to distinguish most sharply the poorly adjusted seminarians from the poorly adjusted members of the other groups.

A study of the tables reveals that 11 of the 40 items found under the seminary group are not found in any of the other groups. Therefore these 11 items in the present interpretation constitute the within-group adjustment which characterizes the seminary group in a specific manner.

It is neither possible nor necessary to cite here the verbal items which correspond to the numbered items referred to throughout this study. The numbering of items employed in the new group form of the MMPI has been followed, and any verbal specification of items which is desired may be had by a simple reference to this booklet. No more than a token presentation of items in verbal form will, therefore, be attempted here. Such a limited presentation may, however, serve as a useful summary of some of the results in terms of test items.

First will be presented the ten items which are, for all five groups combined, the items giving the greatest inter-group differentiation:

116. I enjoy a race or game better when I bet on it. 229. I should like to belong to several clubs or lodges. 316. I think nearly everyone would tell a lie to keep out of trouble. 231. I like to talk about sex. 15. Once in a while I think of things too bad to talk about. 199. Children should be taught all the main facts about sex. 297. I wish I were not bothered by thoughts about sex. 264. I am entirely self-confident. 135. If I could get into a movie without paying and be sure I was not seen I would probably do it. 223. I very much like hunting.

The above ten items are those giving the greatest general inter-group differentiation in adjustment. Before suggesting any comment on these items, the author presents, by way of comparison, the ten items which serve most to specify the adjustment of the seminary group and differentiate it from the adjustment of the other groups. The following are the ten items thus serving to differentiate the adjustment of the seminary group:

297. I wish I were not bothered by thoughts about sex. 229. I should like to belong to several clubs or lodges. 232. I have been inspired to a program of life based on duty which I have since carefully followed. 199. Children should be taught all the main facts about sex. 98. I believe in the second coming of Christ. 102. My hardest battles are with myself. 208. I like to flirt. 285. Once in a while I laugh at a dirty joke. 340. Sometimes I get so excited that I find it hard to get to sleep. 143. When I was a child, I belonged to a crowd or gang that tried to stick together through thick and thin.

A brief comment appears in order. In the first place, three of the ten items serving to specify the adjustment of the seminary group are found among the ten items giving the greatest general inter-group differentiation in adjustment. There are five groups; yet the seminary group contributes three out of the first ten items of general differentiation in adjustment. Clearly a disproportionately large share of inter-group differences is being furnished by the divergence of the seminary from the other groups. This disproportion confirms the previous finding that there are more significant inter-group differences found for the seminary group than for any of the other groups.

Now, however, we have an indication of the reason why the seminary group shows greater differentiation in adjustment than the other groups. It is suggested that the reason is that a large number of the MMPI items do not apply to the seminary group or apply in a quite different way than they do to the other groups.

The author believes that the data substantiate these two statements. Four of the ten items which serve most to differentiate the seminary group from the others are sex items. It is perfectly clear that sex adjustment for seminarians, dedicated as they are to a life of celibacy, is a very different thing than it is even for the unmarried groups comprising the present study. It goes without saying that the divergence of the seminary group from the population at large in this respect would be even greater. It is evident that sex adjustment is very basic, and a radically different orientation in this respect must inevitably color and diversify many of life's attitudes. Items such as item No. 229 (which is found both in the seminary group and in the general list) and item No. 223 do not appear to apply to the seminary group, and hence would be answered by them in a quite different way than they would by the average person. On the other hand, certain items apply to the seminary group in a far fuller and almost completely different way than they do to people in general, as, for instance, item No. 232 and, to a lesser extent, item No. 98.

These items, though few, are sufficient to indicate what would be more adequately demonstrated by a fuller study of the tables involved, namely, that the seminary group is differentiated from the others because a certain number of items either do not apply to the group at all, or apply in a very different way from that in which they apply to the other groups.

We may turn now to the 11 items referred to above as characterizing and specifying the intra-group adjustment of the seminarians:

5. I am easily awakened by noise. 106. Much of the time I feel as if I have done something wrong or evil. 128. The sight of blood neither frightens me nor makes me sick. 165. I like to know some important people because it makes me feel important. 170. What others think of me does not bother me. 186. I frequently notice my hand shakes when I try to do something. 190. I have very few headaches. 241. I dream frequently about things that are best kept to myself. 287. I have very few fears compared to my friends. 321. I am easily embarrassed. 352. I have been afraid of things or people that I knew could not hurt me.

The above items, although they serve to differentiate the intra-group adjustment of the seminary group from that of the other groups, and in this sense to specify it, are not, nevertheless, the items which give the greatest differentiation between the well-adjusted and the poorly adjusted portion of the seminary group. The ten items which give the greatest such contrast are the following:

94. I do many things which I regret afterwards. 217. I frequently find myself worrying about something. 238. I have periods of such great restlessness that I cannot sit long in a chair. 86. I am certainly lacking in self confidence. 170. What others think of me does not bother me. 317. I am more sensitive than most other people. 236. I brood a great deal. 160. I have never felt better in my life than I do now. 138. Criticism or scolding hurts me terribly. 32. I find it hard to keep my mind on a task or job.

The above ten items are those which serve most to discriminate between the well-adjusted and the poorly adjusted seminarian. To form a basis of comparison the following are the ten items which furnish, for all groups combined, the greatest difference between the well-adjusted and the poorly adjusted portion of each group:

217. I frequently find myself worrying about something. 361. I am inclined to take things hard. 3. I wake up fresh and rested most mornings. 67. I wish I could be as happy as some people seem to be. 94. I do many things which I regret afterwards. 317. I am more sensitive than most other people. 142. I certainly feel useless at times. 102. My hardest battles are with myself. 238. I have periods of such great restlessness that I cannot sit long in a chair. 32. I find it hard to keep my mind on a task or job.

A comparison of the two lists of items immediately above reveals that five of the items giving the greatest difference between the well adjusted and the poorly adjusted in the seminary group are also found among the ten items giving the largest such differences for all groups combined. In the inter-group differences, three of the ten seminary items were found among the ten items giving the greatest inter-group differences with all groups combined. If these facts are added to the evidence furnished above with reference to the percentage of overlap of items, the impression seems well founded that a relatively small number of the MMPI items are doing the major task of adjustment differentiation, both within and between groups.

It will be recalled that sex items assumed a rather prominent role in creating inter-group differences in adjustment, a thing which, as pointed out, is quite understandable. It is, therefore, worthy of remark that not a single sex item is to be found among the 31 items cited just above as distinguishing most adequately between the well-adjusted and the poorly adjusted portions of each group.

That some modification of content is desirable if the MMPI is to be employed with a seminary group follows in the author's opinion as a logical consequence from the evidence adduced just above in the verbal consideration of the items which produce the most significant inter-group differences in adjustment. In the present interpretation, the seminary group gives these large inter-group differences in adjustment because a certain number of the MMPI items do not apply to this group at all, or else they have an almost completely altered meaning for the seminary group. It appears that some allowance should be made for these items in interpreting the MMPI results for the seminary group.

The most obvious allowance for the different significance of these items with respect to the seminary group would be made if modified norms were developed on the various MMPI scales for special use with this group. This would be the minimum requirement if this test is to be adapted for use with a special group. On the basis of the present study as revealed, for instance, in Table 1 it would appear that the effect of introducing such modifications in the MMPI norms for the seminary group would be to raise the level of the T scores which would be accepted as normal for this group. In other words, a certain elevation of the MMPI profile would be accepted as normal for this group, and individual interpretation made upon this basis.

It is suggested here, however, that some modification should also be introduced in the content of the MMPI in adapting it to seminary use. More specifically it is suggested that certain items should be eliminated. This proposal is based upon the assumption, expressed above, that certain MMPI items have no application to the seminary group and upon the experimental fact that a number of these items do not discriminate between the well-adjusted and the poorly adjusted seminarians. When these two criteria agree in picking out the same items, the author believes that such items can be eliminated from the test without loss when the test is used with seminary groups. The author wishes, however, to go one step further and suggest that the elimination of these items would be beneficial. If the effect of the presence of such items were merely negative, i.e., if they were merely undiagnostic and nothing more, there would be no harm in allowing them to remain. What, however, if such items are not items that are neutral but rather prejudicial to the effective operation of the test? Such, it is submitted, is the case with the seminary group because the number of unsuitable items is sufficiently large to produce an atmosphere of artificiality and unreality inimical to the test operation.

Let us take, by way of example, two of the items appearing among the ten which served most to differentiate the adjustment of the seminary group from that of the others, item No. 229: "I should like to belong to several clubs or lodges," and item No. 208: "I like to flirt." It will probably be admitted that such items do not apply to the life of a seminarian. What then is the situation created by asking a seminarian to answer them? If he answers them at all, he does so in either of two ways. Either he appeals to the experience he has had previous to entering the seminary to find the answer, or he imagines what he might like or what he would do were he in a state of life where such things were possible. There might be no great harm in a few such items out of the total number, but multiply these two items many times over as you do in the case of a seminary group, and you create an atmosphere of considerable remoteness and artificiality for the respondent.

There is another aspect of the unsuitability of items for the seminary group which may constitute a more basic objection than the one above. Certain religious items of the test are without any diagnostic value with respect to the seminary group, because every member of the group is predisposed to answer the items in exactly the same way. Take the following three items, by way of example: No. 98, "I believe in the second coming of Christ"; No. 249, "I believe there is a Devil and a Hell in after-life"; and No. 258, "I believe there is a God." All diagnostic value for the seminary group is precluded in the case of these items, and on the other hand, they may understandably bring the entire test into disfavor, if not disrepute, with such a group.

In the mind of the writer this leads to the conclusion that the MMPI will function more effectively as a diagnostically useful instrument in testing the adjustment of seminarians if certain items are eliminated. It will be clear from what has been said above that it is no adequate answer to the difficulty to say that the seminarians can simply omit any items which do not apply to them. This solution ignores the difficulty, stressed above, of the unfavorable atmosphere presumably created by the presence in the test of a relatively large number of inapplicable items. Furthermore, unanswered items, as pointed out earlier in the present study, have indeterminate but varied effects on the different MMPI scales, which it is quite impossible to evaluate properly, and thus constitute, in the opinion of the present writer, a limitation in the MMPI test construction. This difficulty would be greatly increased and its effects — whatever they are — much magnified in the case of the seminary group where the number of inapplicable items would be much larger than in the general population.

It may be urged, by way of objection to the present proposal, that this would be true also of other groups, and if followed out would mean that a test such as the MMPI would be made subject to endless adaptations. The author would reply that the seminary is a distinctly more special group than would usually be encountered, and that adaptation, therefore, is not equally necessary in these other instances. Neither can it be objected that by the elimination of items we are cutting down the diagnostic effectiveness of our scales, because we make a prerequisite for elimination the demonstration that the items in question — whatever may be their effectiveness for the general population — for this group are nondiagnostic and nondiscriminatory.

In the opinion of the writer some of the findings of the present investigation may be used as criteria in the work of eliminating certain of the MMPI items if one wished to follow out this suggestion in adapting the inventory for use with seminary groups. The following three criteria are recommended for use in this respect: (1) Inclusion of an item among those which serve to differentiate and specify the adjustment of the seminary group. (2) Inspection of the content of the item creates the presumption of inapplicability to or completely special meaning for the seminary group. (3) Inclusion of the item among those which give no significant differentiation between the well-adjusted and the poorly adjusted seminary groups.

The author would insist that the second criterion of elimination should never be used alone, but only when combined with the first or the third, which are experimentally determined. If an individual item meets all three criteria, it is suggested that it be eliminated in adapting the test for seminary use. If an item satisfies the first and second criteria, or the second and the third, it might profitably be considered for elimination. In this way a tentative adaptation of the MMPI for use with seminary groups could be made.

Frequent reference has been made throughout this study to the goal of adapting the MMPI for use with a seminary group. More specifically the purpose was to evaluate the MMPI with a view to its use as a measure of the suitability, in terms of mental health, of candidates for the priesthood.

The current study has concerned itself only with seminarians and the findings cannot immediately be applied to the seminary candidates. Study of the seminary group was, however, essential for two reasons. In the first place, it is only on a basis of his capacity for adjustment to seminary life that the mental health of the seminary candidate can legitimately be judged. Hence we needed to learn what the picture of seminary adjustment might be. Secondly, the study of seminary adjustment, undertaken in the present investigation, has made it possible to indicate how the MMPI might be modified in its norms, and to a certain extent in its content, in order to accommodate it for use with a seminary group. As the author conceives the task, one step yet remains to be taken. It is now necessary to administer the modified form of the MMPI to seminary candidates on an unselected basis, and then wait for the criterion behavior to appear. It would be even better if during this experimental period both the full and the modified forms of the MMPI could be administered and the results on both forms checked against one another.

The larger number of the candidates, it may be presumed, will adjust satisfactorily to seminary life, will succeed in meeting the academic and other standards required, and will be ordained to the priesthood. Others, however, will not make the necessary adjustment, and will drop out. Those who leave the seminary will do so for a variety of reasons, but a not insignificant number of these reasons can legitimately be classed under the general term of psychological adjustment. Certain of the candidates, therefore, will depart from the seminary because they are not suited for seminary life from a psychological, temperamental, or emotional point of view. If the MMPI at all lives up to the diagnostic promise which it gives, the profiles of those who leave the seminary because of inability to make the psychological adjustment necessary will be distinguishably different from the profiles of those who make a satisfactory adjustment, remain, and are ordained to the priesthood.

For a certain period of time, therefore, until the records have been allowed to accumulate and validate themselves against this objective differentiation, no judgments should be made on a basis of the test results. This sort of validation is admittedly not an easy task, and not one that can be quickly done, but it does have the distinct advantage of furnishing as crucial a test as it is possible to devise. The author considers this period of incubation and validation to be essential, because the matter with which he is dealing — acceptance or rejection of seminary candidates — is too important to rest content with anything less.

When the modified form of the MMPI has been validated in the manner indicated, what may it be expected to accomplish? In the opinion of the writer its essential function would be to screen out those candidates who do not give promise of satisfactory psychological adjustment to seminary life. The number of these will presumably be but a small percentage of the total number of candidates, and even in these cases no categoric judgment could be made on a basis of the test results. The test, however, would pick out those candidates in whose case further and individual investigation on this score would be indicated and advantageous. Clearly there would be many other reasons for the unsuitability of candidates for the priesthood which would be completely beyond the scope of such a test. However, in the area of its competence — the area of psychological, temperamental, and emotional suitability for seminary life — the test, when validated in that manner indicated, would have a modest but solid contribution to make.

ARTICLE 66 *Positive Characteristics of MMPI Elevations in a Nursing Group*

The Problem

IN A previous paper [331 (see V, 34)] results were reported of a study in which observed personality characteristics of student nurses were compared with MMPI profiles produced by them. Attention was given primarily to ascertaining what characteristics might correlate significantly with high and low scores on the various scales, rather than to a special analysis of student nurses as a pre-vocational group. This paper, however, concerns the latter as representing persons making satisfactory adjustments under partially controlled conditions. The total group was comprised of 137 students (an original sample of 97 and a new one of 40) in advanced practicum training at a VA neuropsychiatric hospital, about 20 being in training at any one time for three-month periods. The MMPI was administered to each upon admission. During their stay eight supervisors recorded impromptu observations and impressions, and rated each on a rating scale based on ward practice — which tended to include their observed behavior in general and personal adjustment as well as the main objective of on-the-job performance. Final grades in the course were based primarily on formal subject-matter test scores and the ward-practice ratings.

Results

The present study indicates that student nurses tend to produce a characteristic MMPI profile, with a predominant elevation on the Pd scale, and secondary elevations on the Ma and Hy scales. (The group's mean on Pd was 56.53 with an SE_M of 0.74.) Weisgerber's [614] study of 72 student nurses came out with a composite profile having similar features except that Ma dominated and Pd was secondary. The present author separated the population into three equal-sized groups according to ratings on ward practice, highest third, middle third, and lowest third, and computed a composite profile for each of the three groups. In each instance Pd dominated the profiles. The population was then separated into three equal-sized groups according to scores on formal tests, and again the three composite profiles each had a dominant elevation on Pd. A further check was made by separating out the 17 students who made a final grade of A in the course, and the 18 who made D.

The relationships still held. Throughout these various comparisons, composite scores on Ma and Hy shifted in relative positions between themselves and somewhat with other scales, but the highest score was on Pd every time. Also, about 34 per cent of the students had individual profiles with Pd containing the highest score. Table 1 contains the T scores for the groups separated according to ratings on ward practice, and according to scores on formal tests.

Table 1. T-Score Means and Codes for MMPI Findings on Various Criterion Groups

Group	Hs	D	Hy	Pd	Pa	Pt	Sc	Ma
Ward practice								
High (N = 39)	48.1	48.1	53.3	58.6	49.0	51.8	50.7	54.7
MMPI Code: 49378/612								
Middle (N = 39)	49.2	48.7	54.8	57.4	51.7	51.5	52.1	53.4
MMPI Code: 439867/12								
Low (N = 39)	48.8	48.8	52.3	53.4	50.8	51.6	52.0	51.9
MMPI Code: 438976/12								
Formal tests								
High (N = 45)	48.1	48.3	52.0	54.1	50.5	50.5	51.6	51.6
MMPI Code: 4389 67/21								
Middle (N = 45)	48.2	49.0	53.0	55.9	50.6	50.8	50.6	52.0
MMPI Code: 439 768/21								
Low (N = 45)	49.7	48.6	55.1	59.7	51.0	53.4	53.4	57.5
MMPI Code: 493786/12								

An elevated score on the Pd scale seems to represent something favorable to the practice of nursing, at least for students in training in a neuropsychiatric setting. In Table 1 the mean T score on this scale for the highest group on ward practice is more than five points *above* that for the lowest group on ward practice. (The t is 2.64, which is within the .05 level of significance.) When achievement on formal tests alone is considered, the relationship is reversed; that is, the highest third in this category has a mean Pd score more than five points *below* that of the lowest third. (The t is 2.97, which is within the .01 level.) In this light, elevated Pd seems able to compensate for poor grade-getting ability in formal tests so far as over-all achievement in student nursing is concerned. The 47 students who had profiles with Pd scores being their highest obtained a composite grade in the course comparable to that of the other students, but their numerical rating on ward practice averaged 81.0 as compared with 75.6 for the larger portion of the group. An elevated Pd may reflect something in the personal backgrounds or personalities that motivates a good proportion of them to seek nursing as a career, or that helps them through screening for acceptance as students, or it may reflect something that helps them in the actual work — at least so far as favorably impressing supervisors is concerned. In the previous study the following characteristics were found to be significantly correlated with elevated Pd scores: participates actively in group discussions, is resistant to suggestions, is aggressive, lacks perseverence, is not industrious, likes to have responsibilities, adjusts rapidly, has initiative, is self-confident, is unafraid of mental patients, is not shy, doesn't work persistently with assigned patients, is enthusiastic.

An elevation on Ma seems also to reflect an asset insofar as favorably impressing the supervisors is concerned. Table 1 shows that all composite scores on this scale are somewhat above average. But more noteworthy is the fact that the highest subgroup on formal tests has the lowest Ma elevation (51.6) while the lowest subgroup on such tests has the highest (57.5), suggesting that elevated Ma in some way tended to compensate for inferior test performance just as elevated Pd did, but to a lesser extent. This is further confirmed to some extent by opposite trends for the highest versus lowest subgroups on ward practice. In the previous paper 16 personality characteristics are listed as correlating significantly with elevated Ma, the five with highest significance being the following: has ease of oral expression, participates actively in group discussions, has self-confidence, is not reserved, has initiative. Composite scores on Hy are consistently elevated too. High Hy correlated significantly with friendliness, cooperativeness, and cheerfulness, yet it did so still more with "immaturity."

While looking over the accumulation of MMPI profiles the author noted that a number of them were abnormal in appearance. So, for special scrutiny all the profiles with one or more T scores above 65 were segregated, with the idea of estimating what kinds of diagnostic categories they would be likely to appear under (according to profile shape) should they happen to belong to individuals clinically diagnosed as emotionally ill. There were 43 such profiles out of the total of 137. An *Atlas for the Clinical Use of the MMPI* [307] was used for criteria. It was found that the group of 43 cases were overbalanced with profile potential for behavior disorders, underbalanced for psychoneuroses and psychoses. About 17 per cent of the total of 968 cases in the *Atlas* are categorized under "B" for behavior disorder. In contrast to this 17 per cent, the present elevated profile group contained 67 per cent of profiles with patterns most closely resembling the patterns in the *Atlas* which most frequently represent its behavior-disorder cases. About 45 per cent of the cases in the *Atlas* come under "P," or psychoneuroses. The present group had only 21 per cent psychoneurotic type (*Atlas*) profiles. Approximately 44 per cent of the *Atlas* cases are categorized under "Ps," psychoses; and only 12 per cent of the present group had psychotic-type profiles. The inference can be made that those of the present population who produced elevated profiles had distinctly more potential for behavior disorders than for psychoses or psychoneuroses, when compared with the population of case histories in the *Atlas*. This is consistent with the elevation on Pd mentioned above for the group of students as a whole, as compared with standardization groups.

The group of high-profile individuals received as good a composite rating on ward practice as did the remaining students (about two points higher), and came out with a comparable distribution in grades for the course. And the supervisors noted about the same average number of "positive" personality characteristics as for the remainder (11.0 and 11.1 respectively), and "negative" characteristics (3.9 for both). Hypothetically, if all the students in the study should become involved in situations highly stressful to each of them, a relatively larger proportion of the high-profile group could be expected to present symptoms of mental illness. But at the time of the study this group appeared to have been making as acceptable an adjustment as that achieved by the others.

The question arises as to how the individuals in this group happened to be functioning as effectively as those with more normal profiles. Wiener's [642 (see IV, 22)] "subtle" and "obvious" keys were applied and this procedure failed to differentiate significantly. However, about 85 per cent of the students had higher scores on the subtle items, suggesting that a control factor of some kind pervaded the whole population including the elevated-profile group. The K factor also failed to differentiate. But here again the whole population was loaded with high K (mean, 58.6), bolstering the hypothesis of a control factor which included the elevated-profile group. The previous study revealed that personality assets as well as liabilities are associated with elevated scores on at least most of the scales. For instance score elevations were found to be significantly related to such traits as perseverence, efficiency, dependability, active participation in group discussions, leadership qualities, etc. It seems possible that, in addition to a control factor of some kind, such assets may have been functioning to counterbalance, at least in the training situation, for aberration potentials among the student nurses.

Table 2. Scores on K and Evaluations of Student Nurses by Supervisors
(Numbers in Parentheses are N's)[a]

T Score on K	N	Rating on Ward Practice	N	Desirable Minus Undesirable Traits
Below 50	16	73.4	21	4.33
50–54	17	74.6	21	4.14
Below 55	33	74.0	42	4.24
55–59	26	78.1	33	8.06
60–64	29	77.8	32	9.69
55–64	55	77.9	65	8.86
65 and up	29	73.2	30	5.86

[a] Since the present study was done, 46 additional students have completed the course. Of this new group, those who made K scores below 55 averaged 77.3 on ward practice, and those scoring in the 55–64 range averaged 79.6 on ward practice.

While profiles of the more outstanding students were being inspected, it was noted that some of them not only had high scores among the clinical scales but also elevated scores on K. So all the cases were listed in sequence according to magnitude of K score and broken down into five subgroups. Then it was ascertained how these subgroups turned out on ward practice, and the number of desirable traits minus undesirable ones as noted by supervisors was determined. Table 2 presents the figures.

Those groupings which had K scores of 55–59 and 60–64 averaged higher on both determinations than did any of the other groupings. The subgroups with below-average K and average or just above showed less in the way of competence in ward practice and in presenting desirable traits. The same thing obtained for those with very high K—above 64. The CR's reached the .01 level of significance for the difference between mean ratings on ward practice, and between desirable-minus-undesirable traits. (The CR's were 2.95 and 3.23, respectively.)

This sort of patterning is in harmony with Wiener's [644] studies in which he found that veterans with neuropsychiatric diagnoses who were adjusting outside a hospital, successful salesmen, etc., built up profile scores primarily on subtle items in contrast to hospitalized veterans, unsuccessful salesmen, etc., who admitted more obvious items. The present population of students, when separated into three equal-sized groups arranged according to algebraic T scores for subtle-obvious items, revealed different adjustment levels. The middle group (each individual of which had declared more subtle than obvious items but not to an extreme extent) turned out with better ratings on both ward practice and positive traits than did either group above or below it.

Such findings suggest that an individual who denies personality shortcomings and emotional aberrations to a somewhat greater extent than is usual may function more productively than the average person. On the other hand, however, the individual who goes to the extreme in his denials seems likely to be less efficient. When a clinician examines an MMPI profile and finds an elevated K score or tries during interviews to elicit deviant material and gets only a little, he may be inclined to consider the subject uncooperative, as lacking in insight, a poor psychotherapy prospect. Instead, the subject might be showing an asset, some kind of control such as Wiener mentions, a stabilizing factor, or adaptive suppression, etc. At least those individuals among the student nurses who scored as mildly "defensive" on K and on the subtle-obvious scales showed up in the practicum training situation as superior to the other students.

Since it was found that an elevated score on K is associated more with desirable performance than is the mean on this scale, the various clinical scales were investigated to determine if optimum positions on them might be somewhere other than around the mean T score position of 50. An optimum score position reaching the .05 level of significance showed up for only one of the eight scales (Sc). The group of individuals with T scores within the 45–49 range on this scale obtained higher ward-practice ratings and were credited with higher ratios of positive traits than groups falling within any other range. In fact the group made better showings than did a group of individuals hovering close around the midpoint on the scale. (The optimum T score was 47, but there were only a few cases with exactly this score.) In other words, those individuals who had a little less than average schizoid potential, as measured by the MMPI, tended to show up better in the practicum situation than did those with average, or more than average, or very little potential. An unexpected finding occurred for five of the scales: Hs, D, Pd, Pt, and Ma. Groups scoring in the 55–59 range on every one of these scales obtained lower ward-practice ratings (although not significantly so) than did groups scoring in any other range studied, including a higher one. Table 3 presents the mean ratings on ward practice for successive score ranges. For the purposes of this table, the individual's score is based on her averaged T scores for Hs, D, Pd, Pt, and Ma. The difference between the mean ward-pratice rating for the 55–59 range and the 60-plus range has a t value of 2.88, which is significant at the .01 level. The mean for desirable-minus-undesirable traits for the 55–59 range was lower than for any other range, but differences between means failed to reach statistical significance. As a check on the dip in ward practice when based on averaged scores for the five scales, a different computation was tried. This time the T score on each of the five scales considered separately was used and tabulated with ratings on ward practice, and then these tabulations were accumulated or summated. The results are presented in the lower part of Table 3. Again the rating on ward practice for the 55–59 range is distinctly below that for any of the other ranges, including the higher one.

Table 3. Scores on Hs, D, Pd, Pt, and Ma, and Ratings on Ward Practice [a]

T-Score Ranges	Below 45	45–49	50–54	55–59	60 and up
Ward-practice ratings for subjects [b]	76.6	76.2	76.3	71.4	79.8
Number of subjects	12	28	44	22	11
Ward-practice ratings for scores [c]	76.4	76.3	75.5	72.2	76.5
No. of cases	114	155	140	86	90

[a] A tally has been made on a new group of 46 students who were not included in the study. Means of accumulated scores on the same five scales and ward-practice ratings turned out as follows: below 55, 78.1; 55–59, 77.4; 60 and above, 79.9. (Since these differences and those in Table 3 are based on related measures, they need not be large to be significant.)

[b] This row presents mean ward-practice ratings in terms of the subjects' mean scores on all five scales.

[c] This row presents mean ward-practice ratings for the accumulations of all T scores on each of the five scales.

A similar dip in ward-practice rating occurred for the Pa scale, but it did so at a higher point — at around 60 or a little above. The L scale also contained a dip within the 55–59 range. (Its consistency in this respect with most of the clinical scales presents another bit of evidence that it has value as a clinical scale). The Hy scale presented a plateau throughout the various score ranges except for drops at both ends.

As a tentative interpretation of the dips within the 55–59 ranges, the author applied the hypothesis that these scores represent a falling off in personal effectiveness along with increasing maladjustment potential, and that the secondary rises signify the introduction or increase of something to offset more pronounced maladjustment trends. For the original sample of 97 cases the frequency of occurrence of the various traits reported by supervisors, with T scores of 60 or above on one or more of the five scales, was tabulated, and these frequencies were compared with frequencies for the lower T scores on these scales. In favor of the high scores the following traits showed up with frequencies sufficiently greater to reach the .05 level: is energetic, enthusiastic, industrious, shows initiative, is interested in the course, participates actively in group discussions. Tabulations were then made for the new and smaller population. Differences reaching the .05 level occurred for only two traits, but the magnitudes of the other differences approximated those for the original population.

The data seem to suggest that along with a little more than usual in emotional maladjustment there was a concomitant dropping off in personal effectiveness among the populations of student nurses, but that potential for more extreme maladjustment was compensated for by increased motivation toward personal expression and activity. And this motivation, or whatever it was, seemed to have compensated sufficiently to bring the most maladjusted individuals back up to the general output level of, or higher than, those with no more than ordinary emotional discomfort.

Summary

A group of 137 nurses in practicum training was studied for relationships between rating on ward practice, scores on formal tests, and MMPI profiles. These students tended to produce predominantly elevated scores on the Pd scale, with secondary elevations on Ma and Hy. Such elevations seem favorable in the student practice of nursing, particularly psychiatric nursing. Those students who had the more abnormal-looking profiles, and perhaps expressed higher potential for maladjustment, tended to produce an overload of profiles representative of behavior disorders and relatively small proportions representative of psychoses and psychoneuroses. These same students as a subgroup performed as well as the remainder so far as grades and ratings on ward practice were concerned. In partial explanation of this the operation of some kind of control factor seems plausible, and utilitarian personality characteristics associated with elevated scores or perhaps aberration potentials seem able to compensate for these same potentials. Those students who scored as mildly defensive displayed better adaptation than those who produced either scores around average or who scored as highly defensive. As potential for emotional maladjustment (as measured by most of the MMPI scales) increased beyond the midpoint, personal effectiveness in the practicum situation started to drop off and then build up again as maladjustment potential increased further. This secondary increase seemed due to compensation, some of which may have taken the form of increased personal expression and activity.

Bibliography and Index

BIBLIOGRAPHY

THIS list includes most papers published through December 1954 which make more than casual reference to the MMPI. All references to the articles in this volume are designated by the numbers in this list and in a supplement containing references to non-MMPI materials which follows the bibliography. The numbers in this supplementary list are designated by the letter "r" before the reference number. The papers have been arranged alphabetically except for a few late additions ordered at the end of the bibliography. The editors would appreciate notification of errors or omissions to improve subsequent bibliographic publication.

1. Aaronson, B. S., and G. S. Welsh. The MMPI as diagnostic differentiator: a reply to Rubin. *J. consult. Psychol.*, 1950, 14, 324–326.
2. Abrams, E. N. A comparative factor analytic study of normal and neurotic veterans: a statistical investigation of the interrelationships of intellectual and emotional factors as disclosed in the Primary Mental Abilities Examination and the Minnesota Multiphasic Personality Inventory. Ph.D. dissertation, New York University, 1950. (Also abstracted in *Microfilm Abstracts*, 1950, 10, 94–95.)
3. Abramson, H. A. The effect of alcohol on the Personality Inventory (Minnesota): preliminary report. *Psychosom. Med.*, 1945, 7, 184–185.
4. Abramson, H. A. The Minnesota Personality Test in relation to selection of specialized military personnel. *Psychosom. Med.*, 1945, 7, 178–184.
5. Abramson, H. A. The effect of alcohol on the Personality Inventory. *Ann. N.Y. Acad. Sci.*, 1946, 46, 535–557.
6. Abramson, H. A., and Erna Tiege. Minnesota test as a guide to therapy in multiple sclerosis. *Ann. N.Y. Acad. Sci.*, 1954, 58, 648–655.
7. Abramson, H. A., *et al.* Non-projective personality tests. *Ann. N.Y. Acad. Sci.*, 1946, 46, 531–678.
8. Albee, G. W. Psychological concomitants of pulmonary tuberculosis. *Amer. Rev. Tuberculosis*, 1948, 58, 650–661.
9. Allerhand, M. E., H. G. Gough, and M. L. Grais. Personality factors in neurodermatitis. *Psychosom. Med.*, 1950, 12, 386–390.
10. Altus, W. D. The adjustment of army illiterates. *Psychol. Bull.*, 1945, 42, 461–476.
11. Altus, W. D. A college achiever and non-achiever scale for the MMPI. *J. appl. Psychol.*, 1948, 32, 385–397.
12. Altus, W. D. Some correlates of the group Rorschach and the schizophrenia scale of the group MMPI among two groups of "normal" college students. *J. consult. Psychol.*, 1948, 12, 375–378. (Also abstracted in *Amer. Psychologist*, 1948, 3, 349.)
13. Altus, W. D. Personality correlates of Q-L variability on the ACE. *J. consult. Psychol.*, 1952, 16, 284–291.
14. Altus, W. D. Adjustment items which differentiate between psychiatric categories of military general prisoners. *J. gen. Psychol.*, 1953, 49, 293–301.
15. Altus, W. D., and H. M. Bell. The validity of certain measures of maladjustment in an army special training center. *Psychol. Bull.*, 1945, 42, 98–103.
16. Altus, W. D., and H. M. Bell. An analysis of four orally administered measures of adjustment. *Educ. psychol. Measmt.*, 1947, 7, 101–115.
17. Altus, W. D., and J. H. Clark. The effect of adjustment patterns upon the intercorrelation of intelligence subtest variables. *J. soc. Psychol.*, 1949, 30, 39–48.
18. Altus, W. D., and T. T. Tafejian. MMPI correlates of the California E-F Scale. *J. soc. Psychol.*, 1953, 38, 145–149.
19. Anastasi, Anne. *Psychological testing*. New York: Macmillan, 1954.
20. Andersen, A. L. Personality changes following prefrontal lobotomy in a case of severe psychoneurosis. *J. consult. Psychol.*, 1949, 13, 105–107.
21. Andersen, A. L., and L. J. Hanvik. The psychometric localization of brain lesions: the dif-

ferential effect of frontal and parietal lesions on MMPI profiles. *J. clin. Psychol.*, 1950, 6, 177–180.

22. Apfelbaum, B. E., and A. C. Sherriffs. Factors influencing ratings of recalled experiences. *J. Pers.*, 1954, 22, 557–564.

23. Applezweig, M. H. A statistical analysis of the influence of age, education, and intelligence on the scales of the Minnesota Multiphasic Personality Inventory. *J. Colo.-Wyo. Acad. Sci.*, 1948, 3, 59. (Abstract.)

24. Applezweig, M. H. Educational levels and Minnesota Multiphasic profiles. *J. clin. Psychol.*, 1953, 9, 340–344.

25. Arndt, W. B. MMPI: a supplementary method for its clinical analysis. *Med. Technicians Bull.*, 1954, 5, 267–268.

26. Aronson, M. L. A study of the Freudian theory of paranoia by means of a group of psychological tests. Ph.D. dissertation, University of Michigan, 1951. (Also abstracted in *Microfilm Abstracts*, 1951, 11, 443–444.)

27. Arthur, Grace. An experience in examining an Indian twelfth-grade group with the MMPI. *Ment. Hyg.*, 1944, 28, 243–250.

28. Asch, M. J. Nondirective teaching in psychology: an experimental study. *Psychol. Monogr.*, 1951, 65, No. 4 (Whole No. 321).

29. Auld, F. Influence of social class on personality test responses. *Psychol. Bull.*, 1952, 49, 318–332.

30. Aumack, L. Misconceptions concerning the interpretation of subgroup variations within normative data. *J. Psychol.*, 1954, 38, 79–82.

31. Autrey, O. Ruth. A study of the effects of anxiety and of situational stress on communicative efficiency. M.A. thesis, University of North Carolina, 1954.

32. Axtell, S. B. Diagnostic patterns on the Minnesota Multiphasic Personality Inventory. M.A. thesis, University of California, 1948.

33. Baker, G., and J. G. Peatman. Tests used in Veterans Administration guidance units. *Amer. Psychologist*, 1947, 2, 99–102.

34. Baldwin, Marcella Vig. A clinico-experimental investigation into the psychologic aspects of multiple sclerosis. *J. nerv. ment. Dis.*, 1952, 115, 299–342.

35. Balian, Lucy J. The performance of 80 normal subjects on a German translation of the MMPI. M.A. thesis, University of Minnesota, 1952.

36. Bard, P. A note on MMPI (Pd) scores of state training school boys. *Minn. Counselor*, 1950, 4, 21.

37. Barker, R. G., Beatrice A. Wright, L. Meyerson, and Mollie R. Gonick. *Adjustment to physical handicap and illness: a survey of the social psychology of physique and disability.* New York: Social Science Research Council Bulletin No. 55 (Revised), 1953.

38. Barnabus, B. Twelve tests that have proved practical in commercial application. *Trans. Kans. Acad. Sci.*, 1947, 50, 204–207.

39. Barnabus, B. Validity of personality and interest tests in selection and placement situations. *Trans. Kans. Acad. Sci.*, 1948, 51, 335–339.

40. Barrett, A. M. Personality characteristics under the stress of high intensity sound. Ph.D. dissertation, Pennsylvania State College, 1950.

41. Barron, E. M., and H. H. Donohue. Psychiatric aide selection through psychological examinations: a preliminary report of the screening of applicants at the Arkansas State Hospital. *Amer. J. Psychiat.*, 1951, 107, 859–865.

42. Barron, F. Psychotherapy as a special case of personal interaction: prediction of its course. Ph.D. dissertation, University of California, Berkeley, 1950.

43. Barron, F. Complexity-simplicity as a personality dimension. *J. abnorm. soc. Psychol.*, 1953, 48, 163–172.

44. Barron, F. An ego-strength scale which predicts response to psychotherapy. *J. consult. Psychol.*, 1953, 17, 327–333.

45. Barron, F. Some test correlates of response to therapy. *J. consult. Psychol.*, 1953, 17, 235–241.

46. Barron, F. Ego-strength in normal subjects as measured by an MMPI scale. *Amer. Psychologist*, 1954, 9, 565. (Abstract.)

47. Barron, F. Ego-strength in normal men as measured by an MMPI scale. *J. Psychol.* (in press).

48. Beaver, Alma. Personality factors in choice of nursing. *J. appl. Psychol.*, 1953, 37, 374–379.

49. Bechtoldt, H. P. Response defined anxiety and MMPI variables. *Proc. Iowa Acad. Sci.*, 1953, 60, 495–499.

50. Beier, E. G., and F. Ratzeburg. The parental identifications of male and female college students. *J. abnorm. soc. Psychol.*, 1953, 48, 569–572.

51. Benarick, S. J., G. M. Guthrie and W. U. Snyder. An interpretative aid for the Sc scale of the MMPI. *J. consult. Psychol.*, 1951, 15, 142–144.
52. Bendig, A. W. Age, sex and the Manifest Anxiety Test. *J. consult. Psychol.*, 1954, 18, 16.
53. Benton, A. L. The MMPI in clinical practice. *J. nerv. ment. Dis.*, 1945, 102, 416–420.
54. Benton, A. L. The MMPI: A Review. In O. K. Buros, *The third mental measurements yearbook.* New Brunswick, N.J.: Rutgers University Press, 1949.
55. Benton, A. L. The MMPI: A Review. In O. K. Buros, *The fourth mental measurements yearbook.* Highland Park, N.J.: The Gryphon Press, 1953.
56. Benton, A. L., and Kathryn A. Probst. A comparison of psychiatric ratings with MMPI scores. *J. abnorm. soc. Psychol.*, 1946, 41, 75–78.
57. Berdie, R. F. Range of interests and psychopathologies. *J. clin. Psychol.*, 1946, 2, 161–166.
58. Berdie, R. F. Counseling methods: diagnostics. In C. P. Stone and D. W. Taylor (Eds.), *Annual review of psychology.* Stanford: Annual Reviews, 1950. Vol. I.
59. Berkshire, J. R., S. F. T. Bugental, and F. P. Cassens. Test preferences in guidance centers. *Occupations*, 1948, 26, 337–343.
60. Bier, W. C. (S.J.) A comparative study of a seminary group and four other groups on the MMPI. *Stud. Psychol. Psychiat. Cathol. Univ. Amer.*, 1948, 7, 1–107.
61. Birkner, E. C. The relationship of personality characteristics to the seeking of medical advice. M.A. thesis, Ohio University, 1949.
62. Birnberg, Vita K. The relationship between food aversions and the MMPI for college women. M.A. thesis, University of Minnesota, 1945.
63. Bitterman, M. E., and W. H. Holtzman. Conditioning and extinction of the GSR as a function of anxiety. *J. abnorm. soc. Psychol.*, 1952, 47, 615–623.
64. Bitterman, M. E., and W. H. Holtzman. Development of psychiatric screening of flying personnel. III. Conditioning and extinction of the galvanic skin response in relation to clinical evidence of anxiety. *USAF Sch. Aviat. Med. Proj. Rep.*, 1952, Project No. 21-37-002, Rep. No. 3.
65. Bitterman, M. E., and C. W. Kniffin. Manifest anxiety and "perceptual defense." *J. abnorm. soc. Psychol.*, 1953, 48, 248–252.
66. Black, J. D. The interpretation of MMPI profiles of college women. *Dissertation Abstr.*, 1953, 13, 870–871. (Abstract of Ph.D. dissertation, University of Minnesota, 1953.)
67. Black, J. D. A study of the efficiency of the MMPI for screening college women. *Amer. Psychologist*, 1954, 9, 562. (Abstract.)
68. Blair, W. R. N. A comparative study of disciplinary offenders and non-offenders in the Canadian army, 1948. *Canad. J. Psychol.*, 1950, 4, 49–62.
69. Blake, R. R., and G. P. Wilson. Perceptual selectivity in Rorschach determinants as a function of depressive tendencies. *J. abnorm. soc. Psychol.*, 1950, 45, 459–472.
70. Blanton, R., and T. Landsman. The retest reliability of the group Rorschach and some relationships to the MMPI. *J. consult. Psychol.*, 1952, 16, 265–267. (Also abstracted in *Amer. Psychologist*, 1951, 6, 379.)
71. Blum, L. P. A comparative study of students preparing for five selected professions including teaching. *J. exp. Educ.*, 1947, 16, 31–65.
72. Blum, R. H. The validity of the Machover DAP technique. A study in clinical agreement. *J. clin. Psychol.*, 1954, 10, 120–125.
73. Blumberg, E. M. The results of psychological testing of cancer patients. In J. A. Gengerelli and F. J. Kirkner (Eds.), *The psychological variables in human cancer.* Berkeley: University of California Press, 1954.
74. Blumberg, E. M., P. M. West, and F. W. Ellis. A possible relationship between psychological factors and human cancer. *Psychosom. Med.*, 1954, 16, 277–286.
75. Boland, J. L. A comparison of stutterers and non-stutterers on several measures of anxiety. Ph.D. dissertation, University of Michigan, 1951.
76. Bolander, W. G. A study of the MMPI as an indicator in the prediction of college success. M.A. thesis, University of Oregon, 1947.
77. Bortin, A. W., and I. Brill. Psychiatric studies based on new personality test. *Milit. Surg.*, 1945, 96, 497–503.
78. Botwinick, J., and S. Machover. A psychometric examination of latent homosexuality in alcoholism. *Quart. J. Stud. Alcohol*, 1951, 12, 268–272.
79. Brackbill, G., and K. B. Little. MMPI correlates of the Taylor scale of manifest anxiety. *J. consult. Psychol.*, 1954, 18, 433–436.
80. Bradfield, Anne F. Predicting the success in training of graduate students in school administration. Ph.D. dissertation, Stanford University, 1950.
81. Brockway, Ann L., Goldine Gleser, G. Winokur, and G. A. Ulett. The use of a control

population in neuropsychiatric research (psychiatric, psychological, and EEG evaluation of a heterogeneous sample). *Amer. J. Psychiat.*, 1954, 111, 248–262.

82. Brody, D. S. A genetic study of sociality patterns of college women. *Educ. psychol. Measmt.*, 1950, 10, 513–520.

83. Brothers, W. L. The relationship of certain factors to effectiveness in student teaching in the secondary schools. Ph.D. dissertation, Indiana University, 1950.

84. Brower, D. The relation between intelligence and MMPI scores. *J. soc. Psychol.*, 1947, 25, 243–245.

85. Brower, D. The relations between MMPI scores and cardio-vascular measures before and after experimentally induced visuo-motor conflict. *J. soc. Psychol.*, 1947, 26, 55–60.

86. Brower, D. The relations of visuo-motor conflict to personality traits and cardio-vascular activity. *J. gen. Psychol.*, 1948, 38, 69–99. (Also abstracted in *Amer. Psychologist*, 1946, 1, 244.)

87. Brown, D. G., and W. L. Lowe. A study of religious beliefs and personality differences in college students. M.A. thesis, University of Denver, 1948.

88. Brown, H. S. An investigation of the validity of the MMPI for a college population, and the relationship of certain personality traits to achievement. Ph.D. dissertation, University of Minnesota, 1947.

89. Brown, H. S. Similarities and differences in college populations on the Multiphasic. *J. appl. Psychol.*, 1948, 32, 541–549.

90. Brown, Mary A. Alcoholic profiles on the Minnesota Multiphasic. *J. clin. Psychol.*, 1950, 6, 266–269.

91. Brown, M. N. Evaluating and scoring the Minnesota Multiphasic "Cannot Say" items. *J. clin. Psychol.*, 1950, 6, 180–184.

92. Brozek, J. Psychology of human starvation and nutritional rehabilitation. *Sci. Mon.*, 1950, 70, 270–274.

93. Brozek, J., and Nancy K. Erickson. Item analysis of the psychoneurotic scales on the MMPI in experimental semistarvation. *J. consult. Psychol.*, 1948, 12, 403–411.

94. Brozek, J., H. Guetzkow, A. Keys, R. B. Cattell, Molly R. Harrower, and S. R. Hathaway. A study of personality of normal young men maintained on restricted intakes of vitamins of the B complex. *Psychosom. Med.*, 1946, 8, 98–109.

95. Brozek, J., and A. Keys. Personality changes with age: an item analysis of the Minnesota Multiphasic Personality Inventory. *Amer. Psychologist*, 1951, 6, 397. (Abstract.)

96. Brozek, J., and B. C. Schiele. Clinical significance of the Minnesota Multiphasic F scale evaluated in experimental neurosis. *Amer. J. Psychiat.*, 1948, 105, 259–266.

97. Buechley, R., and H. Ball. A new test of "validity" for the group MMPI. *J. consult. Psychol.*, 1952, 16, 299–301.

98. Bursch, C. W. Teacher satisfaction and teacher complaints. *Phi Delta Kappan*, 1950, 32, 139–140.

99. Bursch, C. W. Certain relationships between the Kuder Preference Record and the Minnesota Multiphasic Personality Inventory. *Calif. J. educ. Res.*, 1952, 3, 224–227.

100. Burton, A. The use of the masculinity-femininity scale of the MMPI as an aid in the diagnosis of sexual inversion. *J. Psychol.*, 1947, 24, 161–164.

101. Burton, A. The use of psychometric and projective tests in clinical psychology. *J. Psychol.*, 1949, 28, 451–456.

102. Burton, A., and C. J. Bright. Adaptation of the MMPI for group administration and rapid scoring. *J. consult. Psychol.*, 1946, 10, 99–103.

103. Burton, A., Sue S. Kalua, and F. J. Gorman. The prediction of suicide by the MMPI. Unpublished manuscript.

104. Butler, J. M., and D. W. Fiske. Theory and techniques of assessment. In C. P. Stone and Q. McNemar (Eds.), *Annual review of psychology.* Stanford: Annual Reviews, 1955. Vol. VI.

105. Caligor, L. The determination of the individual's unconscious conception of his own masculinity-femininity identification. *J. proj. Tech.*, 1951, 15, 494–509. (Same title: Ph.D. dissertation, New York University, 1950.)

106. Calvin, A. D., and W. H. Holtzman. Adjustment and the discrepancy between self-concept and inferred self. *J. consult. Psychol.*, 1953, 17, 39–44.

107. Calvin, A., and J. McConnell. Ellis on personality inventories. *J. consult. Psychol.*, 1953, 17, 462–464.

108. Canning, W., G. Harlow, and C. Regelin. A study of two personality questionnaires. *J. consult. Psychol.*, 1950, 14, 414–415.

109. Canter, A. H. MMPI profiles in multiple sclerosis. *J. consult. Psychol.*, 1951, 15, 253–256.

110. Cantor, J. M. Syndromes found in psychiatric population selected for certain MMPI code endings. Ph.D. dissertation, University of Minnesota, 1952.

111. Capwell, Dora F. Personality patterns of adolescent girls: I. Girls who show improvement in IQ. *J. appl. Psychol.*, 1945, 29, 212–228.

112. Capwell, Dora F. Personality patterns of adolescent girls: II. Delinquents and non-delinquents. *J. appl. Psychol.*, 1945, 29, 289–297.

113. Carp, A. Psychological test performance and insulin shock therapy. Ph.D. dissertation, Stanford University, 1948.

114. Carp, A. MMPI performance and insulin shock therapy. *J. abnorm. soc. Psychol.*, 1950, 45, 721–726.

115. Carpenter, L. G., M. B. Freedman, R. E. Harris, and M. Sokolow. A scale for the measurement of personality in patients with essential hypertension. *Amer. Psychologist*, 1951, 6, 493. (Abstract.)

116. Cauffiel, P. W. A comparison of the P-S experience blank with the MMPI. M.A. thesis, Pennsylvania State College, 1950.

117. Cauffiel, P. W., and W. U. Snyder. A comparison of the performance of a randomly selected college population on the MMPI and the P-S experience blank. *J. clin. Psychol.*, 1951, 7, 267–270.

118. Cerf, A. Z. The Minnesota Multiphasic Personality Inventory, CE437A. In J. P. Guilford and J. I. Lacey (Eds.), *Printed classification tests.* Army Air Forces Aviation Psychology Program Research Reports, Report No. 5, Washington, D.C.: U.S. Government Printing Office, 1947.

119. Challman, R. C. Clinical methods: psychodiagnostics. In C. P. Stone and D. W. Taylor (Eds.), *Annual review of psychology.* Stanford: Annual Reviews, 1951. Vol. II.

120. Charen, S. A note on the use of a pencil and paper form of the MMPI Hs scale for hospital use. *J. consult. Psychol.*, 1954, 18, 344.

121. Child, I. L. Personality. In C. P. Stone and Q. McNemar (Eds.), *Annual review of psychology.* Stanford: Annual Reviews, 1954. Vol. V.

122. Chyatte, C. Personality traits of professional actors. *Occupations*, 1949, 27, 245–250.

123. Clark, G. C., and R. M. Allen. Item analysis aid for the Minnesota Multiphasic Personality Inventory. *J. consult. Psychol.*, 1951, 15, 262.

124. Clark, J. H. Application of the MMPI in differentiating AWOL recidivists from non-recidivists. *J. Psychol.*, 1948, 26, 229–234.

125. Clark, J. H. Clinical use of the Altus thirty-six point adjustment test in screening army AWOL's. *J. consult. Psychol.*, 1948, 12, 276–279. (Also abstracted in *Amer. Psychologist*, 1947, 2, 411.)

126. Clark, J. H. Some MMPI correlates of color responses in the group Rorschach. *J. consult. Psychol.*, 1948, 12, 384–386. (Also abstracted in *Amer. Psychologist*, 1948, 3, 349.)

127. Clark, J. H. Additional applications of the Altus thirty-six point adjustment test as a screening instrument. *J. gen. Psychol.*, 1949, 40, 261–265.

128. Clark, J. H. The adjustment of army AWOL's. *J. abnorm. soc. Psychol.*, 1949, 44, 394–401.

129. Clark, J. H. Intertest variability on the California Test of Mental Maturity in relation to the MMPI. *J. consult. Psychol.*, 1950, 14, 32–34.

130. Clark, J. H. The relationship between MMPI scores and psychiatric classification of Army general prisoners. *J. clin. Psychol.*, 1952, 8, 86–89.

131. Clark, J. H. Additional applications of the AWOL recidivist scale. *J. clin. Psychol.*, 1953, 9, 62–64.

132. Clark, J. H. Grade achievement of female college students in relation to non-intellective factors: MMPI items. *J. soc. Psychol.*, 1953, 37, 275–281.

133. Clark, J. H. The interpretation of the MMPI profiles of college students: a comparison by college major subject. *J. clin. Psychol.*, 1953, 9, 382–384.

134. Cofer, C. N., June Chance, and A. J. Judson. A study of malingering on the MMPI. *J. Psychol.*, 1949, 27, 491–499.

135. Cofer, C. N., A. J. Judson, and D. V. Weick. On the significance of the psychogalvanic response as an indicator of reaction to personality test items. *J. Psychol.*, 1949, 27, 347–354. (Also abstracted in *Amer. Psychologist*, 1948, 3, 303.)

136. Cohen, D. Psychological concomitants of chronic illness: a study of emotional correlates of pulmonary tuberculosis, peptic ulcer, the arthritides, and cardiac disease. Ph.D. dissertation, University of Pittsburgh, 1949.

137. Cook, E. B., and R. J. Wherry. A study of the interrelationships of psychological and physiological measures on submarine enlisted candidates: I. History, experimental design, and statistical treatment of data. Medical Research Laboratory, U.S. Naval Submarine Base, New London, Conn. Report No. 1, Bureau of Medicine and Surgery Research, 1949.

624 BIBLIOGRAPHY

138. Cook, E. B., and R. J. Wherry. A factor analysis of MMPI and aptitude test data. *J. appl. Psychol.*, 1950, 34, 260–265.
139. Cook, W. W., and D. M. Medley. Proposed hostility and pharisaic-virtue scales for the MMPI. *J. appl. Pschol.*, 1954, 30, 414–418.
140. Corsini, R. J. A time and motion study of hand scoring the individual MMPI. *J. consult. Psychol.*, 1949, 13, 62–63.
141. Corsini, R. J., and K. Bartleme. Attitudes of San Quentin prisoners. *J. correctional Educ.*, 1952, 4, 43–46.
142. Cottle, W. C. A factorial study of selected instruments for measuring personality and interest. *Amer. Psychologist*, 1948, 3, 300. (Abstract.)
143. Cottle, W. C. Card versus booklet forms of the MMPI. *J. appl. Psychol.*, 1950, 34, 255–259.
144. Cottle, W. C. A factorial study of the Multiphasic, Strong. Kuder, and Bell inventories using a population of adult males. *Psychometrika*, 1950, 15, 25–47. (Same title: Ph.D. dissertation, Syracuse University, 1949.)
145. Cottle, W. C. Relationships among selected personality and interest inventories. *Occupations*, 1950, 28, 306–310. (Also abstracted in *Amer. Psychologist*, 1949, 4, 292–293.
146. Cottle, W. C. *The MMPI: a review.* Lawrence, Kansas: University of Kansas Press, 1953.
147. Cottle, W. C., W. W. Lewis, Jr., and M. M. Penney. Personal characteristics of counselors: III. An experimental scale. *J. counsel. Psychol.*, 1954, 1, 74–77.
148. Cottle, W. C., and J. O. Powell. Relationship of mean scores on the Strong, Kuder, and Bell inventories with the MMPI Mf scale as a criterion. *Trans. Kans. Acad. Sci.*, 1949, 52, 396–398.
149. Cottle, W. C., and J. O. Powell. The effect of random answers to the MMPI. *Educ. psychol. Measmt.*, 1951, 11, 224–227.
150. Cronbach, L. J. Response sets and test validity. *Educ. psychol. Measmt.*, 1946, 6, 475–494.
151. Cronbach, L. J. *Essentials of psychological testing.* New York: Harper, 1949.
152. Crook, G. H. The measurement of personal characteristics: are available tests of personality of use in the Army? Adjutant General's Office, Personnel Research Section, Report No. 669, 1944.
153. Cross, O. H. Adaptation of the MMPI for use with the blind. M.A. thesis, University of Minnesota, 1945.
154. Cross, O. H. Braille edition of the MMPI for use with the blind. *J. appl. Psychol.*, 1947, 31, 189–198.
155. Crowell, D. H. Personality and physical disease: a test of the Dunbar hypothesis applied to diabetes mellitus and rheumatic fever. *Genet. Psychol. Monogr.*, 1953, 48, 117–153.
156. Cuadra, C. A. A psychometric investigation of control factors in psychological adjustment. Ph.D. dissertation, University of California, 1953.
157. Cuadra, C. A., and C. F. Reed. *An introduction to the MMPI.* Downey, Ill.: Veterans Administration Hospital, 1954.
158. Dahlstrom, W. G. An exploration of mental status syndromes by factor analytic techniques. Ph.D. dissertation, University of Minnesota, 1949.
159. Dahlstrom, W. G. Personnel psychology and small business. *J. appl. Psychol.*, 1954, 38, 203–204.
160. Dahlstrom, W. G. Prediction of adjustment after neurosurgery. *Amer. Psychologist*, 1954, 9, 353. (Abstract.)
161. Dahlstrom, W. G., and Dorothy D. Craven. The MMPI and stuttering phenomena in young adults. *Amer. Psychologist*, 1952, 7, 341. (Abstract.)
162. Daly, Juliette M. Relationship of MMPI and Kuder Preference Record scores. M.A. thesis, Catholic University, 1948.
163. Daniels, E. E., and W. A. Hunter. MMPI personality patterns for various occupations. *J. appl. Psychol.*, 1949, 33, 559–565.
164. Danielson, J. R., and J. H. Clark. A personality inventory for induction screening. *J. clin. Psychol.*, 1954, 10, 137–143.
165. Darley, J. G., M. Gross, and W. E. Martin. Studies of group behavior: stability, change and interrelations of psychometric and sociometric variables. *J. abnorm. soc. Psychol.*, 1951, 46, 565–576.
166. Darley, J. G., and D. G. Marquis. Veterans' guidance centers: a survey of their problems and activities. *J. clin. Psychol.*, 1946, 2, 109–116.
167. Davidson, Marjorie E. A psychological study of successful and unsuccessful first year students at the University of Alberta. M.A. thesis, University of Alberta, 1950.
168. Davis, C. E. The MMPI: a new method of scoring and analysis. *J. clin. Psychol.*, 1947, 3 298–301.

169. Deane, M. A. A factorial study of the Minnesota Multiphasic Inventory. M.A. thesis, University of Utah, 1948.
170. deCillis, Olga E., and W. D. Orbison. A comparison of the Terman-Miles M-F test and the Mf scale of the MMPI. *J. appl. Psychol.*, 1950, 34, 338–342.
171. Deese, J., R. S. Lazarus, and J. Keenan. Anxiety, anxiety reduction, and stress in learning. *J. exp. Psychol.*, 1953, 46, 55–60.
172. Delay, J., P. Pichot, and M. Leroy. Diagnostic de la réticence et de la simulation des tests mentaux. (Diagnosis of reticence and simulation by mental tests.) *Ann. méd.-psychol.*, 1951, 109, 192–196.
173. Derner, G. F. *Aspects of the psychology of the tuberculous.* New York: Hoeber, 1953.
174. Diethelm, O., and C. A. Knehr. The diagnostic use of psychological tests from the psychiatrist's standpoint. In P. H. Hoch and J. Zubin (Eds.), *Relation of psychological tests to psychiatry.* New York: Grune and Stratton, 1952.
175. Dobson, W. R., and D. R. Stone. College freshman responses on the Minnesota Multiphasic Personality Inventory. *J. educ. Res.*, 1951, 44, 611–618.
176. Drake, F. E. A study of the personality traits of students interested in acting. *Speech Monogr.*, 1950, 17, 123–133.
177. Drake, L. E. A social I. E. scale for the MMPI. *J. appl. Psychol.*, 1946, 30, 51–54.
178. Drake, L. E. A method for machine scoring the card form of the MMPI. *J. educ. Res.*, 1947, 41, 139–141.
179. Drake, L. E. Differential sex responses to items of the MMPI. *J. appl. Psychol.*, 1953, 37, 46.
180. Drake, L. E. MMPI profiles and interview behavior. *J. counsel. Psychol.*, 1954, 1, 92–95.
181. Drake, L. E., and W. B. Thiede. Further validation of the social I. E. scale for the MMPI. *J. educ. Res.*, 1948, 41, 551–556.
182. Driscoll, P. J. Factors related to the institutional adjustment of prison inmates. *J. abnorm. soc. Psychol.*, 1952, 47, 593–596.
183. Dunham, R. E. Factors related to recidivism in adults. *J. soc. Psychol.*, 1954, 39, 77–91.
184. Elkin, A. Personality as a variable in serial verbal learning. Ph.D. dissertation, Northwestern University, 1950.
185. Ellis, A. The validity of personality questionnaires. *Psychol. Bull.*, 1946, 43, 385–440.
186. Ellis, A. Personality questionnaires. *Rev. educ. Res.*, 1947, 17, 53–63.
187. Ellis, A. The relationship between personality inventory scores and other psychological test results. *J. soc. Psychol.*, 1948, 28, 287–289.
188. Ellis, A. Recent research with personality inventories. *J. consult. Psychol.*, 1953, 17, 45–49.
189. Ellis, A., and H. S. Conrad. The validity of personality inventories in military practice. *Psychol. Bull.*, 1948, 45, 385–426.
190. Eriksen, C. W. Psychological defenses and "ego strength" in the recall of completed and incompleted tasks. *J. abnorm. soc. Psychol.*, 1954, 49, 45–50.
191. Eriksen, C. W. Some personality correlates of stimulus generalization under stress. *J. abnorm. soc. Psychol.*, 1954, 49, 561–565.
192. Eysenck, H. J. The MMPI: A Review. In O. K. Buros, *The third mental measurements yearbook.* New Brunswick, N.J.: Rutgers University Press, 1949.
193. Eysenck, H. J. *The structure of human personality.* New York: Wiley, 1953.
194. Falls, R. P., and R. R. Blake. A quantitative analysis of the Picture-Frustration study. *J. Pers.*, 1948, 16, 320–325.
195. Farber, I. E., and K. W. Spence. Complex learning and conditioning as a function of anxiety. *J. exp. Psychol.*, 1953, 45, 120–125.
196. Farberow, N. L. Personality patterns of suicidal mental hospital patients. *Genet. Psychol. Monogr.*, 1950, 42, 3–80.
197. Fassett, K. K. Interest and personality measures of veteran and non-veteran university freshman men. *Educ. psychol. Measmt.*, 1950, 10, 338–341.
198. Feather, D. B. The relation of personality maladjustments of 503 University of Michigan students to their occupational interests. *J. soc. Psychol.*, 1950, 32, 71–78.
199. Feil, Madeleine H. A study of leadership and scholastic achievement in their relation to prediction factors. Ph.D. dissertation, Ohio State University, 1949.
200. Feldman, M. J. A prognosis scale for shock therapy. *Psychol. Monogr.*, 1951, 65, No. 10 (Whole No. 327). (Also abstracted in *Amer. Psychologist*, 1948, 3, 348.)
201. Feldman, M. J. The use of the MMPI profile for prognosis and evaluation of shock therapy. *J. consult. Psychol.*, 1952, 16, 376–382.
202. Ferguson, L. W. *Personality measurement.* New York: McGraw-Hill, 1952.
203. Ferguson, R. G. A useful adjunct to the Minnesota Multiphasic Personality Inventory scoring and analysis. *J. clin. Psychol.*, 1946, 2, 248–253.

204. Ferreira, J. A. deA. O inventorio multifasico de personalidade de Minnesota no estude de leucotomizados. (The MMPI in the study of lobotomized persons.) *Med. contemp. Lisb.,* 1953, 71, 531–536.
205. Foster, K. A study of WPA white collar workers with respect to job satisfaction and personality characteristics. M.S. thesis, University of Minnesota, 1941.
206. Francey, Ruth. A study on the "epileptic personality." *Canad. J. Psychol.,* 1950, 4, 81–87.
207. Freeman, R. A., and H. M. Mason. Construction of a key to determine recidivists from non-recidivists using the MMPI. *J. clin. Psychol.,* 1952, 8, 207–208.
208. Friedman, S. H. Psychometric effects of frontal and parietal lobe brain damage. Ph.D. dissertation, University of Minnesota, 1950.
209. Fry, F. D. A study of the personality traits of college students and of state prison inmates as measured by the MMPI. *J. Psychol.,* 1949, 28, 439–449.
210. Fry, F. D. A normative study of the reactions manifested by college students and by state prison inmates in response to the MMPI, the Rosenzweig P-F study and the T.A.T. *J. Psychol.,* 1952, 34, 27–30. (Also abstracted in *Penn. State Coll. Abstracts of Dissertations,* 1952–53, 15, 548–552.)
211. Gallagher, J. J. Manifest anxiety changes concomitant with client-centered therapy. *J. consult. Psychol.,* 1953, 17, 443–446.
212. Gallagher, J. J. MMPI changes concomitant with client-centered therapy. *J. consult. Psychol.,* 1953, 17, 334–338.
213. Gallagher, J. J. The problem of escaping clients in nondirective counseling. In W. U. Snyder (Chairman), *Group report of a program of research in psychotherapy.* State College: Pennsylvania State University Press, 1953.
214. Gallagher, J. J. Test indicators for therapy prognosis. *J. consult. Psychol.,* 1954, 18, 409–413.
215. Gallenbeck, C. G. The effects of prison confinement upon personality adjustment of inmates of Waupun State Prison. M.A. thesis, University of Wisconsin, 1948.
216. Gayral, L., J. Carrié, P. Jardillier, and Genevieve Sciolette. Etude critique de l'inventaire multiphasique de personnalité; "test" de Minnesota. *Ann. méd.-psychol.,* 1951, 2, 166–178.
217. Geist, H. A comparison of personality test scores and medical psychiatric diagnosis by the inverted factor technique. *J. clin. Psychol.,* 1952, 8, 184–188.
218. Gengerelli, J. A. Comparison of the MMPI profile shapes of several nosological groups. *Amer. Psychologist,* 1954, 9, 562. (Abstract.)
219. Gengerelli, J. A., and F. J. Kirkner (Eds.). *The psychological variables in human cancer.* Berkeley: University of California Press, 1954.
220. Gilberstadt, H. An exploratory investigation of the Hathaway-Meehl method of Minnesota Multiphasic Personality Inventory profile analysis with psychiatric clinical data. *Dissertation Abstr.,* 1953, 13, 256–257. (Abstract of Ph.D. dissertation, University of Minnesota, 1952.)
221. Gilbert, W. M. Counseling: therapy and diagnosis. In C. P. Stone and D. W. Taylor (Eds.), *Annual review of psychology.* Stanford: Annual Reviews, 1952. Vol. III.
222. Gill, I. A. An investigation of the psychological effects of the first three months of imprisonment on the personality of the first offender. M.A. thesis, University of North Carolina, 1952.
223. Gilliland, A. R. A comparison of two personality tests. *Amer. Psychologist,* 1949, 4, 258. (Abstract.)
224. Gilliland, A. R. The Humm-Wadsworth and the Minnesota Multiphasic. *J. consult. Psychol.,* 1951, 15, 457–459.
225. Gilliland, A. R., and R. Colgin. Norms, reliability, and forms of the MMPI. *J. consult. Psychol.,* 1951, 15, 435–438.
226. Gjerde, C. M. Parent-child resemblances in vocational interests and personality traits. Ph.D. dissertation, University of Minnesota, 1949.
227. Glaser, R. Predicting achievement in medical school. *J. appl. Psychol.,* 1951, 35, 272–274.
228. Glaser, R. The validity of some tests for predicting achievement in medical school. *Amer. Psychologist,* 1951, 6, 298. (Abstract.)
229. Glenn, R. A study of personality patterns of male defective delinquents as indicated by the Minnesota Multiphasic Personality Inventory. M.S. thesis, Pennsylvania State College, 1949.
230. Goffard, S. J. Some diagnostic correlates of sociometric status. Ph.D. dissertation, University of Minnesota, 1949.
231. Goodstein, L. D. Interrelationships among several measures of anxiety and hostility. *J. consult. Psychol.,* 1954, 18, 349–354.
232. Goodstein, L. D. Regional differences in MMPI responses among male college students. *J. consult. Psychol.,* 1954, 18, 437–441.

233. Gordon, T. The airline pilot's job. *J. appl. Psychol.*, 1949, 33, 122–131.
234. Gough, H. G. Diagnostic patterns on the MMPI. *J. clin. Psychol.*, 1946, 2, 23–37.
235. Gough, H. G. Simulated patterns on the MMPI. *J. abnorm. soc. Psychol.*, 1947, 42, 215–225.
236. Gough, H. G. A new dimension of status: I. Development of a personality scale. *Amer. sociol. Rev.*, 1948, 13, 401–409.
237. Gough, H. G. A new dimension of status: II. Relationship of the St scale to other variables. *Amer. sociol. Rev.*, 1948, 13, 534–537.
238. Gough, H. G. A note on the security-insecurity test. *J. soc. Psychol.*, 1948, 28, 257–261.
239. Gough, H. G. Personality correlates of socio-economic status. *Amer. Psychologist*, 1948, 3, 360. (Abstract.)
240. Gough, H. G. A sociological theory of psychopathy. *Amer. J. Sociol.*, 1948, 53, 359–366.
241. Gough, H. G. Factors relating to the academic achievement of high school students. *J. educ. Psychol.*, 1949, 40, 65–78.
242. Gough, H. G. A new dimension of status: III. Discrepancies between the St scale and "objective status." *Amer. sociol. Rev.*, 1949, 14, 275–281.
243. Gough, H. G. Personality correlates of social and ethnic attitudes among high school students. Ph.D. dissertation, University of Minnesota, 1949.
244. Gough, H. G. A research note on the MMPI social I. E. scale. *J. educ. Res.*, 1949, 43, 138–141.
245. Gough, H. G. The F minus K dissimulation index for the MMPI. *J. consult. Psychol.*, 1950, 14, 408–413.
246. Gough, H. G. Studies of social intolerance: I. Psychological and sociological correlates of anti-Semitism. *J. soc. Psychol.*, 1951, 33, 237–246.
247. Gough, H. G. Studies of social intolerance: II. A personality scale for anti-Semitism. *J. soc. Psychol.*, 1951, 33, 247–255.
248. Gough, H. G. Studies of social intolerance: III. Relationship of the Pr scale to other variables. *J. soc. Psychol.*, 1951, 33, 257–262.
249. Gough, H. G. Studies of social intolerance: IV. Related social attitudes. *J. soc. Psychol.*, 1951, 33, 263–269.
250. Gough, H. G. Identifying psychological femininity. *Educ. psychol. Measmt.*, 1952, 12, 427–439.
251. Gough, H. G. Predicting social participation. *J. soc. Psychol.*, 1952, 35, 227–233.
252. Gough, H. G. The construction of a personality scale to predict academic achievement. *J. appl. Psychol.*, 1953, 37, 361–366.
253. Gough, H. G. A nonintellectual intelligence test. *J. consult. Psychol.*, 1953, 17, 242–246.
254. Gough, H. G. Tests of personality: questionnaires. A. Minnesota Multiphasic Personality Inventory. In A. Weider (Ed.), *Contributions toward medical psychology*. New York: Ronald Press, 1953.
255. Gough, H. G. Some common misconceptions about neuroticism. *J. consult. Psychol.*, 1954, 18, 287–292.
256. Gough, H. G. Some personality differences between high ability high school students who do, and do not, go to college. *Amer. Psychologist*, 1954, 9, 559. (Abstract.)
257. Gough, H. G. Adjectival descriptions of scale deviates among normals. Unpublished manuscript (mimeographed material).
258. Gough, H. G., H. McClosky, and P. E. Meehl. A personality scale for dominance. *J. abnorm. soc. Psychol.*, 1951, 46, 360–366.
259. Gough, H. G., H. McClosky, and P. E. Meehl. A personality scale for social responsibility. *J. abnorm. soc. Psychol.*, 1952, 47, 73–80.
260. Gough, H. G., and G. Mann. Changes in MMPI profiles occurring in a military rehabilitation program. Unpublished manuscript.
261. Gough, H. G., and W. H. Pemberton. Personality characteristics related to success in practice teaching. *J. appl. Psychol.*, 1952, 36, 307–309.
262. Gowan, J. C., and May S. Gowan. A teacher prognosis scale on the MMPI. *Amer. Psychologist*, 1954, 9, 561. (Abstract.)
263. Granick, S., and L. J. Smith. Sex sequence in the Draw-a-Person Test and its relation to the MMPI masculinity-femininity scale. *J. consult. Psychol.*, 1953, 17, 71–73.
264. Grant, H. A rapid personality evaluation based on the MMPI and the Cornell Selectee Index. *Amer. J. Psychiat.*, 1946, 103, 33–41.
265. Grayson, H. The Minnesota Multiphasic Personality Inventory. In E. S. Shneidman, W. Joel, and K. B. Little (Eds.), *Thematic test analysis*. New York: Grune and Stratton, 1951.
266. Grayson, H. M. *A psychological admissions testing program and manual*. Los Angeles: V.A. Center Neuropsychiatric Hospital, 1951.

267. Greenberg, P., and A. R. Gilliland. The relationship between basal metabolism and personality. *J. soc. Psychol.*, 1952, 35, 3–7.

268. Grossman, Donna J. A study of the parents of stuttering and non-stuttering children using the MMPI and the Minnesota Scale of Parents' Opinions. M.A. thesis, University of Wisconsin, 1951. (Abstracted in *Speech Monogr.*, 1952, 19, 193–194.)

269. Guertin, W. H., and V. Zilaitis. A transposed factor analysis of paranoid schizophrenics. *J. consult. Psychol.*, 1953, 17, 455–458.

270. Guetzkow, H., *et al.* Recovery after 12 weeks of controlled nutritional rehabilitation following experimental semistarvation in man: Part III. Personality. *Amer. Psychologist*, 1947, 2, 330–331. (Abstract.)

271. Gulde, C. J., and H. L. Roy. A note on the scoring of the MMPI. *J. consult. Psychol.*, 1947, 11, 221–222.

272. Guthrie, G. M. Six MMPI diagnostic profile patterns. *J. Psychol.*, 1950, 30, 317–323.

273. Guthrie, G. M. A study of the personality characteristics associated with the disorders encountered by an internist. Ph.D. dissertation, University of Minnesota, 1950.

274. Guthrie, G. M. Common characteristics associated with frequent MMPI profile types. *J. clin. Psychol.*, 1952, 8, 141–145.

275. Haertzen, C. A. The value of the MMPI as a predictor of discharge of mentally sick patients at the Rochester State Hospital. *Blocks and Blots*, 1952, 2, 4–5.

276. Hales, W. M., and W. Simon. MMPI patterns before and after insulin shock therapy. *Amer. J. Psychiat.*, 1948, 105, 254–258.

277. Hampton, P. J. The MMPI as a psychometric tool for diagnosing personality disorders among college students. *J. soc. Psychol.*, 1947, 26, 99–108.

278. Hampton, P. J. A psychometric study of drinkers: the development of a personality questionnaire for drinkers. Ph.D. dissertation, Western Reserve University, 1950.

279. Hampton, P. J. Differences in personality traits between alcoholic and nonalcoholic subjects. *Amer. Psychologist*, 1951, 6, 313. (Abstract.)

280. Hampton, P. J. A psychometric study of drinkers. *J. consult. Psychol.*, 1951, 15, 501–504.

281. Hampton, P. J. The development of a personality questionnaire for drinkers. *Genet. Psychol. Monogr.*, 1953, 48, 55–115.

282. Hand, T. J. Personality characteristics of a tuberculosis group. *Amer. J. phys. Med.*, 1952, 31, 95–101.

283. Hanes, B. Reading ease and MMPI results. *J. clin. Psychol.*, 1953, 9, 83–85.

284. Hanley, C. An inventory of personal opinions. Rehabilitation research. USN Retraining Command, Camp Elliott, San Diego, First Technical Report. ONR No. 174–177, 1954.

285. Hanvik, L. J. Some psychological dimensions of low back pain. Ph.D. dissertation, University of Minnesota, 1949.

286. Hanvik, L. J. Some comparisons and correlations between MMPI and Rosenzweig P-F study scores in a neuropsychiatric hospital sample. *J. Colo.-Wyo. Acad. Sci.*, 1950, 4, 70. (Abstract.)

287. Hanvik, L. J. MMPI profiles in patients with low back pain. *J. consult. Psychol.*, 1951, 15, 350–353.

288. Harmon, L. R. Interrelations of patterns on the Kuder Preference Record and the Minnesota Multiphasic Personality Inventory. *Dissertation Abstr.*, 1953, 13, 257–258. (Abstract of Ph.D. dissertation, University of Minnesota, 1952.)

289. Harmon, L. R., and D. N. Wiener. Use of the MMPI in vocational advisement. *J. appl. Psychol.*, 1945, 29, 132–141.

290. Harris, R. E. Measured personality characteristics of convulsive therapy patients: a study of diagnostic and prognostic criteria. *Psychol. Bull.*, 1945, 42, 535. (Abstract.)

291. Harris, R. E., K. M. Bowman, and A. Simon. Studies in electro-narcosis therapy: III. Psychological test findings. *J. nerv. ment. Dis.*, 1948, 107, 371–376.

292. Harris, R. E., and Carole Christiansen. Prediction of response to brief psychotherapy. *J. Psychol.*, 1946, 21, 269–284.

293. Harris, R. E., and V. M. Ives. A study of the personality of alcoholics. *Amer. Psychologist*, 1947, 2, 405. (Abstract.)

294. Hathaway, S. R. The Multiphasic Personality Inventory. *Mod. Hospital*, 1946, 66, 65–67.

295. Hathaway, S. R. *Supplementary manual for the MMPI.* (Part I: The K scale and its use. Part II: The booklet form of the MMPI.) New York: Psychological Corporation, 1946.

296. Hathaway, S. R. A coding system for MMPI profiles. *J. consult. Psychol.*, 1947, 11, 334–337.

297. Hathaway, S. R. Hypochondriasis. In A. Burton and R. E. Harris (Eds.), *Case histories in clinical and abnormal psychology.* New York: Harper, 1947.

298. Hathaway, S. R. Neurasthenia. In A. Burton and R. E. Harris (Eds.), *Case histories in clinical and abnormal psychology.* New York: Harper, 1947.

BIBLIOGRAPHY 629

299. Hathaway, S. R., and J. C. McKinley. The measurement of symptomatic depression with the Minnesota Multiphasic Personality Schedule. *Psychol. Bull.*, 1940, 37, 425. (Abstract.)
300. Hathaway, S. R., and J. C. McKinley. A multiphasic personality schedule (Minnesota): I. Construction of the schedule. *J. Psychol.*, 1940, 10, 249–254.
301. Hathaway, S. R., and J. C. McKinley. A multiphasic personality schedule (Minnesota): III. The measurement of symptomatic depression. *J. Psychol.*, 1942, 14, 73–84.
302. Hathaway, S. R., and J. C. McKinley. *The Minnesota Multiphasic Personality Schedule.* Minneapolis: University of Minnesota Press, 1942.
303. Hathaway, S. R., and J. C. McKinley. *The Minnesota Multiphasic Personality Inventory.* (Rev. ed.) Minneapolis: University of Minnesota Press, 1943.
304. Hathaway, S. R., and J. C. McKinley. *Manual for the MMPI.* New York: Psychological Corporation, 1945.
305. Hathaway, S. R., and J. C. McKinley. *The Minnesota Multiphasic Personality Inventory Manual.* (Revised.) New York: Psychological Corporation, 1951.
306. Hathaway, S. R., and P. E. Meehl. *The K scale for the MMPI.* New York: Psychological Corporation, 1947.
307. Hathaway, S. R., and P. E. Meehl. *An atlas for the clinical use of the MMPI.* Minneapolis: University of Minnesota Press, 1951.
308. Hathaway, S. R., and P. E. Meehl. The Minnesota Multiphasic Personality Inventory. In *Military clinical psychology.* Department of the Army Technical Manual TM 8:242; Department of the Air Force Manual AFM 160–145. Washington, D.C.: U.S. Government Printing Office, 1951.
309. Hathaway, S. R., and P. E. Meehl. MMPI. In E. Stern (Ed.), *Handbuch der Klinischen Psychologie.* Band 1. Zurich: Rascher, 1954.
310. Hathaway, S. R., and E. D. Monachesi. The prediction of juvenile delinquency using the Minnesota Multiphasic Personality Inventory. *Amer. J. Psychiat.*, 1951, 108, 469–473.
311. Hathaway, S. R., and E. D. Monachesi. The MMPI in the study of juvenile delinquents. *Amer. sociol. Rev.*, 1952, 17, 704–710.
312. Hathaway, S. R., and E. D. Monachesi (Eds.). *Analyzing and predicting juvenile delinquency with the MMPI.* Minneapolis: University of Minnesota Press, 1953.
313. Hawkes, G. R. Use of the MMPI in screening college students for counseling purposes. *J. educ. Psychol.*, 1950, 41, 116–121.
314. Heineman, C. E. A forced-choice form of the Taylor Anxiety Scale. *J. consult. Psychol.*, 1953, 17, 447–454.
315. Henderson, C. R., et al. Changes in personality appraisal associated with a restricted intake of B vitamins and protein. *Amer. J. med. Sci.*, 1947, 213, 488–493.
316. Herzberg, F. I. A study of the psychological factors in primary dysmenorrhea. *J. clin. Psychol.*, 1952, 8, 174–178.
317. Heston, J. C. A comparison of four masculinity-femininity scales. *Educ. psychol. Measmt.*, 1948, 8, 375–388.
318. Hewitt, C. C. A personality study of alcohol addiction. *Quart. J. Stud. Alcohol*, 1943, 4, 368–386.
319. Hibbeler, H. L. Personality patterns of white adults with primary glaucoma. *Amer. J. Ophthal.*, 1947, 30, 181–186.
320. Hilgard, E. R., L. V. Jones, and S. J. Kaplan. Conditioned discrimination as related to anxiety. *J. exp. Psychol.*, 1951, 42, 94–99.
321. Hobbs, N., and J. Seeman. Counseling. In C. P. Stone and Q. McNemar (Eds.), *Annual review of psychology.* Stanford: Annual Reviews, 1955. Vol. VI.
322. Holzberg, J. D., and S. Alessi. Reliability of the shortened MMPI. *J. consult. Psychol.*, 1949, 13, 288–292.
323. Holzberg, J. D., Eleanor R. Cahen, and E. K. Wilk. Suicide: a psychological study of self-destruction. *J. proj. Tech.*, 1951, 15, 339–354.
324. Holtzman, W. H., and M. E. Bitterman. Psychiatric screening of flying personnel: VI. Anxiety and reactions to stress. School of Aviation Medicine, Project No. 21-37-002, Report No. 6, 1952.
325. Holtzman, W. H., A. D. Calvin, and M. E. Bitterman. New evidence for the validity of Taylor's Manifest Anxiety Scale. *J. abnorm. soc. Psychol.*, 1952, 47, 853–854.
326. Holtzman, W. H., I. Iscoe, and A. D. Calvin. Rorschach color responses and manifest anxiety in college women. *J. consult. Psychol.*, 1954, 18, 317–324.
327. Houk, T. W. MMPI in diagnosis of psychoneuroses. *Northwest Med.*, 1946, 45, 248–252.
328. Houk, T. W., and Y. Robertson. Diagnosis of hypoglycemic neurosis with the MMPI. *Northwest Med.*, 1946, 45, 923.
329. Hovey, H. B. Detection of circumvention in the MMPI. *J. clin. Psychol.*, 1948, 4, 97.

330. Hovey, H. B. Somatization and other neurotic reactions and MMPI profiles. *J. clin. Psychol.*, 1949, 5, 153–156.
331. Hovey, H. B. MMPI profiles and personality characteristics. *J. consult. Psychol.*, 1953, 17, 142–146.
332. Hovey, H. B. MMPI aberration potentials in a nonclinical group. *J. soc. Psychol.*, 1954, 40, 299–307.
333. Hovey, H. B., and J. C. Stauffacher. Intuitive versus objective prediction from a test. *J. clin. Psychol.*, 1953, 9, 349–351.
334. Hoyt, D. P., and T. M. Magoon. A validation study of the Taylor Manifest Anxiety Scale. *J. clin. Psychol.*, 1954, 10, 357–361.
335. Hoyt, D. P., and W. T. Norman. Adjustment and academic predictability. *J. counsel. Psychol.*, 1954, 1, 96–99.
336. Hughes, H. B., J. L. Sprague, and A. W. Bendig. Anxiety level, response alternation, and performance in serial learning. *J. Psychol.*, 1954, 38, 421–426.
337. Hunt, E. L., and G. F. J. Lehner. Relationships of the Hildreth feeling and attitude scale to the MMPI. *J. clin. Psychol.*, 1948, 4, 412–414. (Also abstracted in *Amer. Psychologist*, 1947, 2, 417.)
338. Hunt, H. F. A study of the effect of the K correction on the differential diagnostic efficiency of the MMPI. *Amer. Psychologist*, 1947, 2, 272–273. (Abstract.)
339. Hunt, H. F. The effect of deliberate deception on MMPI performance. *J. consult. Psychol.*, 1948, 12, 396–402. (Also abstracted in *Amer. Psychologist*, 1948, 3, 349.)
340. Hunt, H. F. Clinical methods: psychodiagnostics. In C. P. Stone and D. W. Taylor (Eds.), *Annual review of psychology*. Stanford: Annual Reviews, 1950. Vol. I.
341. Hunt, H. F., et al. A study of the differential diagnostic efficiency of the MMPI. *J. consult. Psychol.*, 1948, 12, 331–336. (Also abstracted in *Amer. Psychologist*, 1947, 2, 417.)
342. Hunt, W. A., and Iris Stevenson. Psychological testing in military clinical psychology: II. Personality testing. *Psychol. Rev.*, 1946, 53, 107–115.
343. James, R. W. Selection of graduate students: I. The adequacy of certain measures for differentiating between two groups of masters candidates; II. The value of these measures in prognosing graduate academic achievement. Ph.D. dissertation, New York University, 1950. (Also abstracted in *Microfilm Abstracts*, 1951, 11, 53–54.)
344. Janda, E. J. On the relationship between anxiety and night vision. Ph.D. dissertation, University of Michigan, 1951.
345. Jeffrey, Mary E. Some factors influencing answers on the Multiphasic K scale. Ph.D. dissertation, University of Minnesota, 1946.
346. Jenkins, W. L. The Minnesota Multiphasic Personality Inventory applied to the problem of prognosis in schizophrenia. Ph.D. dissertation, University of Minnesota, 1952.
347. Jennings, L. S. MMPI: differentiation of psychologically good and poor combat risks among flying personnel. *J. Aviat. Med.*, 1948, 19, 222–226, 237.
348. Jensen, M. B., and J. B. Rotter. The value of thirteen psychological tests in officer candidate screening. *J. appl. Psychol.*, 1947, 31, 312–322.
349. Johnson, R. H., and G. L. Bond. Reading ease of commonly used tests. *J. appl. Psychol.*, 1950, 34, 319–324.
350. Johnson, Ruth L. E. The relation of religious attitudes and selected personality characteristics. M.A. thesis, University of Minnesota, 1948.
351. Johnson, W., F. L. Darley, and D. C. Spriestersbach. *Diagnostic manual in speech correction: a professional training workbook*. New York: Harper, 1952.
352. Kahn, H., and E. Singer. An investigation of the factors related to success or failure of school of commerce students. *J. educ. Psychol.*, 1949, 40, 107–117.
353. Kahn, M. W. The role of perceptual consistency and generality change in Rorschach and psychotherapy behavior. In W. U. Snyder, *Group report of a program of research in psychotherapy*. State College: Pennsylvania State University Press, 1953.
354. Kalhorn, Joan. Personality and parent behavior. *Amer. Psychologist*, 1947, 2, 425. (Abstract.)
355. Kamman, G. R. Psychosomatic diagnosis. *Lancet*, 1947, 67, 102–107.
356. Kaufmann, P. Changes in the Minnesota Multiphasic Personality Inventory as a function of psychiatric therapy. *J. consult. Psychol.*, 1950, 14, 458–464.
357. Kazan, A. T., and I. M. Sheinberg. Clinical note on the significance of the validity score (F) in the MMPI. *Amer. J. Psychiat.*, 1945, 102, 181–183.
358. Kelly, E. L. Theory and techniques of assessment. In C. P. Stone and Q. McNemar (Eds.), *Annual review of psychology*. Stanford: Annual Reviews, 1954. Vol. V.
359. Kelly, E. L., and D. W. Fiske. *The selection of clinical psychologists. Progress report and preliminary findings*. Ann Arbor: Edwards Letter Shop, 1948.

360. Kelly, E. L., and D. W. Fiske. *The prediction of performance in clinical psychology.* Ann Arbor: University of Michigan Press, 1951.
361. Kendall, E. The validity of Taylor's Manifest Anxiety Scale. *J. consult. Psychol.,* 1954, 18, 429–432.
362. Keys, A. Rehabilitation following experimental starvation in man. Laboratory of Physiological Hygiene Report, University of Minnesota, 1946.
363. Keys, A. Later stages of rehabilitation following experimental starvation in man. Laboratory of Physiological Hygiene Report, University of Minnesota, 1946.
364. Keys, A., et al. *Biology of human starvation.* Vol. II. Minneapolis: University of Minnesota Press, 1950.
365. Kinsala, J. E., and E. L. Phillips. Personality characteristics of veterans with no primary interest on the Strong Vocational Interest Test. *Minn. Counselor,* 1949, 4, 13–17.
366. Kirkwood, J. W. Incidence, contributory etiological factors, and use of the Minnesota Multiphasic Personality Inventory as a prognostic and diagnostic instrument of psychopathological conditions among public school teachers in California. Ph.D. dissertation, University of California, 1949.
367. Kline, M. V. Visual imagery and a case of experimental hypnotherapy. *J. gen. Psychol.,* 1952, 46, 159–167.
368. Knehr, C. A., and N. Fuller. Sensory vs. autonomous control of span of apprehension. *J. Psychol.,* 1954, 37, 65–73.
369. Kooser, E. deT. The relationship of masculinity-femininity orientation to self-report of anxiety. M.A. thesis, University of North Carolina, 1954.
370. Koskaff, Y. D., and E. Wheeler. Psychometric evaluation of noninstitutionalized epileptic patients with varying degrees of cerebral dysrhythmia. *Trans. Amer. Neurol. Assoc.,* 1946, 173. (Abstract.)
371. Kostlan, A. A method for the empirical study of psychodiagnosis. *J. consult. Psychol.,* 1954, 18, 83–88.
372. Krise, E. M. A short method of scoring the MMPI. *J. clin. Psychol.,* 1947, 3, 386–392.
373. Krise, E. M. A common error in scoring the MMPI. *J. clin. Psychol.,* 1949, 5, 180–181.
374. Kuder, G. F. Expected developments in interest and personality inventories. *Educ. psychol. Measmt.,* 1954, 14, 265–271.
375. Laforge, R., T. F. Leary, H. Naboisek, H. S. Coffey, and M. B. Freedman. The interpersonal dimension of personality. II. An objective study of repression. *J. Pers.,* 1954, 23, 129–153.
376. Lagerstedt, B. Investigation of personality and attitudinal changes in three SPAN groups. M.A. thesis, University of Minnsota, 1950.
377. Lander, E. K. An explorative study of some effects of therapy on adult stutterers. M.S. thesis, University of Minnesota, 1949. (Also abstracted in *Speech Monogr.,* 1950, 17, 295.)
378. La Tourelle, C. W. A study of the relationship of the subtest deviations on the Wechsler-Bellevue Intelligence Scale and scores of the MMPI. M.A. thesis, University of Southern California, 1946.
379. Lauterbach, C. An empirical study of the Manifest Anxiety Scale and its relationship to other clinical measures of anxiety. Ph.D. dissertation, State University of Iowa, 1952.
380. Layton, W. L. The variability of individuals' scores upon successive testings on the MMPI. *Educ. psychol. Measmt.,* 1954, 14, 634–640.
381. Lazarus, R. S., et al. Anxiety and stress in learning: the role of intraserial duplication. *J. exp. Psychol.,* 1954, 47, 111–114.
382. Lehman, C. F. A comparative study of instrumental musicians on the basis of the Kwalwasser-Dykema Music Tests, the Otis IQ Intelligence Test and the Minnesota Multiphasic Personality Inventory. Ph.D. dissertation, Syracuse University, 1949.
383. Lehman, C. F. A comparative study of instrumental musicians on the basis of the Otis Intelligence Test, the Kwalwasser-Dykema Music Test and the Minnesota Multiphasic Personality Inventory. *J. educ. Res.,* 1950, 44, 57–61.
384. Lehner, G. F. J., W. M. Wheeler, and K. B. Little. A factor analysis of the MMPI. *Amer. Psychologist,* 1950, 5, 471. (Abstract.)
385. Leton, D. A study of the relationship between the Kuder Preference Record and the MMPI. *Minn. Counselor,* 1949, 4, 18–22.
386. Leverenz, C. W. MMPI: an evaluation of its usefulness in the psychiatric service of a station hospital. *War Med.,* 1943, 4, 618–629.
387. Levine, S. The relationship between personality and efficiency in various hospital occupations. Ph.D. dissertation, New York University, 1951.
388. Levinson, Maria H. Psychological ill-health in relation to potential fascism: a study of psychiatric clinic patients. In T. W. Adorno, Else Frenkel-Brunswik, D. Levinson, and R. N. Sanford, *The authoritarian personality.* New York: Harper, 1950.

389. Levitt, E. E. A note on the Welsh MMPI anxiety index. *J. consult. Psychol.*, 1954, 18, 112.
390. Levy, S., *et al.* The outstanding personality factors among the population of a state penitentiary: a preliminary report. *J. clin. exp. Psychopath.*, 1952, 13, 117–130.
391. Lewis, J. A. Occupational interests and personality tendencies. M.A. thesis, University of Minnesota, 1946.
392. Lewis, J. A. Kuder Preference Record and MMPI scores for two occupational groups. *J. consult. Psychol.*, 1947, 11, 194–201.
393. Lindgren, H. C. The development of a scale of cultural idealization based on the California Test of Personality. *J. educ. Psychol.*, 1952, 43, 81–91.
394. Lingoes, J. C., R. E. Harris, and S. R. Hathaway. Two personality profiles associated with cardiovascular measures. *Amer. Psychologist*, 1954, 9, 561. (Abstract.)
395. Little, J. W. An analysis of the Minnesota Multiphasic Personality Inventory. M.A. thesis, University of North Carolina, 1949.
396. Little, K. B., and E. S. Shneidman. The validity of MMPI interpretations. *J. consult. Psychol.*, 1954, 18, 425–428.
397. Lively, Mary L. An investigation of some clinical aspects of the Heidbreder introversion-extroversion variable. M.A. thesis, University of Minnesota, 1943.
398. Lockman, R. F. Some relationships between the MMPI and a problem checklist. *J. appl. Psychol.*, 1954, 38, 264–267.
399. Loth, Nancy N. Correlations between the Guilford-Martin Inventory of Factors STDCR and the MMPI at the college level. M.A. thesis, University of Minnesota, 1945.
400. Lough, Orpha M. Teachers college students and the MMPI. *J. appl. Psychol.*, 1946, 30, 241–247.
401. Lough, Orpha M. Women students in liberal arts, nursing, and teacher training curricula and the MMPI. *J. appl. Psychol.*, 1947, 31, 437–445.
402. Lough, Orpha M. Correction for "Women students in liberal arts, nursing, and teacher training curricula and the MMPI." *J. appl. Psychol.*, 1951, 35, 125–126.
403. Lough, Orpha M., and Mary E. Green. Comparison of the Minnesota Multiphasic Personality Inventory and the Washburne S-A Inventory as measures of personality of college women. *J. soc. Psychol.*, 1950, 32, 23–30.
404. Louttit, C. M., and C. G. Browne. The use of psychometric instruments in psychological clinics. *J. consult. Psychol.*, 1947, 11, 49–54.
405. Low, G. M., and B. V. Sheets. The relation of psychometric factors to stage fright. *Speech Monogr.*, 1951, 18, 266–271.
406. Lucas, J. D. The interactive effects of anxiety, failure, and intraserial duplication. *Amer. J. Psychol.*, 1952, 65, 59–66.
407. Ludolph, M. The Guilford-Martin Inventory of Factors GAMIN and its relation to the MMPI. Unpublished paper, University of Minnesota, 1944.
408. McAllister, Catherine. A study of item behavior in the depression scale of the MMPI. M.S. thesis, Pennsylvania State College, 1950.
409. McClelland, W. A. A preliminary test of role-playing ability. *J. consult. Psychol.*, 1951, 15, 102–108.
410. McCollum, E. L. Personality alteration during reduced caloric intake under survival conditions in the subarctic. Arctic Aeromedical Laboratory, Project No. 21-01-025. Distribution No. 1517, SAM, San Antonio, 1950.
411. McCollum, E. L. Selection of men best qualified for subarctic and arctic duty: an 18-month longitudinal study of airmen assigned to Alaskan duty. Arctic Aeromedical Laboratory, Project No. 21-01-007, Part B. Ladd AFB, Alaska, 1951.
412. McCollum, E. L. Survey of human adjustment problems in the northern latitudes: a study of military offenders. Arctic Aeromedical Laboratory, Project No. 21-01-22, Program F, Part 1. Ladd AFB, Alaska, 1951.
413. McCreary, Joyce B., and A. W. Bendig. Comparison of two forms of the Manifest Anxiety Scale. *J. consult. Psychol.*, 1954, 18, 206.
414. McCrory, Anita T. The Minnesota Multiphasic Personality Inventory: a tool for detecting personality problems among senior high school students. M.A. thesis, University of Southern California, 1948.
415. MacDonald, G. L. A study of the shortened group and individual forms of the MMPI. *J. clin. Psychol.*, 1952, 8, 309–311.
416. MacDonald, G. L. Effect of test-retest interval and item arrangement on the shortened forms of the MMPI. *J. clin. Psychol.*, 1952, 8, 408–410.
417. McGee, Shanna. Measurement of hostility: a pilot study. *J. clin. Psychol.*, 1954, 10, 280–282.

418. Machover, S., and Helen J. Anderson. Validity of a paper-and-pencil form of the MMPI psychopathic deviate scale. *J. consult. Psychol.*, 1953, 17, 459–461.
419. Machover, S., and A. Schwartz. A homeostatic effect of mood on associative abstractness and reaction time. *J. Pers.*, 1952, 21, 59–67.
420. McKinley, J. C., and S. R. Hathaway. A multiphasic personality schedule (Minnesota): II. A differential study of hypochondriasis. *J. Psychol.*, 1940, 10, 255–268.
421. McKinley, J. C., and S. R. Hathaway. A multiphasic personality schedule (Minnesota): IV. Psychasthenia. *J. appl. Psychol.*, 1942, 26, 614–624.
422. McKinley, J. C., and S. R. Hathaway. The identification and measurement of the psychoneuroses in medical practice. *J. Amer. med. Ass.*, 1943, 122, 161–167.
423. McKinley, J. C., and S. R. Hathaway. The MMPI: V. Hysteria, hypomania and psychopathic deviate. *J. appl. Psychol.*, 1944, 28, 153–174.
424. McKinley, J. C., S. R. Hathaway, and P. E. Meehl. The MMPI: VI. The K scale. *J. consult. Psychol.*, 1948, 12, 20–31.
425. MacLean, A. G., A. T. Tait, and C. D. Catterall. The F minus K index on the MMPI. *J. appl. Psychol.*, 1953, 37, 315–316.
426. McNemar, Q. A review: E. L. Kelly and D. W. Fiske, The prediction of performance in clinical psychology. *J. abnorm. soc. Psychol.*, 1952, 47, 857–860.
427. McQuary, J. P., and W. E. Truax, Jr. A comparison of the group and individual forms of the MMPI. *J. educ. Res.*, 1952, 45, 609–614.
428. Mann, W. A. Validation of the Cornell Index for freshmen at Michigan State College. Ph.D. dissertation, Michigan State College, 1949.
429. Manson, M. P. A psychometric analysis of psychopathic characteristics of alcoholics. *J. consult. Psychol.*, 1949, 13, 111–118.
430. Manson, M. P., and H. M. Grayson. Key-sort method of scoring the MMPI. *J. appl. Psychol.*, 1946, 30, 509–516.
431. Matarazzo, J. D., G. A. Ulett, S. B. Guze, and G. Saslow. The relationship between anxiety level and several measures of intelligence. *J. consult. Psychol.*, 1954, 18, 201–205.
432. Mathews, Ravenna, C. Hardyck, and T. R. Sarbin. Self-organization as a factor in the performance of selected cognitive tasks. *J. abnorm. soc. Psychol.*, 1953, 48, 500–502.
433. Meehl, P. E. The dynamics of "structured" personality tests. *J. clin. Psychol.*, 1945, 1, 296–303.
434. Meehl, P. E. A general normality or control factor in personality testing. Ph.D. dissertation, University of Minnesota, 1945.
435. Meehl, P. E. An investigation of a general normality or control factor in personality testing. *Psychol. Monogr.*, 1945, 59, No. 4 (Whole No. 274).
436. Meehl, P. E. Profile analysis of the MMPI in differential diagnosis. *J. appl. Psychol.*, 1946, 30, 517–524.
437. Meehl, P. E. Schizophrenia, catatonic form. In A. Burton and R. E. Harris (Eds.), *Case histories in clinical and abnormal psychology*. New York: Harper, 1947.
438. Meehl, P. E. Configural scoring. *J. consult. Psychol.*, 1950, 14, 165–171.
439. Meehl, P. E. *Research results for counselors*. St. Paul, Minn.: Dept. of Education, 1951.
440. Meehl, P. E. *Clinical versus statstical prediction: a theoretical analysis and a review of the evidence*. Minneapolis: University of Minnesota Press, 1954.
441. Meehl, P. E., and S. R. Hathaway. The K factor as a suppressor variable in the MMPI. *J. appl. Psychol.*, 1946, 30, 525–564.
442. Michael, J. C., and Charlotte Bühler. Experiences with personality testing in a neuropsychiatric department of a public general hospital. *Dis. nerv. Syst.*, 1945, 6, 205–211.
443. Michaelis, J. U., and F. T. Tyler. MMPI and student teaching. *J. appl. Psychol.*, 1951, 35, 122–124.
444. Miller, Christine. Consistency of cognitive behavior as a function of personality characteristics. *J. Pers.*, 1954, 23, 233–249.
445. Miller, D. R. Levels of aspiration of hysterics and neurasthenics. *Amer. Psychologist*, 1947, 2, 406. (Abstract.)
446. Miller, D. R. Responses of psychiatric patients to threat of failure. *J. abnorm. soc. Psychol.*, 1951, 46, 378–387.
447. Mitchell, Mildred B., and H. F. Rothe. Validity of an emotional key on a short industrial personality questionnaire. *J. appl. Psychol.*, 1950, 34, 329–332.
448. Mochel, Marguerite. The Minnesota Multiphasic Personality Inventory as a factor in the selection and guidance of physical education major students. Ph.D. dissertation, University of Southern California, 1949.
449. Modlin, H. C. A study of the MMPI in clinical practice with notes on the Cornell Index. *Amer. J. Psychiat.*, 1947, 103, 758–769.

450. Monachesi, E. D. Some personality characteristics of delinquents and non-delinquents. *J. crim. Law Criminol.*, 1948, 38, 487–500.
451. Monachesi, E. D. American studies in the prediction of recidivism. *J. crim. Law Criminol.*, 1950, 41, 268–289.
452. Monachesi, E. D. Personality characteristics and socio-economic status of delinquents and non-delinquents. *J. crim. Law Criminol.*, 1950, 40, 570–583.
453. Monachesi, E. D. Personality characteristics of institutionalized and non-institutionalized male delinquents. *J. crim. Law Criminol.*, 1950, 41, 167–179.
454. Montague, E. K. The role of anxiety in serial rote learning. *J. exp. Psychol.*, 1953, 45, 91–96.
455. Morgan, H. H. A psychometric comparison of achieving and non-achieving college students of high ability. *J. consult. Psychol.*, 1952, 16, 292–298.
456. Morris, W. W. A preliminary evaluation of the MMPI. *J. clin. Psychol.*, 1947, 3, 370–374. (Also abstracted in *Amer. Psychologist*, 1946, 1, 264.)
457. Morton, Mary A. The army adaptation of the MMPI. *Amer. Psychologist*, 1948, 3, 271–272. (Abstract.)
458. Mullen, F. A. The MMPI: an extension of the Davis scoring method. *J. clin. Psychol.*, 1948, 4, 86–88.
459. Naffziger, J. V. A study of the personality characteristics of juniors in a teacher education program as revealed by the Minnesota Multiphasic Personality Inventory. M.S. thesis, Illinois State Normal University, 1950.
460. Nance, R. D. Masculinity-femininity in prospective teachers. *J. educ. Res.*, 1949, 42, 658–666.
461. Narciso, J. C., Jr. Some psychological aspects of dermatosis. *J. consult. Psychol.*, 1952, 16, 199–201.
462. Navran, L. A rationally derived MMPI scale for dependence. Ph.D. dissertation, Stanford University, 1951.
463. Navran, L. A rationally derived MMPI scale to measure dependence. *J. consult. Psychol.*, 1954, 18, 192.
464. Noll, V. H. Simulation by college students of a prescribed pattern on a personality scale. *Educ. psychol. Measmt.*, 1951, 11, 478–488.
465. Norman, R. D., and Miriam Redlo. MMPI personality patterns for various college major groups. *J. appl. Psychol.*, 1952, 36, 404–409.
466. O'Gorman, W. D., and E. C. Kunkle. Study of the relation between MMPI scores and "pilot error" in aircraft accidents. *J. Aviat. Med.*, 1947, 18, 31–38.
467. Olson, G. W. The Hastings short form of the group MMPI. *J. clin. Psychol.*, 1954, 10, 386–388.
468. Osler, Sonia F. Intellectual performance as a function of two types of psychological stress. *J. exp. Psychol.*, 1954, 47, 115–121.
469. Owens, W. A., and Wilma C. Johnson. Some measured personality traits of collegiate underachievers. *J. educ. Psychol.*, 1949, 40, 41–46. (Also abstracted in *Amer. Psychologist*, 1948, 3, 363.)
470. Pacella, B. L., Z. Piotrowski, and N. D. C. Lewis. The effects of electric convulsive therapy on certain personality traits in psychiatric patients. *Amer. J. Psychiat.*, 1947, 104, 83–91.
471. Page, R. B. Application of the MMPI to tuberculosis patients. Ph.D. dissertation, University of Minnesota, 1947.
472. Patten, J. Personality patterns and written expression. *Calif. J. educ. Res.*, 1951, 2, 119–123. (Same title: Ph.D. dissertation, Stanford University, 1950.)
473. Pearson, J. S. Prediction of the response of schizophrenic patients to electroconvulsive therapy. *J. clin. Psychol.*, 1950, 6, 285–287.
474. Pearson, J. S., and W. M. Swenson. A note on extended findings with the MMPI in predicting response to electroconvulsive therapy. *J. clin. Psychol.*, 1951, 7, 288.
475. Pedrelli, M. Il MMPI di Hathaway e McKinley. *Riv. sper. freniat.*, 1954, 78, 51–84.
476. Penrose, L. S. The MMPI: A Review. In O. K. Buros, *The third mental measurements yearbook*. New Brunswick, N.J.: Rutgers University Press, 1949.
477. Perlman, M. Social class membership and test-taking attitude. M.A. thesis, University of Chicago, 1950.
478. Peterson, D. R. The diagnosis of subclinical schizophrenia. *J. consult. Psychol.*, 1954, 18, 198–200.
479. Peterson, D. R. Predicting hospitalization of psychiatric outpatients. *J. abnorm. soc. Psychol.*, 1954, 49, 260–265.
480. Phillips, E. L., and D. N. Wiener. Relationships between selected disability and disease groups and the MMPI. *Amer. Psychologist*, 1947, 2, 274. (Abstract.)
481. Pierce-Jones, J. The readability of certain standard tests. *Calif. J. educ. Res.*, 1954, 5, 80–82.

482. Pizzat, F. J. A personality study of college stutterers. M.S. thesis, University of Pittsburgh, 1949. (Also abstracted in *Speech Monogr.*, 1951, 18, 240–241.)

483. Portenier, Lillian G. Personality tests in a university guidance program. *J. educ. Psychol.*, 1948, 39, 479–487. (Also abstracted in *J. Colo.-Wyo. Acad. Sci.*, 1948, 3, 51–52.)

484. Potter, C. S. A method of using the Minnesota Multiphasic Personality Inventory with the blind. In Wilma Donahue and D. Dabelstein (Eds.), *Psychological diagnosis and counseling of the adult blind: selected papers from the proceedings of the University of Michigan Conference for the Blind, 1947*. New York: American Foundation for the Blind, 1950.

485. Pugh, R. W. A specific relapse phenomenon during the course of electric convulsive therapy. *J. consult. Psychol.*, 1953, 17, 87–91.

486. Quay, H., and A. Sweetland. The relationship of the Rosenzweig P-F study to the MMPI. *J. clin. Psychol.*, 1954, 10, 296–297.

487. Rashkis, H. A., and D. A. Shaskan. The effects of group psychotherapy on personality inventory scores. *Amer. J. Orthopsychiat.*, 1946, 16, 345–349.

488. Redlo, Miriam. MMPI personality patterns for several academic major groups. M.A. thesis, University of New Mexico, 1951.

489. Renaud, H. R. Clinical correlates of the masculinity-femininity scale of the Minnesota Multiphasic Personality Inventory. Ph.D. dissertation, University of California, 1950.

490. Richards, T. W. *Modern clinical psychology*. New York: McGraw-Hill, 1946.

491. Richards, T. W. Personality of the convulsive patient in military service. *Psychol. Monogr.*, 1952, 66, No. 14 (Whole No. 346).

492. Rinne, K. W. A differential analysis of various group responses to characteristics of personality as measured by the MMPI. *Dissertation Abstr.*, 1953, 13, 1263–1264. (Abstract of Ph.D. dissertation, Indiana University, 1953.)

493. Roessel, F. P. MMPI results for high school drop-outs and graduates: a comparison of results obtained from the MMPI and from the study of school records of drop-outs and graduates from the same school system. Ph.D. dissertation, University of Minnesota, 1954.

494. Rogers, C. R., and Rosalind F. Dymond (Eds.). *Psychotherapy and personality change: coordinated research studies in the client-centered approach*. Chicago: University of Chicago Press, 1954.

495. Rorabaugh, M. E., and G. Guthrie. The personality characteristics of tuberculous patients who leave the tuberculosis hospital against medical advice. *Amer. Rev. Tuberc.*, 1953, 67, 432–439.

496. Rose, Annelies A. A study of homesickness in college freshmen. *J. soc. Psychol.*, 1947, 26, 185–202.

497. Rosen, A. Development of some new MMPI scales for differentiation of psychiatric syndromes within an abnormal population. Ph.D. dissertation, University of Minnesota, 1952.

498. Rosen, A. Test-retest stability of MMPI scales for a psychiatric population. *J. consult. Psychol.*, 1953, 17, 217–221.

499. Rosen, A., W. M. Hales, and W. Simon. Classification of "suicidal" patients. *J. consult. Psychol.*, 1954, 18, 359–362.

500. Rosen, E. Some personality and attitude differences between volunteers and non-volunteers for a psychological experiment. Ph.D. dissertation, University of California, 1950.

501. Rosen, E. Differences between volunteers and non-volunteers for psychological studies. *J. appl. Psychol.*, 1951, 35, 185–193.

502. Rosen, E. MMPI and Rorschach correlates of the Rorschach white space response. *J. clin. Psychol.*, 1952, 8, 283–288.

503. Rosen, H. Correlations between the Schellenberg free association test and the MMPI. M.A. thesis, University of Minnesota, 1944.

504. Rosenzweig, S. The dynamics of an amnesic personality. *J. Pers.*, 1946, 15, 121–142.

505. Rosenzweig, S., and Kate L. Kogan. *Psychodiagnosis: an introduction to tests in the clinical practice of psychodynamics*. New York: Grune and Stratton, 1949.

506. Rotter, J. B. The MMPI: A Review. In O. K. Buros, *The third mental measurements yearbook*. New Brunswick, N.J.: Rutgers University Press, 1949.

507. Rotter, J. B. Clinical methods: psychodiagnostics. In C. P. Stone and D. W. Taylor (Eds.), *Annual review of psychology*. Stanford: Annual Reviews, 1953. Vol. IV.

508. Rotter, J. B. *Social learning and clinical psychology*. New York: Prentice-Hall, 1954.

509. Rubin, H. The MMPI as a diagnostic aid in a veterans hospital. *J. consult. Psychol.*, 1948, 12, 251–254.

510. Rubin, H. A note on "Reply to Rubin." *J. consult. Psychol.*, 1950, 14, 327–328.

511. Rubin, H. Validity of a critical-item scale for schizophrenia on the MMPI. *J. consult. Psychol.*, 1954, 18, 219–220.

512. Ruesch, J. Personality structure, lactic acid production and work performance in psychiatric patients. *J. Psychol.*, 1945, 20, 381–390.
513. Ruesch, J. Psychophysiological relations in cases with head injuries. *Psychosom. Med.*, 1945, 7, 158–168.
514. Ruesch, J. Psychological invalidism in thyroidectomized patients. *Psychosom. Med.*, 1947, 9, 77–91.
515. Ruesch, J., and K. Bowman. Prolonged post-traumatic syndromes following head injury. *Amer. J. Psychiat.*, 1945, 102, 145–163.
516. Ruesch J., R. E. Harris, and K. Bowman. *Pre- and post-traumatic personality in head injuries.* Assoc. Res. Nerv. Ment. Dis. Monogr. 24. Baltimore: Williams and Wilkins Co., 1945.
517. Ruesch, J., *et al. Chronic disease and psychological invalidism: a psychosomatic study.* Amer. Soc. Res. Psychosom. Problems. New York: Hoeber, 1946.
518. Ruesch, J., *et al. Duodenal ulcer: a socio-psychological study of naval personnel and civilians.* Berkeley: University of California Press, 1948.
519. Ruja, D. H. Personality changes following prefrontal lobotomy in 25 schizophrenic patients. *Amer. Psychologist*, 1951, 6, 499. (Abstract.)
520. Sampson, H., and D. Bindra. "Manifest" anxiety, neurotic anxiety, and the rate of conditioning. *J. abnorm. soc. Psychol.*, 1954, 49, 256–259.
521. Sanders, M. W. The prediction of academic success among university freshmen in a school of education. Ph.D. dissertation, New York University, 1950. (Also abstracted in *Microfilm Abstracts*, 1951, 11, 63–64.)
522. Sanderson, J. W. An evaluation of a technique of profile classification for the MMPI. Ph.D. dissertation, University of California, Los Angeles, 1952.
523. Sanford, R. N. Clinical methods: psychotherapy. In C. P. Stone and D. W. Taylor (Eds.), *Annual review of psychology.* Stanford: Annual Reviews, 1953. Vol. IV.
524. Santini, G. Osservagioni sul MMPI. (Study of the MMPI.) *Riv. sper. freniat.*, 1954, 78, 441–442.
525. Schiele, B. C., A. B. Baker, and S. R. Hathaway. The Minnesota Multiphasic Personality Inventory. *Lancet*, 1943, 63, 292–297.
526. Schiele, B. C., and J. Brozek. "Experimental neurosis" resulting from semistarvation in man. *Psychosom. Med.*, 1948, 10, 31–50.
527. Schmid, J., Jr. Factor analysis of prospective teachers' differences. *J. exp. Educ.*, 1950, 18, 287–319. (Same title: Ph.D. dissertation, University of Wisconsin, 1949).
528. Schmidt, H. O. Test profiles as a diagnostic aid: the Minnesota Multiphasic Inventory. *J. appl. Psychol.*, 1945, 29, 115–131.
529. Schmidt, H. O. Notes on the MMPI: the K factor. *J. consult. Psychol.*, 1948, 12, 337–342.
530. Schmidt, H. O. Comparison of women students in occupational therapy and in nursing. *J. Psychol.*, 1951, 31, 161–174.
531. Schneck, J. M. Clinical evaluation of the F scale on the MMPI. *Amer. J. Psychiat.*, 1948, 104, 440–442.
532. Schneck, J. M. The double-spike pattern on the MMPI. *Amer. J. Psychiat.*, 1948, 104, 443–445.
533. Schneider, R. A., J. S. Gray, and C. U. Culmer. Psychological evaluation of surgical patients: a correlation between preoperative psychometric studies and recovery. *Bull. Univ. of Minn. Hospital and Minn. Medical Fdn.*, 1948, 20, 201–211. (Same title: *Wisc. med. J.*, 1950, 49, 285–290.)
534. Schofield, W. Minnesota Multiphasic Personality Inventory response changes with certain therapies. Ph.D. dissertation, University of Minnesota, 1948.
535. Schofield, W. Changes in responses to the MMPI following certain therapies. *Psychol. Monogr.*, 1950, 64, No. 5 (Whole No. 311).
536. Schofield, W. A further study of the effects of therapies on MMPI responses. *J. abnorm. soc. Psychol.*, 1953, 48, 67–77.
537. Schofield, W. A study of medical students with MMPI: I. Scale norms and profile patterns. *J. Psychol.*, 1953, 36, 59–65.
538. Schofield, W. A study of medical students with MMPI: II. Group and individual changes after two years. *J. Psychol.*, 1953, 36, 137–141.
539. Schofield, W. A study of medical students with MMPI: III. Personality and academic success. *J. appl. Psychol.*, 1953, 37, 47–52.
540. Scodel, A. Passivity in a class of peptic ulcer patients. *Psychol. Monogr.*, 1953, 67, No. 10 (Whole No. 360).
541. Scodel, A., and P. Mussen. Social perceptions of authoritarians and nonauthoritarians. *J. abnorm. soc. Psychol.*, 1953, 48, 181–184.

542. Seeman, W. "Subtlety" in structured personality tests. *J. consult. Psychol.*, 1952, 16, 278–283.
543. Seeman, W. Concept of "subtlety" in structured psychiatric and personality tests: an experimental approach. *J. abnorm. soc. Psychol.*, 1953, 48, 239–247.
544. Schacter, Helen. Personality profiles of psychoneurotics before and after treatment. *Amer. Psychologist*, 1947, 2, 420. (Abstract.)
545. Shaffer, G. W., and R. S. Lazarus. *Fundamental concepts in clinical psychology.* New York: McGraw-Hill, 1952.
546. Shepler, B. F. A comparison of masculinity-femininity measures. *J. consult. Psychol.*, 1951, 15, 484–486.
547. Sheriffs, A. C., and D. S. Boomer. Who is penalized by the penalty for guessing? *J. educ. Psychol.*, 1954, 45, 81–90.
548. Sherman, A. W. Personality factors in the psychological weaning of college women. *Amer. Psychologist*, 1947, 2, 423. (Abstract.)
549. Shneidman, E. S. A short method of scoring the MMPI. *J. consult. Psychol.*, 1946, 10, 143–145.
550. Shneidman, E. S. Prospectus of the Make-A-Picture Story (MAPS) projective personality test. *Amer. Psychologist*, 1947, 2, 407. (Abstract.)
551. Shneidman, E. S., W. Joel, and K. B. Little. An empirical categorization of psychological test report items. *Amer. Psychologist*, 1951, 6, 492. (Abstract.)
552. Shuttleworth, Margaret. An investigation of the relationship between certain psychological factors and childbirth. Ph.D. dissertation, State University of Iowa, 1954.
553. Siegel, S. Certain determinants and correlates of authoritarianism. *Genet. Psychol. Monogr.*, 1954, 49, 187–229.
554. Simon, W. Attempted suicide among veterans. *J. nerv. ment. Dis.* (in press).
555. Simon, W., and H. Gilberstadt. MMPI patterns before and after carbon dioxide inhalation therapy. *J. nerv. ment. Dis.*, 1954, 119, 523–529.
556. Simon, W., and W. M. Hales. Note on a suicide key in the MMPI. *Amer. J. Psychiat.*, 1949, 106, 222–223.
557. Sipprelle, C. An empirical test of Pascal's formula. *J. Pers.*, 1954, 23, 195–206.
558. Sisk, H. L. A reply to Winfield's study of the multiple choice Rorschach. *J. appl. Psychol.*, 1947, 31, 446–448.
559. Smith, J. G. Influence of failure, expressed hostility and stimulus characteristics on verbal learning and recognition. *J. Pers.*, 1954, 22, 475–493.
560. Smykal, A., and F. C. Thorne. Etiological studies of psychopathic personality: II. Asocial type. Case study. *J. clin. Psychol.*, 1951, 7, 299–316.
561. Snoke, Mary, and N. Ziesner. Relationship between subtle-obvious keys and K scale of the MMPI. Minneapolis: V.A. Voc. Rehab. and Educ. Div. Advisement Bulletin No. 6, 1946.
562. Snyder, W. U., and Barbara J. Snyder. Implications for therapy of personality changes resulting from a course in mental hygiene. *Amer. Psychologist*, 1948, 3, 286–287. (Abstract.)
563. Sopchak, A. L. College student norms for the MMPI. *J. consult. Psychol.*, 1952, 16, 445–448.
564. Sopchak, A. L. Parental "identification" and "tendency toward disorders" as measured by the MMPI. *J. abnorm. soc. Psychol.*, 1952, 47, 159–165.
565. Spence, K. W. Current interpretations of learning data and some recent developments in stimulus-response theory. In *Learning theory, personality theory and clinical research: the Kentucky symposium.* New York: Wiley, 1954.
566. Spence, K. W., and I. E. Farber. Conditioning and extinction as a function of anxiety. *J. exp. Psychol.*, 1953, 45, 116–119.
567. Spence, K. W., and Janet A. Taylor. Anxiety and strength of the UCS as determiners of the amount of eyelid conditioning. *J. exp. Psychol.*, 1951, 42, 183–188.
568. Spence, K. W., and Janet A. Taylor. The relation of conditioned response strength to anxiety in normal, neurotic and psychotic subjects. *J. exp. Psychol.*, 1953, 45, 265–272.
569. Spiaggia, M. An investigation of the personality traits of art students. *Educ. psychol. Measmt.*, 1950, 10, 285–293.
570. Staudt, Virginia M. The relationship of certain personality traits to errors and correct responses in several types of tasks among college women under varying test conditions. *J. Psychol.*, 1949, 27, 465–478. (Also abstracted in *Amer. Psychologist*, 1948, 3, 273.)
571. Stout, Marjory. An analysis of the structure of the Minnesota Multiphasic Personality Inventory. M.A. thesis, Pennsylvania State College, 1949.
572. Strangio, V. A psychiatric test for general practice: Part I. The personality in terms of the psychiatric components. *J. Osteopathy*, 1950, 57, 20–23.
573. Strangio, V. A psychiatric test for general practice: Part II. Clinical applications. *J. Osteopathy*, 1950, 57, 16–19.

574. Strother, G. B., Margaret M. Barnett, and P. C. Apostolakos. The use of cartoons as a projective device. *J. clin. Psychol.*, 1954, 10, 38–42.

575. Sullivan, P. L., and G. S. Welsh. A technique for objective configural analysis of MMPI profiles. *J. consult. Psychol.*, 1952, 16, 383–388.

576. Sundberg, N. D. The relationship of psychotherapeutic skill and experience to knowledge of other people. Ph.D. dissertation, University of Minnesota, 1952.

577. Super, D. E. *Appraising vocational fitness by means of psychological tests.* New York: Harper, 1949.

578. Sutton, Mary L. Profile patterning and descriptive correlates of patients having low scores on scale 9 of the MMPI. Ph.D. dissertation, University of Minnesota, 1952.

579. Swan, R., Jr. The application of a couple analysis approach to the Minnesota Multiphasic Personality Inventory in marriage counseling. *Dissertation Abstr.*, 1953, 13, 1095–1096. (Abstract of Ph.D. dissertation, University of Minnesota, 1953.)

580. Sweet, Blanche S. A study of insight: its operational definition and its relationship to psychological health. Ph.D. dissertation, University of California, 1953.

581. Sweetland, A. Hypnotic neurosis: hypochondriasis and depression. *J. gen. Psychol.*, 1948, 39, 91–105.

582. Sweetland, A., and H. Quay. An experimental investigation of the hypnotic dream. *J. abnorm. soc. Psychol.*, 1952, 47, 678–682.

583. Sweetland, A., and H. Quay. A note on the K scale of the MMPI. *J. consult. Psychol.*, 1953, 17, 314–316.

584. Tafejian, T. T. The E-F scale, the MMPI, and Gough's Pr scale. *Amer. Psychologist*, 1951, 6, 501. (Abstract.)

585. Taylor, Elaine, I. E. Farber, and R. P. Kabrick. New evidence of a favorability effect upon scores on the Taylor Manifest Anxiety Scale. *Proc. Iowa Acad. Sci.*, 1953, 60, 562–565.

586. Taylor, Janet A. The relationship of anxiety to the conditioned eyelid response. *J. exp. Psychol.*, 1951, 41, 81–92.

587. Taylor, Janet A. A personality scale of manifest anxiety. *J. abnorm. soc. Psychol.*, 1953, 48, 285–290.

588. Taylor, Janet A., and K. W. Spence. The relationship of anxiety level to performance in serial learning. *J. exp. Psychol.*, 1952, 44, 61–64.

589. Taylor, Janet A., and K. W. Spence. Conditioning level in the behavior disorders. *J. abnorm. soc. Psychol.*, 1954, 49, 497–502.

590. Thompson, Grace M. MMPI correlates of certain movement responses in the group Rorschachs of two college samples. *J. consult. Psychol.*, 1948, 12, 379–383. (Also abstracted in *Amer. Psychologist*, 1948, 3, 348.)

591. Thorn, Katherine F. A study of the personality of stutterers as measured by the Minnesota Multiphasic Personality Inventory. Ph.D. dissertation, University of Minnesota, 1950.

592. Toobert, S., et al. A scale for pedophilia. Unpublished studies at the state prison, San Quentin, California.

593. Torrens, J. K. An investigation and evaluation of the Guilford Inventory of Factors STDCR with special reference to the MMPI. Unpublished paper, University of Minnesota, 1944.

594. Traxler, A. E., and R. Jacobs. Construction and educational significance of structured inventories in personality measurement. *Rev. educ. Res.*, 1950, 20, 38–50.

595. Triggs, F. O. A study of the relationship of measured interests to measured mechanical aptitude, personality, and vocabulary. *Amer. Psychologist*, 1947, 2, 296–297. (Abstract.)

596. Trumbull, R. A study of relationships between factors of personality and intelligence. *J. soc. Psychol.*, 1953, 38, 161–173.

597. Tydlaska, Mary, and R. Mengel. A scale for measuring work attitudes for the MMPI. *J. appl. Psychol.*, 1953, 37, 474–477.

598. Tyler, F. T. A factorial analysis of fifteen MMPI scales. *J. consult. Psychol.*, 1951, 15, 541–546.

599. Tyler, F. T., and J. U. Michaelis. A comparison of manual and college norms for the MMPI. *J. appl. Psychol.*, 1953, 37, 273–275.

600. Tyler, F. T., and J. U. Michaelis. K-scores applied to MMPI scales for college women. *Educ. psychol. Measmt.*, 1953, 13, 459–466.

601. Van Vorst, R. B. An evaluation of test performances of a group of psychopathic delinquents. *Psychol. Bull.*, 1943, 50, 583. (Abstract.)

602. Varva, F. A study of deception on the Minnesota Multiphasic Personality Inventory. M.S. thesis, Pennsylvania State College, 1949.

603. Verniaud, W. M. Occupational differences in the MMPI. *J. appl. Psychol.*, 1946, 30, 604–613.

604. Vernon, P. E. *Personality tests and assessments.* New York: Holt, 1953.

605. Vidor, Martha. Personality changes following pre-frontal leucotomy as reflected by the Minnesota Multiphasic Personality Inventory and the results of psychometric testing. *J. ment. Sci.*, 1951, 97, 159–173.

606. Vig, Marcella J. (Baldwin, Marcella J. V.) A clinical investigation into the psychological aspects of multiple sclerosis. Ph.D. dissertation, University of Minnesota, 1947.

607. Walch, A. E., and R. A. Schneider. The MMPI: an evaluation of its use in private practice. *Minn. Med.*, 1947, 30, 753–758.

608. Walnut, F. A personality inventory item analysis of individuals who stutter and individuals who have other handicaps. *J. Speech Hearing Disorders*, 1954, 19, 220–227.

609. Waters, R. O. V., and E. V. Semrad. Use of the MMPI in assessing the Pd factor in psychopathic personalities. *Dis. nerv. Syst.*, 1949, 10, 267–272.

610. Watson, G., and A. L. Comrey. Nutritional replacement for mental illness. *J. Psychol.*, 1954, 38, 251–264.

611. Watt, G. D. An evaluation of non-directive counseling in the treatment of delinquents. *J. educ. Res.*, 1949, 42, 343–352.

612. Wauck, L. A. Schizophrenia and the MMPI. *J. clin. Psychol.*, 1950, 6, 279–284.

613. Webster, H. Derivation and use of the masculinity-femininity variable. *J. clin. Psychol.*, 1953, 9, 33–36.

614. Weisgerber, C. A. The predictive value of the Minnesota Multiphasic Personality Inventory with student nurses. *J. soc. Psychol.*, 1951, 33, 3–11.

615. Weisgerber, C. A. Norms for the MMPI with student nurses. *J. clin. Psychol.*, 1954, 10, 192–194.

616. Weisgerber, C. A. The relationship of perseveration to a number of personality traits and to adjustment. *J. gen. Psychol.*, 1954, 50, 3–13.

617. Welsh, G. S. An extension of Hathaway's MMPI profile coding system. *J. consult. Psychol.*, 1948, 12, 343–344.

618. Welsh, G. S. A projective figure-preference test for diagnosis of psychopathology: I. A preliminary investigation. Ph.D. dissertation, University of Minnesota, 1949.

619. Welsh, G. S. Some practical uses of MMPI profile coding. *J. consult. Psychol.*, 1951, 15, 82–84.

620. Welsh, G. S. An anxiety index and an internalization ratio for the MMPI. *J. consult. Psychol.*, 1952, 16, 65–72.

621. Welsh, G. S. A factor study of the MMPI using scales with item overlap eliminated. *Amer. Psychologist*, 1952, 7, 341. (Abstract.)

622. Welsh, G. S. An interpretation of a general factor on the MMPI. *Amer. Psychologist*, 1952, 7, 528. (Abstract.)

623. Welsh, G. S. A review: S. R. Hathaway and P. E. Meehl, An atlas for the clinical use of the MMPI. *J. appl. Psychol.*, 1952, 36, 279.

624. Welsh, G. S. Factor dimensions of the MMPI. Mimeographed material, University of North Carolina, 1954.

625. Welsh, G. S., and M. Roseman. A graphic method for showing therapeutic change by the use of MMPI factor scales. Paper presented at meetings of S.E.P.A., May 1955.

626. Welsh, G. S., and P. L. Sullivan. Booklet-card, card-booklet item conversion tables for MMPI. Published by authors, 1951.

627. Wenar, C. Reaction time as a function of manifest anxiety and stimulus intensity. *J. abnorm. soc. Psychol.*, 1954, 49, 335–340.

628. Wesley, Elaine. Correlations between the Guilford-Martin Personality Factors O, Ag, Co and the MMPI at the college level. M.A. thesis, University of Minnesota, 1945.

629. Wesley, S. M., B. Stewart, and D. Corey. A study of the intra-individual relationships between interest and ability. *Amer. Psychologist*, 1947, 2, 411. (Abstract.)

630. West, L. J. Measurement of changing psychopathology with the MMPI. *Amer. J. Psychiat.*, 1953, 109, 922–928.

631. West, P. M., E. M. Blumberg, and F. W. Ellis. An observed correlation between psychological factors and growth rate of cancer in man. *Cancer Res.*, 1952, 12, 306–307. (Abstract.)

632. Wheeler, Erma T. A study of certain aspects of personality as related to the electroencephalogram. Ph.D. dissertation, University of Pittsburgh, 1947.

633. Wheeler, W. M. The internal structure of three clinical instruments. *Amer. Psychologist*, 1950, 5, 470. (Abstract.)

634. Wheeler, W. M., K. B. Little, and G. F. J. Lehner. The internal structure of the MMPI. *J. consult. Psychol.*, 1951, 15, 134–141.

635. White, A. A. Evaluation of psychogenic symptoms in general medicine. *J. Amer. med. Ass.*, 1951, 147, 1521–1526.

636. Whooley, J. P. The application of the MMPI to hospitalized tuberculous patients. M.A. thesis, Catholic University, 1952.
637. Wiener, D. N. Advisement factors in successful and unsuccessful rehabilitation trainees. Minneapolis: V.A. Voc. Rehab. and Educ. Div. Advisement Bulletin No. 6, 1946.
638. Wiener, D. N. Differences between the individual and group forms of the MMPI. *J. consult. Psychol.*, 1947, 11, 104–106.
639. Wiener, D. N. MMPI K-correction results for non-institutionalized neuropsychiatric cases. *Minn. Counselor*, 1948, 3, 12–13.
640. Wiener, D. N. Personality characteristics of selected disability groups. *J. clin. Psychol.*, 1948, 4, 285–290. (Same title: *Genet. Psychol. Monogr.*, 1952, 45, 175–255.)
641. Wiener, D. N. Selecting salesmen with subtle-obvious keys for the MMPI. *Amer. Psychologist*, 1948, 3, 364. (Abstract.)
642. Wiener, D. N. Subtle and obvious keys for the MMPI. *J. consult. Psychol.*, 1948, 12, 164–170. (Also abstracted in *Amer. Psychologist*, 1947, 2, 296.)
643. Wiener, D. N. The subtle-obvious factor in vocational and educational success. *Amer. Psychologist*, 1948, 3, 299. (Abstract.)
644. Wiener, D. N. A control factor in social adjustment. *J. abnorm. soc. Psychol.*, 1951, 46, 3–8.
645. Wiener, D. N., and L. R. Harmon. Subtle and obvious keys for the MMPI: their development. Minneapolis: V.A. Advisement Bulletin No. 16, 1946.
646. Wiener, D. N., and E. L. Phillips. A study of progress in psychotherapy. *J. clin. Psychol.*, 1948, 4, 201–206.
647. Wiener, D. N., and W. Simon. Personality characteristics of embalmer trainees. *J. appl. Psychol.*, 1950, 34, 391–393.
648. Willerman, B. The relation of motivation and skill to active and passive participation in the group. *J. appl. Psychol.*, 1953, 37, 387–390.
649. Williams, H. L. The development of a caudality scale for the MMPI. *J. clin. Psychol.*, 1952, 8, 293–297.
650. Williams, H. L. Differential effects of focal brain damage on the MMPI. Ph.D. dissertation, University of Minnesota, 1952.
651. Williams, H. L., and J. F. Lawrence. Comparison of the Rorschach and MMPI by means of factor analysis . *J. consult. Psychol.*, 1954, 18, 193–197.
652. Williams, Janet T. A study of the parents of cerebral palsied and non-cerebral palsied children using the MMPI. M.A. thesis, University of Wisconsin, 1951. (Also abstracted in *Speech Monogr.*, 1952, 19, 199.)
653. Williamson, E. G., and D. Hoyt. Measured personality characteristics of student leaders. *Educ. psychol. Measmt.*, 1952, 12, 65–78.
654. Winberg, W. C. Some personality traits of collegiate underachievers. *Proc. Iowa Acad. Sci.*, 1947, 54, 267–270.
655. Windle, C. Psychological tests in psychopathological prognosis. *Psychol. Bull.*, 1952, 49, 451–482.
656. Windle, C. Test-retest effect on personality questionnaires. *Educ. psychol. Measmt.*, 1954, 14, 617–633.
657. Winfield, D. L. An investigation of the relationship between intelligence and the statistical reliability of the Minnesota Multiphasic Personality Inventory. *J. clin. Psychol.*, 1952, 8, 146–148.
658. Winfield, D. L. The relationship between IQ scores and Minnesota Multiphasic Personality Inventory scores. *J. soc. Psychol.*, 1953, 38, 299–300.
659. Winfield, M. C. The use of the Harrower-Erickson multiple choice Rorschach test with a selected group of women in military service. *J. appl. Psychol.*, 1946, 30, 481–487.
660. Winne, J. F. The factorial composition of normal and neurotic responses to an adaptation of the Minnesota Multiphasic Personality Inventory. Ph.D. dissertation, University of Pennsylvania, 1950. (Also abstracted in *Microfilm Abstracts*, 1950, 10, 311–313.)
661. Winne, J. F. A scale of neuroticism: an adaptation of the Minnesota Multiphasic Personality Inventory. *J. clin. Psychol.*, 1951, 7, 117–122.
662. Wrenn, C. G. Counseling methods. In C. P. Stone and Q. McNemar (Eds.), *Annual review of psychology.* Stanford: Annual Reviews, 1954. Vol. V.
663. Yacorzynski, G. K. *Medical psychology: a basis for psychiatry and clinical psychology.* New York: Ronald Press, 1951.
664. Young, N., and E. L. Gaier. A preliminary investigation into the prediction of suggestibility from selected personality variables. *J. soc. Psychol.*, 1953, 37, 53–60.
665. Young, R. H., and G. A. Pierson. The professional aptitude test, 1947: a preliminary evaluation. *J. ass. Amer. med. Coll.*, 1948, 23, 176–179.

666. Zubin, J., and C. Windle. Psychological prognosis of outcome in the mental disorders. *J. abnorm. soc. Psychol.*, 1954, 49, 272–281.

667. Zwerling, I. Psychological factors in susceptibility to motion sickness. *J. Psychol.*, 1947, 23, 219–239.

668. Analysis of item responses of WACs and WAC applicants on the MMPI and Cornell Selectee Index. U.S. Army, Adjutant General's Office, PRS No. 726, 1944.

669. Measurement of personal characteristics of War Department personnel. U.S. Army, Adjutant General's Office, PRS No. 669, 1944.

670. Research on personality testing. U.S. Army, Adjutant General's Office, PRS. *Bull. Milit. clin. Psychol.*, 1946, 1, 33–41.

671. A study of the Bell Adjustment Inventory and deviant scores on the MMPI. U.S.V.A., Guidance Center, St. Cloud, Minn. *Minn. Counselor*, 1948, 3, 1–7.

672. Validation of the West Point Biographical Inventory WPB-1 against first year aptitude for service ratings. U.S. Army, Adjutant General's Office, PRS No. 3693, 1950.

673. Borko, H. *A factor-analytic study of the MMPI: using a transpose matrix, Q-technique.* Los Angeles: VA Center, NP Hospital, 1952. (Also abstracted in *Amer. Psychologist*, 1952, 7, 342.)

674. Burdock, E. I. A statistical technique for the isolation of personality types by means of the MMPI. Ph.D. dissertation, University of California, Los Angeles, 1954.

675. Cline, V., *et al. Task: fighter.* Research report of the Human Research Unit No. 2, OCAFF, Fort Ord, California, 1954.

676. Glasscock, E. M. An investigation of the value of the MMPI as a prognostic instrument. Ph.D. dissertation, Washington University, 1954.

677. Goulding, C. W. A study of the distribution of MMPI profiles in a college population. M.A. thesis, University of Minnesota, 1951.

678. Leary, T. F., and H. Coffey. The prediction of interpersonal behavior in group psychotherapy. *Group Psychotherapy*, 1954, 7, 1.

679. Mowrer, O. H. (Ed.) *Psychotherapy: theory and research.* New York: Ronald Press, 1953.

680. Mozak, H. H. Evaluation of psychotherapy: a study of some current measures. Ph.D. dissertation, University of Chicago, 1950.

681. Pearson, J. S. Psychometric correlates of emotional immaturity. Ph.D. dissertation, University of Minnesota, 1954.

682. Pemberton, W. H. Test characteristics of student teachers rated at the extremes of teaching ability. Ph.D. dissertation, University of California, Berkeley, 1950.

683. Phillips, F. A. Correlations between the Johnson Temperament Analysis and the MMPI based on 100 male counselees. M.A. thesis, Municipal University of Omaha, 1951.

684. Roseman, M. The sensitivity of repeated MMPI administrations to changes in patient behavior accompanying insulin coma therapy. *Amer. Psychologist*, 1954, 9, 555. (Abstract.)

685. Schultz, S. D. A differentiation of several forms of hostility by a scale empirically constructed from significant items on the MMPI. Ph. D. dissertation, Pennsylvania State University, 1954.

686. Shoben, E. J. The Wechsler-Bellevue in the detection of anxiety: a test of the Rashkis-Welsh hypothesis. *J. consult. Psychol.*, 1950, 14, 40–45.

687. Tiedman, D. V., and K. M. Wilson. Development and application of non-projective tests of personality. *Rev. educ. Res.*, 1953, 23, 56–69.

688. Welsh, G. S. A measure of general maladjustment on the MMPI. Paper read at the San Francisco Bay Area Clinical Psychology meeting, February 1952.

689. Witkin, H. A., *et al. Personality through perception.* New York: Harper, 1953.

SUPPLEMENTARY REFERENCES

r1. Adams, C. R. A new measure of personality. *J. appl. Psychol.*, 1941, 25, 141–151.
r2. Adler, Alexandra. Mental symptoms following head injury. A statistical analysis of 200 cases. *Arch. Neurol. Psychiat.*, 1945, 53, 34–43.
r3. Adorno, T. W., Else Frenkel-Brunswik, D. Levinson, and R. N. Sanford. *The authoritarian personality.* New York: Harper, 1950.
r4. Alexander, F. The influence of psychological factors upon gastrointestinal disorders. *Psychoanal. Quart.*, 1934, 3, 501–588.
r5. Allport, G. W. A test for ascendance-submission. *J. abnorm. soc. Psychol.*, 1928, 23, 118–136.
r6. Allport, G. W. *Personality: a psychological interpretation.* New York: Holt, 1937.
r7. Allport, G. W. *The use of personal documents in psychological science.* New York: Social Science Research Council Bulletin No. 49, 1942.
r8. Andersen, A. L. The effect of laterality localization of brain damage on Wechsler-Bellevue indices of deterioration. *J. clin. Psychol.*, 1950, 6, 191–194.
r9. Andersen, A. L. The effect of laterality localization of focal brain lesions on the Wechsler-Bellevue subtests. *J. clin. Psychol.*, 1951, 7, 149–153.
r10. Arnold, D. A. The clinical validity of the Humm-Wadsworth temperament scale in psychiatric diagnosis. Ph.D. dissertation, University of Minnesota, 1942.
r11. Asch, S. Effects of group pressure upon the modification and distortion of judgments. Swarthmore College: Progress Report on Office of Naval Research Project, Task Order N70nr-38003, 1950.
r12. Ash, P. The reliability of psychiatric diagnoses. *J. abnorm. soc. Psychol.*, 1949, 44, 272–276.
r13. Bacon, C. L., R. Renneker, and M. Cutler. A psychosomatic survey of cancer of the breast. *Psychosom. Med.*, 1952, 14, 453.
r14. Barker, R., Beatrice A. Wright, and Molly R. Gonick. *Adjustment to physical handicap and illness: a survey of the social psychology of physique and disability.* New York: Social Science Research Council Bulletin No. 55, 1946.
r15. Bennett, A. E. Faulty management of psychiatric syndromes simulating organic disease. *J. Amer. med. Ass.*, 1946, 130, 1203–1208.
r16. Benton, A. L. The interpretation of questionnaire items in a personality schedule. *Arch. Psychol.*, 1935, 190.
r17. Bernreuter, R. G. Theory and construction of the personality inventory. *J. soc. Psychol.*, 1933, 4, 387–405.
r18. Bernreuter, R. G. Validity of the personality inventory. *Personnel J.*, 1933, 11, 383–386.
r19. Bernreuter, R. G. The present status of personality trait tests. *Educ. Rec. Supp.*, 1940, 21, 160–171.
r20. Bills, Marion. Selection of casualty and life insurance agents. *J. appl. Psychol.*, 1941, 25, 6–10.
r21. Block, J. *A cluster-analysis of the IPAR Q-sort items.* Berkeley, Calif.: Research Bulletin of the Institute of Personality Assessment and Research, 1954.
r22. Bordin, E. S. A theory of vocational interests as dynamic phenomena. *Educ. psychol. Measmt.*, 1943, 3, 49–65.
r23. Brozek, J., J. C. Franklin, H. Guetzkow, and A. Keys. Human behavior in prolonged experimental semistarvation. *Amer. Psychologist*, 1946, 1, 269. (Abstract.)
r24. Brozek, J., J. C. Franklin, H. Guetzkow, and A. Keys. Recovery after 12 weeks of controlled rehabilitation following experimental semistarvation in man. *Amer. Psychologist*, 1947, 2, 329. (Abstract.)
r25. Brozek, J., S. Wells, and A. Keys. Medical aspects of semistarvation in Leningrad (siege 1941–1942). *Amer. Rev. Soviet Med.*, 1946, 4, 70.
r26. Brunswik, E. *Systematic and representative design of psychological experiments.* Berkeley: University of California Press, 1949.

642

r27. Buchberg, A., R. Lubliner, and E. H. Rubin. Cancer of the lung: duration of life in individuals not treated surgically. *Dis. Chest*, 1951, 20, 257.

r28. Burke, H. H. *Personality traits of successful minor seminarians.* Washington: The Catholic University of America Press, 1947.

r29. Cady, V. M. The estimation of juvenile incorrigibility. *J. Delinqu. Monogr.*, 1923, No. 2.

r30. Canter, A. H. Direct and indirect measures of psychological deficit in multiple sclerosis. *J. gen. Psychol.*, 1951, 44, 3–50.

r31. Cantril, H. The place of personality in social psychology. *J. soc. Psychol.*, 1947, 24, 25.

r32. Cattell, R. B. *Description and measurement of personality.* New York: World Book Co., 1946.

r33. Centers, R. The American class structure. In T. M. Newcomb and E. L. Hartly (Eds.), *Readings in social psychology.* New York: Holt, 1947.

r34. Chapin, F. S. *Experimental designs in sociological research.* New York: Harper, 1947.

r35. Chase, L., and S. Silverman. Prognostic criteria in schizophrenia. *Amer. J. Psychiat.*, 1941, 98, 360–368.

r36. Clark, R. E. Psychoses: income and occupational prestige. *Amer. J. Sociol.*, 1949, 54, 433–440.

r37. Cleckley, H. *The mask of sanity.* St. Louis: Mosby, 1941.

r38. Cowen, E. L., and A. W. Combs. Follow-up study of 32 cases treated by nondirective therapy. *J. abnorm. soc. Psychol.*, 1950, 45, 232–258.

r39. Cronbach, L. J. Statistical methods applied to Rorschach scores: a review. *Psychol. Bull.*, 1949, 46, 393–429.

r40. Cronbach, L. J., and P. E. Meehl. Construct validity in psychological tests. *Psychol. Bull.*, 1955, 52, 281–302.

r41. Darley, J. G. Changes in measured attitudes and adjustments. *J. soc. Psychol.*, 1938, 9, 189–199.

r42. Davis, A. Child training and social class. In R. G. Barker, J. S. Kounin, and H. F. Wright, *Child behavior and development.* New York: McGraw-Hill, 1943.

r43. Davis, W. A., and R. J. Havighurst. *Father of the man.* Boston: Houghton-Mifflin, 1947.

r44. Day, G. The psychosomatic approach to pulmonary tuberculosis. *Lancet*, 1951, 19, 1025.

r45. Du Mas. F. M. On the interpretation of personality profiles. *J. clin. Psychol.*, 1947, 3, 57–65.

r46. Dunham, H. W., and B. S. Meltzer. Predicting length of hospitalization of mental patients. *Amer. J. Sociol.*, 1946, 52, 123–131.

r47. Dunbar, H. F. *Psychosomatic diagnosis.* New York: Hoeber, 1943.

r48. Dunbar, H. F. *Mind and body: psychosomatic medicine.* New York: Random House, 1947.

r49. Dunphy, J. E. Some observations on the natural behavior of cancer in man. *New England J. Med.*, 1950, 242, 167.

r50. Dvorak, B. J. *Differential occupational ability patterns.* Minneapolis: University of Minnesota Press, Employment Stabilization Research Institute Bulletin No. 8, Vol. 3, 1935.

r51. Dynes, J. B. Mental breaking point. *New England J. Med.*, 1946, 234, 42–45.

r52. Eisenberg, P. Individual interpretation of psychoneurotic inventory items. *J. gen. Psychol.*, 1941, 25, 19–40.

r53. Eisenberg, P., and A. Wesman. Consistency in response and logical interpretation of psychoneurotic inventory items. *J. educ. Psychol.*, 1941, 32, 321–338.

r54. Evans, Catharine, and T. R. McConnell. A new measure of introversion-extroversion. *J. Psychol.*, 1941, 12, 111–124.

r55. Eysenck, H. J. The effects of psychotherapy: an evaluation. *J. consult. Psychol.*, 1952, 16, 319–324.

r56. Fenichel, O. *Psychoanalytical theory of the neuroses.* New York: Norton, 1945.

r57. Fisher, W., and S. P. Hayes, Jr. Maladjustment in college predicted by Bernreuter Inventory scores and family position. *J. appl. Psychol.*, 1941, 25, 86–96.

r58. Frank, L. K. Projective methods for the study of personality. *J. Psychol.*, 1939, 8, 389–413.

r59. Franklin, J. C., B. C. Schiele, J. Brozek, and A. Keys. Observations on human behavior in experimental semistarvation and rehabilitation. *J. clin. Psychol.*, 1948, 4, 28–45.

r60. Frenkel-Brunswik, Else. Mechanisms of self-deception. *J. soc. Psychol.*, 1939, 10, 409–420.

r61. Frenkel-Brunswik, Else, and R. N. Sanford. Some personality factors in anti-Semitism. *J. Psychol.*, 1945, 20, 271–291.

r62. Gengerelli, J. A. A factorial method whose factors are empirical tests. *Amer. Psychologist*, 1949, 4, 245–246.

r63. Gough, H. G. The relationship of socioeconomic status to personality inventory and achievement test scores. *J. educ. Psychol.*, 1946, 37, 527–540.

r64. Gough, H. G. A short social status inventory. *J. educ. Psychol.*, 1949, 40, 52–56.

r65. Green, A. W. The middle class male child and neurosis. *Amer. sociol. Rev.*, 1946, 11, 31–41.
r66. Grinker, R., G. C. Ham, and F. P. Robbins. Some psychodynamic factors in multiple sclerosis. *Proc. 28th annu. Meet. Ass. Res. nerv. ment. Dis.*, 1948.
r67. Guilford, J. P., and Ruth B. Guilford. Personality factors S, E, and M, and their measurement. *J. Psychol.*, 1936, 2, 109–127.
r68. Guilford, J. P., and Ruth B. Guilford. Personality factors D, R, T, and A. *J. abnorm. soc. Psychol.*, 1939, 34, 21–36.
r69. Haggard, H. W., and E. M. Jellinek. *Alcohol explored.* New York: Doubleday, Doran, 1942.
r70. Hartshorne, H., and M. A. May. *Studies in deceit.* New York: Macmillan, 1928.
r71. Hartshorne, H., M. A. May, and F. K. Shuttleworth. *Studies in the nature of character: III. Studies in the organization of character.* New York: Macmillan, 1930.
r72. Hathaway, S. R. The personality inventory as an aid in the diagnosis of psychopathic inferiors. *J. consult. Psychol.*, 1939, 3, 112–117.
r73. Henderson, D. K. *Psychopathic states.* New York: Norton, 1939.
r74. Hendrickson, G. Attitudes and interests of teachers and prospective teachers. Paper given before Section Q, AAAS, Atlantic City, 1932 (unpublished).
r75. Hertz, Marguerite R. *Frequency tables to be used in scoring responses to the Rorschach ink-blot test.* (3rd Ed.) Cleveland: Western Reserve University, 1946.
r76. Horst, P. *The prediction of personal adjustment.* New York: Social Science Research Council Bulletin No. 48, 1941.
r77. Horst, P. Pattern analysis and configural scoring. *J. clin. Psychol.*, 1954, 10, 3–11.
r78. Hovey, H. B. A self-interview inventory. *J. clin. Psychol.*, 1947, 3, 191–193.
r79. Humm, D. G., and Kathryn A. Humm. Validity of the Humm-Wadsworth temperament scale: with consideration of the effects of subjects' response-bias. *J. Psychol.*, 1944, 18, 55–64.
r80. Humm, D. G., R. C. Storment, and M. E. Iorns. Combination scores for the Humm-Wadsworth temperament scale. *J. Psychol.*, 1939, 7, 227–253.
r81. Humm, D. G., and G. W. Wadsworth. The Humm-Wadsworth temperament scale. *Amer. J. Psychiat.*, 1935, 92, 163–200.
r82. Hunt, W. A. New evaluative methods and future prospects. *Ment. Hyg.*, 1946, 30, 21–32.
r83. Hutt, M. L. The use of projective methods of personality measurement in Army medical installations. *J. clin. Psychol.*, 1945, 1, 134–140.
r84. Johnson, P. O. *Statistical methods in research.* New York: Prentice-Hall, 1949.
r85. Jurgensen, C. E. Report on the "classification inventory," a personality test for industrial use. *J. appl. Psychol.*, 1944, 28, 445–460.
r86. Jurgensen, C. E. Table for determining phi coefficients. *Psychometrika*, 1947, 12, 17–29.
r87. Kant, O. The evaluation of prognostic criteria in schizophrenia. *J. nerv. ment. Dis.*, 1944, 100, 598–605.
r88. Kelly, E. L., C. C. Miles, and L. M. Terman. Ability to influence one's score on a typical pencil and paper test of personality. *J. Pers.*, 1936, 4, 206–215.
r89. Kerr, W. A., and H. H. Remmers. *Manual for the American Home Scale.* Chicago: Science Research Associates, 1942.
r90. Keys, A. Human starvation and its consequences. *J. Amer. diet. Ass.*, 1946, 22, 582–587.
r91. Klopfer, B., and D. M. Kelley. *The Rorschach technique.* Yonkers, N.Y.: World Book Co., 1946.
r92. Laird, D. A. Detecting abnormal behavior. *J. abnorm. soc. Psychol.*, 1925, 20, 128–141.
r93. Landis, C., and S. E. Katz. The validity of certain questions which purport to measure neurotic tendencies. *J. appl. Psychol.*, 1934, 18, 343–356.
r94. Landis, C., J. Zubin, and S. E. Katz. Empirical evaluation of three personality adjustment inventories. *J. educ. Psychol.*, 1935, 26, 321–330.
r95. Levinson, D. J., and R. N. Sanford. A scale for the measurement of anti-Semitism. *J. Psychol.*, 1944, 17, 339–370.
r96. Lewis, N. D. C. *Research in dementia praecox.* New York: Nat. Comm. Ment. Hygiene, 1936.
r97. Leyton, G. B. Effects of slow starvation. *Lancet*, 1946, 2, 73.
r98. Lindquist, E. L. *Design and analysis of experiments.* Boston: Houghton-Mifflin, 1953.
r99. Linton, R. *The cultural background of personality.* New York: Appleton-Century, 1945.
r100. Little, K. B., and E. S. Shneidman. The validity of thematic projective technique interpretations. *J. Pers.*, 1955, 23, 285–294.
r101. Lorr, M. Multidimensional scale for rating psychiatric patients, hospital form. VA Tech. Bull. 10–507. Washington, D.C.: U.S. Govt. Printing Office, 1953.

r102. Lundberg, G. A. The measurement of socio-economic status. *Amer. J. Sociol.*, 1940, 5, 29–39.
r103. Lykken, D. T., and H. L. Williams. The products of individual sample probabilities — their significance to the null hypothesis. Unpublished paper.
r104. McCarthy, Dorothea. Language development in children. In L. Carmichael, (Ed.), *Manual of child psychology*. New York: Wiley, 1946.
r105. McFarland, R. A., E. Gellhorn, E. F. Adolph, N. W. Shock, and C. P. Richter. The internal environment and behavior: a symposium. *Amer. J. Psychiat.*, 1941, 97, 858–893, 1204–1218, 1365–1396.
r106. McKinley, J. C. (Ed.) *An outline of neuropsychiatry*. St. Louis: John S. Swift, 1944.
r107. McNemar, Q. The mode of operation of suppressant variables. *Amer. J. Psychol.*, 1945, 58, 544–555.
r108. McNemar, Q. *Psychological statistics*. New York: Wiley, 1949.
r109. Maddy, Nancy R. Comparison of children's personality traits, attitudes, and intelligence with parental occupation. *Genet. Psychol. Monogr.*, 1943, 27, 3–65.
r110. Maller, J. B. The effect of signing one's name. *Sch. & Soc.*, 1930, 31, 882–884.
r111. Maller, J. B. *Character sketches*. New York: Bureau of Publications, Teachers College, Columbia University, 1932.
r112. Maslow, A. H., Elisa Hirsh, Marcella Stein, and Irma Honigmann. A clinically derived test for measuring psychological security-insecurity. *J. gen. Psychol.*, 1945, 33, 21–41.
r113. Masserman, J. H. *Principles of dynamic psychiatry*. Philadelphia: Saunders, 1946.
r114. Mayer-Gross, W., and N. P. Moore. Schizophrenia. *J. ment. Sci.*, 1944, 90, 231–255.
r115. Meehl, P. E. A simple algebraic development of Horst's suppressor variables. *Amer. J. Psychol.*, 1945, 58, 550–554.
r116. Menninger, K. A. Preface. In D. Rappaport, *Manual of diagnostic psychological testing*. New York: Josiah Macy, Jr., Foundation, 1944.
r117. Menninger, K. A. *The human mind*. (3rd Ed.) New York: Knopf, 1947.
r118. Metfessel, M. Personality factors in motion picture writing. *J. abnorm. soc. Psychol.*, 1935, 30, 333–347.
r119. Miller, N. E., and J. Dollard. *Social learning and imitation*. New Haven: Yale University Press, 1941.
r120. Mills, C. W. The middle classes in middle-sized cities. *Amer. sociol. Rev.*, 1946, 11, 520–529.
r121. Minot, G. B., T. E. Buckman, and R. Isaacs. Chronic myelogenous leukemia: age incidence, duration, and benefit derived from irradiation. *J. Amer. med. Ass.*, 1924, 82, 1489.
r122. Minot, G. B., and R. Isaacs. Lymphatic leukemia: age incidence, duration, and benefit derived from irradiation. *Boston med. surg. J.*, 1924, 191, 1.
r123. Moses, L. E. Non-parametric statistics for psychological research. *Psychol. Bull.*, 1952, 49, 122–143.
r124. Mosier, C. I. A note on item analysis and the criterion of internal consistency. *Psychometrika*, 1936, 1, 275–282.
r125. Mosier, C. I., E. E. Cureton, R. A. Katzell, and R. J. Wherry. Symposium: the need and means of cross-validation. *Educ. psychol. Measmt.*, 1951, 2, 5–28.
r126. Murphy, G. *Personality: a biosocial approach to origins and structure*. New York: Harper, 1947.
r127. Murray, H. A. *Explorations in personality*. New York: Oxford University Press, 1938.
r128. Nathanson, I. T., and C. E. Welch. Life expectancy and incidence of malignant disease: I. Cancer of the breast. *Amer. J. Cancer*, 1936, 28, 40.
r129. Nathanson, I. T., and C. E. Welch. Life expectancy and incidence of malignant disease: V. Malignant lymphoma, fibrosarcoma, malignant melanoma and osteogenic sarcoma. *Amer. J. Cancer*, 1937, 31, 598.
r130. Olson, W. C. The waiver of signature in personal reports. *J. appl. Psychol.*, 1936, 20, 442–450.
r131. Page, J., C. Landis, and S. E. Katz. Schizophrenic traits in the functional psychoses and in normal individuals. *Amer. J. Psychiat.*, 1934, 13, 1213–1225.
r132. Pavlov, I. P. *Conditioned reflexes and psychiatry*. New York: International Press, 1941.
r133. Pear, T. H. Personality in its cultural context. *Bull. of the John Rylands Library*, 1946, 30, 16.
r134. Rabin, A. I. The use of the Wechsler-Bellevue scales with normal and abnormal persons. *Psychol. Bull.*, 1945, 42, 410–422.
r135. Rabin, A. I., and W. H. Guertin. Research with the Wechsler-Bellevue test. 1945–1950. *Psychol. Bull.*, 1951, 48, 211–242.
r136. Rashkis, H. A., and G. S. Welsh. Detection of anxiety by use of the Wechsler scale. *J. clin. Psychol.*, 1946, 2, 354–357.

r137. Renneker, R., and M. Cutler. Psychological problems of adjustment to cancer of the breast. *J. Amer. med. Ass.*, 1952, 148, 833.

r138. Rosanoff, A. J. *Manual of psychiatry.* (7th Ed.) New York: Wiley, 1938.

r139. Rosenzweig, S. A suggestion for making verbal personality tests more valid. *Psychol. Rev.*, 1934, 41, 400–401.

r140. Rosenzweig, S. A basis for the improvement of personality tests with special reference to the M-F battery. *J. abnorm. soc. Psychol.*, 1938, 33, 476–488.

r141. Ross, N. D., and F. L. McNaughton. Head injury: a study of patients with chronic post-traumatic complaints. *Arch. Neurol. Psychiat.*, 1944, 52, 255–269.

r142. Ruch, F. L. A technique for detecting attempts to fake performance on a self-inventory type of personality test. In Q. McNemar and M. A. Merrill, *Studies in personality.* New York: McGraw-Hill, 1942.

r143. Sargent, Helen. Projective methods: their origins, theory, and application in personality research. *Psychol. Bull.*, 1945, 42, 257–293.

r144. Schneidler, G. G., and R. F. Berdie. Representativeness of college students who received counseling. *J. educ. Psychol.*, 1942, 33, 545–551.

r145. Schofield, W. Critique of scatter and profile analysis of psychometric data. *J. clin. Psychol.*, 1952, 8, 16–22.

r146. Shimkin, M. B. Duration of life in untreated cancer. *Cancer*, 1951, 4, 1.

r147. Shimkin, M. B., S. R. Mettier, and H. R. Bierman. Myelocytic leukemia: an analysis of incidence, distribution and fatality. *Ann. Int. Med.*, 1951, 35, 194.

r148. Shneidman, E. S. (Ed.). *Thematic test analysis.* New York: Grune and Stratton, 1951.

r149. Sims, V. M. *Sims Score Card for socio-economic status.* Bloomington, Ill.: Public School Publishing Co., 1927.

r150. Sorokin, P. A. *Man and society in calamity.* New York: Dutton, 1942.

r151. Sorokin, P. A. *Society, culture, and personality: their structure and dynamics.* New York: Harper, 1947.

r152. Spencer, D. Frankness of subjects on personality measures. *J. educ. Psychol.*, 1938, 28, 26–35.

r153. Steinmetz, H. C. Measuring ability to fake occupational interest. *J. appl. Psychol.*, 1932, 16, 123–130.

r154. Stephenson, W. S. *The study of behavior.* Chicago: University of Chicago Press, 1953.

r155. Strecker, E. A., and F. T. Chambers, Jr. *Alcohol — one man's meat.* New York: Macmillan, 1938.

r156. Strong, E. K. *Vocational interests of men and women.* Stanford: Stanford University Press, 1943.

r157. Sugar, C., and R. Nadell. Mental symptoms in multiple sclerosis. *J. nerv. ment. Dis.*, 1948, 98, 267–280.

r158. Super, D. E. Strong's vocational interests of men and women. *Psychol. Bull.*, 1945, 42, 359–371.

r159. Symonds, P. M. *Diagnosing personality and conduct.* New York: Appleton-Century, 1932.

r160. Terman, L. M., and Catherine C. Miles. *Sex and personality.* New York: McGraw-Hill, 1936.

r161. Trunnell, J. B. *Second report on institutional research grants of the American Cancer Society.* New York: American Cancer Society, 1952.

r162. Tryon, R. C. *Cluster analysis.* Ann Arbor: Edwards Brothers, 1939.

r163. Tucker, J. E. A multiple criterion of success in client-centered therapy. In *Group report of a program of research in psychotherapy.* Psychotherapy Research Group, Pennsylvania State College, 1953.

r164. Vernon, P. E. The attitude of the subject in personality testing. *J. appl. Psychol.*, 1934, 18, 165–177.

r165. Washburne, A. C. Seven-year report from Neuropsychiatric Department, Student Health Service, University of Wisconsin. *Wisc. med. J.*, 1946, 45, 195–204.

r166. Washburne, J. N. A test of social adjustment. *J. appl. Psychol.*, 1935, 19, 125–144.

r167. Wechsler, D. *The measurement of adult intelligence.* (3rd Ed.) Baltimore: Williams and Wilkins, 1944.

r168. Weider, A., K. Brodman, B. Mittelmann, D. Wechsler, and H. G. Wolff. Cornell Service Index: a method for quickly assaying personality and psychosomatic disturbances in men in the armed forces. *War Med.*, 1945, 7, 209–213.

r169. Weider, A., B. Mittelmann, D. Wechsler, and H. G. Wolff. The Cornell Selective Index, a method for quick testing of selectees for the armed forces. *J. Amer. med. Ass.*, 1944, 124, 224–228.

r170. Willoughby, R. R. The concept of reliability. *Psychol. Rev.*, 1935, 42, 153–165.

r171. Willoughby, R. R., and M. E. Morse. Spontaneous reactions to a personality inventory. *Amer. J. Orthopsychiat.*, 1936, 6, 562–575.

r172. Wittman, Phyllis. A scale for measuring prognosis in schizophrenic patients. *Elgin Papers*, 1941, 4, 20–33.

r173. Wolf, S. Experimental research into psychosomatic phenomena in medicine. *Science*, 1948, 107, 637–639.

r174. Wright, D. G. Foreword. In G. R. Pascal and Barbara J. Suttell, *The Bender-Gestalt Test*. New York: Grune and Stratton, 1951.

r175. Yule, G. U. *Introduction to the theory of statistics*. (14th Ed.) London: C. Griffin, 1950.

r176. Zubin, J. The method of internal consistency for selecting test items. *J. educ. Psychol.*, 1934, 25, 345–356.

r177. The experience of the American Friends Service Committee in civilian public service under the Selective Training and Service Act of 1940 (1941–1945). Philadelphia: American Friends Service Committee, 1946.

r178. Psychometrics. V.A. Advisement and Guidance Bulletin No. 9, Minneapolis, 1946.

r179. Schedule for rating disabilities. (1945 Ed.) Washington, D.C.: U.S. Govt. Printing Office, 1945.

r180. Statistical abstract of the United States. U.S. Department of Commerce, Bureau of the Census, 1948.

r181. Technical recommendations for psychological tests and diagnostic techniques. Published by the American Psychological Association as a supplement to *Psychol. Bull.*, 1954, 51, No. 2, Part 2.

INDEX

A priori methods, and clinical stereotypes, 51. *See also* Scale construction

A (anxiety) scale (Taylor), 179: changes in client-centered therapy, 513–514; correlation with Tucker's criterion of improvement, 514

A (anxiety) scale (Welsh): items in, 268–272, 281; correlations with regular scales, 270, 277; level of and code frequencies, 272–275; in factor study, 275–276; and communicative efficiency, 276–277; correlations with CPI scales, 277; and psychiatric diagnosis, 277; personality correlates in normals, 277–278; distributional characteristics, 279, 281; T-score values, 280. *See also* Ja scale

A (anxiety) score (Modlin), 364, 393

Abramson, H. A., on over-conventionality, 252–253

Ac (achievement) scale, 207

Adjective check list: reliability of Black list, 151; items on Black list, 152; items on Hathaway-Meehl list, 153; Gough list and Es scale, 229

Adler, A., and individual psychology, 597

Affective disorders, *see* Psychosis, depression; Psychosis, hypomania

Age differences: on K scale, 38; on scale 2, 80, 590, 591; on scale 7, 85; on scale 4, 103; and scale elevation, 590–591; adjustment for, 590, 591

Aggressiveness: in college groups, 175–176, 563, 569–570; and Es scale, 582, 584

Alcoholics: use of MMPI with, 135, 397–398, 419–426; code of female, 420; code of male, 420; symptomatic drinking, 422–423

Alcoholics Anonymous, 419–420, 424–426

American Council on Education Test, 38

American Home Scale: and ethnic prejudice, 206, 207; and Do scale, 217

Analysis, configural, *see* Configural analysis

Analysis, item, *see* Item analysis

Analysis, pattern, *see* Pattern analysis

Analysis, profile, *see* Pattern analysis

Anonymity: and item response, 13; and card form, 14; secret coding, 14; and inventory performance, 589–590

Anti-Semitism, and response to therapist, 523. *See also* Ethnocentrism

Anxiety: in psychasthenia, 81; and diagnosis and treatment, 298; measurement of, 298–307, 389; and length of hospitalization, 304; and client-centered therapy, 512–515

Anxiety index: formula for, 300, 301; distributional characteristics, 301–303; and therapy change, 304–306, 513–514; advantages of, 306

Anxiety neurosis, *see* Psychoneurosis, anxiety

Anxiety pattern, 299, 493–494

Anxiety scales, *see* A scale (Taylor); A scale (Welsh)

Anxiety score, 364, 393

Arthritis, 442, 443, 444

Asch, S., group conformity study, 580

Asthma, 443, 444

Athletic interest, in college women, 563, 570–571

Atlas for the Clinical Use of the MMPI, 111, 146, 315, 612

Autrey, Olive Ruth, on communicative efficiency, 276–277

Av (average) score, 393

Barker, R. G., on psychosomatic relations, 440

Behavior disorder pattern, in student nurses, 612

Behavior disorders, *see* Psychopathic personality

Bernreuter Personality Inventory, 12–13, 33, 98

Bird, C., and faking of specific syndromes, 323

"Bootstraps" effect, in test development, 107–108

Borderline profiles: interpretive difficulty, 27; of surgical patients, 378; of soldiers, 389–390; in normals, 396; in psychiatric patients, 396. *See also* Profile elevation

Box form, *see* Card form

Ca (caudality) scale: list of items, 223–224; correlation with other scales, 224; T scores for, 225

Cady, V. M., modification of Woodworth Psychoneurotic Inventory, 16

California Psychological Inventory (CPI): relation to Es scale, 230; relation to A and R scales, 277–278

M

J